GCSE
Combined Science
Foundation Level

GCSE Combined Science is certainly not a Bohr...
and this spectacular all-in-one CGP book puts the cool in molecule!

It's the ultimate revision triple-threat — everything you need to know for Combined
Science Biology, Chemistry and Physics. Plus, there are exam-style questions
for every topic, a full set of practice papers, <u>and</u> a free online edition.

You'll also find links to our fantastic online content, with video solutions for practice
questions, as well as Retrieval Quizzes to help you nail down all the facts you need to learn.

Unlock your free online extras!

Just go to **cgpbooks.co.uk/extras** and enter this code or scan the QR codes in the book.

4395 6239 4466 5473

By the way, this code only works for one person. If somebody else has used
this book before you, they might have already claimed the Online Edition.

Complete
Revision & Practice
<u>Everything</u> you need to pass the exams!

Contents

Throughout this book you'll see grade stamps like these:

These grade stamps help to show how difficult the questions are.
Remember — to get a top grade you need to be able to answer **all** the questions, not just the hardest ones.

In the real exams, some questions test how well you can write (as well as your scientific knowledge).
In this book, we've marked these questions with an asterisk (*).

Topic C1 — Atomic Structure and the Periodic Table

Topic C2 — Bonding, Structure and Properties of Matter

Topic C3 — Quantitative Chemistry

Topic C4 — Chemical Changes

Topic C5 — Energy Changes

Topic C6 — The Rate and Extent of Chemical Change

Topic P3 — Particle Model of Matter

Topic P4 — Atomic Structure

Topic P5 — Forces

Topic P6 — Waves

Topic P7 — Magnetism and Electromagnetism

You'll see **QR codes** throughout the book that you can scan with your smartphone.

A QR code next to a tip box question takes you to a **video** that talks you through solving the question. You can access **all** the videos by scanning this code here.

Video Solutions

A QR code on a 'Revision Summary' page takes you to a **Retrieval Quiz** for that topic. You can access **all** the quizzes by scanning this code here.

Retrieval Quizzes

You can also find the **full set of videos** at cgpbooks.co.uk/GCSEScienceFoundation/Videos and the **full set of quizzes** at cgpbooks.co.uk/GCSEScienceFoundation/Quiz

For useful information about **What to Expect in the Exams** and other exam tips head to cgpbooks.co.uk/GCSEScienceFoundation/Exams

Published by CGP

From original material by Richard Parsons.

Editors: Emily Garrett, Rob Hayman, Paul Jordin, Sharon Keeley-Holden, Duncan Lindsay, Sarah Pattison, Rachael Rogers

Contributors: Paddy Gannon

With thanks to Emily Smith for the copyright research.

Stopping distance data used on pages 367 and 484 from the Highway Code.
Contains public sector information licensed under the Open Government Licence v3.0.
http://www.nationalarchives.gov.uk/doc/open-government-licence/version/3/

Printed by Elanders Ltd, Newcastle upon Tyne.
Clipart from Corel®

Illustrations by: Sandy Gardner Artist, email sandy@sandygardner.co.uk

The Scientific Method

*This section **isn't** about how to 'do' science — but it does show you the way **most scientists** work.*

Science is All About **Testing Hypotheses**

Scientists Make an **Observation**

1) Scientists <u>OBSERVE</u> (look at) something they don't understand.
2) They come up with a <u>possible explanation</u> for what they've observed.
3) This explanation is called a <u>HYPOTHESIS</u>.

About 100 years ago, scientists thought that atoms looked like this.

They **Test** Their Hypothesis

1) Next, they test whether the hypothesis is <u>right or not</u>.
2) They do this by making a <u>PREDICTION</u> — a statement based on the hypothesis that can be tested.
3) They then <u>TEST</u> this prediction by carrying out <u>experiments</u>.
4) If their prediction is <u>right</u>, this is <u>EVIDENCE</u> that their <u>hypothesis might be right</u> too.

Other Scientists Test the Hypothesis Too

1) Other scientists <u>check</u> the evidence — for example, they check that the experiment was carried out in a <u>sensible</u> way. This is called <u>PEER-REVIEW</u>.
2) Scientists then <u>share their results</u>, e.g. in scientific papers.
3) Other scientists carry out <u>more experiments</u> to test the hypothesis.
4) Sometimes these scientists will find <u>more evidence</u> that the <u>hypothesis is RIGHT</u>.
5) Sometimes they'll find <u>evidence</u> that shows the <u>hypothesis is WRONG</u>.

After more evidence was gathered, they changed their hypothesis to this.

The Hypothesis is **Accepted** or **Rejected**

1) If <u>all the evidence</u> that's been found <u>supports</u> the <u>hypothesis</u>, it becomes an <u>ACCEPTED THEORY</u> and goes into <u>textbooks</u> for people to learn.
2) If the <u>evidence</u> shows that the hypothesis is <u>wrong</u>, scientists must:
3) <u>Change the hypothesis</u>, OR
4) Come up with a <u>new hypothesis</u>.

Now we think it's more like this.

Scientific models are constantly being refined...

You can see just how much testing has to be done before something gets accepted as a theory. If scientists aren't busy testing their own hypothesis, then they're busy testing someone else's.

(WORKING SCIENTIFICALLY)

Models and Communication

*Once scientists have made a **new discovery**, they **don't** just keep it to themselves. Oh no. Time to learn about how scientific discoveries are **communicated**, and the **models** that are used to represent theories.*

Theories Can Involve **Different Types** of **Models**

1) A <u>model</u> is a <u>simple way</u> of <u>describing</u> or <u>showing</u> what's going on in <u>real life</u>.
2) Models can be used to <u>explain ideas</u> and <u>make predictions</u>. For example:

- The <u>Bohr model</u> of an <u>atom</u> is a simple <u>picture</u> of what an atom looks like (see p.177).
- It can be used to explain <u>trends</u> in the <u>periodic table</u> (see p.180 for more).

3) All models have <u>limits</u> — a single model <u>can't explain</u> everything about an idea.

It's Important to **Tell People** About Scientific Discoveries

1) Scientific discoveries can make a big difference to <u>people's lives</u>.
2) So scientists need to <u>tell the world</u> about their discoveries.
3) They might need to tell people to <u>change their habits</u>, e.g. stop smoking to protect against lung cancer.
4) They might also need to tell people about new <u>technologies</u>. For example:

The discovery of molecules called <u>fullerenes</u> has led to a new technology that delivers medicine to <u>body cells</u>. <u>Doctors</u> and <u>patients</u> might need to be given <u>information</u> about this technology.

Scientific **Evidence** can be **Presented** in a **Biased Way**

1) <u>Reports</u> about scientific discoveries in the <u>media</u> (e.g. newspapers or television) can be <u>misleading</u>.
2) The data might be <u>presented</u> in a way that's <u>not quite right</u> — or it might be <u>oversimplified</u>.
3) This means that people may not <u>properly understand</u> what the scientists found out.
4) People who want to make a point can also sometimes <u>present data</u> in a <u>biased way</u> (in a way that's <u>unfair</u> or <u>ignores</u> one side of the argument). For example:

- A <u>scientist</u> may talk a lot about <u>one particular relationship</u> in the data (and not mention others).
- A <u>newspaper article</u> might describe data <u>supporting</u> an idea without giving any evidence <u>against</u> it.

Companies can present biased data to help sell products...

Sometimes a company may only want you to see half of the story so they present the data in a <u>biased way</u>. For example, a medicines company may want to encourage you to buy their drugs. They might tell you about all the <u>positives</u>, but not report the results of any <u>unfavourable studies</u>.

Issues Created by Science

*Science has helped us to **make progress** in loads of areas, from medicine to space travel.
But science still has its **issues**. And it **can't answer everything**, as you're about to find out.*

Scientific Developments are Great, but they can Raise Issues

1) Scientific developments include <u>new technologies</u> and <u>new advice</u>.

2) These developments can create <u>issues</u>. For example:

> <u>Economic (money) issues:</u> Society <u>can't</u> always <u>afford</u> to do things scientists recommend, like spend money on green energy sources.

> <u>Social (people) issues:</u> Decisions based on scientific evidence affect <u>people</u> — e.g. should alcohol be banned (to prevent health problems)?

> <u>Personal issues:</u> Some decisions will affect <u>individuals</u> — e.g. people may be upset if a <u>wind farm</u> is built next to their house.

> <u>Environmental issues:</u> <u>Human activity</u> often affects the <u>environment</u> — e.g. some people think that <u>genetically modified crops</u> (see p.135) could cause <u>environmental problems</u>.

Science Can't Answer Every Question — Especially Ethical Ones

1) At the moment scientists <u>don't agree</u> on some things — like what the Universe is made of.

2) This is because there <u>isn't</u> enough <u>data</u> to <u>support</u> the scientists' hypotheses.

3) But <u>eventually</u>, we probably <u>will</u> be able to answer these questions once and for all.

4) Experiments <u>can't tell us</u> whether something is <u>ethically right or wrong</u>. For example, whether it's right for people to use new drugs to help them do better in exams.

5) The best we can do is make a decision that <u>most people</u> are more or less happy to live by.

There are often issues with new scientific developments...

The trouble is, there's often <u>no clear right answer</u> where these issues are concerned. Different people have <u>different views</u>, depending on their priorities. These issues are full of <u>grey areas</u>.

Risk

*Scientific discoveries are often great, but they can prove **risky**. With dangers all around, you've got to be aware of hazards — this includes **how likely** they are to **cause harm** and **how serious** the effects may be.*

Nothing is Completely Risk-Free

1) A <u>hazard</u> is something that could <u>cause harm</u>.

2) All hazards have a <u>risk</u> attached to them — this is the <u>chance</u> that the hazard will cause harm.

3) <u>New technology</u> can bring <u>new risks</u>. E.g. scientists are creating technology to <u>capture</u> and <u>store</u> carbon dioxide. But if the carbon dioxide leaked out it could <u>damage</u> soil or water supplies. These risks need to be considered <u>alongside</u> the <u>benefits</u> of the technology, e.g. lower greenhouse gas emissions.

4) To make a <u>decision</u> about activities that involve <u>hazards</u>, we need to think about:
   - the <u>chance</u> of the hazard causing harm,
   - how <u>bad</u> the <u>outcome</u> (consequences) would be if it did.

People Make Their Own Decisions About Risk

1) Not all risks have the same <u>consequences</u>. For example, if you chop veg with a sharp knife you risk <u>cutting your finger</u>, but if you go scuba-diving you risk <u>death</u>.

2) Most people are happier to accept a risk if the consequences <u>don't last long</u> and <u>aren't serious</u>.

3) People tend to think <u>familiar</u> activities are <u>low-risk</u>. They tend to think <u>unfamiliar</u> activities are <u>high-risk</u>. But this <u>isn't always true</u>. For example:

   - Cycling on roads is often <u>high-risk</u>. But it's a <u>familiar</u> activity, so many people are happy to do it.
   - Air travel is actually pretty <u>safe</u>, but a lot of people think it is <u>high-risk</u>.

4) The best way to <u>estimate</u> the <u>size of a risk</u> is to look at <u>data</u>. E.g. you could estimate the risk of a driver crashing by recording <u>how many people</u> in a group of 100 000 drivers crashed their cars over a year.

The pros and cons of new technology must be weighed up...

The world's a <u>dangerous</u> place and it's impossible to rule out the chance of an accident altogether. But if you can recognise <u>hazards</u> and take steps to reduce the <u>risks</u>, you're more likely to stay <u>safe</u>.

Designing Investigations

*Dig out your lab coat and dust down your safety goggles... it's **investigation time**.*
*Investigations include **lab experiments** and **studies** done in the **real world**.*

Evidence Can Support or Disprove a Hypothesis

1) Scientists <u>observe</u> things and come up with <u>hypotheses</u> to explain them (see p.2).
   You need to be able to do the same. For example:

   > <u>Observation</u>: People have big feet and spots. <u>Hypothesis</u>: Having big feet causes spots.

2) To <u>find out</u> if your hypothesis is <u>right</u>, you need to do an <u>investigation</u> to gather evidence.

3) To do this, you need to use your hypothesis to make a <u>prediction</u> — something you think <u>will happen</u>
   that you can <u>test</u>. E.g. people who have bigger feet will have more spots.

4) Investigations are used to see if there are <u>patterns</u> or <u>relationships</u> between <u>two variables</u> (see below).

Make an Investigation a Fair Test By Controlling the Variables

1) In a lab experiment you usually <u>change one thing</u> (a variable)
   and <u>measure</u> how it affects <u>another thing</u> (another variable).

   > <u>EXAMPLE:</u> you might <u>change</u> the <u>concentration</u> of a reactant
   > and <u>measure</u> how it affects the <u>temperature change</u> of the reaction.

2) <u>Everything else</u> that could affect the results needs to <u>stay the same</u>.
   Then you know that the thing you're <u>changing</u> is the <u>only</u> thing that's affecting the results.

   > <u>EXAMPLE continued:</u> you need to keep the volume of the reactants the same.
   > If you don't, you won't know if any change in the temperature is caused by
   > the change in concentration, or the change in volume.

3) The variable that you <u>CHANGE</u> is called the <u>INDEPENDENT</u> variable.

4) The variable you <u>MEASURE</u> is called the <u>DEPENDENT</u> variable.

5) The variables that you <u>KEEP THE SAME</u> are called
   <u>CONTROL</u> variables.

   > <u>EXAMPLE continued:</u>
   > Independent = concentration
   > Dependent = temperature
   > Control = volume of
   >   reactants, pH, etc.

6) Because you can't always control all the variables,
   you often need to use a <u>CONTROL EXPERIMENT</u>.

7) This is an experiment that's kept under the <u>same conditions</u> as the rest of the investigation, but <u>doesn't</u>
   have anything <u>done</u> to it. This is so that you can see what happens when you don't change <u>anything</u>.

Evidence Needs to be Repeatable, Reproducible and Valid

1) <u>REPEATABLE</u> means that if the <u>same person</u> does the experiment again, they'll get <u>similar results</u>.
   To check your results are repeatable, <u>repeat</u> the readings <u>at least three times</u>.
   Then check the repeat results are all similar.

2) <u>REPRODUCIBLE</u> means that if <u>someone else</u> does the experiment, the results will still be <u>similar</u>.
   To make sure your results are reproducible, get <u>another person</u> to do the experiment too.

3) <u>VALID results</u> come from experiments that were designed to be a <u>fair test</u>.
   They're also repeatable and reproducible.

   If data is repeatable and reproducible, scientists are more likely to trust it.

Designing Investigations

The **Bigger** the **Sample Size** the **Better**

1) Sample size is how many things you test in an investigation, e.g. 500 people or 20 types of metal.

2) The bigger the sample size the better — to reduce the chance of any weird results.

3) But scientists have to be realistic when choosing how big their sample should be. E.g. if you were studying how lifestyle affects weight it'd be great to study everyone in the UK (a huge sample), but it'd take ages and cost loads.

4) When you choose a sample, you need to make sure you've got a range of different people.

5) For example, both men and women with a range of different ages.

Your Data Should be **Accurate** and **Precise**

1) ACCURATE results are results that are really close to the true answer.

2) The accuracy of your results usually depends on your method. You need to make sure you're measuring the right thing.

3) You also need to make sure you don't miss anything that should be included in the measurements. For example:

> If you're measuring the volume of gas released by a reaction, make sure you collect all the gas.

4) PRECISE results are ones where the data is all really close to the mean (average) of your repeated results.

Repeat	Data set 1	Data set 2
1	12	11
2	14	17
3	13	14
Mean	13	14

Data set 1 is more precise than data set 2 — the results are all close to the mean (not spread out).

Your **Equipment** has to be **Right for the Job**

1) The measuring equipment you use has to be able to accurately measure the chemicals you're using. E.g. if you need to measure out 11 cm³ of a liquid, use a measuring cylinder that can measure to 1 cm³ — not 5 or 10 cm³.

2) You also need to set up the equipment properly. For example, make sure your mass balance is set to zero before you start weighing things.

Designing Investigations

You Need to Look out for **Errors** and **Anomalous Results**

1) The results of your experiment will always <u>vary a bit</u> because of <u>RANDOM ERRORS</u> — for example, mistakes you might make while <u>measuring</u>.

2) You can <u>reduce</u> the effect of random errors by taking <u>repeat readings</u> and finding the <u>mean</u>. This will make your results <u>more precise</u>.

3) If a measurement is wrong by the <u>same amount every time</u>, it's called a <u>SYSTEMATIC ERROR</u>. For example:

> If you measure from the <u>very end</u> of your <u>ruler</u> instead of from the <u>0 cm mark</u> every time, <u>all</u> your measurements would be a bit <u>small</u>.

Always measure from here...

...not here.

4) If you know you've made a systematic error, you might be able to <u>correct it</u>. For example, by adding a bit on to all your measurements.

5) Sometimes you get a result that <u>doesn't fit in</u> with the rest. This is called an <u>ANOMALOUS RESULT</u>.

6) You should try to <u>work out what happened</u>. If you do (e.g. you find out you measured something wrong) you can <u>ignore</u> it when processing your results (see next page).

Investigations Can Have **Hazards**

1) Hazards from science experiments include things like:

<u>microorganisms</u> (e.g. bacteria)

<u>chemicals</u>

<u>electricity</u>

<u>fire</u>

2) When you <u>plan</u> an investigation you need to make sure that it's <u>safe</u>.

3) You should <u>identify</u> all the hazards that you might come across.

4) Then you should think of ways of <u>reducing the risks</u>. For example:

- If you're working with <u>sulfuric acid</u>, always wear gloves and safety goggles. This will reduce the risk of the acid <u>burning</u> your skin and eyes.
- If you're using a <u>Bunsen burner</u>, stand it on a heat proof mat. This will reduce the risk of starting a fire.

There's more on safety in experiments on page 395.

Designing an investigation is an involved process...

WORKING SCIENTIFICALLY

Collecting <u>data</u> is what investigations are all about. Designing a good investigation is really important to make sure that any data collected is <u>accurate</u>, <u>precise</u>, <u>repeatable</u> and <u>reproducible</u>.

Processing Data

*Processing your data means doing some **calculations** with it to make it **more useful**.*

Data Needs to be Organised

1) <u>Tables</u> are useful for <u>organising data</u>.
2) When you draw a table <u>use a ruler</u>.
3) Make sure <u>each column</u> has a <u>heading</u> (including the <u>units</u>).

Test tube	Repeat 1 (cm³)	Repeat 2 (cm³)
A	28	37
B	47	51

There are Different Ways of Processing Your Data

1) When you've done repeats of an experiment you should always calculate the <u>mean</u> (a type of average).
2) You might also need to calculate the <u>range</u> (how spread out the data is).

> **EXAMPLE**
>
> **The results of an experiment to find the volume of gas produced in a reaction are shown in the table below. Calculate the mean volume and the range.**
>
> | Volume of gas produced (cm³) | | |
> |---|---|---|
> | Repeat 1 | Repeat 2 | Repeat 3 |
> | 28 | 37 | 32 |
>
> 1) To calculate the <u>mean</u>, <u>add together</u> all the data values. Then <u>divide</u> by the <u>total number</u> of values in the sample.
>
> $(28 + 37 + 32) \div 3$ $= 32$ cm³
>
> 2) To calculate the <u>range</u>, <u>subtract</u> the <u>smallest</u> number from the <u>largest</u> number.
>
> $37 - 28 = 9$ cm³

3) To find the <u>median</u>, put all your data in <u>order</u> from smallest to largest. The median is the <u>middle value</u>.
4) The number that appears <u>most often</u> is the <u>mode</u>.

> E.g. if you have the data set: 1 2 1 1 3 4 2
> The <u>median</u> is: 1 1 1 <u>2</u> 2 3 4. The <u>mode</u> is <u>1</u> because 1 appears most often.

If you have an even number of values, the median is halfway between the middle two values.

5) When calculating any of these values, always <u>ignore</u> any <u>anomalous results</u>.

Round to the Lowest Number of Significant Figures

1st significant figure

0.0307

2nd 3rd

1) The <u>first significant figure</u> of a number is the first digit that's <u>not zero</u>.
2) The second and third significant figures come <u>straight after</u> (even if they're zeros).
3) In <u>any</u> calculation, you should round the answer to the <u>lowest number of significant figures</u> (s.f.) given.
4) If your calculation has more than one step, <u>only</u> round the <u>final</u> answer.

> **EXAMPLE**
>
> **The mass of a solid is 0.24 g and its volume is 0.715 cm³. Calculate the density of the solid.**
>
> Density = 0.24 g ÷ 0.715 cm³ = 0.33566... = 0.34 g/cm³ (2 s.f.)
>
> 2 s.f.   3 s.f.
>
> *Final answer should be rounded to 2 s.f.*

Don't forget your calculator...

EXAM TIP In the exam you could be given some <u>data</u> and be expected to <u>process it</u> in some way. Make sure you keep an eye on <u>significant figures</u> in your answers and <u>always write down your working</u>.

Presenting Data

*Once you've processed your data, e.g. by calculating the mean, you can present your results in a nice **chart** or **graph**. This will help you to **spot any patterns** in your data.*

If Your Data Comes in **Categories**, Present it in a **Bar Chart**

If the independent variable comes in <u>clear categories</u> (e.g. blood group, types of metal) or can be <u>counted exactly</u> (e.g. number of protons) you should use a <u>bar chart</u> to display the data. Here's what to do:

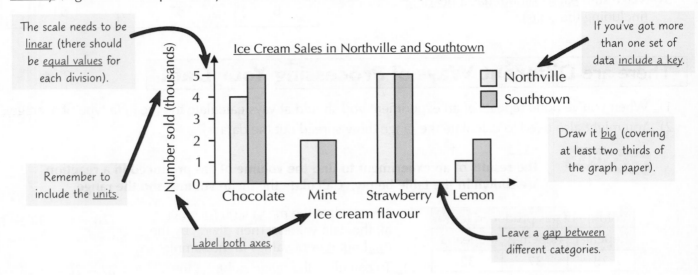

The scale needs to be <u>linear</u> (there should be <u>equal values</u> for each division).

Remember to include the <u>units</u>.

Label both axes.

If you've got more than one set of data <u>include a key</u>.

Draw it <u>big</u> (covering at least two thirds of the graph paper).

Leave a <u>gap between</u> different categories.

If Your Data is **Continuous**, Plot a **Graph**

If both variables can have any value <u>within a range</u> (e.g. length, volume) use a <u>graph</u> to display the data. Here are the rules for plotting points on a graph:

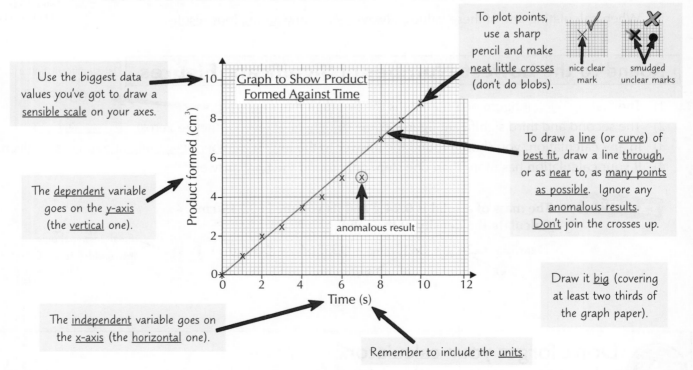

Use the biggest data values you've got to draw a <u>sensible scale</u> on your axes.

The <u>dependent</u> variable goes on the <u>y-axis</u> (the <u>vertical</u> one).

The <u>independent</u> variable goes on the <u>x-axis</u> (the <u>horizontal</u> one).

To plot points, use a sharp pencil and make <u>neat little crosses</u> (don't do blobs).

To draw a <u>line</u> (or <u>curve</u>) of <u>best fit</u>, draw a line <u>through</u>, or as <u>near</u> to, as <u>many points as possible</u>. Ignore any <u>anomalous results</u>. <u>Don't</u> join the crosses up.

Draw it <u>big</u> (covering at least two thirds of the graph paper).

Remember to include the <u>units</u>.

More on Graphs

*Graphs aren't just fun to plot, they're also really useful for showing **trends** in your data.*

You Can Calculate the **Rate** of a Reaction from the **Gradient** of a Graph

1) This is the <u>formula</u> you need to calculate the <u>gradient</u> (slope) of a graph:

$$\text{gradient} = \frac{\text{change in } y}{\text{change in } x}$$

2) You can use it to work out the <u>rate of a reaction</u> (how <u>quickly</u> the reaction happens).

 The graph shows the volume of gas produced in a reaction against time. Calculate the rate of reaction.

1) To calculate the <u>gradient</u>, pick <u>two points</u> on the line that are easy to read. They should also be a <u>good distance</u> apart.

2) Draw a line <u>down</u> from the higher point. Then draw a line <u>across</u> from the other, to make a <u>triangle</u>.

3) The line drawn <u>down the side</u> of the triangle is the <u>change in y</u>. The line <u>across the bottom</u> is the <u>change in x</u>.

4) Read the x and y values of the points <u>off the graph</u> and work out the change in y and the change in x:

Change in y = 6.8 − 2.0 = 4.8 cm³   Change in x = 5.2 − 1.6 = 3.6 s

To calculate a rate, the graph must have time on the x-axis.

5) Then put these numbers in the formula above to find the rate of the reaction:

$$\text{Rate} = \text{gradient} = \frac{\text{change in } y}{\text{change in } x} = \frac{4.8 \text{ cm}^3}{3.6 \text{ s}} = 1.3 \text{ cm}^3/\text{s}$$

The units are (units of y)/(units of x). cm³/s can also be written as cm³ s⁻¹.

Graphs Show the **Relationship** Between Two Variables

1) You can get <u>three</u> types of <u>correlation</u> (relationship) between variables:

<u>POSITIVE</u> correlation: as one variable <u>increases</u> the other <u>increases</u>.

<u>INVERSE (negative)</u> correlation: as one variable <u>increases</u> the other <u>decreases</u>.

<u>NO</u> correlation: <u>no relationship</u> between the two variables.

2) A correlation <u>doesn't mean</u> the change in one variable is <u>causing</u> the change in the other (see page 14).

 ## Graphs make it much easier to see relationships in data...

If you can't work out what kind of correlation a graph shows, just remember that an inverse correlation gives a line of best fit that slopes downwards, so it looks like the letter N (for <u>N</u>egative).

Rearranging Equations and Units

*Graphs and maths skills are all very well, but the numbers don't mean much if you don't get the **units** right.*

You Can **Rearrange** Equations

1) Equations show <u>relationships</u> between <u>variables</u>. For example, speed = $\dfrac{\text{distance}}{\text{time}}$.

2) The <u>subject</u> of an equation is the variable <u>by itself</u> on one side of the equals sign. So <u>speed</u> is the <u>subject</u> in the equation above.

3) To <u>change</u> the <u>subject</u> of an equation do the same thing to <u>both sides</u> of the equation until you've got the subject you <u>want</u>.

> **EXAMPLE** **Make distance the subject of the equation above.**
>
> 1) <u>Multiply</u> both sides by <u>time</u>. $\text{speed} = \dfrac{\text{distance}}{\text{time}}$
>
> ➡ $\text{speed} \times \text{time} = \dfrac{\text{distance} \times \text{time}}{\text{time}}$
>
> 2) 'Time' is now on the top <u>and</u> the bottom of the fraction, so it cancels out: $\text{speed} \times \text{time} = \dfrac{\text{distance} \times \cancel{\text{time}}}{\cancel{\text{time}}}$
>
> 3) This leaves <u>distance</u> by itself. So it's the <u>subject</u>: $\text{speed} \times \text{time} = \text{distance}$

S.I. Units Are Used All Round the World

1) All scientists use the same <u>units</u> to measure their data.

2) These are <u>standard units</u>, called S.I. units.

3) Here are some S.I. units you might see:

Quantity	S.I. Base Unit
mass	kilogram, kg
length	metre, m
time	second, s
temperature	kelvin, K

S.I. units help scientists to compare data...

You can only really <u>compare</u> things if they're in the <u>same units</u>. E.g. if the rate of blood flow was measured in ml/min in one vein and in l/day in another vein, it'd be hard to know which was faster.

More on Units

*You can **convert units**, which can save you from having to write a lot of 0's...*

Different Units Help you to Write Large and Small Quantities

1) Quantities come in a huge <u>range</u> of sizes.

2) To make the size of numbers <u>easier to handle</u>, larger or smaller units are used.

3) Larger and smaller units are written as the <u>S.I. base unit</u> with a <u>little word</u> in <u>front</u> (a prefix). Here are some <u>examples</u> of <u>prefixes</u> and what they mean:

Kilogram is an exception. It's an S.I. unit with the prefix already on it.

Prefix	mega (M)	kilo (k)	deci (d)	centi (c)	milli (m)	micro (μ)
How it compares to the base unit	1 000 000 times bigger	1000 times bigger	10 times smaller	100 times smaller	1000 times smaller	1 000 000 times smaller

E.g. 1 <u>kilo</u>metre is <u>1000</u> metres.   E.g. there are <u>1000</u> milli<u>metres</u> in 1 metre.

You Need to be Able to Convert Between Units

You need to know how to <u>convert</u> (change) one unit into another. Here are some useful conversions:

Mass can have units of kg and g.

Energy can have units of kJ and J.

MULTIPLY to go from a bigger unit to a smaller unit.

DIVIDE to go from a smaller unit to a bigger unit.

Length can have lots of units including m, mm and μm.

Always make sure the values you put into an equation or formula have the right units.

EXAMPLE

A car has travelled 0.015 kilometres. How many metres has it travelled?

1 km = 1000 m. So to convert from km (a bigger unit) to m (a smaller unit) you need to <u>multiply</u> by 1000.   0.015 km × 1000 = 15 m

MATHS TIP

To convert from bigger units to smaller units...

...you need to <u>multiply</u>, and to convert from <u>smaller units</u> to <u>bigger units</u>, you need to <u>divide</u>. Don't get this the wrong way round or you'll get answers that are far too big or far too small.

Drawing Conclusions

*Once you've carried out an experiment and processed your data, it's time to work out **what your data shows**.*

You Can **Only Conclude** What the Data Shows and **NO MORE**

1) To come to a conclusion, <u>look at your data</u> and <u>say what pattern you see</u>.

<u>EXAMPLE</u>: The table on the right shows the heights of pea plant seedlings grown for three weeks with different fertilisers.

Fertiliser	Mean growth / mm
A	13.5
B	19.5
No fertiliser	5.5

<u>CONCLUSION</u>: <u>Pea plant</u> seedlings grow taller over a <u>three week</u> period with fertiliser B than with fertiliser A.

2) It's important that the conclusion <u>matches the data</u> it's based on — it <u>shouldn't go any further</u>.

<u>EXAMPLE continued</u>: You can't conclude that <u>any other type of plant</u> grows taller with fertiliser B than with fertiliser A — the results could be totally different.

3) You also need to be able to <u>use your results</u> to <u>justify your conclusion</u> (i.e. back it up).

<u>EXAMPLE continued</u>: The pea plants grow 6 mm more on average with fertiliser B than with fertiliser A.

4) When writing a conclusion you need to say whether or not the data <u>supports</u> the <u>original hypothesis</u>:

<u>EXAMPLE continued</u>: The hypothesis might have been that adding different types of fertiliser would affect the growth of pea plants by different amounts. If so, the data <u>supports</u> the hypothesis.

Correlation **DOES NOT** Mean **Cause**

1) If two things are <u>correlated</u>, there's a <u>relationship</u> between them — see page 11.

2) But a correlation <u>doesn't always</u> mean that a change in one variable is <u>causing</u> the change in the other.

3) There are <u>three possible reasons</u> for a correlation:

1) <u>CHANCE</u>: The results happened <u>by chance</u>. Other scientists <u>wouldn't</u> get a correlation if they carried out the same investigation.

2) <u>LINKED BY A 3RD VARIABLE</u>: There's <u>another factor</u> involved.

E.g. there's a correlation between water temperature and shark attacks. They're linked by a <u>third variable</u> — the number of people swimming (more people swim when the water's hotter, which means you get more shark attacks).

3) <u>CAUSE</u>: Sometimes a change in one variable does <u>cause</u> a change in the other. You can only conclude this when you've <u>controlled all the variables</u> that could be affecting the result.

Uncertainty

*Uncertainty is how sure you can really be about your data. There's a little bit of **maths** to do, and also a formula to learn. But don't worry too much — it's no more than a simple bit of subtraction and division.*

Uncertainty is the Amount of Error Your Measurements Might Have

1) Measurements you make will have some <u>uncertainty</u> in them (i.e. they won't be completely perfect).

2) This can be due to <u>random errors</u> (see page 8). It can also be due to <u>limits</u> in what your <u>measuring equipment</u> can measure.

3) This means that the <u>mean</u> of your results will have some uncertainty to it.

4) You can <u>calculate</u> the uncertainty of a <u>mean result</u> using this equation:

$$\text{uncertainty} = \frac{\text{range}}{2}$$

← The range is the largest value minus the smallest value (p.9).

5) The <u>less precise</u> your results are, the <u>higher</u> the uncertainty will be.

6) Uncertainties are shown using the '±' symbol.

EXAMPLE

The table below shows the results of an experiment to determine the speed of a trolley as it moves along a horizontal surface. Calculate the uncertainty of the mean.

Repeat	1	2	3	mean
Speed (m/s)	2.02	1.98	2.00	2.00

1) First work out the range:

Range = 2.02 − 1.98 = 0.04 m/s

2) Use the range to find the uncertainty:

Uncertainty = range ÷ 2 = 0.04 ÷ 2 = 0.02 m/s

So the uncertainty of the mean = 2.00 ± 0.02 m/s

MATHS TIP

The smaller the uncertainty, the more precise your results...

Remember that equation for <u>uncertainty</u>. You never know when you might need it — you could be expected to use it in the exams. You need to make sure all the <u>data</u> is in the <u>same units</u> though. For example, if you had some measurements in metres, and some in centimetres, you'd need to convert them all into either metres or centimetres before you set about calculating uncertainty.

Evaluations

*Hurrah! The end of another investigation. Well, now you have to work out all the things you did **wrong**. That's what **evaluations** are all about I'm afraid. Best get cracking with this page...*

Evaluations — Describe **How** it Could be **Improved**

In an evaluation you look back over the whole investigation.

1) You should comment on the <u>method</u> — was it <u>valid</u>?
   Did you control all the other variables to make it a <u>fair test</u>?

2) Comment on the <u>quality</u> of the <u>results</u> — was there <u>enough evidence</u> to reach a valid <u>conclusion</u>?
   Were the results <u>repeatable</u>, <u>reproducible</u>, <u>accurate</u> and <u>precise</u>?

3) Were there any <u>anomalous</u> results? If there were <u>none</u> then <u>say so</u>.
   If there were any, try to <u>explain</u> them — were they caused by <u>errors</u> in measurement?

4) You should comment on the level of <u>uncertainty</u> in your results too.

5) Thinking about these things lets you say how <u>confident</u> you are that your conclusion is <u>right</u>.

6) Then you can suggest any <u>changes</u> to the <u>method</u> that would <u>improve</u> the
   quality of the results, so you could have <u>more confidence</u> in your conclusion.

7) For example, taking measurements at <u>narrower intervals</u>
   could give you a <u>more accurate result</u>. E.g.

- Say you do an experiment to find the <u>temperature</u> at which an enzyme <u>works best</u>.
- You take measurements at <u>30 °C</u>, <u>40 °C</u> and <u>50 °C</u>.
  The results show that the enzyme works best at <u>40 °C</u>.
- To get a more accurate result, you could <u>repeat</u> the experiment and take <u>more measurements</u>
  <u>around 40 °C</u>. You might then find that the enzyme actually works best at <u>42 °C</u>.

8) You could also make more <u>predictions</u> based on your conclusion.
   You could then carry out <u>further experiments</u> to test the new predictions.

Always look for ways to improve your investigations

So there you have it — <u>Working Scientifically</u>. Make sure you know this stuff like the back of your hand. It's not just in the lab or the field, when you're carrying out your groundbreaking <u>investigations</u>, that you'll need to know how to work scientifically. You can be asked about it in the <u>exams</u> as well. So swot up...

Cells

*Cells are the **building blocks** of **every organism on the planet**.*

Cells can be **Prokaryotic** or **Eukaryotic**

1) All living things are made of cells.

2) Eukaryotic cells are complex. All animal and plant cells are eukaryotic.

3) Prokaryotic cells are smaller and simpler. Bacteria are prokaryotic cells.

Plant and Animal Cells have Similarities and Differences

The different parts of a cell are called subcellular structures.

Animal Cells

Most animal cells have these subcellular structures:

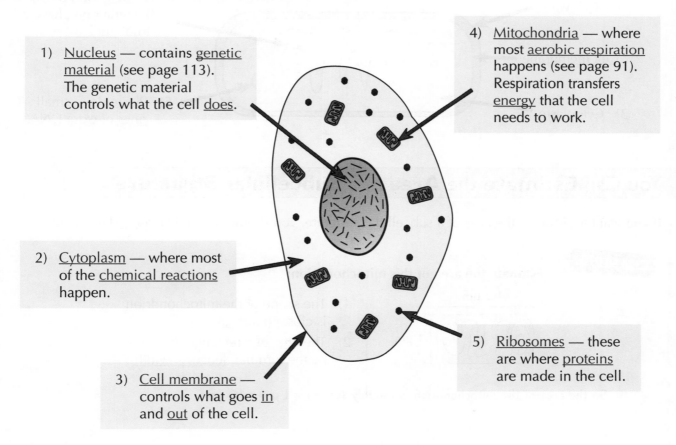

1) Nucleus — contains genetic material (see page 113). The genetic material controls what the cell does.

4) Mitochondria — where most aerobic respiration happens (see page 91). Respiration transfers energy that the cell needs to work.

2) Cytoplasm — where most of the chemical reactions happen.

3) Cell membrane — controls what goes in and out of the cell.

5) Ribosomes — these are where proteins are made in the cell.

Subcellular structures are all the different parts of a cell

Make sure you get to grips with the different subcellular structures that animal cells contain before you move on to the next page. There are more subcellular structures coming up that you need to know...

Cells

Plant Cells

Plant cells usually have <u>all the bits</u> that <u>animal</u> cells have.
They also have:

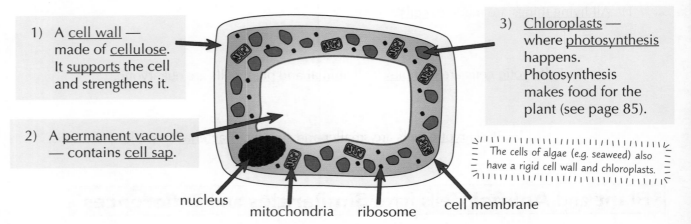

1) A <u>cell wall</u> —
made of <u>cellulose</u>.
It <u>supports</u> the cell
and strengthens it.

2) A <u>permanent vacuole</u>
— contains <u>cell sap</u>.

3) <u>Chloroplasts</u> —
where <u>photosynthesis</u>
happens.
Photosynthesis
makes food for the
plant (see page 85).

The cells of algae (e.g. seaweed) also
have a rigid cell wall and chloroplasts.

nucleus   mitochondria   ribosome   cell membrane

Bacterial Cells Have These Subcellular Structures:

1) <u>Cell wall</u>

2) <u>Cell membrane</u>

3) Cytoplasm

4) A <u>single loop</u> of <u>DNA</u>.
Bacteria <u>don't</u> have a
'true' <u>nucleus</u>.

5) <u>Plasmids</u> — small
<u>rings</u> of <u>extra DNA</u>.

You Can Estimate the Area of a Subcellular Structure

If you want to <u>estimate</u> the <u>area</u> of a subcellular structure, you should treat it like a <u>regular shape</u>:

EXAMPLE

Estimate the area of this mitochondrion:

10 μm

1 μm

1) The shape of the mitochondrion
is close to a <u>rectangle</u>.

2) The <u>area</u> of a rectangle is found
by the formula: <u>length × width</u>

So the area of the mitochondrion is roughly 10 μm × 1 μm = 10 μm²

REVISION TIP

There's quite a bit to learn in biology — but that's life, I guess...

On these pages are a <u>typical animal cell</u>, <u>plant cell</u> and <u>bacterial cell</u>. Make sure you're
familiar with all their <u>structures</u>. A good way to check that you know what all the bits and pieces
are is to copy out the diagrams and see if you can remember all the labels. No cheating.

Microscopy

Microscopes are pretty important for biology. So here are a couple of pages all about them...

Microscopes **Magnify** Things (Make Them Look **Bigger**)

1) The ways we can use microscopes have developed over the years. This is because technology and knowledge have improved.

2) Light microscopes can be used to look at cells. They let us see large subcellular structures (like the nucleus).

3) Electron microscopes have a higher resolution than light microscopes — they show things in more detail.

4) Electron microscopes also have a higher magnification than light microscopes. They can let us see really small things like ribosomes and plasmids.

5) Electron microscopes were invented after light microscopes. They helped scientists understand more about subcellular structures.

> See the next page for how to use a light microscope.

You Need to be Able to Use the **Formula** for **Magnification**

Magnification is how many times bigger the image is than the real thing. You can work out the magnification of an image using this formula:

$$\text{magnification} = \frac{\text{image size}}{\text{real size}}$$

Image size and real size should have the same units.

EXAMPLE

The width of a cell is 0.02 mm. The width of its image under a microscope is 8 mm. What magnification was used to view the cell?

magnification = 8 mm ÷ 0.02 mm = × 400

You Can Write Numbers in **Standard Form**

Standard form is useful for writing very big or very small numbers in a simpler way.

EXAMPLE   **Write 0.0025 mm in standard form.**

1) The first number needs to be between 1 and 10 so the decimal point needs to move after the '2'.

2) Count how many places the decimal point has moved — this is the power of 10.

3) The power of 10 is positive if the decimal point is moved to the left. It's negative if the decimal point has moved to the right. Here, the decimal point has moved right, so it needs a minus sign.

0.0025 → 2.5
1 2 3

The decimal point has moved 3 places = 10^3

2.5×10^{-3}

Standard form saves you from having to write a lot of zeros

Remember, when you're writing a number in standard form, you've got to move the decimal point to just after the first digit that's not a zero. E.g. 342 000 is 3.42×10^5, and 0.0009513 is 9.513×10^4.

Q1 A cheek cell is viewed under a microscope with × 40 magnification. The image of the cell is 2.4 mm wide. Calculate the real width of the cheek cell. Give your answer in μm. [2 marks]

Q1 Video Solution

Microscopy

*So you know what microscopes **do**... now you need to know how to **use** one.*

You Need to **Prepare** Your **Slide**

Lots of different animal and plant cells can be looked at under a light microscope.

1) Add a <u>drop of water</u> to the middle of a clean slide.

2) Cut up an onion and take off one <u>layer</u>.

3) Use <u>tweezers</u> to peel off some <u>epidermal tissue</u> (the clear 'skin') from the <u>bottom</u> of the layer.

4) Using the tweezers, place the skin into the <u>water</u> on the slide.

5) Add a drop of <u>iodine solution</u>. Iodine solution is a <u>stain</u>. Stains can make different parts of a cell <u>easier to see</u>.

6) Place a <u>cover slip</u> on top. Try <u>not</u> to get any <u>air bubbles</u> under it.

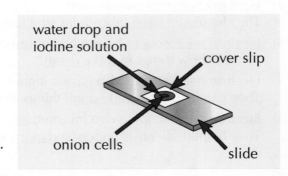
water drop and iodine solution
cover slip
onion cells
slide

Know the Parts of a **Light Microscope**

To look at your prepared slides, you need to know how to use a light microscope. Here are the main parts you'll use:

Eyepiece
Coarse adjustment knob
Fine adjustment knob
High and low power objective lenses
Stage
Light

Stains can make subcellular structures easier to see

Carry on to the next page for <u>how to use</u> the microscope above to view your specimen.

Microscopy

Use a **Light Microscope** to Look at Your **Slide**

1) Clip the <u>slide</u> onto the <u>stage</u>.

2) Select the <u>objective lens</u> with the lowest magnification.

3) Use the <u>coarse adjustment knob</u> to move the stage up to <u>just below</u> the objective lens.

4) Look down the <u>eyepiece</u>. Move the stage downwards until the image is <u>roughly in focus</u>.

5) Move the <u>fine adjustment knob</u>, until you get a <u>clear image</u> of what's on the slide.

6) If you want a bigger image, use an <u>objective lens</u> with a <u>higher magnification</u> and refocus.

Draw Your Observations **Neatly** with a **Pencil**

1) You should use a <u>pencil</u> with a <u>sharp point</u> to draw <u>what you see</u> under the microscope.

2) Use <u>smooth lines</u> to draw the <u>outlines</u> of the <u>main features</u> (e.g. nucleus, chloroplasts).

3) <u>Don't</u> do any <u>shading</u> or <u>colouring in</u>.

4) <u>Label</u> the features with <u>straight lines</u>. Make sure the lines <u>don't cross over</u> each other.

5) The drawing should take up <u>at least half</u> the space available.

6) Include a <u>title</u> and a <u>scale</u>.

7) Write down the <u>magnification</u> that it was observed under.

You can measure the real size of the cells using a ruler that fits onto your microscope (see p.394).

Your microscope might look a bit different

The appearance of light microscopes can <u>vary</u> (e.g. they might have two eyepieces rather than one) but they should have the <u>same basic features</u> shown on the previous page.

Warm-Up & Exam Questions

So, hopefully you've read the last five pages. But could you cope if a question on cells or microscopes came up in the exam? See what happens when you try out these questions...

Warm-Up Questions

1) Name the subcellular structures where aerobic respiration takes place.
2) Give two ways in which animal cells are different from plant cells.
3) True or false? Bacterial cells have a nucleus.
4) What type of microscope should be used to look at ribosomes and plasmids?
5) Write the number 0.00045 μm in standard form.

Exam Questions

1 Which of the following cells is an example of a prokaryotic cell? Tick **one** box. *(Grade 3-4)*

☑ bacterial cell ☐ animal cell ☐ plant cell ☐ sperm cell

[1 mark]

2 **Figure 1** shows a typical plant cell. *(Grade 3-4)*

Figure 1

2.1 Which label points to a chloroplast? Tick **one** box.

☐ A ☐ B ☑ C ☐ D

[1 mark]

2.2 What is the function of a chloroplast? Tick **one** box.

☑ allows photosynthesis to take place ☐ contains genetic material ☐ contains cell sap

[1 mark]

2.3 **Figure 1** also shows ribosomes.
What is the function of a ribosome? Tick **one** box.

☐ aerobic respiration ☑ making proteins ☐ storing extra DNA

[1 mark]

PRACTICAL

3 A light microscope can be used to observe a layer of onion cells on a slide. *(Grade 4-5)*

3.1* Describe how you would prepare a slide to observe a layer of onion cells.

[4 marks]

3.2 When the onion cell is viewed with × 100 magnification, the image of the cell is 7.5 mm wide.

Calculate the real width of the onion cell in micrometres (μm). Complete the following steps.

Calculate the real width in mm using the formula: $\text{real size} = \dfrac{\text{image size}}{\text{magnification}}$

Convert mm to μm.   7.5 ÷ 100 = 0.075

[2 marks]

Topic B1 — Cell Biology

Cell Differentiation and Specialisation

*Cells **don't** all look the **same**. They have **different structures** to suit their **different functions**.*

Specialised Cells are Cells that Carry Out a Specific Function

1) The process by which cells <u>change</u> to become <u>specialised</u> is called <u>differentiation</u>.

2) As cells change, they develop <u>different subcellular structures</u>.
   They turn into <u>different types of cells</u>. This allows them to carry out <u>specific functions</u>.

undifferentiated
cell

differentiated
white blood cell

3) Most differentiation occurs as an organism <u>develops</u>.

4) Most <u>animal</u> cells can only differentiate at an <u>early stage</u> of the animal's life.

5) But lots of <u>plant</u> cells can differentiate for the <u>whole</u> of the plant's life.

6) The cells that differentiate in <u>adult animals</u> are mainly used for <u>repairing</u> and <u>replacing cells</u>.

7) Some cells are <u>undifferentiated</u> — they are called <u>stem cells</u>.
   There's more about them on pages 25-26.

There Are Many Examples of Specialised Cells...

Sperm Cells Take the Male DNA to the Egg

1) A sperm cell has a <u>tail</u> to help it <u>swim</u> to the egg.

2) It has a lot of <u>mitochondria</u> (see p.17).
   These provide <u>energy</u> for swimming.

Nerve Cells Carry Electrical Signals Around the Body

1) Nerve cells are <u>long</u> to cover <u>more distance</u> in the body.

2) They have <u>branches</u> at the end to <u>connect</u> to other nerve cells.

Cell Specialisation

Muscle Cells Contract (Shorten)

1) Muscle cells are <u>long</u> so they have space to <u>contract</u>.

2) They have <u>lots of mitochondria</u>. These provide <u>energy</u> for contracting.

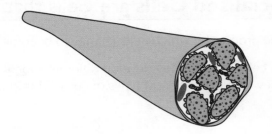

Root Hair Cells Absorb Water and Minerals

1) Root hair cells grow into long "<u>hairs</u>" that stick out into the soil.

2) This gives the plant a <u>big surface area</u> for absorbing <u>water</u> and <u>mineral ions</u> from the soil.

Phloem Cells Transport Food and Xylem Cells Transport Water

1) <u>Phloem</u> and <u>xylem cells</u> form phloem and xylem <u>tubes</u>.

2) To form the tubes, the cells are <u>long</u> and joined <u>end to end</u>.

3) Xylem cells are <u>hollow</u> and phloem cells have <u>very few</u> subcellular structures. So there's lots of space inside the cells for stuff to <u>flow through</u> them.

phloem   xylem

There's more about phloem and xylem on page 67.

Cells have the same basic bits but are specialised for their function

Not all cells contain <u>all</u> of the bits shown on pages 17-18. This is because some specialised cells don't have a use for certain subcellular structures — it depends on their <u>function</u>. For example, root hair cells grow <u>underground</u> in the soil. They <u>don't need chloroplasts</u> because they don't photosynthesise.

Stem Cells

*Stem cell research has exciting **possibilities**, but **not everyone agrees** with some of the uses of stem cells.*

Stem Cells can Differentiate into Different Types of Cells

1) Cells <u>differentiate</u> (change) to become <u>specialised</u> for their job (see page 23).

2) <u>Undifferentiated</u> cells are called <u>stem cells</u>.

3) Stem cells can produce lots <u>more</u> undifferentiated cells and differentiate into <u>different types of cell</u>.

4) Stem cells found in early <u>human embryos</u> are called <u>embryonic stem cells</u>.

5) Embryonic stem cells can turn into <u>any</u> kind of cell at all.

6) <u>Adults</u> also have stem cells. They're only in <u>certain places</u> in the body, like <u>bone marrow</u> (a tissue inside bones).

7) Adult stem cells can <u>only</u> produce <u>certain types</u> of specialised cell, e.g. blood cells.

8) Stem cells from embryos and bone marrow can be <u>cloned</u> (copied) in a lab. The cloned cells can be used in <u>medicine</u> or <u>research</u>.

An embryo is an unborn baby at an early stage of growth.

Stem Cells May Be Able to Cure Many Diseases

1) <u>Embryonic stem cells</u> could be used to <u>replace faulty cells</u> in sick people.

> E.g. you could make <u>nerve cells</u> for people with <u>paralysis</u> (where they can't move part of the body due to an injury to their spine) or <u>insulin-producing cells</u> for people with <u>diabetes</u> (see page 106).

2) It's possible to <u>make an embryo</u> that has the <u>same genes</u> as a <u>patient</u>. This is called <u>therapeutic cloning</u>.

3) This means that the <u>stem cells</u> from the embryo <u>wouldn't</u> be <u>rejected</u> by the patient's body.

4) However, there are <u>risks</u> involved in using stem cells in medicine. For example, the stem cells could be <u>infected</u> with a <u>virus</u>. The virus could be <u>passed on</u> to a patient and make them <u>sicker</u>.

Stem Cells

Some People Are **Against Stem Cell Research**

1) Some people feel embryos <u>shouldn't</u> be used for research because each one could be a <u>human life</u>.

2) Others think that <u>curing patients</u> who are <u>suffering</u> is <u>more important</u> than the rights of embryos.

3) They argue that the embryos used in the research are usually <u>unwanted ones</u> from <u>fertility clinics</u>. If they weren't used for research, they would probably just be <u>destroyed</u>.

4) Some people feel that scientists should be finding <u>other sources</u> of stem cells.

Stem Cells Can Produce **Identical Plants**

1) Plants have tissues called <u>meristems</u>. Meristems are where <u>growth</u> occurs — in the tips of <u>roots</u> and <u>shoots</u>.

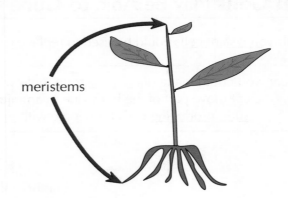

meristems

2) The meristems contain <u>stem cells</u> that can differentiate into <u>any type</u> of plant cell. They can do this all through the plant's <u>entire life</u>.

3) These stem cells can be used to make <u>clones</u> (identical copies) of plants <u>quickly</u> and <u>cheaply</u>. Clones can be made of:

- <u>rare species</u> (to prevent them being wiped out).
- <u>crop plants</u> that have <u>features</u> that are useful for farmers, e.g. plants <u>aren't killed</u> by a <u>disease</u>.

Getting stem cells from other places would avoid the disagreements

Scientists are looking into ways of getting human stem cells without using embryos. Whatever your opinion of stem cell research is, it's good to know what their <u>uses</u> are and the arguments <u>for</u> and <u>against</u> using them.

Chromosomes and Mitosis

*In order to survive and grow, our cells have got to be able to **divide**. And that means our DNA does as well...*

Chromosomes Contain Genetic Information

1) The <u>nucleus</u> of a cell contains <u>chromosomes</u>.

2) Chromosomes are <u>coiled up</u> lengths of <u>DNA molecules</u>.

3) Each chromosome carries a <u>large number</u> of genes.

4) Different genes <u>control</u> the development of different <u>characteristics</u>, e.g. hair colour.

5) <u>Body cells</u> normally have <u>two copies</u> of each <u>chromosome</u>.

6) There are <u>23 pairs of chromosomes</u> in a human cell.

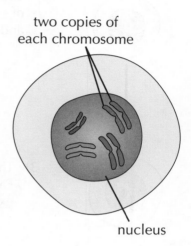

two copies of each chromosome

nucleus

The Cell Cycle Makes New Cells

1) <u>Body cells</u> in <u>multicellular organisms</u> (e.g. like you, me or a plant) <u>divide</u> to make new cells. This is part of a series of stages called the <u>cell cycle</u>.

2) The stage of the cell cycle when the cell <u>divides</u> is called <u>mitosis</u>.

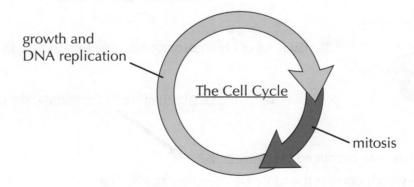

growth and DNA replication

The Cell Cycle

mitosis

3) Multicellular organisms use <u>mitosis</u> to <u>grow</u> and <u>develop</u>.

4) You need to know about the main stages of the <u>cell cycle</u> shown on the next page.

The cell cycle is important for growth and repair

When a cell goes through the cell cycle, you end up with <u>two cells</u> where you originally had just one. The body <u>controls</u> which cells divide and when — if this control <u>fails</u>, it can result in <u>cancer</u> (see page 64).

Chromosomes and Mitosis

*There are two main stages of the **cell cycle**...*

Growth and DNA Replication

Before it divides:

1) The cell <u>grows</u> and <u>increases</u> the amount of <u>subcellular structures</u> such as <u>ribosomes</u> and <u>mitochondria</u> (see page 17).

2) The DNA is <u>replicated</u> (copied) — so there's one copy for each new cell.

3) The DNA forms <u>X-shaped</u> chromosomes. Each 'arm' of the chromosome is an <u>exact copy</u> of the other.

The <u>left arm</u> has the same DNA as the <u>right arm</u> of the chromosome.

Mitosis

The cell is now ready for <u>dividing</u>...

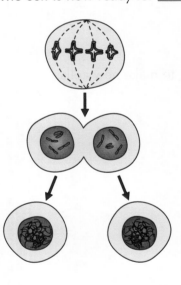

4) The chromosomes <u>line up</u> at the centre of the cell.

5) The <u>two arms</u> of each chromosome are <u>pulled apart</u> to <u>opposite ends</u> of the cell.

6) This <u>divides</u> the <u>nucleus</u>.

7) Each set of chromosomes become the <u>nucleus</u> of a new cell.

8) The <u>cytoplasm</u> and <u>cell membrane</u> divide.

The cell has now produced <u>two new cells</u>.

- They both contain the <u>same DNA</u> — they're <u>identical</u>.
- They're also <u>identical</u> to the <u>original cell</u>.

Mitosis produces two identical cells

Mitosis can seem tricky at first. But don't worry — just go through it slowly, <u>one step at a time</u>.

Q1 Video Solution

Q1 A student looks at cells in the tip of a plant root under a microscope.
She counts 11 cells that are undergoing mitosis and 62 cells that are not.
a) Calculate the percentage of cells that are undergoing mitosis. [1 mark]
b) Suggest how the student can tell whether a cell is undergoing mitosis or not. [1 mark]

Warm-Up & Exam Questions

There's only one way to do well in the exam — learn the facts and then practise lots of exam questions to see what it'll be like on the big day. We couldn't have made it easier for you — so do it.

Warm-Up Questions

1) What is the name of the process where cells become specialised for their job?
2) Describe how a root hair cell is specialised for its function.
3) How many copies of each chromosome does a normal body cell have?
4) Where in the cell are chromosomes found?
5) True or false? The cells produced in mitosis are genetically identical.

Exam Questions

1 Draw **one** line from each cell type to its adaptation. Grade 1-3

Cell type

| Sperm cell |

| Nerve cell |

| Muscle cell |

Adaptation

| Many mitochondria to provide energy for contracting |

| Very few subcellular structures, so there is more space inside the cell |

| A tail for swimming |

| Branches to connect to other cells |

[3 marks]

2 Stem cells are cells produced by both plants and animals that can develop into any type of cell. Grade 4-5

2.1 Draw **two** arrows on **Figure 1** to show two places where stem cells are produced in plants.

Figure 1

[2 marks]

2.2 Describe **one** way that plant stem cells can be used by farmers to increase crop yields.

[2 marks]

2.3 Stem cells might be useful for the treatment of human diseases.
Give **one** health condition that could possibly be treated with stem cells.

[1 mark]

Diffusion

*Diffusion is **really important** in living organisms — it's how a lot of **substances** get **in** and **out** of cells.*

Don't Be Put Off by the **Fancy Word**

1) "<u>Diffusion</u>" is the <u>movement</u> of particles from where there are <u>lots</u> of them to where there are <u>fewer</u> of them.

2) You have to learn this fancy way of saying it:

> <u>DIFFUSION</u> is the <u>SPREADING OUT</u> of <u>particles</u> from an area of <u>HIGHER CONCENTRATION</u> to an area of <u>LOWER CONCENTRATION</u>.

3) Diffusion happens in <u>solutions</u> and <u>gases</u>. For example, the smell of perfume <u>diffuses</u> through the <u>air</u> in a room:

air

perfume particles

perfume particles diffused in the air

4) The <u>difference</u> in concentration is called the <u>concentration gradient</u>. The <u>bigger</u> the <u>difference</u> in concentration, the <u>faster</u> the diffusion rate.

5) A <u>higher temperature</u> will also give a <u>faster</u> diffusion rate. This is because the particles have <u>more energy</u>, so move around faster.

Cell Membranes Are Kind of **Clever**...

Oxygen is needed for aerobic respiration — see page 91.

1) Cell membranes let stuff diffuse <u>in and out</u> of the cell.

2) Only very <u>small</u> molecules can <u>fit</u> through cell membranes, e.g. <u>oxygen</u>, <u>glucose</u>, <u>amino acids</u> and <u>water</u>.

3) <u>Big</u> molecules like <u>starch</u> and <u>proteins</u> can't fit through the membrane:

protein

starch

glucose

amino acid

4) Molecules flow through the membrane from where there's a <u>higher concentration</u> (a lot of them) to where there's a <u>lower concentration</u> (not such a lot of them).

5) They actually move <u>both</u> ways — but if there are a lot <u>more</u> particles on one side of the membrane, there's a <u>net</u> (overall) movement <u>from</u> that side.

6) The <u>larger</u> the <u>surface area</u> of the membrane, the <u>faster</u> the diffusion rate. This is because <u>more</u> particles can pass through <u>at the same time</u>.

Diffusion is just particles spreading out

<u>Really tiny particles</u> can go through cell membranes to <u>even up the concentration</u> on either side.

Q1 Video Solution

Q1 A student adds a drop of ink to a glass of cold water.
    a) What will the student observe to happen to the drop of ink. Explain your answer. [2 marks]
    b) How might the observation differ if the ink was added to a glass of warm water? [1 mark]

Q2 Explain how the surface area of a membrane affects the rate of diffusion. [2 marks]

Osmosis

*If you've got your head round **diffusion**, osmosis will be a **breeze**.*
If not, have another look at the previous page...

Osmosis is the Movement of **Water Molecules**

OSMOSIS is the movement of water molecules across a partially permeable membrane from a less concentrated solution to a more concentrated solution.

1) A partially permeable membrane is just one with very small holes in it.

2) Tiny molecules (like water) can pass through it, but bigger molecules (e.g. sucrose) can't.

3) Water molecules actually pass both ways through the membrane during osmosis.

4) But overall, the water molecules move from the less concentrated solution (where there are lots of water molecules) to the more concentrated solution (where there are fewer water molecules).

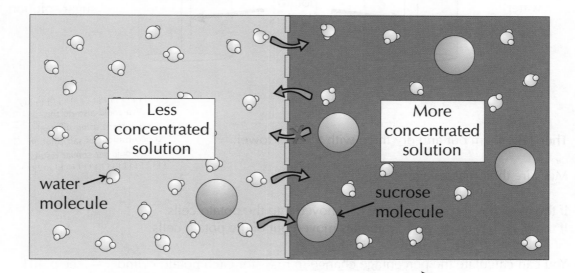

Less concentrated solution

More concentrated solution

water molecule

sucrose molecule

Overall movement of water molecules

5) This means the more concentrated solution gets more dilute.

6) The water acts like it's trying to "even up" the concentration either side of the membrane.

Diffusion is movement from where there's lots to where there's few...

...so osmosis is really just a fancy word for the diffusion of water molecules. It's simple really.

Osmosis

*There's an **experiment** you can do to show osmosis at work.*

You can **Observe** the Effect of **Sugar Solutions** on **Plant Tissue**

1) First, cut up a <u>potato</u> into cylinders with the <u>same length and width</u>.

2) Then get two beakers — one with <u>pure water</u> and another with a <u>very concentrated sugar solution</u> (e.g. 1 mol/dm³).

3) You can also have a few other beakers with <u>less concentrated sugar solutions</u> (e.g. 0.2 mol/dm³, 0.4 mol/dm³, etc).

4) Measure the <u>mass</u> of each potato cylinder, then put <u>one</u> in each beaker.

5) Leave the potato cylinders for <u>twenty four hours</u>.

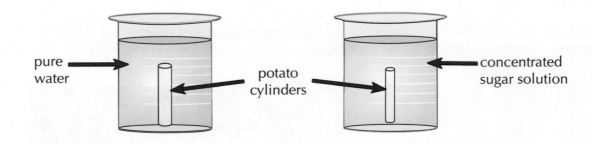

6) Then take them out and <u>dry</u> them with a paper towel.

7) Measure their masses <u>again</u>.

8) If the <u>mass has increased</u>, water has moved <u>into</u> the potato cells. If the <u>mass has decreased</u>, water has moved <u>out</u> of the potato cells.

9) You can calculate the <u>percentage change in mass</u> for each potato cylinder — see p.401. This means you can <u>compare</u> the <u>effects</u> of each sugar solution.

10) The only thing you should <u>change</u> in this experiment is the <u>concentration</u> of the <u>sugar solution</u>. <u>Everything else</u> (e.g. volume of solution, temperature, time, type of sugar used) should <u>stay the same</u>.

> You could also do this experiment using different concentrations of salt solution. You should see similar results.

Osmosis is the reason why it's bad to drink sea-water...

The high <u>salt</u> content means you end up with a much <u>lower water concentration</u> in your blood and tissue fluid than in your cells. All the water is sucked out of your cells and they <u>shrivel and die</u>.

Q1　Explain what will happen to the mass of a piece of potato added to a concentrated salt solution.

[2 marks]

Q1 Video Solution

Active Transport

*Sometimes substances need to be absorbed from an area where they are in **low concentration** into an area where they are in **high concentration**. This happens by a process called **active transport**.*

Root Hairs Take In Minerals and Water

1) Plant roots are covered in <u>millions</u> of <u>root hair cells</u>.

2) These cells <u>stick out</u> into the soil.

3) The "hairs" give the roots a <u>large surface area</u>.

4) This is useful for absorbing <u>water</u> and <u>mineral ions</u> from the soil.

5) Plants <u>need</u> mineral ions for <u>healthy growth</u>.

root hair cell

Root Hairs Take in Minerals Using Active Transport

1) The concentration of minerals is usually <u>higher</u> in the <u>root hair cells</u> than in the <u>soil</u> around them.

2) So the root hair cells <u>can't</u> use <u>diffusion</u> to take up minerals from the soil.

3) They use <u>active transport</u> instead.

4) Active transport allows the plant to absorb minerals from a very <u>dilute</u> solution in the soil — it moves the minerals <u>against</u> the <u>concentration gradient</u>.

5) But active transport needs <u>ENERGY</u> from <u>respiration</u> to make it work.

Water is taken into root hair cells by osmosis (see page 31).

mineral ions

higher concentration

to the rest of the plant

mineral ions

lower concentration

We Need Active Transport to Stop Us Starving

1) The body needs to <u>absorb nutrients</u> (e.g. glucose and amino acids) from <u>food</u> to <u>survive</u>.

2) The nutrients have to move from the <u>gut</u> into the <u>blood</u>.

3) When there's a <u>higher concentration</u> of nutrients in the gut, they <u>diffuse</u> into the blood.

4) Sometimes there's a <u>lower concentration</u> of nutrients in the gut than there is in the blood.

5) The body uses <u>active transport</u> to move the nutrients (like glucose) from a <u>lower concentration</u> in the <u>gut</u> to a <u>higher concentration</u> in the <u>blood</u>.

6) This means <u>glucose</u> can be taken into the blood <u>against</u> the concentration gradient. The glucose is then transported to <u>cells</u>, where it's used for <u>respiration</u> (see page 91).

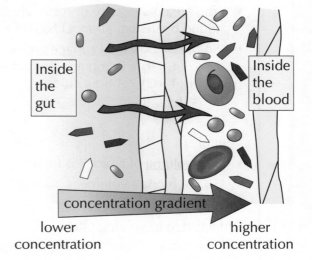

Inside the gut

Inside the blood

concentration gradient

lower concentration

higher concentration

Active transport uses energy

An important difference between <u>active transport</u> and <u>diffusion</u> is that active transport uses <u>energy</u>.

Exchanging Substances

*How easily stuff **moves** between an **organism** and its **environment** depends on its **surface area to volume ratio**.*

Organisms Exchange Substances with their Environment

1) Cells can use <u>diffusion</u> to <u>take in</u> substances from the <u>environment</u>, such as <u>oxygen</u>.

2) They also use diffusion to <u>get rid</u> of <u>waste products</u>, such as:

- <u>Carbon dioxide</u> (from <u>respiration</u>).
- <u>Urea</u> (from the <u>breakdown</u> of <u>proteins</u>) — urea diffuses from <u>cells</u> into the <u>blood plasma</u> (see p.53). It is then removed from the body by the <u>kidneys</u>.

3) How <u>easy</u> it is for an organism to <u>exchange</u> (swap) substances with its environment depends on the organism's <u>surface area to volume ratio</u>.

You Can Calculate an Organism's Surface Area to Volume Ratio

1) A <u>ratio</u> shows <u>how big</u> one value is <u>compared</u> to another.

2) So a <u>surface area to volume ratio</u> shows how big a shape's <u>surface</u> is compared to its <u>volume</u>.

E.g. a <u>2 cm × 4 cm × 4 cm block</u> can be used to <u>estimate</u> the surface area to volume ratio of a <u>hippo</u>:

Surface area
- The <u>area</u> of a square or rectangle is found by the equation: LENGTH × WIDTH.
- So the hippo's <u>total surface area</u> is:
  (4 × 4) × 2 (top and bottom surfaces)
  + (4 × 2) × 4 (four sides)
  = <u>64 cm²</u>.

Volume
- The <u>volume</u> of a block is found by the equation: LENGTH × WIDTH × HEIGHT.
- So the hippo's <u>volume</u> is 4 × 4 × 2 = <u>32 cm³</u>.

Surface area to volume ratio
- The surface area to volume ratio (<u>SA : V</u>) of the hippo can be written as <u>64 : 32</u>.
- To get the ratio so that volume is equal to <u>one</u>, <u>divide both sides</u> of the ratio by the <u>volume</u>.

  64 ÷ 32 = 2   32 ÷ 32 = 1   So the SA : V of the hippo is <u>2 : 1</u>.

Exchanging Substances

*Now for some more on **surface area to volume ratios**, and why they're important in biology...*

Larger Objects Usually Have Smaller Surface Area to Volume Ratios

1) A 1 cm × 1 cm × 1 cm block can be used to
estimate the surface area to volume ratio of a mouse.

It's found that the SA : V of the mouse is 6 : 1.

2) The larger the organism, the smaller its surface area is compared to its volume.

> Example: The surface area of the mouse is six times its volume.
> The surface area of the hippo (see previous page) is only two times its volume.
>
> So the hippo has a smaller surface area compared to its volume.

3) The smaller its surface area compared to its volume, the harder it is
for an organism to exchange substances with its environment.

Multicellular Organisms Need Exchange Surfaces

1) Single-celled organisms have a large surface area compared to their volume.

2) So, they can exchange all the substances they need across their surface (the cell membrane).

3) Multicellular organisms (such as animals) have a smaller surface area compared to their volume.

4) They can't normally exchange enough substances across their outside surface alone.

5) Instead, multicellular organisms have specialised exchange surfaces
— see the next page and page 37 for some examples.

6) They also have transport systems that carry substances to and from their exchange surfaces.

7) The exchange surfaces are ADAPTED to allow enough of different substances to pass through:

- They have a thin membrane (so substances only have a short distance to diffuse).

- They have a large surface area (so lots of a substance can diffuse at once).

- Exchange surfaces in animals have lots of blood vessels
(so stuff can get into and out of the blood quickly).

- Gas exchange surfaces in animals (e.g. alveoli) are ventilated too — air moves in and out.

Surface area to volume ratios crop up a lot in biology...

...so it's a good idea to try to understand them now. Remember that, generally speaking,
a smaller object has a larger surface area to volume ratio than a bigger object.

Q1 Video Solution

Q1 A bacterial cell can be represented by a 2 μm × 2 μm × 1 μm block.
Calculate the cell's surface area to volume ratio.

[3 marks]

More on Exchanging Substances

*Here are a couple of examples of **exchange surfaces** inside your body...*

Gas Exchange Happens in the Lungs

1) Oxygen (O_2) and carbon dioxide (CO_2) are exchanged in the lungs.

2) The lungs contain millions of little air sacs called alveoli. This is where gas exchange happens.

3) The alveoli are specialised for the diffusion of oxygen and carbon dioxide. They have:
   - A large surface area.
   - Very thin walls (so gases don't have far to diffuse).
   - A good blood supply.

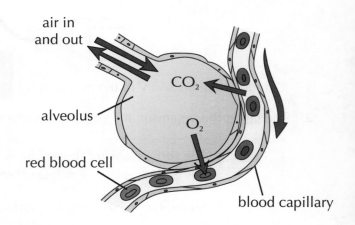

air in and out

CO_2

alveolus

O_2

red blood cell

blood capillary

The Villi Provide a Really Big Surface Area

1) The inside of the small intestine is covered in millions of villi.

2) They increase the surface area so that digested food is absorbed more quickly into the blood.

3) They have:
   - a single layer of surface cells,
   - a very good blood supply.

The digested food moves into the blood by diffusion and by active transport (see page 33).

villi

single layer of cells

lots of capillaries

Humans need alveoli for gas exchange

Q1 Give one way in which alveoli are adapted for gas exchange.

[1 mark]

Q2 Video Solution

Q2 Coeliac disease causes inflammation of the small intestine, which can damage the villi. Suggest why a person with coeliac disease might have low levels of iron in their blood.

[2 marks]

More on Exchanging Substances

*More stuff on exchange surfaces for diffusion now — only this time they're in **plants** and **fish**.*

The **Structure of Leaves** Lets Gases **Diffuse** In and Out of Cells

1) Plant leaves need to <u>take in carbon dioxide</u> for photosynthesis, and <u>get rid</u> of <u>oxygen</u> and <u>water vapour</u>.

2) The underneath of the leaf is an <u>exchange surface</u>. It's covered in small <u>holes</u> called <u>stomata</u>.

3) <u>Carbon dioxide diffuses</u> through the stomata <u>into</u> the leaf.

4) <u>Oxygen</u> and <u>water vapour</u> diffuse <u>out</u> through the stomata.

5) The size of the stomata are controlled by <u>guard cells</u> — see page 68.

6) The <u>flattened shape</u> of the leaf increases the <u>area</u> of its exchange surface.

7) The <u>walls of the cells</u> inside the leaf are another exchange surface.
Gases diffuse <u>into</u> and <u>out of</u> the cells through these walls.

8) There are <u>air spaces</u> inside the leaf to <u>increase</u> the <u>area</u> of these surfaces.

cell wall
air space

Oxygen and water vapour diffuse <u>out of</u> the leaf

guard cell

stomata

CO_2 diffuses <u>into</u> leaf

Gills Have a **Large Surface Area** for **Gas Exchange**

1) The <u>gills</u> are the <u>gas exchange surface</u> in <u>fish</u>.

2) Water (containing <u>oxygen</u>) flows into the fish's <u>mouth</u> and passes out through the <u>gills</u>.

3) In the gills, <u>oxygen</u> diffuses from the <u>water</u> into the <u>blood</u>. <u>Carbon dioxide</u> diffuses from the <u>blood</u> into the <u>water</u>.

4) The gills are made up of lots of <u>thin plates</u>. This gives them a <u>large surface area</u> for <u>gases</u> to be <u>exchanged</u>.

5) The plates have lots of <u>blood capillaries</u>. So they have a <u>good blood supply</u> to <u>speed up diffusion</u>.

6) They also have a <u>thin layer</u> of surface cells. So the gases only have to diffuse a <u>short distance</u>.

mouth

water

gill

Exchange surfaces make diffusion quick and easy

Multicellular organisms are really <u>well adapted</u> for getting the substances they need to their cells. It makes sense — if they couldn't do this well, they'd die out. A <u>large surface area</u> is a key way that organisms' exchange surfaces are made more effective — molecules can only diffuse through a membrane when they're right next to it, and a large surface area means that <u>a lot more molecules</u> are close to the membrane.

Warm-Up & Exam Questions

Question time again — Warm-Up first, then Exam (or the other way round if you want to be different).

Warm-Up Questions

1) What is the word for the spreading out of particles from an area of higher concentration to an area of lower concentration?
2) True or false? Larger objects usually have smaller surface area to volume ratios than smaller objects.
3) How do villi in the small intestine help food to be absorbed more quickly?
4) Name one other exchange surface in humans.
5) What is the name of the small holes for exchanging gases on the underside a leaf?
6) Give one way in which the structure of a gill is adapted for effective gas exchange.

Exam Questions

1 **Figure 1** shows a cup of water which has just had a drop of dye added to it. *(Grade 3-4)*

Figure 1

water particle

dye particle

Drop of dye added　　　　**One hour later**

1.1 Complete **Figure 1** by drawing the molecules of dye in the cup after one hour.

[1 mark]

1.2 Describe the effect that a lower temperature would have on diffusion.

[1 mark]

2 Active transport is an important form of transport in organisms. *(Grade 3-4)*

2.1 Which of the following is a correct description of active transport?
Tick **one** box.

☐ The movement of substances from an area of higher concentration to an area of lower concentration, without requiring energy.

☐ The movement of substances from an area of lower concentration to an area of higher concentration, without requiring energy.

☐ The movement of substances from an area of higher concentration to an area of lower concentration, requiring energy.

☐ The movement of substances from an area of lower concentration to an area of higher concentration, requiring energy.

[1 mark]

Exam Questions

2.2 Which of the following processes involve active transport?
Tick **two** boxes.

☐ Movement of mineral ions from the soil into root hair cells

☐ Movement of carbon dioxide from the air into the stomata of leaves

☐ Movement of oxygen from the water into the blood of fish

☐ Movement of nutrients, such as glucose, from the gut into the blood

[2 marks]

3 **Figure 2** shows a tank divided in two by the structure labelled **X**. Osmosis will occur between the two sides of the tank.

Grade 3-4

Figure 2

3.1 Name the structure labelled **X** on **Figure 2**.

[1 mark]

3.2 Which of the following will happen to the level of liquid on side **B**? Tick **one** box.

☐ The liquid level on side B will remain the same.

☐ The liquid level on side B will fall.

☐ The liquid level on side B will rise.

[1 mark]

PRACTICAL

4 In an experiment, four 50 mm long cylinders were cut from a fresh potato. The cylinders were then placed in different sugar solutions. After 24 hours the potato cylinders were removed and measured. The results are shown in **Table 1**.

Grade 4-5

Table 1

Cylinder	1	2	3	4
Length after 24 hours (mm)	40	43	51	55
Change in length (mm)				+5

4.1 Complete **Table 1** by calculating the change in length for cylinders 1-3.

[1 mark]

4.2 Explain the change that occurred to the length of cylinder 4.

[2 marks]

Cell Organisation

*Some organisms are made of **lots** of cells. To get a **working** organism, these cells need to be **organised**.*

Large Multicellular Organisms are Made Up of Organ Systems

1) <u>Cells</u> are the <u>basic building blocks</u> that make up <u>all living organisms</u>.
2) <u>Specialised cells</u> carry out a <u>particular function</u> (see p.23-24).
3) These specialised cells form <u>tissues</u>, which form <u>organs</u>, which form <u>organ systems</u> (see below).
4) <u>Large multicellular organisms</u> (e.g. humans) have different <u>systems</u> inside them for <u>exchanging</u> and <u>transporting</u> materials.

Epithelial cell

Similar Cells Make Up Tissues

1) A <u>tissue</u> is a <u>group</u> of <u>similar cells</u> that work together to carry out a <u>function</u>.
2) E.g. <u>epithelial tissue</u> is a type of tissue made of <u>epithelial cells</u>. It <u>covers</u> some parts of the human body, e.g. the <u>inside</u> of the <u>gut</u>.

Epithelial tissue

Tissues Make Up Organs

1) An <u>organ</u> is a group of <u>different tissues</u> that work together to perform a certain <u>function</u>.
2) For example, the <u>stomach</u> is an organ. <u>Epithelial tissue</u> lines the inside and outside of the stomach.

Stomach

Organs Make Up Organ Systems

1) An <u>organ system</u> is a <u>group of organs</u> working together to perform a <u>function</u>.
2) The <u>digestive system</u> is an organ system found in humans and other mammals.
3) It <u>breaks down</u> and <u>absorbs</u> food.
4) It's made up of these organs:

You need to know where these organs are on a diagram.

Digestive system

<u>Salivary glands</u>
Produce digestive juices.

<u>Liver</u>
Produces bile.

<u>Large intestine</u>
Absorbs water from undigested food, leaving faeces (poo).

<u>Stomach</u>
Digests food.

<u>Pancreas</u>
Produces digestive juices.

<u>Small intestine</u>
Digests food and absorbs soluble food molecules, e.g. glucose.

5) Organ systems work together to make entire <u>organisms</u>.

Remember — cells, tissues, organs, organ systems

OK, so from this page you should know that <u>cells</u> are organised into <u>tissues</u>, the tissues into <u>organs</u>, the organs into <u>organ systems</u> and the organ systems into a whole <u>organism</u>.

Enzymes

Chemical reactions are what make you work. And **enzymes** are what make them work.

Enzymes Are **Catalysts**

1) <u>Living things</u> have tons of <u>reactions</u> going on inside their cells.

2) These reactions are <u>controlled</u> by <u>enzymes</u>.

Enzymes are important in metabolism — see page 94.

3) Enzymes are <u>large proteins</u>.

4) They <u>speed up</u> reactions inside living things by acting as <u>catalysts</u>:

> A <u>CATALYST</u> is a substance which <u>INCREASES</u> the speed of a reaction, without being <u>CHANGED</u> or <u>USED UP</u> in the reaction.

Enzymes Have **Special Shapes**

1) <u>Chemical reactions</u> usually involve things either being <u>split apart</u> or <u>joined together</u>.
2) <u>Every</u> enzyme has an <u>active site</u> with a <u>unique shape</u>.
3) The substance involved in the reaction has to <u>fit</u> into the <u>active site</u> for the enzyme to work.
4) So enzymes are really <u>picky</u> — they usually only catalyse <u>one specific reaction</u>.
5) This diagram shows the <u>'lock and key'</u> model of enzyme action:

The substance that an enzyme acts on is called the substrate.

active site

enzyme

substrate

enzyme unchanged after reaction

products

This is a useful model but it's a bit simpler than how enzymes actually work.

Enzymes speed up chemical reactions

Just like you've got to have the correct key for a lock, you've got to have the right substrate for an enzyme. As you can see in the diagram above, if the substrate <u>doesn't fit</u>, the enzyme <u>won't</u> catalyse the reaction...

Enzymes

*Enzymes are clearly very clever, but they need just the right **conditions** if they're going to work properly.*

Enzymes Need the **Right Temperature**...

1) <u>Temperature</u> affects the <u>rate</u> of a reaction involving an enzyme.
2) A higher temperature <u>increases</u> the rate at first.
3) But if it gets <u>too hot</u>, some of the <u>bonds</u> holding the enzyme together <u>break</u>.
4) This changes the shape of the enzyme's <u>active site</u>, so the substrate <u>won't fit</u> any more — the enzyme is <u>denatured</u>.
5) All enzymes have a <u>temperature</u> that they work best at — their <u>optimum</u> temperature.

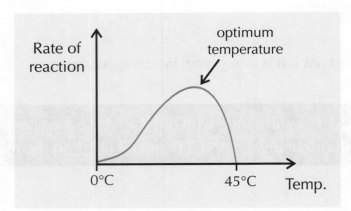

... and the **Right pH**

1) <u>pH</u> can affect the rate of a reaction involving an enzyme.
2) If the pH is <u>too high</u> or <u>too low</u>, it affects the <u>bonds</u> holding the enzyme together.
3) This changes the <u>shape</u> of the <u>active site</u>, and <u>denatures</u> the enzyme.
4) All enzymes have a <u>pH</u> that they work best at — their <u>optimum</u> pH.

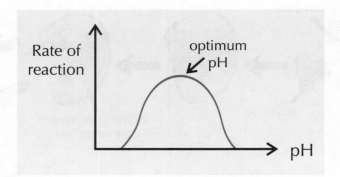

Most enzymes catalyse just one reaction

The <u>optimum temperature</u> for most human enzymes is around <u>normal body temperature</u>.
And <u>stomach enzymes</u> work best at <u>low pH</u>, but the enzymes in your <u>small intestine</u> like a <u>higher pH</u>.

Investigating Enzymatic Reactions

*Give this page a read and you'll soon know how to investigate the effect of **pH** on the rate of **enzyme activity**.*

You Can **Investigate** the Effect of **pH** on **Enzyme Activity** PRACTICAL

1) The enzyme <u>amylase</u> catalyses the breakdown of <u>starch</u> to <u>sugar</u>.

2) You can <u>detect starch</u> using <u>iodine solution</u> — if starch is present, the iodine solution will change from <u>browny-orange</u> to <u>blue-black</u>.

1) Put a <u>drop</u> of <u>iodine solution</u> into every <u>well</u> of a <u>spotting tile</u>.

2) Set up a <u>water bath</u> at 35 °C.
   (You could use a Bunsen burner and a beaker of water, or an electric water bath.)

3) Add some <u>amylase solution</u> and a <u>buffer solution</u> with a <u>pH</u> of <u>5</u> to a boiling tube.

4) Put the boiling tube in the water bath and wait for five minutes.

5) Add some <u>starch solution</u> to the boiling tube, <u>mix</u>, and start a <u>stop clock</u>.

6) <u>Every 30 seconds</u>, take a <u>sample</u> from the boiling tube using a dropping pipette.

7) Put a <u>drop</u> of the sample into a <u>well</u> on the spotting tile.

8) When the iodine solution <u>stays browny-orange</u>, all the starch in the sample has been broken down. <u>Record how long</u> this takes.

amylase, starch and buffer solution

mixture sampled every 30 seconds

dropping pipette

drop of iodine solution

spotting tile

9) <u>Repeat</u> the experiment with buffer solutions of different <u>pH values</u>.

10) As the <u>pH changes</u>, the <u>time</u> it takes for the starch to be broken down should also <u>change</u>.

11) Remember to <u>control any variables</u> each time you repeat the experiment. This will make it a <u>fair test</u>. For example, the <u>concentration</u> and <u>volume</u> of the <u>amylase solution</u> should always be the <u>same</u>.

Here's How to **Calculate** the **Rate of Reaction**

1) <u>Rate</u> is a measure of <u>how much</u> something <u>changes</u> over <u>time</u>.

2) For the <u>experiment above</u>, you can calculate the rate of reaction using <u>this formula</u>:

$$\text{Rate} = \frac{1000}{\text{time}}$$

EXAMPLE

The time taken for amylase to break down all of the starch in a solution was 90 seconds. Calculate the rate of the reaction. Write your answer in s^{-1}.

Rate of reaction = 1000 ÷ time = 1000 ÷ 90 s
= 11 s^{-1}

 s^{-1} just means 'per second'.

You can investigate other factors too...

You could easily <u>adapt</u> this experiment to investigate how factors <u>other than pH</u> affect the rate of amylase activity. For example, you could use a <u>water bath</u> to investigate the effect of <u>temperature</u>.

Q1   Calculate the rate of a reaction that finished in 2.5 minutes.
     Give your answer in s^{-1}.

[2 marks]

 Q1 Video Solution

Enzymes and Digestion

*The **enzymes** used in **digestion** are produced by **cells**. They're released into the **gut** to mix with food.*

Digestive Enzymes Break Down **Big Molecules**

1) Starch, proteins and fats are BIG molecules.
2) They're too big to pass through the walls of the digestive system.
3) So digestive enzymes break these BIG molecules down into smaller ones.
4) These smaller, soluble molecules can easily be absorbed into the bloodstream.

Carbohydrases

- Amylase is an example of a carbohydrase.
- Amylase is made in the salivary glands, pancreas and small intestine.
- It works in the mouth and small intestine.

 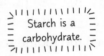

starch → amylase enzyme → sugars

Starch is a carbohydrate.

Proteases

- Proteases are made in the stomach, pancreas and small intestine.
- They work in the stomach and small intestine.

proteins → protease enzymes → amino acids

Lipases

- Lipases are made in the pancreas and small intestine.
- They work in the small intestine.

 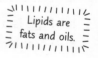

lipid → lipase enzymes → glycerol and fatty acids

Lipids are fats and oils.

5) The products of digestion can be used to make new carbohydrates, proteins and lipids.
6) Glucose is a sugar produced by digestion. Some of it is used in respiration (see p.91-92).

Bile **Neutralises** the Stomach Acid and **Emulsifies** Fats

1) Bile is produced in the liver. It's stored in the gall bladder before it's released into the small intestine.
2) Bile is alkaline. It neutralises hydrochloric acid (from the stomach) and makes conditions alkaline.
3) The enzymes in the small intestine work best in these alkaline conditions.
4) Bile also emulsifies fats. Emulsify means that it breaks the fats down into tiny droplets.
   This gives a bigger surface area of fat for lipase to work on. This makes its digestion faster.

Food Tests

*There are some clever ways to **identify** what type of **food molecule** a sample contains.*

Prepare Your Food Sample First

For each test, you need to prepare a <u>food sample</u>. It's the same each time though — here's what you'd do:

1) Get a piece of food and <u>break it up</u> using a <u>pestle and mortar</u>.
2) Transfer the ground up food to a <u>beaker</u> and add some <u>distilled water</u>.
3) Give the mixture a good <u>stir</u> with a glass rod to <u>dissolve</u> some of the food.
4) <u>Filter</u> the solution using a <u>funnel</u> lined with <u>filter paper</u>. This will <u>get rid</u> of the <u>solid</u> bits of food.

Use the **Benedict's Test** to Test for **Sugars**

Glucose is a reducing sugar.

The <u>Benedict's test</u> is used to test for a type of sugar called a <u>reducing sugar</u>. Here's how you do it:

1) Prepare a <u>food sample</u> and transfer <u>5 cm³</u> to a test tube.

2) Prepare a <u>water bath</u> so that it's set to <u>75 °C</u>.

3) Add some <u>Benedict's solution</u> to the test tube (about <u>10 drops</u>) using a pipette.

4) Place the test tube in the water bath using a test tube holder. Leave it in there for <u>5 minutes</u>.

5) If the food sample contains a reducing sugar, the solution in the test tube will change from the normal <u>blue</u> colour to <u>green</u>, <u>yellow</u> or <u>brick-red</u>. The colour change depends on <u>how much</u> sugar is in the food.

Benedict's solution

water bath

food sample

colour change if reducing sugar present

higher sugar concentration

Use **Iodine Solution** to Test for **Starch**

1) Make a <u>food sample</u> and transfer <u>5 cm³</u> to a test tube.

2) Add a few drops of <u>iodine solution</u>. <u>Gently shake</u> the tube to mix the contents.

3) If the sample contains <u>starch</u>, the colour of the solution will change from <u>browny-orange</u> to <u>black</u> or <u>blue-black</u>.

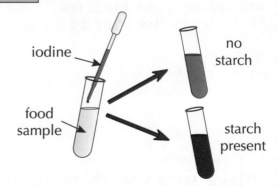
iodine

food sample

no starch

starch present

There are four food molecules you should know how to test for

You're halfway through them now. Turn the page to read about the other two — <u>proteins</u> and <u>lipids</u>...

Food Tests

*There are a couple more **food tests** coming up on this page — for proteins and for lipids. As with the other tests, you need to use the method on the previous page to prepare a **sample** of your food first.*

Use the **Biuret Test** to Test for **Proteins**

1) Prepare a <u>sample</u> of your food and transfer <u>2 cm³</u> to a test tube.

2) Add 2 cm³ of <u>biuret solution</u> to the sample.
   Mix the contents of the tube by <u>gently shaking</u> it.

3) If the food sample contains <u>protein</u>, the solution will change from <u>blue</u> to <u>purple</u>.

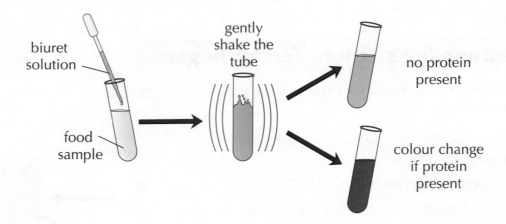

biuret solution

food sample

gently shake the tube

no protein present

colour change if protein present

Use the **Sudan III Test** to Test for **Lipids**

1) Prepare a <u>food sample</u> using the method on the previous page but <u>don't</u> filter it. Transfer <u>5 cm³</u> to a test tube.

2) Add <u>3 drops</u> of <u>Sudan III stain solution</u> to the test tube. <u>Gently shake</u> the tube.

3) If the sample contains <u>lipids</u>, the mixture will separate out into <u>two layers</u>. The top layer will be <u>bright red</u>.

Sudan III stain solution

food sample

gently shake the tube

separates into two layers if lipids are present

the top layer is red

Make sure you think about all of the hazards...

<u>Iodine</u> is an <u>irritant</u> to the <u>eyes</u>, and the chemicals in the <u>biuret solution</u> are <u>dangerous</u>, so wear <u>safety goggles</u> for food tests. If you <u>spill</u> any of the chemicals on your <u>skin</u>, wash it off <u>straight away</u>. Be careful around the <u>water bath</u> in the <u>Benedict's test</u>, too. And if that's not enough to be cautious about, <u>Sudan III stain solution</u> is <u>flammable</u>, so keep it away from any <u>lit Bunsen burners</u>.

Warm-Up & Exam Questions

Doing well in exams isn't just about remembering all the facts, although that's important. You have to get used to the way the exam questions are phrased and make sure you always read them carefully.

Warm-Up Questions

1) Is the stomach a tissue or an organ?
2) What is the name for the part of an enzyme that a substrate fits into?
3) Which enzyme digests starch?
4) What are the products when lipids are broken down?
5) True or false? Protease enzymes are made in the liver.
6) Describe how you would prepare a food sample before testing it for the presence of different food molecules.

Exam Questions

1   **Figure 1** shows the human digestive system. **Figure 1**

1.1   Which label, **A-D**, shows the place where bile is produced?

[1 mark]

1.2   Use words from the box to complete the sentences below.

acidic	alkaline	neutral
lipids	starch	proteins

Bile makes conditions in the small intestine ....

Bile also emulsifies ....

[2 marks]

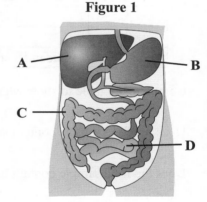

2   **Figure 2** shows the effect of temperature on the action of an enzyme.

2.1   At what temperature does the enzyme work best?

[1 mark]

2.2   What name is given to the temperature at which an enzyme works best?

[1 mark]

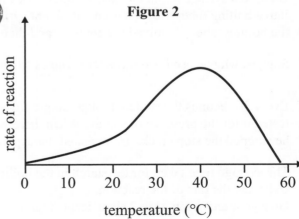

Figure 2

Exam Questions

3 **Figure 3** represents the action of an enzyme in catalysing a biological reaction.

3.1 In terms of the enzyme's shape, explain why an enzyme only catalyses one reaction.

[1 mark]

Figure 3

3.2 The optimum pH of the enzyme is pH 7. Explain what effect a very low pH would have on the activity of the enzyme.

[2 marks]

PRACTICAL

4 A student wanted to know which substances were present in a food sample. She prepared a solution containing the food, and added some of the solution to each of three test tubes. She then added different chemicals to each test tube, to test for different food molecules. Her results are shown in **Table 1**.

Table 1

Test tube	Chemical added to test tube	Description of solution in test tube
A	Iodine	Blue-black
B		Blue
C	Sudan III stain solution	In two layers. Top layer red.

4.1 Complete the table to show what solution would have been added to test tube **B** to test for proteins.

[1 mark]

4.2 Does the food sample contain starch? Explain your answer.

[1 mark]

4.3 Does the food sample contain lipids? Explain your answer.

[1 mark]

PRACTICAL

5 A student was investigating the effect of pH on the rate of amylase activity. He used a syringe to put amylase solution and a buffer solution with a pH of 6 into a boiling tube. He then used a different syringe to add a starch solution to the boiling tube. He mixed the contents and then started a stop clock.

5.1 Suggest why he used two different syringes when adding substances to the boiling tube.

[1 mark]

Every 30 seconds the student took a sample from the boiling tube and tested it for the presence of starch. When there was no starch present he stopped the stop clock. He repeated the experiment three times.

5.2 The average time taken for the starch in the boiling tube to be broken down was 60 seconds. Calculate the rate of the reaction. Give your answer in s^{-1} to 2 significant figures. Use the formula: $\text{rate} = \dfrac{1000}{\text{time}}$

[2 marks]

The Lungs

*You need **oxygen** to supply your **cells** for **respiration** (see p.91-92). You also need to get rid of **carbon dioxide**. This all happens in your **lungs** when you breathe air in and out.*

Air Moves In and Out of the Lungs

1) This diagram shows the <u>structure</u> of the lungs:
2) The air that you breathe in goes through the <u>trachea</u>.
3) Then it passes through the <u>bronchi</u>, then the <u>bronchioles</u> and ends up in the <u>alveoli</u> (small air sacs).

> One bronchus, two bronchi.
> One alveolus, many alveoli.

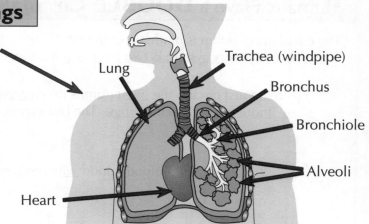

Alveoli Carry Out Gas Exchange

1) <u>Alveoli</u> in the lungs are surrounded by <u>blood capillaries</u>.
2) <u>Blood</u> comes <u>into</u> the lungs through the capillaries. It contains <u>lots</u> of <u>carbon dioxide</u> and <u>very little oxygen</u>.
3) <u>Oxygen</u> diffuses (see p.30) <u>out</u> of the <u>air</u> in the alveolus (where there's a <u>higher</u> concentration) <u>into</u> the <u>blood</u> (where there's a <u>lower</u> concentration).
4) <u>Carbon dioxide</u> diffuses <u>out</u> of the <u>blood</u> (higher concentration) <u>into</u> the <u>air</u> in the alveolus (lower concentration).
5) The blood then leaves the lungs and travels around the <u>body</u>.

You Can Calculate the Breathing Rate

<u>Breathing rate</u> is how <u>fast</u> a person moves air in and out of their lungs. Here's how to calculate it:

EXAMPLE

Bob takes 91 breaths in 7 minutes. Calculate his average breathing rate in breaths per minute.

breaths per minute = number of breaths ÷ number of minutes

= 91 ÷ 7

= 13 breaths per minute

Take a deep breath...

...and make sure you get to grips with the <u>layout</u> of the innards of your <u>chest</u>.

Q1   Aaqib jogged around the park for 8 minutes. During his jog he took 304 breaths. Calculate his average breathing rate in breaths per minute.   [1 mark]

Q1 Video Solution

Circulatory System — The Heart

*The circulatory system carries **food** and **oxygen** to every cell in the body.*
*It also carries **waste products** to where they can be removed from the body.*

Humans Have a **DOUBLE** Circulatory System

The circulatory system is made up of the <u>heart</u>, <u>blood vessels</u> and <u>blood</u>.
A <u>double circulatory system</u> is <u>two circuits</u> joined together:

1) In the first circuit, the <u>heart</u> pumps <u>deoxygenated</u> blood (blood <u>without oxygen</u>) to the <u>lungs</u>. The blood picks up oxygen in the lungs.

2) <u>Oxygenated</u> blood (blood <u>with oxygen</u>) then <u>returns</u> to the heart.

3) In the second circuit, the <u>heart</u> pumps <u>oxygenated</u> blood around all the <u>other organs</u> of the <u>body</u>. This delivers oxygen to the body cells.

4) <u>Deoxygenated</u> blood <u>returns</u> to the heart to be pumped out to the <u>lungs</u> again.

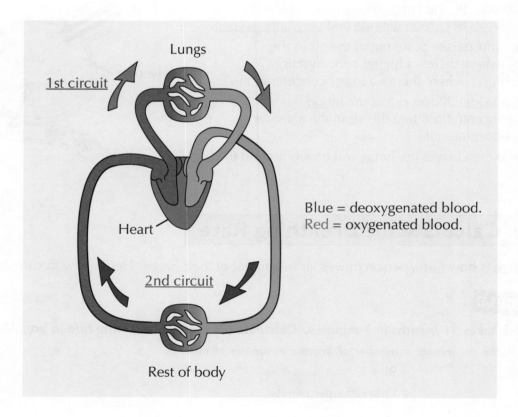

Blue = deoxygenated blood.
Red = oxygenated blood.

First, blood goes to the lungs to pick up oxygen...

...then it takes the oxygen around the rest of the body to all of the cells. The next few pages are also about the circulatory system, so make sure you understand what a <u>double circulatory system</u> is before moving on.

Circulatory System — The Heart

*Now you know how the circulatory system works **overall**, it's time to look at the individual **parts** of it. First up, the **heart**...*

The **Heart Pumps Blood** Around The Body

1) The <u>heart</u> is an organ with <u>four chambers</u>. The walls of the chambers are mostly made of <u>muscle tissue</u>.

2) This muscle tissue is used to <u>pump blood</u> around the body. Here's how:

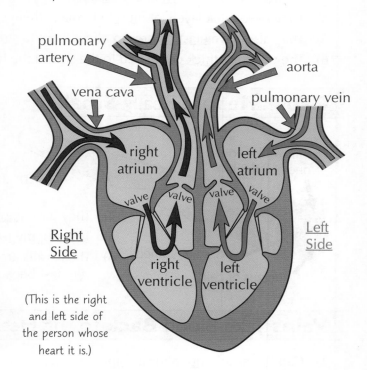

1) <u>Blood flows into</u> the two <u>atria</u> from the <u>vena cava</u> and the <u>pulmonary vein</u>.

2) The <u>atria pump</u> the blood into the <u>ventricles</u>.

3) The <u>ventricles</u> pump the blood <u>out</u> of the heart:
   - Blood from the <u>right ventricle</u> goes through the <u>pulmonary artery</u> to the <u>lungs</u>.
   - Blood from the <u>left ventricle</u> goes through the <u>aorta</u> to the rest of the <u>body</u>.

4) The blood then flows to the <u>organs</u> through <u>arteries</u>, and <u>returns</u> through <u>veins</u> (see next page).

5) The atria fill again — the whole cycle <u>starts over</u>.

(This is the right and left side of the person whose heart it is.)

Atrium is when there is just one. Atria is plural.

3) The <u>valves</u> in the heart stop the blood flowing <u>backwards</u>.

4) The heart also needs its <u>own</u> supply of <u>oxygenated</u> blood.

5) It gets oxygenated blood from arteries called <u>coronary arteries</u>. These branch off the <u>aorta</u> and <u>surround</u> the heart.

The **Heart** Has a **Pacemaker**

1) Your resting heart rate is <u>controlled</u> by a group of cells in the <u>right atrium</u> wall.

2) These cells act as a <u>pacemaker</u> — they tell the heart <u>when</u> to <u>pump blood</u>.

3) A pacemaker that doesn't work properly causes an <u>irregular heartbeat</u>. An <u>artificial pacemaker</u> (a small electrical device) can be used to keep the heart beating <u>regularly</u>.

REVISION TIP

Make sure you know the names of the parts of the heart

The heart diagram on this page is really important. Try copying it out a few times to get yourself really familiar with it. If you get your <u>atria</u> and <u>ventricles</u> mixed up, think about how the shape of the heart comes to a point at the bottom, just like a letter V, which is where the <u>v</u>entricles are.

Circulatory System — Blood Vessels

Blood needs a good set of 'tubes' to carry it round the body. Here's a page on the different types:

Arteries Carry Blood Under Pressure

elastic fibres and muscle
lumen

1) Arteries carry blood <u>away</u> from the heart.
2) The heart pumps the blood out at <u>high pressure</u>.
3) So artery walls are <u>strong</u> and <u>elastic</u>.
4) They have thick layers of <u>muscle</u> to make them <u>strong</u>.
5) They also have <u>elastic fibres</u> to allow them to <u>stretch</u> and <u>spring back</u>.
6) The walls are <u>thick</u> compared to the size of the hole down the middle (the "<u>lumen</u>").

Capillaries are Really Small

thin wall — only one cell thick
very small lumen
nucleus of cell

1) Arteries branch into <u>capillaries</u>.
2) Capillaries are really <u>tiny</u> — too small to see.
3) They carry the blood <u>really close</u> to <u>every cell</u> in the body to <u>exchange substances</u> with them.
4) They have <u>gaps</u> in their walls, so substances can <u>diffuse</u> in and out.
5) They supply <u>food</u> and <u>oxygen</u>, and take away <u>waste</u> like <u>CO_2</u>.
6) Their walls are usually <u>only one cell thick</u>. This means that diffusion is <u>very fast</u> because there is only a <u>short distance</u> for molecules to travel.

Veins Take Blood Back to the Heart

elastic fibres and muscle
large lumen
valve

1) Capillaries <u>join up</u> to form <u>veins</u>.
2) The blood is at <u>lower pressure</u> in the veins. This means the walls don't need to be as <u>thick</u> as artery walls.
3) Veins have a <u>bigger lumen</u> than arteries. This helps the blood <u>flow</u> despite the lower pressure.
4) They also have <u>valves</u>. These help keep the blood flowing in the <u>right direction</u>.

You Can Calculate the Rate of Blood Flow

The <u>rate of blood flow</u> is the amount of blood that passes through a blood vessel in a given <u>time</u>. Here's how to <u>calculate</u> it:

EXAMPLE
1300 ml of blood passed through an artery in 4 minutes.
Calculate the rate of blood flow through the artery in ml per minute.

rate of blood flow = volume of blood ÷ number of minutes
= 1300 ÷ 4 = 325 ml per minute

Veins have valves — arteries carry blood away from the heart

Q1 Video Solution

Q1 2.175 litres of blood passed through a vein in 8.7 minutes.
Calculate the rate of blood flow through the vein in ml/min. [2 marks]

Q2 Describe how the features of veins help them to carry blood back to the heart. [2 marks]

Circulatory System — Blood

Blood is a **tissue** *(see p.40). One of its jobs is to act as a huge* **transport** *system. It has four main parts...*

Red Blood Cells Carry Oxygen

1) The job of red blood cells is to <u>carry oxygen</u> from the lungs to all the cells in the body.
2) Their shape gives them a <u>large surface area</u> for <u>absorbing oxygen</u>.
3) They contain a red substance called <u>haemoglobin</u>.
4) Haemoglobin is the stuff that allows red blood cells to <u>carry oxygen</u>.
5) Red blood cells <u>don't</u> have a <u>nucleus</u> — this leaves more space for carrying oxygen.

White Blood Cells Defend Against Infection

1) White blood cells are part of your <u>immune system</u> — see page 78.
2) Some can change shape to gobble up unwelcome <u>microorganisms</u>.
3) Others produce molecules called <u>antibodies</u> and <u>antitoxins</u> to defend against microorganisms.
4) Unlike red blood cells, they <u>do</u> have a <u>nucleus</u>.

Platelets Help Blood Clot

1) These are <u>small fragments</u> of <u>cells</u>. They have <u>no nucleus</u>.
2) They help the blood to <u>clot</u> (clump together) at a wound.
3) This stops all your <u>blood pouring out</u>.
4) It also stops any <u>microorganisms</u> getting in.

Plasma is the Liquid That Carries Everything in Blood

This is a pale straw-coloured <u>liquid</u>. It <u>carries</u>:
1) <u>Red</u> and <u>white blood cells</u> and <u>platelets</u>.
2) Food molecules (like <u>glucose</u> and <u>amino acids</u>).
3) <u>Waste products</u> (like <u>carbon dioxide</u> and <u>urea</u>).
4) <u>Hormones</u>.
5) <u>Proteins</u>.

Blood — red blood cells, white blood cells, platelets and plasma

<u>Blood tests</u> can be used to diagnose loads of things — not just disorders of the blood. This is because the blood transports <u>so many chemicals</u> produced by <u>so many organs</u>.

Q2 Video Solution

Q1   Describe the purpose of platelets in blood. [1 mark]

Q2   State the function of the cell labelled X in the image on the right. [1 mark]

Warm-Up & Exam Questions

There are some nice diagrams to learn on the previous few pages. If you don't bother, you'll feel pretty silly if you turn over the exam paper and the first question asks you to label a diagram of the heart. Just saying... Anyway, let's see if these questions get your blood pumping...

Warm-Up Questions

1) What is the name of the tubes that the trachea splits into?
2) What is the function of the coronary arteries?
3) What does an artificial pacemaker do?
4) What do veins do?
5) True or false? Red blood cells don't have a nucleus.

Exam Questions

1   **Figure 1** shows the human heart and four blood vessels, as seen from the front. The left ventricle and the right atrium have been labelled.

Figure 1

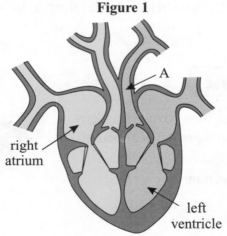

1.1   Name the part labelled **A**.

[1 mark]

1.2   What is the function of the left ventricle? Tick **one** box.

☐ It pumps blood to the lungs.

☑ It pumps blood around the body.

☐ It prevents the backflow of blood.

[1 mark]

1.3   Complete the sentence.

Deoxygenated blood enters the right atrium through the ......vena cava...... .

[1 mark]

Exam Questions

2 Draw **one** line from each part of the blood to its function.

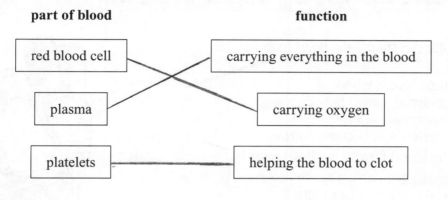

part of blood	function
red blood cell	carrying everything in the blood
plasma	carrying oxygen
platelets	helping the blood to clot

[2 marks]

3 The cell shown in **Figure 2** transports oxygen around the body.

Figure 2

View
from above

Cut through
view

Explain how the shape of the cell in **Figure 2** is adapted for transporting oxygen.

[1 mark]

4 A student ran for 12 minutes.

4.1 During this 12 minute run, the student took 492 breaths.
Calculate his average breathing rate in breaths per minute.

41 breaths per minute

[1 mark]

4.2 The student also measured his heart rate before and during his run.
Before his run, the student's heart rate was at its natural resting rate.
Outline how natural resting heart rate is controlled.

By how fit you are so if you exercise a lot/ your heart is stronger and needs less pumps.

[1 mark]

5 Blood cells are carried in the bloodstream inside blood vessels.

5.1* Capillaries are one type of blood vessel.
Explain how the structure of a capillary allows it to carry out its function.

[4 marks]

5.2 Blood flows through different types of blood vessels at different rates.
The volume of blood that passed through an artery in 150 seconds was 1155 ml.
Calculate the rate of blood flow through the artery in ml/min.

[2 marks]

Topic B2 — Organisation

Cardiovascular Disease

Cardiovascular diseases are diseases of the *heart or blood vessels*. *One example is **coronary heart disease**.*

Coronary Heart Disease is a Disease of the Coronary Arteries

1) The <u>coronary arteries</u> supply the <u>heart muscle</u> with blood.

2) <u>Coronary heart disease</u> is when <u>layers of fatty material</u> (called <u>fatty deposits</u>) build up in the coronary arteries. This causes the arteries to become <u>narrow</u>.

3) This <u>reduces</u> the <u>blood flow</u> to the heart muscle.

4) This means <u>less oxygen</u> can get to the heart muscle. This can result in a <u>heart attack</u>.

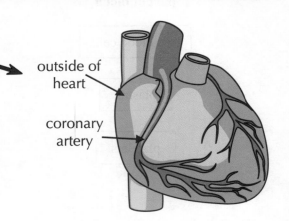

outside of heart

coronary artery

Stents Keep Coronary Arteries Open

1) <u>Stents</u> are <u>tubes</u> that are put <u>inside</u> coronary arteries by surgery. They keep the arteries <u>open</u>.

2) This allows blood to reach the heart muscles and reduces the risk of a <u>heart attack</u>.

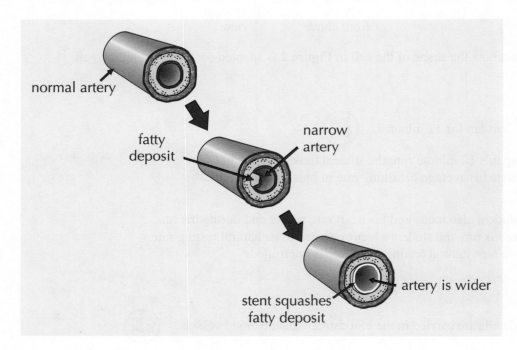

normal artery

fatty deposit

narrow artery

stent squashes fatty deposit

artery is wider

3) Stents are <u>effective</u> for a <u>long time</u>. <u>Recovery time</u> from the surgery is also quite <u>quick</u>.

4) But there are <u>risks</u>. These include having a <u>heart attack</u> during the operation, or getting an <u>infection</u> after surgery. Patients may also develop a <u>blood clot</u> near the stent.

Coronary heart disease is a type of cardiovascular disease

Coronary heart disease is caused by the arteries being <u>blocked</u> by <u>fatty material</u> — if the <u>heart muscle</u> can't get enough <u>oxygen</u>, then it <u>can't work properly</u>. And if the heart can't work properly, well, you're in trouble.

Cardiovascular Disease

*You've read about stents, so now it's time for a second treatment for coronary heart disease — **statins**.*

Statins Reduce Cholesterol in the Blood

1) Cholesterol is a lipid that your body needs.
2) However, too much cholesterol can cause fatty deposits to form inside arteries.
3) Statins are drugs that can reduce the amount of cholesterol in the blood.
4) This slows down the rate of fatty deposits forming.

Advantages

1) Statins reduce the risk of strokes, coronary heart disease and heart attacks.
2) Some studies suggest that statins may also help prevent some other diseases.

Disadvantages

1) Statins must be taken regularly over a long time. A person could forget to take them.
2) Statins can cause unwanted side effects, for example, headaches.
3) The effect of statins isn't instant. It takes time for their effect to work.

Faulty Heart Valves Can Be Replaced

1) The valves (see p.51) in the heart can be damaged by heart attacks, infection or old age.

2) This may cause the valve to stiffen, so it won't open properly.

3) A valve may also become leaky — blood flows in both directions instead of just forward.

4) This means that blood doesn't flow around the body as well as normal.

5) Damaged valves may be replaced by biological valves — valves from humans or other mammals (e.g. cows or pigs). Or they can be replaced by mechanical valves — these are man-made valves.

6) Replacing a valve is less risky than a heart transplant (see next page). But as it requires surgery, there is a risk of bleeding and infection. There can also be problems with blood clots.

valves ⟶   ⟵ valves

There are risks with any treatment for cardiovascular disease

Anything involving surgery on the heart is going to be risky, but even taking statins comes with a risk of side effects. Doctors and patients have to weigh up the benefits against the risks.

More on Cardiovascular Disease

*One final page on cardiovascular disease. Having the valves replaced isn't the only surgery for cardiovascular disease — when someone has heart failure, surgeons can **replace** the **whole heart**.*

An **Artificial Heart** Can **Pump Blood** Round the Body

1) A heart transplant is when a person's heart is replaced by a donor heart (a heart from someone who has recently died).

2) This can happen if someone has heart failure. Heart failure is when the heart can't pump enough blood.

3) The lungs may also be replaced if they are diseased.

4) If a donor heart isn't available, doctors may fit an artificial heart (a machine that pumps blood around the body).

5) Artificial hearts can be used to keep a person alive until a donor heart is available. Or they can help a person recover by allowing the heart to rest and heal.

6) Sometimes artificial hearts are permanent, so a donor heart isn't needed anymore.

7) Here are some of the advantages and disadvantages of artificial hearts:

Advantage

Artificial hearts are made from metals or plastics. This makes them less likely to be attacked by the body's immune system (see page 78) than a donor heart.

Disadvantages

1) Surgery to fit an artificial heart can lead to bleeding and infection. (This can also happen with transplant surgery.)

2) Artificial hearts don't work as well as healthy natural ones.

3) Blood doesn't flow through artificial hearts as smoothly as through a natural heart. This can cause blood clots and lead to strokes.

Some of the disadvantages of an artificial heart are advantages of a donor heart.

4) The patient has to take drugs to thin their blood. This means they can bleed a lot more than is usual if they have an accident.

EXAM TIP

Don't lose heart...

You could be asked to evaluate treatments for cardiovascular disease. Don't panic — just use any information you're given and your own knowledge to weigh up the advantages and disadvantages. Make sure your answer doesn't just focus on one side — e.g. don't just talk about the advantages and ignore the disadvantages. You should also include a conclusion that you can back up.

Warm-Up & Exam Questions

Hopefully I've persuaded you by now that it's a good idea to try these questions. Believe me, when you're sitting with your real exam paper in front of you, you'll feel so much better knowing that you've already been through loads of practice questions. So off you go...

Warm-Up Questions

1) Which vessels are affected in coronary heart disease?
2) If someone has heart failure, and there is no donor heart available, how might they be treated?
3) What is an artificial heart?

Exam Questions

1 There are different ways to treat coronary heart disease.

1.1 Complete **Table 1** to give the names of the treatments described.

Table 1

Description of treatment	Name of treatment
Tubes that are put inside arteries to keep them open	
Drugs that reduce cholesterol in the blood	

[2 marks]

1.2 Suggest **one** disadvantage to a patient of taking drugs to reduce blood cholesterol.

[1 mark]

2 A patient is taken into hospital. They are diagnosed as having a leaky heart valve. The doctor decides that a surgeon should replace the valve.

2.1 Give the **two** types of valve that the surgeon might use.

[2 marks]

2.2 Suggest **one** risk of replacing the faulty valve.

[1 mark]

3 **Figure 1** shows a cross-section of a blood vessel in someone with coronary heart disease.

3.1 Name the substance labelled **X** on **Figure 1**.

[1 mark]

3.2 Explain how the presence of this substance can affect oxygen delivery to the heart muscle.

[2 marks]

Figure 1

Health and Disease

*Try as we might, it's unlikely that we'll be in tip-top condition for all of our lives — **disease** tends to get us all at some point. There are lots of **different types** of diseases we could get...*

Diseases are a Major Cause of Ill Health

1) <u>Health</u> is the <u>state</u> of <u>physical</u> and <u>mental wellbeing</u>.

2) This means that both the <u>body</u> and <u>mind</u> are <u>well</u>.

3) Diseases are often responsible for causing <u>ill health</u>.

4) Diseases can be <u>communicable</u> or <u>non-communicable</u>:

Communicable diseases are sometimes called infectious diseases.

Communicable Diseases

1) These are diseases that can <u>spread</u> from <u>person to person</u> or between <u>animals</u> and <u>people</u>.
2) Communicable diseases can be caused by <u>bacteria</u>, <u>viruses</u>, <u>parasites</u> or <u>fungi</u>.
3) <u>Measles</u> and <u>malaria</u> are examples of communicable diseases. See pages 73-76 for more.

Non-Communicable Diseases

1) These are diseases that <u>cannot spread</u> between people or between animals and people.
2) <u>Coronary heart disease</u> (see page 56) is an example of a non-communicable disease.

Different Types of Disease Can Interact

Sometimes a disease can cause <u>other</u> physical and mental health issues. Here are a few examples:

1) The <u>immune system</u> helps to fight off <u>pathogens</u> (see page 78). Some people have <u>problems</u> with their immune system. This makes them <u>more likely</u> to <u>suffer</u> from communicable diseases.

Pathogen is just the fancy term for a microorganism that can cause disease.

2) An <u>immune system reaction</u> (caused by a pathogen) may lead to an <u>allergic</u> reaction, such as a <u>skin rash</u>. Or it may worsen the symptoms of <u>asthma</u> for asthma sufferers.
3) <u>Viruses</u> infect <u>cells</u> in the body. This can lead to some types of <u>cancer</u>.
4) <u>Physical</u> health problems may also lead to <u>mental</u> health problems. For example, a person may become <u>depressed</u> if they can't carry out <u>everyday activities</u> because of <u>ill health</u>.

Communicable diseases can spread...

...but <u>non-communicable</u> diseases <u>can't</u>. Remember that — it's really important.

Health and Disease

Ill health isn't just about having a disease — there are plenty of other causes.
And then there's the cost of ill health to consider too — there might be more to it than you'd first thought...

Other Factors Can Also Affect Your Health

There are plenty of factors other than diseases that can also affect your health. For example:

1) A poor diet can affect your physical and mental health. A good diet is balanced and provides your body with everything it needs, in the right amounts.

2) Being constantly under lots of stress can lead to poor health.

3) Your life situation can affect your health. This is because it affects how easily you can access medicine or things that prevent you from getting ill. E.g. being able to buy condoms to prevent the spread of some sexually transmitted diseases.

Non-Communicable Diseases Can Be Costly

The Human Cost

1) Tens of millions of people around the world die from non-communicable diseases every year.
2) People with these diseases may have a lower quality of life or a shorter lifespan — this is the human cost.

The Financial Cost

1) The financial cost of researching and treating these diseases is huge.
2) It can also be expensive for individuals if they have to move or adapt their home because of a disease. If a person has to give up work or if they die, then their family's income will be reduced.
3) A reduction in the number of people able to work can also affect a country's economy.

Lots of things affect health, and ill health can be costly

A human cost is the effect something has on humans. A financial cost is to do with how much spending something results in. When you're studying biology, you'll come across lots of things that have a human cost or a financial cost (or both). Some things can have quite far-reaching knock-on effects.

Risk Factors for Non-Communicable Diseases

You've probably heard the term 'risk factor' before. These next couple of pages have lots of info on them. There's nothing too tricky, but there's quite a bit to read — take it slowly and make sure it goes in.

Risk Factors Increase Your Chance of Getting a Disease

1) Risk factors are things that are linked to an <u>increased chance</u> of getting a certain disease.

2) However, risk factors <u>don't mean</u> that someone <u>will</u> definitely get the disease.

3) They can be:
   - part of a person's <u>lifestyle</u> (for example, how much exercise they do),
   - substances in a person's <u>environment</u> (e.g. air pollution),
   - substances in a person's <u>body</u> (e.g. asbestos fibres in the lungs can cause cancer).

4) Many <u>non-communicable</u> diseases are caused by <u>several</u> risk factors that <u>interact</u> with each other.

5) Lifestyle factors can have different effects <u>locally</u>, <u>nationally</u> and <u>globally</u>.
   - <u>Globally</u>, non-communicable diseases are <u>more common</u> in developed countries. This is because people in developed countries generally <u>earn more</u> and can buy <u>high-fat</u> food.
   - <u>Nationally</u>, cardiovascular disease, obesity and Type 2 diabetes are more common in <u>poorer</u> areas. This is because people in <u>poorer areas</u> are <u>more likely</u> to smoke, have a poor diet and not exercise.
   - Your <u>individual choices</u> affect how common a disease is <u>locally</u>.

Some Risk Factors Can Cause a Disease Directly

Some risk factors are able to <u>directly cause</u> a disease. For example:

> Smoking can cause <u>cardiovascular disease</u>, <u>lung disease</u> and <u>lung cancer</u>. It damages the <u>walls</u> of <u>arteries</u> and the <u>lining</u> of the <u>lungs</u>.

Lifestyle can have a big impact on a person's health

Smoking makes a person <u>more likely</u> to get certain diseases. The next page has some more risk factors.

Risk Factors for Non-Communicable Diseases

Here are a few <u>more risk factors</u> that can <u>directly</u> cause <u>disease</u>:

<u>Obesity</u> may cause <u>Type 2 diabetes</u> by making the body <u>less sensitive</u> or <u>resistant to</u> (not affected by) insulin.

There's more about Type 2 diabetes on page 106.

Drinking <u>too much alcohol</u> can damage the <u>brain</u> and the <u>liver</u>.

<u>Smoking</u> and drinking <u>alcohol</u> when <u>pregnant</u> can cause <u>health problems</u> for the <u>unborn baby</u>.

Cancer can be caused by <u>exposure</u> to certain <u>substances</u> or <u>radiation</u>. Things that cause cancer are known as <u>carcinogens</u>. <u>Ionising radiation</u> (e.g. from X-rays) is an example of a <u>carcinogen</u>.

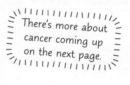
There's more about cancer coming up on the next page.

Risk Factors Can be **Identified** Using **Correlation**

Some risk factors don't <u>directly cause</u> a disease.
BUT there is a <u>correlation</u> between the risk factor and the disease.

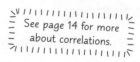
See page 14 for more about correlations.

For example, a <u>lack of exercise</u> and a <u>high fat diet</u> are risk factors for <u>cardiovascular disease</u>, but they can't cause the disease. It's the resulting <u>high cholesterol levels</u> (see p.57) that can <u>cause</u> it.

WORKING SCIENTIFICALLY

It's hard to avoid all risk factors of disease...

...but remember that risk factors that <u>cause disease</u> don't mean you'll <u>definitely</u> get the disease. They just increase the chance of it happening. Also, remember that <u>not all</u> risk factors <u>cause</u> disease. Many are just <u>correlated</u> with the disease, meaning there is a relationship between them.

Cancer

*The more we understand **cancer**, the better our chances of **avoiding** and **beating** it.*

Cancer is Caused by Uncontrolled Cell Growth and Division

1) Changes in cells can lead to <u>uncontrolled</u> growth and division. This results in a <u>tumour</u> (a mass of cells).

2) Tumours can be <u>benign</u> or <u>malignant</u>:

1) <u>Benign</u> tumours are masses of <u>abnormal cells</u>.	1) <u>Malignant</u> tumours spread to other parts of the body.
2) They stay in <u>one place</u> (usually within a membrane).	2) The cells can <u>break off</u> and travel in the <u>bloodstream</u>.
3) They don't <u>invade</u> other parts of the body.	3) The cells <u>get into</u> healthy tissues and form <u>secondary tumours</u>.
4) This type <u>isn't</u> normally dangerous, and the tumour <u>isn't</u> cancerous.	4) Malignant tumours are <u>dangerous</u> and can be fatal — <u>they are cancers</u>.

Risk Factors Can Increase the Chance of Some Cancers

Scientists have identified <u>lots</u> of risk factors for cancers. For example:

Lifestyle Factors

1) <u>Smoking</u> — Smoking is linked to <u>many types</u> of cancer.

2) <u>Obesity</u> — Obesity has also been linked to <u>many different cancers</u>.

3) <u>Viral infection</u> — Infection with some viruses can <u>increase</u> the chances of developing <u>certain types</u> of cancer.

4) <u>UV exposure</u> — The Sun produces <u>UV radiation</u>. This radiation has been linked to an increased chance of developing skin cancer.

Genetic Factors

1) Genes are passed on (<u>inherited</u>) from <u>parent</u> to <u>offspring</u> — see page 114.

2) Sometimes you can <u>inherit faulty genes</u> that make you <u>more likely</u> to get cancer.

People are Now More Likely to Survive Cancer

People have become <u>more likely</u> to <u>survive</u> cancer because:

1) <u>Treatments</u> have improved.

2) Doctors can diagnose cancer <u>earlier</u>.

3) More people are being <u>screened</u> (tested) for cancer.

4) People know more about the <u>risk factors</u> for cancer.

Knowing about the risk factors can help to protect people

E.g. people are now more aware that wearing <u>sun block</u> reduces the risk of skin cancer from UV radiation.

Warm-Up & Exam Questions

It's time for some more questions — don't just assume that you've remembered everything you just read on the past few pages. Give these a go, and then go back over anything that you struggled with.

Warm-Up Questions

1) True or false? Health is the state of physical wellbeing only.
2) What does it mean if a disease is 'communicable'?
3) True or false? Physical health problems may lead to mental health problems.
4) What disease can uncontrolled cell division lead to?

Exam Questions

1   Diseases can be communicable or non-communicable. **(Grade 1-3)**
What is meant by a non-communicable disease?
Tick **one** box.

☐   A disease that can be spread between people or between animals and people.

☐   A disease that cannot be spread between people or between animals and people.

☐   A disease cause by uncontrolled cell growth and division.

☐   A disease caused by the build-up of fatty material in the coronary arteries.

[1 mark]

2   Tumours can be either benign or malignant. **(Grade 3-4)**

Complete **Table 1** to show whether each statement is true for benign tumours, malignant tumours, or both.
Put **one or two** ticks in each row.

Table 1

	Benign	Malignant
The tumour is made up of a mass of cells formed by uncontrollable division and growth.		
The tumour cells can break off and travel into the bloodstream.		
The tumour is cancerous.		

[3 marks]

3   Many diseases have risk factors. **(Grade 4-5)**

3.1   What is meant by the term 'risk factor'?

[1 mark]

3.2   Give **one** risk factor for lung disease.

[1 mark]

3.3   Name **one** carcinogen that is a risk factor for cancer.

[1 mark]

Plant Cell Organisation

*Just like in animals, plant cells are also organised. Here are a few examples of plant **tissues** and **organs**.*

Plant Cells Are Organised Into Tissues And Organs

1) Plants are made of <u>organs</u>. These organs <u>work together</u> to make <u>organ systems</u>.

2) For example, <u>stems</u>, <u>roots</u> and <u>leaves</u> are all plant organs.
They work together to <u>transport</u> (carry) substances around the plant.

3) Plant <u>organs</u> are made of <u>tissues</u>. Examples of plant tissues are:

For more on
photosynthesis,
see page 85.

- <u>Epidermal tissue</u> — this <u>covers</u> the whole plant.
- <u>Palisade mesophyll tissue</u> — this is the part of the leaf where most <u>photosynthesis</u> happens.
- <u>Spongy mesophyll tissue</u> — this is the part of the leaf that has big <u>air spaces</u>.
  This allows <u>gases</u> to <u>diffuse</u> in and out of cells.
- <u>Xylem</u> and <u>phloem</u> — these transport things like <u>water</u>, <u>mineral ions</u> and <u>food</u>
  around the roots, stems and leaves (see next page).
- <u>Meristem tissue</u> — this is found at the <u>growing tips</u> of <u>shoots</u> and <u>roots</u>.

Leaves Contain Epidermal, Mesophyll, Xylem and Phloem Tissue

1) The leaf is where <u>photosynthesis</u> and <u>gas exchange</u> happens in a plant.

2) The <u>structures</u> of the tissues in a leaf are <u>related</u> to their <u>function</u>:

<u>Upper epidermis</u>
This layer is <u>transparent</u>
(see-through). This lets light
through to the palisade layer.

<u>Palisade layer</u>
This has lots of <u>chloroplasts</u>
(see page 18). They are
near the <u>top</u> of the leaf
to get <u>more light</u>.

<u>Spongy mesophyll</u>
This contains <u>air spaces</u>
which increase the rate
of <u>diffusion</u> of <u>gases</u>.

<u>Lower epidermis</u>

<u>Stomata</u>
These let gases <u>diffuse</u> into and out of
the leaf. They are opened and closed
in response to the <u>environment</u>.
This is controlled by <u>guard cells</u>.

<u>Xylem and phloem</u>
These bring <u>water</u> and
<u>nutrients</u> to the leaf and
take away <u>glucose</u> produced
by photosynthesis.
They also <u>support</u> the leaf.

REVISION TIP

Each tissue in a leaf is adapted for its function
There are a lot of weird names here, so make sure you spend plenty of time on this page.
Try <u>drawing</u> your own leaf diagram. <u>Label</u> it with the different tissues and <u>describe</u> each type.

Transpiration and Translocation

*Flowering plants have **two** separate types of vessel — **xylem** and **phloem** — for transporting stuff around.*
***Both** types of vessel go to **every part** of the plant, but they are totally **separate**.*

Phloem Tubes Transport Food

Food (mainly dissolved sugars)

1) Phloem tubes are made of <u>elongated</u> (stretched out) <u>living cells</u>.

2) There are <u>end walls</u> between the cells.
These have <u>pores</u> (small holes) to allow <u>cell sap</u> to flow through.

3) Plants make <u>food substances</u> (e.g. dissolved <u>sugars</u>) in their <u>leaves</u>.

4) Phloem tubes transport these <u>food substances</u>
around the plant for <u>immediate use</u> or for <u>storage</u>.

5) The transport goes in <u>both directions</u>.

6) This process is called <u>translocation</u>.

Cell sap is a liquid that's made up of the substances being transported and water.

Xylem Tubes Take Water Up

1) Xylem tubes are made of <u>dead cells</u>.

2) The cells are joined together with a <u>hole</u> down the <u>middle</u>.

3) There are no <u>end walls</u> between the cells.

4) The cells are <u>strengthened</u> with a material called <u>lignin</u>.

5) Xylem tubes carry <u>water</u> and <u>mineral ions</u>
from the <u>roots</u> to the <u>stem</u> and <u>leaves</u>.

6) The movement of water from the <u>roots</u>, through the <u>xylem</u> and
out of the <u>leaves</u> is called the <u>transpiration stream</u> (see next page).

Water and minerals

REVISION TIP

Xylem vessels carry water, phloem vessels carry sugars

Make sure you don't get your phloem <u>mixed up</u> with your xylem. To help you to learn which is which, you could remember that ph<u>lo</u>em transports substances in b<u>o</u>th directions, but xylem only transports things upwards — x<u>y</u> to the sky. It might just bag you a mark or two on exam day...

Transpiration

*If you don't water a house plant for a few days it starts to go all droopy. Plants need **water**.*

Transpiration is the **Loss of Water** from the Plant

1) Transpiration is caused by <u>evaporation</u> and <u>diffusion</u> of water from a plant's surface (mainly the leaves).

2) Here's how it happens:

Evaporation is when water turns from a liquid into a gas. See page 30 for more on diffusion.

1) Water <u>evaporates</u> from the leaves and <u>diffuses</u> into the air.

2) This creates a slight <u>shortage</u> of water in the leaf. More water is drawn up from the rest of the plant through the <u>xylem tubes</u> to replace it.

3) This means more water is drawn up from the <u>roots</u>.

Head back to page 33 to see how root hair cells are adapted for taking up water.

3) There's a constant <u>stream of water</u> through the plant. This is called the <u>transpiration stream</u>.

Guard Cells Control Gas Exchange and Water Loss

guard cell

stoma
(plural — stomata)

1) Water is <u>lost</u> from a plant's leaves through the <u>stomata</u>.

2) Stomata are surrounded by <u>guard cells</u>.

3) These <u>change shape</u> to control the size of the stomata.

4) When the plant has <u>lots</u> of water the guard cells fill with it and get <u>fat</u>. This makes the stomata <u>open</u> so <u>gases</u> can be exchanged for <u>photosynthesis</u>.

5) When the plant is <u>short</u> of water, the guard cells lose water and become <u>floppy</u>. This makes the stomata <u>close</u>. This helps stop too much water vapour <u>escaping</u>.

6) There are usually <u>more</u> stomata on the <u>bottoms</u> of leaves than on the tops. This is because the <u>lower surface</u> is <u>cooler</u> — so <u>less water</u> gets <u>lost</u>.

Transpiration involves evaporation and diffusion

A big tree loses about a <u>thousand litres</u> of water from its leaves <u>every single day</u> — it's a fact.
That's as much water as the average person drinks in a whole year, so the <u>roots</u> have to be very effective at drawing in water from the soil. Which is why they have all those root <u>hairs</u>, you see.

The Rate of Transpiration

*The **rate of transpiration** varies according to the **environmental conditions**...*

Transpiration Rate is Affected by Four Main Things:

Air Flow

1) The <u>more windy</u> it is, the <u>faster</u> transpiration happens.
2) <u>Fast</u> moving air means that water vapour around the leaf is <u>swept away</u>.
3) This means there's a <u>higher concentration</u> of water vapour <u>inside</u> the leaf compared to <u>outside</u>. So water will diffuse out of the leaf <u>more</u> quickly.

Temperature

1) The <u>warmer</u> it is, the <u>faster</u> transpiration happens.
2) This is because the water particles have <u>more energy</u>. So they <u>evaporate</u> and <u>diffuse</u> out of the stomata faster.

Many factors affect transpiration rate by affecting the rate of diffusion of water. There's more about diffusion on page 30.

Humidity

1) If the air is <u>humid</u> there's a lot of water in it already.
2) This means there isn't much of a <u>difference</u> between the inside and the outside of the leaf.
3) This means that <u>diffusion</u> will not happen very fast.
4) The <u>drier</u> the air around a leaf, the <u>faster</u> transpiration happens.

Light Intensity

1) The <u>brighter</u> the light, the <u>greater</u> the transpiration rate.
2) Photosynthesis can't happen in the dark, so stomata begin to <u>close</u> as it gets darker.
3) When the stomata are closed, very little water can <u>escape</u>.

Transpiration is fastest when it's windy, warm, dry and bright

Make sure you know these <u>four</u> factors, and that you understand <u>why</u> they affect transpiration rates.

Q1   Aloe vera plants grow in hot, dry areas. Primroses grow in cool, wet areas.
Predict which plant will have fewer stomata per cm^2 on the underside of its leaves.
Explain your answer.   [2 marks]

Q2   Explain how low light intensity affects the rate of transpiration.   [3 marks]

Q1 Video Solution

Warm-Up & Exam Questions

Just a few simple Warm-Up Questions and a few slightly harder Exam Questions stand between you and mastering cell organisation and transport in plants...

Warm-Up Questions

1) Where is meristem tissue found in a plant?
2) Which layer of plant tissue contains lots of chloroplasts?
3) True or false? Substances pass in both directions through xylem vessels.
4) State one of the main factors that affects the rate of transpiration in plants.

Exam Questions

1 Leaves contain many types of tissue. **Grade 3-4**

1.1 Which type of plant tissue contains air spaces for the diffusion of gases?
Tick **one** box.

☐ epidermal tissue

☐ xylem tissue

☐ spongy mesophyll tissue

[1 mark]

1.2 Which type of plant tissue forms the transparent layer covering the outside of plant?
Tick **one** box.

☐ epidermal tissue

☐ palisade mesophyll tissue

☐ spongy mesophyll tissue

[1 mark]

2 **Figure 1** shows a vessel that transports cell sap. **Grade 3-4**

Figure 1

2.1 Name the type of vessel shown in **Figure 1**.

[1 mark]

2.2 Explain why the vessel has the pores labelled **X** on **Figure 1**.

[1 mark]

2.3 Name the movement of cell sap through the plant's transport vessels.

[1 mark]

Exam Questions

3   Stomata are found on the surface of leaves.

3.1   Complete the sentence below about stomata.

Stomata are opened and closed by cells called ....

[1 mark]

3.2   **Figure 2** shows a stoma in different conditions.

Figure 2

Condition **A**   Condition **B**

Which condition, **A** or **B**, shows a stoma when the plant is short of water? Explain your answer.

[1 mark]

4   Plants absorb water and mineral ions through their root hair cells.
Xylem vessels transport water and mineral ions from the roots of a plant to the leaves.

4.1   Describe the structure of xylem vessels.

[3 marks]

4.2   Name the process of water transport through a plant.

[1 mark]

5   The water loss from a plant during two different days is shown on the graph in **Figure 3**.
One of the days was hot and dry, and the other day was cold and wet.

5.1   Which line, **A** or **B**, shows water loss on the
hot, dry day? Explain your answer.

[1 mark]

5.2*   Explain how the rate of water loss from a plant
would be affected by windy weather.

[4 marks]

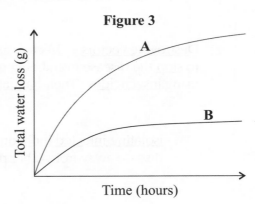

Figure 3

Communicable Disease

*If you're hoping I'll ease you gently into this new topic... no such luck. Straight on to the **baddies** of biology.*

There Are **Several Types** of **Pathogen**

1) Pathogens are <u>microorganisms</u> that enter the body and cause <u>disease</u>.
2) They cause <u>communicable</u> (infectious) diseases.
3) Communicable diseases are diseases that can <u>spread</u> (see p.60).
4) Both <u>plants</u> and <u>animals</u> can be infected by pathogens.
5) There are <u>four main types</u> of pathogens:

<u>Bacteria</u>   <u>Viruses</u>   <u>Protists</u>   <u>Fungi</u>

Pathogens Can Be **Spread** in **Different Ways**

Here are a few ways that pathogens can be <u>spread</u>:

Air

Pathogens can be carried in the <u>air</u> and can then be <u>breathed in</u>. Some pathogens are carried in the air in <u>droplets</u> made when you <u>cough</u> or <u>sneeze</u>.

Water

Some pathogens can be picked up by <u>drinking</u> or <u>bathing</u> in <u>dirty water</u>.

Direct Contact

Some pathogens can be picked up by <u>touching</u> surfaces they're on (e.g. the skin).

The **Spread** of Disease Can Be **Reduced** or **Prevented**

There are things that we can do to <u>reduce</u> or <u>prevent</u> the spread of disease, such as...

1) <u>Being hygienic</u> (clean) — For example, <u>washing your hands</u> before making food can stop you <u>spreading pathogens</u> onto the food and infecting a person who <u>eats</u> it.

2) <u>Destroying vectors</u> — Vectors are <u>organisms</u> that <u>spread disease</u>. Killing them helps to <u>stop</u> the disease from being passed on. Vectors that are <u>insects</u> can be killed using <u>insecticides</u>. Their <u>habitats</u> can also be destroyed so that they can't <u>breed</u>.

3) <u>Isolating infected individuals</u> — If you keep someone who has a communicable disease away from other people, it <u>prevents</u> them from <u>passing it on</u> to anyone else.

4) <u>Vaccination</u> (see page 80) — Vaccinations can <u>stop</u> people and animals from <u>getting</u> a communicable disease. This also stops them <u>passing it on</u> to others.

Bacterial Diseases

*First up from the **pathogen** hall of fame are... **bacteria**.*

Bacteria are Very Small **Living Cells**

1) Bacteria <u>reproduce rapidly</u> inside your body.
2) They can make you <u>feel ill</u> by <u>producing toxins</u> (poisons).
3) Toxins <u>damage</u> your <u>cells and tissues</u>.

Salmonella and **Gonorrhea** Are Two **Bacterial Diseases**

Salmonella

1) *Salmonella* is a type of <u>bacteria</u>. It causes <u>food poisoning</u>.

2) Infected people can suffer from <u>fever</u>, <u>stomach cramps</u>, <u>vomiting</u> and <u>diarrhoea</u>. These symptoms are caused by <u>toxins</u> from the bacteria.

3) You can get *Salmonella* food poisoning by:

- Eating <u>food</u> that's got *Salmonella* bacteria in it already, e.g. eating chicken that caught the disease whilst it was alive.
- Eating food that has been <u>made</u> where the bacteria is present, e.g. in an <u>unclean kitchen</u> or on the <u>hands</u> of the person making the food.

4) In the UK, most <u>poultry</u> (e.g. chickens and turkeys) are given a <u>vaccination</u> against *Salmonella*. This is to control the <u>spread</u> of the disease.

Gonorrhoea

1) Gonorrhoea is caused by <u>bacteria</u>.
2) <u>Gonorrhoea</u> is a <u>sexually transmitted disease</u> (STD).
3) STDs are passed on by <u>sexual contact</u>, e.g. having unprotected sex.
4) A person with gonorrhoea will get <u>pain</u> when they <u>urinate</u> (wee). Another symptom is a thick yellow or green <u>discharge</u> (fluid) from the <u>vagina</u> or the <u>penis</u>.
5) Gonorrhoea <u>used to be treated</u> with an <u>antibiotic</u> called <u>penicillin</u>. There are now <u>new strains</u> (types) of gonorrhoea that are <u>resistant</u> to (not killed by) penicillin. So this antibiotic <u>doesn't work</u> anymore.
6) To prevent the <u>spread</u> of gonorrhoea:

- People can be treated with <u>other antibiotics</u>,
- People should use <u>barrier methods</u> of contraception (see page 110), such as <u>condoms</u>.

Viral Diseases

Viruses may be tiny but there are lots of diseases caused by them.

Viruses Are Not Cells — They're Much Smaller

1) Viruses <u>reproduce rapidly</u> inside your body.

2) They <u>live inside</u> your cells.

3) Inside your cells, they make <u>lots of copies</u> of themselves.

4) The cells will usually then <u>burst</u>, releasing all the new viruses.

5) This <u>cell damage</u> is what makes you feel ill.

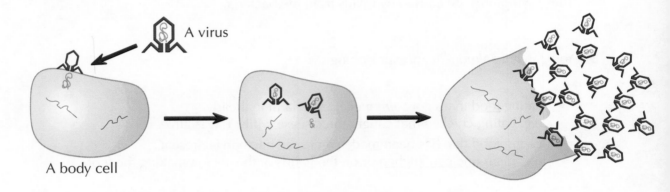

A virus

A body cell

Different Viruses Cause Different Diseases, Such as...

Measles

1) Measles is a <u>viral</u> disease. It is spread by <u>droplets</u> from an infected person's <u>sneeze</u> or <u>cough</u>.

2) People with measles develop a <u>red skin rash</u>.

3) They'll also show signs of a <u>fever</u> (a high temperature).

4) Measles can be <u>very serious</u>. People can <u>die</u> from measles if there are <u>complications</u> (problems).

5) Because of this, most people are <u>vaccinated</u> against measles when they're <u>young</u>.

Viral Diseases

HIV

1) <u>HIV</u> is a <u>virus</u> spread by <u>sexual contact</u> or by exchanging <u>bodily fluids</u> (e.g. blood). This can happen when people <u>share needles</u> when taking drugs.

2) To start with, HIV causes <u>flu-like symptoms</u> for a few weeks.

3) After that the person <u>doesn't</u> usually have any symptoms for several years.

4) HIV can be controlled with <u>antiretroviral drugs</u>. These stop the virus <u>copying itself</u> in the body.

5) If it's not controlled, the virus attacks the <u>immune cells</u> (see page 78).

6) If the body's immune system is badly damaged, it <u>can't cope</u> with <u>other infections</u> or <u>cancers</u>. At this stage, the virus is known as <u>late stage HIV infection</u> or <u>AIDS</u>.

Tobacco Mosaic Virus

1) <u>Tobacco mosaic virus</u> (<u>TMV</u>) is a <u>virus</u> that affects many species of <u>plants</u>, e.g. <u>tomatoes</u>.

2) It causes parts of the <u>leaves</u> to become <u>discoloured</u>. This gives them a <u>mosaic pattern</u>.

3) The discoloured leaves have <u>less chlorophyll</u> to absorb <u>light</u> (see p.85).

4) This means <u>less photosynthesis</u> happens in the leaves, so the plant can't make <u>enough food</u> to <u>grow</u>.

EXAM TIP

Don't be put off by something you haven't heard of...

If you're given some information about a disease you've <u>never heard of before</u>, don't panic. You just need to <u>use what you know</u> and <u>apply</u> it to the disease in the question. For example, if the disease is viral, just use what you know about viruses to answer the question.

Fungal and Protist Diseases

*Sorry — I'm afraid there are some more **diseases** to learn about here...*

Rose Black Spot is a Fungal Disease

1) <u>Rose black spot</u> is a disease caused by a <u>fungus</u>.

2) The fungus causes <u>purple or black spots</u> on the <u>leaves</u> of <u>rose plants</u>. The leaves can then turn <u>yellow</u> and <u>drop off</u>.

3) This means that less <u>photosynthesis</u> can happen, so the plant doesn't <u>grow</u> very well.

4) It is spread in <u>water</u> or by the <u>wind</u>.

5) Gardeners can treat the disease using <u>fungicides</u> (chemicals that kill fungi).

6) They can also <u>strip</u> the <u>affected leaves</u> off the plant. These leaves then need to be <u>destroyed</u> so that the fungus can't spread to other rose plants.

Malaria is a Disease Caused by a Protist

1) <u>Malaria</u> is caused by a <u>protist</u>.

2) Part of the protist's <u>life cycle</u> takes place inside the mosquito.

3) The mosquitoes are <u>vectors</u>. They help <u>spread</u> malaria like this...

- The mosquitoes <u>pick up</u> the protist when they <u>feed</u> on an <u>infected animal</u>.
- The mosquitoes <u>don't</u> get malaria.
- They <u>pass on</u> the protist to other animals (like us) when they <u>bite</u> them.
- These animals <u>get malaria</u>.

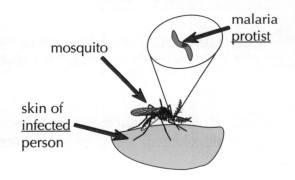

4) Malaria causes <u>repeating</u> episodes of <u>fever</u>. People can <u>die</u> from malaria.

5) The <u>spread</u> of malaria can be reduced by stopping the <u>mosquitoes</u> from <u>breeding</u>.

6) People can be protected from mosquito bites using <u>mosquito nets</u>.

Hang in there, this stuff is pretty gross, but it's nearly over...

Try drawing out a <u>table</u> with columns for 'disease', 'type of pathogen it's caused by', 'symptoms' and 'how it's spread', then fill it in for all the diseases on this page and the previous three. See how much you can write down <u>without</u> looking back at the page.

Warm-Up & Exam Questions

Have a go at these questions to test whether you know about each of the diseases covered on the previous pages, including their symptoms and how they are spread.

Warm-Up Questions

1) True or false? A communicable disease is a disease that can spread.
2) How is gonorrhoea passed between individuals?
3) Where do viruses live inside the human body?
4) What symptom of measles is shown on the skin?
5) Which disease causes the leaves of tomato plants to become discoloured?
6) What effect does rose black spot disease have on plants?

Exam Questions

1 Which of the following statements about malaria is **not** correct? Tick **one** box. *(Grade 1-3)*

☐ People with malaria can have repeating episodes of fever.

☐ Mosquitos are the vectors of malaria.

☐ Malaria is caused by a virus.

☐ People can be protected from mosquito bites by using mosquito nets.

[1 mark]

2 The spread of disease can be reduced or prevented in many ways. *(Grade 1-3)*

2.1 Which method is used to prevent the spread of *Salmonella* between people? Tick **one** box.

☐ hand-washing ☐ stopping vectors from breeding ☐ vaccinating people

[1 mark]

2.2 Which method is used to prevent the spread of measles between people? Tick **one** box.

☐ hand-washing ☐ stopping vectors from breeding ☐ vaccinating people

[1 mark]

3 Diseases are often recognised by their symptoms. *(Grade 3-4)*

3.1 Describe the first symptoms of HIV infection.

[1 mark]

3.2 Give **one** symptom of gonorrhoea.

[1 mark]

3.3 A person has food poisoning caused by *Salmonella*. Give **one** symptom that they may have.

[1 mark]

Fighting Disease

*The human body has some pretty neat features when it comes to **fighting disease**.*

Your Body Has a Pretty Good **Defence System**

The human body has got features that stop a lot of nasties getting inside. For example:

1) The <u>skin</u> — It <u>stops pathogens</u> getting <u>inside</u> you.
It also <u>releases substances</u> that <u>kill pathogens</u>.

2) <u>Nose hairs</u> — They <u>trap</u> particles that could contain pathogens.

3) <u>Mucus</u> (<u>snot</u>) — The <u>trachea</u> and <u>bronchi</u> (airways — see page 49) release <u>mucus</u> to <u>trap</u> pathogens.

4) <u>Cilia</u> (hair-like structures) — The <u>trachea</u> and <u>bronchi</u> are lined with <u>cilia</u>.
They <u>move</u> the <u>mucus</u> up to the back of the throat where it can be <u>swallowed</u>.

5) <u>Stomach acid</u> — The stomach makes <u>hydrochloric acid</u>.
This <u>kills pathogens</u> in the stomach.

Your **Immune System** Can **Attack Pathogens**

1) If pathogens do make it into your body, your <u>immune system</u> kicks in to <u>destroy</u> them.
2) The most important part of your immune system is the <u>white blood cells</u>.
3) When they come across an invading pathogen they have <u>three lines of attack</u>:

Phagocytosis

White blood cells can <u>engulf</u> (surround) pathogens and <u>digest</u> them. This is called <u>phagocytosis</u>.

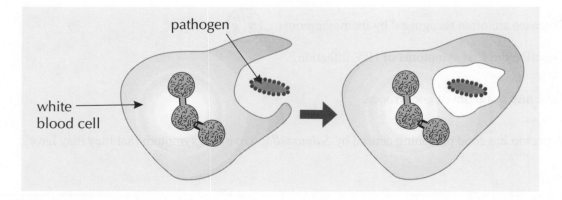

pathogen

white blood cell

Topic B3 — Infection and Response

Fighting Disease

Producing **Antibodies**

1) Every invading pathogen has <u>unique molecules</u> on its surface. These molecules are called <u>antigens</u>.

2) When some types of white blood cell come across a <u>foreign antigen</u> (i.e. one they don't know), they will start to make <u>antibodies</u>.

3) Antibodies <u>lock onto</u> the invading pathogens. The antibodies made are <u>specific</u> to that type of antigen — they won't lock on to any others.

4) The antibodies make sure the pathogens can be <u>found</u> and <u>destroyed</u> by other white blood cells.

5) If the person is infected with the <u>same pathogen</u> again, the white blood cells will <u>rapidly</u> make the antibodies to kill it. This means the person is <u>naturally immune</u> to that pathogen and <u>won't get ill</u>.

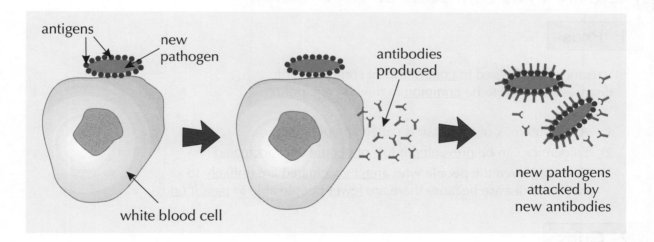

antigens
new pathogen
antibodies produced
white blood cell
new pathogens attacked by new antibodies

Producing **Antitoxins**

These <u>stop toxins</u> produced by the <u>invading bacteria</u> from working.

Fighting disease is one thing the body is really good at...

The <u>immune system</u> attacks pathogens that get <u>inside</u> the body. There are <u>three</u> ways that white blood cells <u>kill</u> pathogens — <u>phagocytosis</u>, making <u>antibodies</u> and making <u>antitoxins</u>. Make sure you know them <u>all</u>.

Fighting Disease — Vaccination

Vaccinations mean we don't always have to treat a disease — we can **stop** the disease in the first place.

Vaccination — **Protects** from **Future Infections**

1) <u>Vaccinations</u> involve injecting <u>small</u> amounts of <u>dead</u> or <u>inactive</u> pathogens into the body.
2) These pathogens have <u>antigens</u> on their surface.
3) The antigens cause your white blood cells to produce <u>antibodies</u> to attack the pathogens.
4) If you're infected with the <u>same</u> pathogen later, your white blood cells <u>quickly produce</u> lots of antibodies.
5) These antibodies <u>kill the pathogen</u> so you <u>don't become ill</u>.

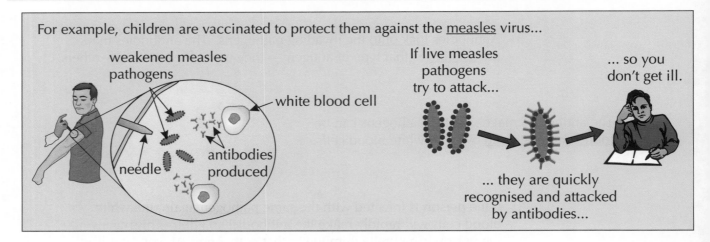

For example, children are vaccinated to protect them against the <u>measles</u> virus...

weakened measles pathogens

white blood cell

needle

antibodies produced

If live measles pathogens try to attack...

... they are quickly recognised and attacked by antibodies...

... so you don't get ill.

There are **Pros** and **Cons** of **Vaccination**

1. Pros

Vaccines have helped to <u>control</u> lots of communicable diseases that used to be <u>common</u> in the UK, e.g. polio.

1) A big outbreak of a disease is called an <u>epidemic</u>.
2) Epidemics can be <u>prevented</u> if <u>lots of people</u> are <u>vaccinated</u>.
3) That way, even the people who <u>aren't vaccinated</u> are <u>unlikely</u> to catch the disease because there are <u>fewer</u> people able to <u>pass it on</u>.

2. Cons

1) Vaccines <u>don't always work</u> — sometimes they <u>don't</u> give you <u>immunity</u>.
2) You can sometimes have a <u>bad reaction</u> to a vaccine (e.g. swelling or a fever).

Prevention is better than cure...

Although vaccinations <u>aren't perfect</u>, it's better to have a vaccine than risk catching a <u>nasty disease</u>.

Q1 Basia is vaccinated against flu and Cassian isn't. They are both exposed to a flu virus. Cassian falls ill whereas Basia doesn't. Explain why. [2 marks]

Q1 Video Solution

Fighting Disease — Drugs

*You've probably had to take some sort of **medicine** if you've been ill, e.g. cough remedies, painkillers.*

Some Drugs **Get Rid of Symptoms** — Others **Cure** the Problem

1) Some drugs help to <u>get rid</u> of the <u>symptoms</u> of a disease, e.g. <u>painkillers reduce pain</u>.

2) But these drugs <u>don't kill</u> the pathogens that cause the disease.

A flu virus

3) <u>Antibiotics</u> (e.g. penicillin) <u>kill bacteria</u>.

4) <u>Different antibiotics</u> kill <u>different types</u> of bacteria, so it's important to be treated with the <u>right one</u>.

5) The use of antibiotics has <u>greatly reduced</u> the number of deaths from communicable diseases caused by bacteria.

6) Antibiotics <u>don't destroy viruses</u> (e.g. <u>flu</u> viruses).

7) Viruses reproduce <u>using your own body cells</u>. This makes it very <u>difficult</u> to develop <u>drugs</u> that <u>destroy the virus</u> without <u>killing the body's cells</u>.

Bacteria Can Become **Resistant** to **Antibiotics**

1) Bacteria can <u>mutate</u> (change).

2) Some of these mutations cause the bacteria to become <u>resistant</u> to (not be killed by) an <u>antibiotic</u>.

3) <u>Resistant strains</u> (<u>types</u>) of bacteria, e.g. <u>MRSA</u>, have increased as a result of <u>natural selection</u> (see page 130).

Many **Drugs** First Came From **Plants**

1) <u>Plants</u> produce <u>chemicals</u> to <u>defend</u> themselves against <u>pests</u> and <u>pathogens</u>.

2) Some of these chemicals can be used as <u>drugs</u> to <u>treat</u> human diseases or <u>relieve symptoms</u>.

3) A lot of our <u>medicines</u> were found by studying plants used in <u>old-fashioned cures</u>. For example:

> 1) <u>Aspirin</u> is used as a <u>painkiller</u>. It was made from a chemical found in <u>willow</u>.
>
> 2) <u>Digitalis</u> is used to treat <u>heart conditions</u>. It was made from a chemical found in <u>foxgloves</u>.

4) Some drugs have come from <u>microorganisms</u>. For example:

> 1) Alexander Fleming found that a type of <u>mould</u> (called *Penicillium*) makes a <u>substance</u> that <u>kills bacteria</u>.
>
> 2) This substance is called <u>penicillin</u>.
>
> 3) Penicillin is used as an <u>antibiotic</u>.

5) These days, <u>new drugs</u> are <u>made</u> by the <u>pharmaceutical industry</u> (companies that make and sell drugs).

6) The drugs are made by <u>chemists</u> in <u>labs</u>.

7) The process of making the drugs still might start with a chemical <u>taken</u> from a <u>plant</u>.

Developing Drugs

*New drugs are always being developed. But before they can be given to people like you and me, they have to go through **a lot** of **tests**. This is what usually happens...*

There Are **Different Stages** in the **Development** of **New Drugs**

1) Once a possible drug has been <u>discovered</u>, it needs to be <u>developed</u>.
2) This involves <u>preclinical</u> and <u>clinical testing</u>.

Preclinical Testing

1) Drugs are <u>first</u> tested on <u>human cells and tissues</u> in the lab.
2) Next the drug is tested on <u>live animals</u>. This is to <u>find out</u>:

- Its <u>efficacy</u> (whether the drug <u>works</u> and has the effect you're looking for).
- Its <u>toxicity</u> (how <u>harmful</u> it is and whether it has any <u>side effects</u>).
- Its <u>dosage</u> (the <u>concentration</u> of the drug that works <u>best</u> and how <u>often</u> it should be taken).

Clinical Testing

If the drug <u>passes</u> the tests on animals then it's tested on <u>human volunteers</u> in a <u>clinical trial</u>.

1) First, the drug is tested on <u>healthy volunteers</u>. This is to make sure it doesn't have any <u>harmful side effects</u> when the body is working <u>normally</u>.
2) At the start of the trial, a <u>very low dose</u> of the drug is given. This dose is <u>increased</u> little by little.
3) If these results are <u>good</u>, the drugs can be tested on <u>patients</u> (people with the <u>illness</u>).
4) The <u>optimum dose</u> is found — this is the dose of drug that is the <u>most effective</u> and has <u>few side effects</u>.
5) To test how well the drug works, patients are put into <u>two groups</u>...

> Group 1 is given the <u>new drug</u>.

> Group 2 is given a <u>placebo</u> (a substance that's like the drug being tested but doesn't do anything).

6) The doctor <u>compares</u> the two groups of patients to see if the drug makes a <u>real difference</u>.
7) Clinical trials are <u>blind</u> — the patient <u>doesn't know</u> whether they're getting the drug or the placebo.
8) In fact, they're often <u>double-blind</u> — neither the <u>patient nor the doctor</u> knows who's taken the drug and who's taken the placebo until all the results have been gathered.
9) The results of these tests aren't <u>published</u> until they've been through <u>peer review</u>. This helps to prevent <u>false claims</u>.

Peer review is when other scientists check the work — see page 2.

The placebo effect doesn't work with revision...

... you can't just expect to get a good mark and then magically get it. I know, I know, there's a lot of information to take in on this page, but just read it through <u>slowly</u>. There's nothing too tricky here — it's just a case of going over it <u>again and again</u> until you've got it all firmly lodged in your memory.

Warm-Up & Exam Questions

It's easy to think you've learnt everything in the section until you try the Warm-Up Questions.
Don't panic if there's a bit you've forgotten, just go back over that bit until it's firmly fixed in your brain.

Warm-Up Questions

1) How does the skin defend the body against pathogens?
2) What is the role of the immune system?
3) What is meant by the term 'antigen'?
4) How do bacteria become resistant to antibiotics?
5) What is meant by the efficacy of a drug?

Exam Questions

1 Many of the drugs used today first came from plants or microorganisms. Grade 1-3

1.1 Draw **one** line from each drug to where it was originally extracted from.

Aspirin	Mould
Digitalis	Willow
Penicillin	Foxgloves

[2 marks]

1.2 State what aspirin is used for.

[1 mark]

1.3 State what penicillin is used for.

[1 mark]

2 The human immune system fights pathogens using a number of different methods. Grade 3-4
One process for destroying pathogens is shown in **Figure 1**.

Figure 1

white blood cell

pathogen

nucleus

2.1 Name the process shown in **Figure 1**.

[1 mark]

2.2 Antibodies play a role in the immune response. Complete the sentences about antibodies.

Antibodies are produced by ....

They attach to specific antigens on the surface of the ....

[2 marks]

Exam Questions

3 A scientist is carrying out a clinical trial. *(Grade 3-4)*

3.1 What is a drug tested on in a clinical trial? Tick **one** box.

☐ human cells

☐ human volunteers

☐ live animals

☐ human tissue

[1 mark]

3.2 The clinical trial is double-blind. What is meant by 'double-blind'? Tick **one** box.

☐ The patient does not know whether they are receiving the drug or placebo, but the doctor does.

☐ All the patients are given a placebo first, followed by the drug.

☐ Neither the patient or the doctor know who is receiving the drug and who is receiving the placebo.

☐ All the patients are given the drug first, followed by a placebo.

[1 mark]

4 There are many different lines of defence in the human body that help to prevent pathogens from entering the blood. *(Grade 4-5)*

4.1 What is the role of the hairs and mucus in the nose?

[1 mark]

4.2 How do the cilia in the trachea and bronchi help to defend the body?

[1 mark]

4.3 What does the stomach produce to kill pathogens?

[1 mark]

5 Rubella is a communicable viral disease. *(Grade 4-5)*

The rubella virus is spread in droplets through the air when an infected person coughs, sneezes or talks.

The virus causes symptoms including fever and painful joints. The spread of the disease can be reduced by vaccination.

5.1* Explain how being vaccinated against rubella can prevent a person from catching the disease. In your answer, suggest why vaccinating a large number of people reduces the risk of someone who hasn't been vaccinated from catching rubella.

[6 marks]

5.2 Suggest **one** reason why some individuals may choose not to receive a vaccination against a disease.

[1 mark]

Photosynthesis

*First, the **photosynthesis equation**. Then onto how plants use **glucose**...*

Photosynthesis Produces **Glucose** Using **Light**

1) <u>Photosynthesis</u> uses <u>energy</u> to change <u>carbon dioxide</u> and <u>water</u> into <u>glucose</u> and <u>oxygen</u>.
2) It takes place in <u>chloroplasts</u> in <u>plant cells</u>.
3) Chloroplasts contain <u>chlorophyll</u> that <u>absorbs light</u>.
4) Energy is <u>transferred</u> to the <u>chloroplasts</u> from the environment by <u>light</u>.
5) Photosynthesis is an <u>endothermic</u> reaction.
   This means that <u>energy</u> is <u>transferred</u> from the <u>environment</u> during the reaction.
6) You need to learn the <u>word equation</u> for photosynthesis:

$$\text{carbon dioxide} + \text{water} \xrightarrow{\text{light}} \text{glucose} + \text{oxygen}$$

7) You also need to know the <u>chemical symbols</u> for the substances involved in photosynthesis:

carbon dioxide: CO_2 water: H_2O glucose: $C_6H_{12}O_6$ oxygen: O_2

Plants Use Glucose in **Five** Main Ways...

1) <u>For respiration</u> — This <u>transfers energy</u> from glucose (see p.91). This allows the plants to <u>change</u> the rest of the glucose into <u>other useful substances</u>.

2) <u>For making cell walls</u> — <u>Glucose</u> is changed into <u>cellulose</u> for making strong <u>plant cell walls</u> (see p.18).

3) <u>For making amino acids</u> — <u>Glucose</u> is combined with <u>nitrate ions</u> to make <u>amino acids</u>. Nitrate ions are <u>absorbed</u> from the <u>soil</u>. Amino acids are used to make <u>proteins</u>.

4) <u>Stored as oils or fats</u> — Glucose is turned into <u>lipids</u> (<u>fats</u> and <u>oils</u>) for <u>storing in seeds</u>.

5) <u>Stored as starch</u> — <u>Glucose</u> is turned into <u>starch</u> and <u>stored</u> in roots, stems and leaves.
   - Plants can <u>use</u> this starch when photosynthesis <u>isn't happening</u>.
   - <u>Starch</u> is <u>insoluble</u> (it can't be <u>dissolved</u>).
   - Being insoluble makes starch much <u>better</u> for <u>storing</u> than glucose. This is because a cell with <u>lots of glucose</u> in would draw in loads of water and <u>swell up</u>.

The Rate of Photosynthesis

*The **rate** of photosynthesis can be **affected** by **a few** different things. These are called **limiting factors**...*

Light, Temperature and CO_2 Affect the Rate of Photosynthesis

1) The underlined rate of photosynthesis is affected by intensity of underlined light (how bright the light is), concentration of CO_2 and underlined temperature.

2) Any of these things can become the underlined limiting factor of photosynthesis.

3) A limiting factor is something that stops photosynthesis from happening any underlined faster.

4) underlined Chlorophyll can also be a underlined limiting factor of photosynthesis.
   - The underlined amount of chlorophyll in a plant can be affected by underlined disease.
   - It can also be affected by underlined changes in the environment, such as underlined a lack of nutrients.
   - These factors can cause underlined chloroplasts to become underlined damaged or to underlined not make underlined enough chlorophyll.
   - This means they underlined can't absorb as much underlined light. The rate of photosynthesis is underlined reduced.

Three Important Graphs for Rate of Photosynthesis

1. Not Enough Light Slows Down the Rate of Photosynthesis

1) At first, the underlined more light there is, the underlined faster photosynthesis happens.

2) This means the underlined rate of photosynthesis depends on the underlined amount of light. underlined Light is the underlined limiting factor.

3) After a certain point the graph underlined flattens out. Here photosynthesis underlined won't go any faster — even if you increase the light intensity.

4) This is because light is underlined no longer the limiting factor. Now it's either the underlined temperature or the amount of underlined carbon dioxide that's the underlined limiting factor.

CO$_2$ or temp needs to be increased

rate increases with light intensity

light intensity

The amount of light is called light intensity.

'Photo' means light and 'synthesis' means putting together...

...so photosynthesis means 'putting together using light'. And the thing being put together is underlined glucose. Well, I guess that's one way of remembering it... (Maybe just underlined learn the underlined word equation instead.)

The Rate of Photosynthesis

2. Too Little **Carbon Dioxide** Also Slows it Down

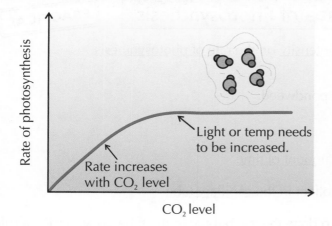

Light or temp needs to be increased.

Rate increases with CO_2 level

CO_2 level

1) The more carbon dioxide (CO_2) there is, the faster photosynthesis happens.
2) This means the amount of CO_2 is the limiting factor.
3) After a certain point, photosynthesis won't go any faster because CO_2 is no longer the limiting factor.
4) If there's plenty of light and carbon dioxide then it must be the temperature that's the limiting factor.

3. The **Temperature** has to be Just Right

1) Usually, if the temperature is the limiting factor it's because it's too low.

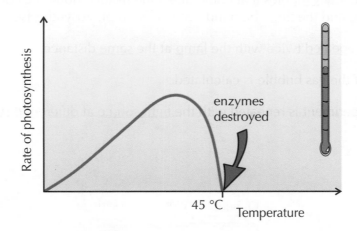

enzymes destroyed

45 °C   Temperature

2) This is because the enzymes (see page 41) needed for photosynthesis work more slowly at low temperatures.

3) But if the plant gets too hot, photosynthesis won't happen at all.

4) This is because the enzymes are damaged if the temperature's too high (over about 45 °C).

Graphs, graphs and more graphs

Q1   a) The graph on the right shows how light intensity affects the rate of photosynthesis. State at which point (A-D) the light intensity stops being the limiting factor. [1 mark]
      b) Suggest what the limiting factor could be at point D. [1 mark]

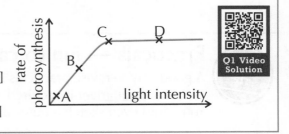

Q1 Video Solution

Measuring the Rate of Photosynthesis

*It's practical time again. This one lets you see how changing **light intensity** affects the **rate of photosynthesis**.*

Oxygen Production Shows the Rate of Photosynthesis

<u>Pondweed</u> can be used to measure the effect of <u>light intensity</u> on the <u>rate of photosynthesis</u>.
Here's how the experiment works:

1) A <u>ruler</u> is used to measure a <u>set distance</u> from the pondweed.

2) A <u>light</u> is placed at that distance.

3) The pondweed is left to photosynthesise for a <u>set amount of time</u>.

4) As it photosynthesises, the oxygen released will collect in the <u>capillary tube</u>.

5) At the end of the experiment, the <u>syringe</u> is used to draw the gas bubble in the tube up alongside a ruler.

6) The <u>length</u> of the <u>gas bubble</u> is <u>measured</u>.

7) The <u>length</u> of the gas bubble tells you <u>how much</u> oxygen has been produced during that amount of time. This means that the <u>longer</u> the gas bubble, the <u>faster</u> the rate of photosynthesis.

8) For this experiment, any <u>variables</u> that could affect the results should be <u>controlled</u>. E.g. the <u>temperature</u> and the <u>time</u> the pondweed is left to photosynthesise.

9) The experiment is <u>repeated</u> twice with the <u>lamp</u> at the <u>same</u> distance.

10) The <u>mean</u> length of the gas bubble is calculated.

11) Then the whole experiment is repeated with the <u>light source</u> at <u>different distances</u> from the pondweed.

You can compare the results at different light intensities by giving the rate as the length of the bubble per unit time, e.g. cm/min.

Practicals — fun to carry out, not so fun to answer questions on

A good way to revise practicals is to scribble down as much as you can remember.
List what <u>equipment</u> is required and write out the <u>method</u> step-by-step.
You could even sketch a quick diagram of the <u>apparatus</u> all set up and practise labelling it.

Warm-Up & Exam Questions

Time for a break in the topic and some questions. Do them now, whilst all that learning is fresh in your mind. Using that knowledge will help you to remember it all, and that's what this game is all about.

Warm-Up Questions

1) What substance do chloroplasts contain that absorbs light?
2) Where does the energy for photosynthesis come from?
3) True or false? Photosynthesis is an exothermic reaction.
4) True or false? Glucose is used for respiration.

Exam Questions

1 Photosynthesis involves a number of substances. *Grade 1-3*

1.1 Draw **one** line from each substance to its chemical symbol.

glucose		O_2
oxygen		H_2O
water		$C_6H_{12}O_6$

[2 marks]

1.2 Carbon dioxide is another substance involved in photosynthesis.
What is the chemical symbol for carbon dioxide?

[1 mark]

2 Photosynthesis produces glucose using light. *Grade 3-4*

2.1 Complete the word equation for photosynthesis.

light
carbon dioxide + ... → glucose + ...

[2 marks]

2.2 Plants use glucose to make a substance which strengthens their cell walls.
Which of the following substances strengthens cells walls? Tick **one** box.

☐ cellulose   ☐ oils   ☐ starch   ☐ fats

[1 mark]

2.3 Which of the following is another way that plants use glucose? Tick **one** box.

☐ making nitrates   ☐ storage as oils   ☐ making chlorophyll

[1 mark]

Exam Questions

3 Plants store glucose as starch. (Grade 3-4)

3.1 Which of the following is a characteristic of starch that makes it suitable for storage? Tick **one** box.

☐ it contains carbon ☐ it is soluble ☐ it is insoluble ☐ starch molecules are large

[1 mark]

3.2 Explain why plants use starch as a source of glucose when photosynthesis is **not** happening.

[1 mark]

4 A student investigated the effect of increasing carbon dioxide concentration on the rate of photosynthesis of a plant. The results are shown in **Figure 1**. (Grade 4-5)

Figure 1

4.1 Describe the trend shown on the graph at point **A**.

[1 mark]

4.2 Give the limiting factor at point **A** on the curve.

[1 mark]

4.3 Explain why the curve is flattening out at point **B**.

[2 marks]

4.4 Explain why low temperatures limit the rate of photosynthesis.

[1 mark]

PRACTICAL

5 A student did an experiment to see how the rate of photosynthesis depends on light intensity. **Figure 2** shows some of her apparatus. (Grade 4-5)

5.1 How can the student measure the rate of photosynthesis?

[1 mark]

Figure 2

5.2 State the dependent variable in this experiment.

[1 mark]

5.3 State the independent variable in this experiment.

[1 mark]

5.4 State **one** factor that should be kept constant during this experiment.

[1 mark]

Aerobic Respiration

*You need **energy** to keep your body going. Energy comes from **food**, and it's **transferred** by **respiration**.*

Respiration is **NOT** "Breathing In and Out"

1) <u>All living things respire</u>.
2) <u>Respiration</u> is the process of <u>transferring energy</u> from the <u>breakdown of glucose</u> (a sugar).
3) Respiration goes on in <u>every cell</u> in your body <u>all the time</u>.
4) The energy transferred from respiration is used for <u>all living processes</u> (everything a cell needs to do).

> <u>RESPIRATION</u> is the process of <u>TRANSFERRING ENERGY</u>
> <u>FROM GLUCOSE</u>, which goes on <u>IN EVERY CELL</u>.

5) Respiration is <u>exothermic</u>. This means it <u>transfers energy</u> to the <u>environment</u>.

Respiration **Transfers Energy** for All Kinds of Things

Here are <u>three examples</u> of how organisms <u>use</u> the <u>energy</u> transferred by respiration:

> 1) To build up <u>larger molecules</u> from <u>smaller</u> ones.
> 2) In animals, to <u>move</u> about.
> 3) In <u>mammals</u> and <u>birds</u>, to keep warm.

Aerobic Respiration Needs Plenty of **Oxygen**

1) <u>Aerobic respiration</u> is respiration using <u>oxygen</u>.
2) Aerobic respiration goes on <u>all the time</u> in <u>plants</u> and <u>animals</u>.
3) Most of the reactions in <u>aerobic respiration</u> happen inside <u>mitochondria</u> (see page 17).
4) You need to learn the overall <u>word equation</u> for respiration:

> glucose + oxygen $\longrightarrow$ carbon dioxide + water

5) You also need to know the <u>chemical symbols</u> for the substances involved:
glucose: $C_6H_{12}O_6$ oxygen: O_2 carbon dioxide: CO_2 water: H_2O

Anaerobic Respiration

*Anaerobic respiration is just as important as aerobic respiration — especially when there's **not enough oxygen**...*

Anaerobic Respiration is Used if There's **Not Enough Oxygen**

1) When you do hard exercise, your body sometimes can't supply enough <u>oxygen</u> to your muscles.

2) When this happens, they start doing <u>anaerobic respiration</u> as well as aerobic respiration.

3) Anaerobic respiration is the <u>incomplete breakdown</u> of glucose (the glucose isn't broken down properly).

4) Here's the <u>word equation</u> for anaerobic respiration in muscle cells:

glucose ⟶ lactic acid

5) <u>Anaerobic respiration</u> does <u>not</u> transfer anywhere near as much <u>energy</u> as aerobic respiration.

6) This is because the <u>glucose</u> has <u>not combined</u> with oxygen like it does in aerobic respiration.

7) The posh way of saying this is that the <u>oxidation</u> of glucose is <u>not complete</u>.

Anaerobic Respiration in **Plants** and **Yeast** is Slightly **Different**

1) <u>Plants</u> and <u>yeast cells</u> can respire <u>without oxygen</u> too.

2) Here is the <u>word equation</u> for anaerobic respiration in <u>plants</u> and <u>yeast cells</u>:

Yeast are single-celled organisms.

glucose ⟶ ethanol + carbon dioxide

3) Anaerobic respiration in <u>yeast cells</u> is called <u>fermentation</u>.

4) In the <u>food and drinks industry</u>, <u>fermentation</u> by yeast is of <u>great value</u>.

5) It's used to make <u>bread</u>. It's the <u>carbon dioxide</u> from fermentation that makes bread <u>rise</u>.

6) It's used to make <u>alcoholic drinks</u> (<u>beer</u> and <u>wine</u>). It's the fermentation process that produces <u>alcohol</u>.

Respiration releases energy from glucose

So... respiration is a pretty important thing — the <u>energy transferred</u> from <u>glucose</u> is used to make <u>molecules</u> that our cells need. When it comes to this topic, make sure you know the <u>word equations</u> from this page and the previous page and can compare the processes of <u>aerobic</u> and <u>anaerobic</u> respiration.

Exercise

*When you **exercise**, your body responds in different ways to get enough **energy** to your **cells**.*

When You **Exercise** You **Respire More**

1) Muscles need <u>energy</u> from respiration to <u>contract</u> (shorten).
2) When you exercise, some of your muscles contract more often. This means you need <u>more energy</u>.
3) This energy comes from <u>increased respiration</u>.
4) The increase in respiration in your cells means you need to get <u>more oxygen</u> into them. To do this:

> 1) Your <u>breathing rate</u> (how fast you breathe) <u>increases</u>.
> 2) Your <u>breath volume</u> (how deep the breaths you take are) <u>increases</u>.
> 3) Your <u>heart rate</u> (how fast your heart beats) <u>increases</u>.

5) Increasing your breathing rate and breath volume gets <u>oxygen</u> into your <u>blood quicker</u>. Blood containing oxygen is called <u>oxygenated blood</u>.
6) Your <u>heart rate</u> increases to get this oxygenated blood <u>around the body</u> faster.

An unfit person's heart rate goes up a lot more during exercise than a fit person, and they take longer to recover.

Hard Exercise Can Lead to **Anaerobic Respiration**

1) When you do <u>really hard exercise</u>, your body can't supply <u>oxygen</u> to your muscles quickly enough.

2) This means your muscles start doing <u>anaerobic respiration</u> (see the previous page).

3) This is <u>NOT the best way to transfer energy from glucose</u>. This is because <u>lactic acid</u> builds up in the muscles, which gets <u>painful</u>.

4) <u>Long periods</u> of exercise also cause <u>muscle fatigue</u>. This is when the muscles get <u>tired</u> and <u>stop contracting efficiently</u>.

Anaerobic Respiration Leads to an **Oxygen Debt**

1) After <u>anaerobic respiration</u> stops, you'll have an "<u>oxygen debt</u>".
2) An oxygen debt is the <u>amount</u> of <u>extra oxygen</u> your body needs <u>after exercise</u>.
3) Your lungs, heart and blood <u>couldn't keep up</u> with the demand for oxygen earlier on. So you have to "<u>repay</u>" the oxygen that you didn't get to your muscles in time.
4) This means you have to keep <u>breathing hard</u> for a while after you stop.
5) This gets <u>more oxygen</u> into your blood, which is transported to the muscle cells.

Very hard exercise = anaerobic respiration = oxygen debt

Q1 A scientist measured the concentration of lactic acid in her blood after walking for 5 minutes. She also measured the concentration of lactic acid in her blood after running for 5 minutes. Suggest why the concentration of lactic acid in her blood was higher after running than after walking.

Q1 Video Solution

[3 marks]

Metabolism

*Metabolism is going on **all of the time**. Right now. And now. Even now. Okay, you get the picture. Time to read all about it.*

Metabolism is ALL the Chemical Reactions in an Organism

1) In a cell there are lots of chemical reactions happening all the time.

2) These reactions are controlled by enzymes.

There's more about enzymes on page 41

3) In some of these reactions, larger molecules are made from smaller ones. For example:

> 1) Lots of small glucose (sugar) molecules are joined together in reactions to form:
>   - starch (a storage molecule in plant cells),
>   - glycogen (a storage molecule in animal cells),
>   - cellulose (a component of plant cell walls).

> 2) Lipid molecules are each made from one molecule of glycerol and three fatty acids.

> 3) Glucose is combined with nitrate ions to make amino acids. These are then made into proteins.

4) In other reactions, larger molecules are broken down into smaller ones. For example:

> 1) Glucose is broken down in respiration.
>   - Respiration transfers energy to power all the reactions in the body that make molecules.

> 2) Excess protein is broken down in a reaction to produce urea. Urea is then excreted in urine.

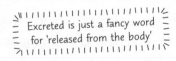
Excreted is just a fancy word for 'released from the body'

5) The sum (total) of all of the reactions that happen in a cell or the body is called its metabolism.

It's still going on now

Remember, the energy for metabolism comes from respiration. This energy allows cells to make larger molecules from smaller ones, and to break larger molecules down into smaller ones. Enzymes are key to metabolism, so if you need a reminder about them, now is a good time to head back to page 41.

Warm-Up & Exam Questions

You know the drill by now — work your way through the Warm-Up questions, then the Exam Questions.

Warm-Up Questions

1) True or false? All living things respire.
2) What is anaerobic respiration in yeast cells called?
3) Give one way that the body gets more oxygen into cells during exercise.
4) What is excess protein broken down into?

Exam Questions

1   In the human body, respiration may be aerobic or anaerobic at different times. (Grade 3-4)

1.1   Which of the following is the word equation for anaerobic respiration in humans. Tick **one** box.

☐ glucose → lactic acid + carbon dioxide   ☐ glucose → lactic acid

☐ glucose → ethanol + carbon dioxide   ☐ glucose → ethanol

[1 mark]

1.2   The body uses anaerobic respiration during hard exercise.
Complete the sentences about anaerobic respiration during exercise.

Muscles start using anaerobic respiration when they don't get enough ....

This causes a build up of ....

After anaerobic respiration stops, the body is left with an oxygen ....

[3 marks]

2   Metabolism is a process in which larger molecules are made or broken down. (Grade 3-4)

Which of the following molecules is **not** formed by
joining lots of glucose molecules together? Tick **one** box.

☐ starch   ☐ glycogen   ☐ protein   ☐ cellulose

[1 mark]

3   Respiration is a process carried out by all living cells. (Grade 4-5)
It can take place aerobically or anaerobically.

3.1   Give **two** differences between aerobic and anaerobic respiration.

[2 marks]

3.2   Complete the word equation for aerobic respiration.

$$\text{glucose} + ... \xrightarrow{\text{light}} \text{carbon dioxide} + ...$$

[2 marks]

Revision Summary for Topics B1-4

Well, it's all over for Topics B1-4 folks — I know you'll miss them, so here are some questions on them...

For even more practice, try the Retrieval Quizzes for Topics B1-4 — just scan the QR codes!

- Try these questions and tick off each one when you get it right.
- When you're completely happy with a topic, tick it off.

Topic B1 — Cell Biology (p.17-37) ☑

1) Name five subcellular structures that both plant and animal cells have.
2) Where is the genetic material found in: a) animals cells   b) bacterial cells?
3) Give two ways that a sperm cell is adapted for swimming to an egg.
4) Give one way that embryonic stem cells could be used to cure diseases.
5) What are chromosomes?
6) What is diffusion?
7) What type of molecules move by osmosis?
8) Give three ways that exchange surfaces can be adapted for diffusion.
9) Give two ways that the villi in the small intestine are adapted for absorbing digested food.

Topic B2 — Organisation (p.40-69) ☑

10) What is a tissue?
11) What does it mean when an enzyme has been 'denatured'?
12) Describe how you could investigate the effect of pH on the rate of amylase activity.
13) Name the solution that you would use to test for the presence of sugars in a food sample.
14) Where does gas exchange happen in the lungs?
15) How are arteries adapted to carry blood away from the heart?
16) Why do red blood cells not have a nucleus?
17) What is the difference between biological and mechanical replacement heart valves?
18) Give an example of different types of disease interacting in the body.
19) Give two lifestyle factors that increase the chance of cancer.
20) Explain how the structure of the palisade layer in a leaf is related to its function.
21) What is the function of phloem tubes?

Topic B3 — Infection and Response (p.72-82) ☑

22) Give one way that pathogens can be spread.
23) Why does tobacco mosaic virus affect photosynthesis?
24) What are the vectors for malaria?
25) Give three ways that white blood cells can defend against pathogens.
26) Why is it difficult to develop drugs that kill viruses?

Topic B4 — Bioenergetics (p.85-94) ☑

27) Where in a plant cell does photosynthesis take place?
28) Why would a low concentration of chlorophyll limit photosynthesis?
29) Describe how you could measure the effect of light intensity on the rate of photosynthesis.
30) What is the word equation for anaerobic respiration in yeast cells?
31) Name two products of the food and drink industry that fermentation is needed for.

Homeostasis

Homeostasis — a word that strikes fear into the heart of many a GCSE student. But it's really not that bad at all. This page is a brief **introduction** to the topic, so you need to **nail all of this** before you can move on.

Homeostasis — Keeping **Conditions Inside Your Body Steady**

1) <u>Homeostasis</u> is the fancy word for keeping the <u>conditions</u> in your body and cells at the <u>right level</u>. This happens in response to <u>changes</u> inside and outside of the body.

2) This is really important because your <u>cells</u> need the <u>right conditions</u> to <u>work properly</u>.

3) This includes having the right conditions for <u>enzymes</u> to work (see p.41).

Your Body Uses **Control Systems** for **Homeostasis**

1) You have loads of <u>control systems</u> that keep the conditions in your body <u>steady</u>. For example, they keep your <u>body temperature</u>, <u>blood glucose level</u> and <u>water level</u> steady.

2) These control systems are <u>automatic</u> — you don't have to think about them.

3) They can control conditions in the body using the <u>nervous system</u> or <u>hormones</u>.

4) Control systems are made up of <u>three main parts</u>:

- <u>receptors</u>,
- <u>coordination centres</u> (including the brain, spinal cord and pancreas),
- <u>effectors</u>.

5) When the level of something (e.g. blood glucose) gets <u>too high</u> or <u>too low</u>, its control system brings it back to <u>normal</u>.

> If the level is <u>too HIGH</u>, the control system <u>DECREASES</u> the level.
> If the level is <u>too LOW</u>, the control system <u>INCREASES</u> the level.

6) Here's how a control system works:

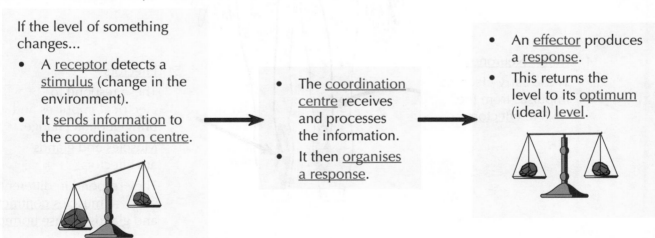

If the level of something changes...
- A <u>receptor</u> detects a <u>stimulus</u> (change in the environment).
- It <u>sends information</u> to the <u>coordination centre</u>.

- The <u>coordination centre</u> receives and processes the information.
- It then <u>organises a response</u>.

- An <u>effector</u> produces a <u>response</u>.
- This returns the level to its <u>optimum</u> (ideal) <u>level</u>.

Homeostasis is always happening without us thinking about it

Homeostasis is really important for keeping processes in your body working. It does this by keeping everything at the <u>right level</u>. Make sure you know what <u>receptors</u>, <u>coordination centres</u> and <u>effectors</u> do.

The Nervous System

*Organisms need to **respond to stimuli** (changes in the environment). That's where the **nervous system** comes in — it picks up information from the environment and brings about a **response**.*

The **Nervous System Detects** and **Reacts** to **Stimuli**

1) The <u>nervous system</u> means that humans can <u>react to their surroundings</u> and <u>coordinate their behaviour</u>.

2) The nervous system is made up of <u>different parts</u>:

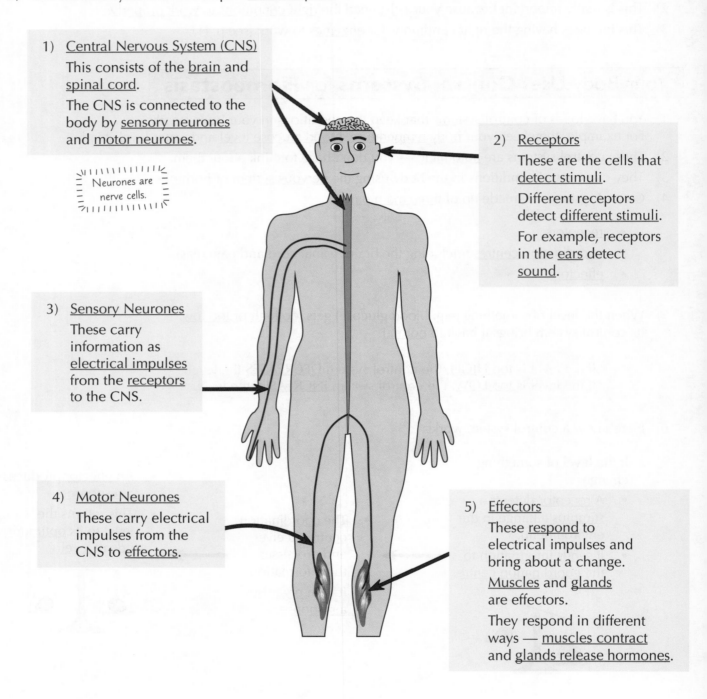

1) <u>Central Nervous System (CNS)</u>
   This consists of the <u>brain</u> and <u>spinal cord</u>.
   The CNS is connected to the body by <u>sensory neurones</u> and <u>motor neurones</u>.

   Neurones are nerve cells.

2) <u>Receptors</u>
   These are the cells that <u>detect stimuli</u>.
   Different receptors detect <u>different stimuli</u>.
   For example, receptors in the <u>ears</u> detect <u>sound</u>.

3) <u>Sensory Neurones</u>
   These carry information as <u>electrical impulses</u> from the <u>receptors</u> to the CNS.

4) <u>Motor Neurones</u>
   These carry electrical impulses from the CNS to <u>effectors</u>.

5) <u>Effectors</u>
   These <u>respond</u> to electrical impulses and bring about a change.
   <u>Muscles</u> and <u>glands</u> are effectors.
   They respond in different ways — <u>muscles contract</u> and <u>glands release hormones</u>.

Learn the different parts of the nervous system

Don't be confused by the terms '<u>nervous system</u>' and '<u>central nervous system</u>'. The 'nervous system' includes <u>all</u> of the parts above, but the '<u>central</u> nervous system' means just the <u>brain</u> and <u>spinal cord</u>.

The Nervous System

*Now for some detail about how the parts of the nervous system on the previous page **work together**.*

The **Central Nervous System** (CNS) **Coordinates** the **Response**

1) The CNS is a <u>coordination centre</u>.
2) It receives <u>information</u> from the <u>receptors</u> and then <u>coordinates a response</u> (decides what to do about it).
3) The response is carried out by <u>effectors</u>.

> For example, a small bird is eating some seed...
>
> 1) ...when it spots a cat coming towards it (this is the <u>stimulus</u>).
> 2) The <u>receptors</u> in the bird's eye are <u>stimulated</u> (activated).
> 3) <u>Sensory neurones</u> carry the information <u>from</u> the <u>receptors</u> to the <u>CNS</u>.
> 4) The CNS <u>decides</u> what to do about it.
> 5) The CNS sends information to the muscles in the bird's wings (the <u>effectors</u>) along <u>motor neurones</u>.
> 6) The <u>muscles contract</u> and the bird flies away to safety.
>
>
>
> | Stimulus | Receptor | Sensory neurone | CNS | Motor neurone | Effector | Response |
>
> receptors in the eye

Synapses Connect Neurones

1) A <u>synapse</u> is where two neurones <u>join together</u>.
2) The <u>electrical impulse</u> is passed from one neurone to the next by <u>chemicals</u>.
3) These chemicals <u>move</u> across the gap.
4) The chemicals set off a <u>new electrical impulse</u> in the <u>next</u> neurone.

chemicals released

end of neurone one

electrical impulse

start of neurone two

Don't let the thought of exams play on your nerves...

Cover up the page and practise writing out the <u>order of events</u> from <u>stimulus</u> to <u>response</u>. Pay attention to <u>names</u> of the neurones — you don't want to be getting them mixed up in the exam.

The Nervous System

Neurones transmit information **very quickly** to and from the brain, and your brain **quickly decides** how to respond to a stimulus. But **reflexes** are even quicker...

Reflexes Help Prevent Injury

1) Reflexes are automatic responses — you don't have to think about them.

> *Reflexes are also called reflex reactions.*

2) This makes them really quick.

3) They can help stop you getting injured.

4) The passage of information in a reflex (from receptor to effector) is called a reflex arc.

5) The neurones in reflex arcs go through the spinal cord or through an unconscious part of the brain (part of the brain not involved in thinking).

Here's an example of how a reflex arc would work if you were stung by a bee:

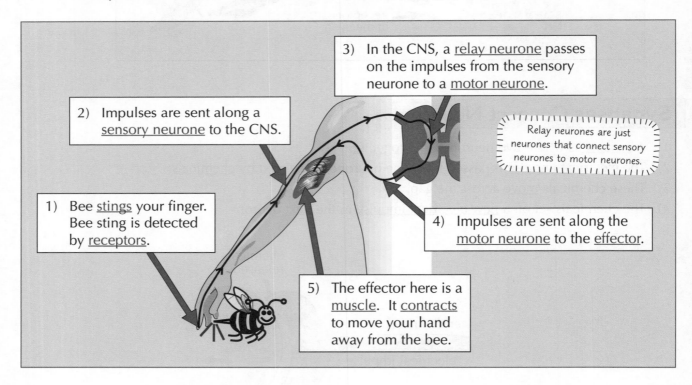

2) Impulses are sent along a sensory neurone to the CNS.

3) In the CNS, a relay neurone passes on the impulses from the sensory neurone to a motor neurone.

> *Relay neurones are just neurones that connect sensory neurones to motor neurones.*

1) Bee stings your finger. Bee sting is detected by receptors.

4) Impulses are sent along the motor neurone to the effector.

5) The effector here is a muscle. It contracts to move your hand away from the bee.

Reflexes are super speedy

Reflexes don't involve your conscious brain at all when a quick response is essential.

Q1   What is a reflex action?   [1 mark]

Q2   A chef touches a hot pan. A reflex reaction causes him to immediately move his hand away.
    a) State the effector in this reflex reaction.   [1 mark]
    b) Describe the pathway of the reflex from stimulus to effector.   [4 marks]

> Q2 Video Solution

Investigating Reaction Time

*Reaction time is the time it takes to **respond to a stimulus** — it's often **less** than a **second**.*
*It can be **affected** by factors such as **age**, **gender** or **drugs**.*

Reaction Time is How Quickly You Respond

1) Reaction time is the time it takes to <u>respond to a stimulus</u>.

2) It's often <u>less</u> than a <u>second</u>. This means it may be measured in <u>milliseconds</u> (ms).

3) It can be <u>affected</u> by factors such as <u>age</u>, <u>gender</u> or <u>drugs</u>.

You Can Measure Reaction Time

<u>Caffeine</u> is a <u>drug</u>. It can <u>speed up</u> a person's reaction time.
The <u>effect of caffeine</u> on reaction time can be <u>measured</u> like this...

1) The person being tested should sit with their arm resting on the edge of a table.

2) Hold a <u>ruler</u> upright between their thumb and forefinger. Make sure that the <u>zero end</u> of the ruler is <u>level</u> with their thumb and finger. <u>Don't</u> let them <u>grip</u> the ruler.

3) Then <u>let go</u> without giving any warning.

4) The person being tested should try to <u>catch the ruler</u> as quickly as they can.

5) Reaction time is measured by the <u>number</u> on the ruler <u>where it's caught</u>.

- The number should be read from the <u>top</u> of the person's <u>thumb</u>.
- The <u>higher the number</u>, the <u>slower</u> their reaction time.

6) <u>Repeat</u> the test several times then calculate the <u>mean distance</u> that the ruler fell.

7) Now give the person being tested a <u>caffeinated drink</u> (e.g. cola).

8) After 10 minutes, repeat steps 1 to 6.

9) You need to <u>control any variables</u> to make sure that this is a fair test. For example:

- Use the <u>same person</u> to catch the ruler each time.
- That person should always use the <u>same hand</u> to catch the ruler.
- The ruler should always be dropped from the <u>same height</u>.

As with any practical, you need to control the variables

Q1 Some students investigated the effect of an energy drink on reaction time. They measured their reaction times using a computer test. They had to click the mouse when the screen changed from red to green. Each student repeated the test five times before having an energy drink, and five times afterwards.

  a) The results for one of the students before having the energy drink were as follows: 242 ms, 256 ms, 253 ms, 249 ms, 235 ms. Calculate the mean reaction time. [2 marks]

  b) Suggest two variables that the students needed to control during their investigation. [2 marks]

Warm-Up & Exam Questions

Welcome to some questions. There are quite a few of them, but that's because they're pretty important...

Warm-Up Questions

1) State one thing that is controlled by homeostasis in the human body.
2) What name is given to the connection between two neurones?
3) True or false? You don't have to think about reflex responses.
4) Students are investigating reaction time by measuring how quickly a ruler can be caught before and after drinking caffeine. Give one variable that would have to be controlled.

Exam Questions

1   A man picked up a plate in the kitchen without realising it was hot, then immediately dropped it. **Figure 1** shows the reflex arc for this incident.

Figure 1

What type of neurone is labelled **X** in **Figure 1**?
Tick **one** box.

☐   motor neurone   ☐   sensory neurone   ☐   relay neurone

[1 mark]

PRACTICAL

2   A student is taking part in an experiment to test reaction times. Every time a red triangle appears on the computer screen in front of her, she has to click the mouse.

2.1   Suggest what the stimulus is in this experiment.

[1 mark]

2.2   Suggest what the receptors are in this experiment.

[1 mark]

2.3   Suggest what the effectors are in this experiment.

[1 mark]

2.4   The student took the test three times. Her reaction time in test 1 was 328 ms.
Her reaction time in test 2 was 346 ms. Her mean reaction time was 343 ms.
Calculate her reaction time for test 3.

[2 marks]

The Endocrine System

*The other way to send information around the body (apart from along nerves) is by using **hormones**.*

Hormones Are Chemical Messengers Sent in the Blood

1) Hormones are chemicals released by glands. They're released directly into the blood.

2) These glands are called endocrine glands. They make up your endocrine system.

3) Hormones are carried in the blood to other parts of the body.

4) They only affect particular cells in particular organs (called target organs).

Hormones and Nerves Have Differences

Hormones and nerves do similar jobs — they both carry information and instructions around the body. But there are some important differences between them:

Nerves

1) Very FAST action.

2) Act for a very SHORT TIME.

3) Act on a very PRECISE AREA.

Hormones

1) SLOWER action.

2) Act for a LONG TIME.

3) Act in a more GENERAL way.

If you're not sure whether a response is nervous or hormonal, have a think about the speed of the reaction and how long it lasts.

Nerves, hormones — no wonder revision makes me tense...

Hormones control various organs and cells in the body, though they tend to control things that aren't immediately life-threatening (so things like sexual development, blood sugar level, water content, etc.).

The Endocrine System

*Hormones are released by **endocrine glands**. There are a few examples you need to learn on this page.*

Endocrine Glands Are Found in Different Places in The Body

PITUITARY GLAND
1) Sometimes called the 'master gland'.
2) This is because it produces many hormones that regulate body conditions.
3) These hormones act on other glands. They make the glands release hormones that bring about change.

THYROID
1) Produces thyroxine.
2) This is involved in regulating things like the rate of metabolism, heart rate and temperature.

OVARIES (females only)
1) Produce oestrogen.
2) This is involved in the menstrual cycle (see page 108).

ADRENAL GLAND
1) Produces adrenaline.
2) This is used to prepare the body for a 'fight or flight' response.

THE PANCREAS
1) Produces insulin.
2) This is used to regulate the blood glucose level (see next page).

TESTES (males only)
1) Produce testosterone.
2) This controls puberty and sperm production in males (see page 108).

You need to know where these glands are in the body

Draw a rough outline of the human body and see if you can draw each of these endocrine glands onto it in the right place. Don't forget you need to remember both the testes and the ovaries.

REVISION TIP

Controlling Blood Glucose

*You should remember from page 97 that **homeostasis** is all about keeping conditions inside the body **stable**. **Blood glucose** is controlled as part of homeostasis — **insulin** is an important **hormone** in this.*

Insulin Reduces the Blood Glucose Level

1) Eating <u>carbohydrates</u> puts <u>glucose</u> (a type of sugar) into the <u>blood</u>.

2) Glucose is <u>removed</u> from the blood by <u>cells</u> (which use it for <u>energy</u>).

3) When you <u>exercise</u>, a lot <u>more</u> glucose is removed from the blood.

4) <u>Changes</u> in the <u>blood glucose concentration</u> are monitored and controlled by the <u>pancreas</u>.

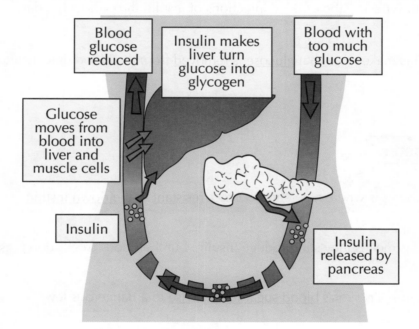

5) If blood glucose concentration gets <u>too high</u>, the pancreas releases the hormone <u>insulin</u>.

6) Insulin causes glucose to <u>move into cells</u> (so it <u>removes</u> glucose from the blood).

7) Glucose can be <u>stored</u> as <u>glycogen</u>.

8) Glucose is converted to glycogen in <u>liver</u> and <u>muscle cells</u>.

Glucose in the blood needs to be kept at a safe level

This stuff can seem a bit confusing at first, but if you learn that <u>diagram</u>, it should get a bit easier.

Q1   The graph shows the changes in concentration of glucose and insulin in a person's blood over time, after they ate a meal.
Which curve represents insulin? Explain your answer.   [2 marks]

Controlling Blood Glucose

Sometimes, homeostasis goes wrong. **Diabetes** *is an example of this.*

With **Diabetes**, You **Can't Control** Your **Blood Sugar Level**

There are two types of diabetes:

Type 1 Diabetes

1) Type 1 diabetes is where the pancreas produces little or no insulin.

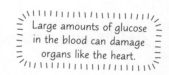

Large amounts of glucose in the blood can damage organs like the heart.

2) This means a person's blood glucose level can rise to a level that can kill them.

3) People with Type 1 diabetes need injections of insulin throughout the day.

4) This makes sure that glucose is removed from the blood quickly after the food is digested.

Type 2 Diabetes

1) Type 2 diabetes is where a person becomes resistant to their own insulin.

2) This means they still produce insulin, but their body's cells don't respond properly to it.

3) This can cause a person's blood sugar level to rise to a dangerous level.

4) Being obese (very overweight) can increase your chance of developing Type 2 diabetes.

5) Type 2 diabetes can be controlled by eating a carbohydrate-controlled diet.

6) This is a diet where the amount of carbohydrates eaten is carefully measured.

7) Type 2 diabetes can also be controlled by taking regular exercise.

EXAM TIP

Be prepared to interpret graphs in the exam

You could be asked to interpret a graph showing the effects of insulin on the blood sugar levels of people with and without diabetes. Don't panic — just study the graph carefully (including the axes labels) so you know exactly what it's showing you. Then apply your blood sugar knowledge.

Topic B5 — Homeostasis and Response

Warm-Up & Exam Questions

If these questions don't get your adrenaline pumping, I don't know what will. Better get started...

Exam Questions

1 Hormones are produced in endocrine glands.

Complete **Table 1** to show which endocrine glands the hormones are released from.

Table 1

Hormone	Gland the hormone is released from
Testosterone	
	Adrenal gland
Oestrogen	

[3 marks]

2 **Figure 1** shows how the body responds when the glucose concentration of the blood gets too high.

Figure 1

Step 1) Blood glucose level is too high.

Step 2) Insulin is released by the ....

Step 3) Insulin causes glucose to move from blood into cells.

Step 4) Liver and muscle cells convert glucose into ....

Complete **Step 2** and **Step 4** in **Figure 1**.

[2 marks]

Puberty and the Menstrual Cycle

*The monthly **release of an egg** from a woman's ovaries is part of the **menstrual cycle**.*

Hormones Cause Sexual Characteristics To Develop at Puberty

1) At <u>puberty</u>, your body starts releasing <u>sex hormones</u>.

2) These sex hormones trigger <u>secondary sexual characteristics</u>.
   For example, the development of <u>facial hair</u> in men and <u>breasts</u> in women.

3) Female sex hormones also cause <u>eggs</u> to <u>mature</u> (develop) in women.

4) In <u>men</u>, the main reproductive hormone is <u>testosterone</u>.
   It's produced by the <u>testes</u>. It stimulates <u>sperm production</u>.

5) In <u>women</u>, the main reproductive hormone is <u>oestrogen</u>. It's produced by the <u>ovaries</u>.
   Oestrogen is involved in the <u>menstrual cycle</u>.

The Menstrual Cycle Has Four Stages

Stage 1

<u>Day 1 is when menstruation (bleeding) starts</u>. The uterus lining breaks down for about four days.

Stage 2

<u>The uterus lining builds up again</u> from day 4 to day 14.
It builds into a thick spongy layer full of blood vessels. It's now ready to receive a fertilised egg.

Stage 3

<u>An egg develops and is released</u> from the ovary at day 14. This is called <u>ovulation</u>.

An egg is released once every 28 days.

Stage 4

<u>The wall is then maintained (kept the same)</u> for about 14 days until day 28.
If no fertilised egg has landed on the uterus wall by day 28,
the spongy lining starts to break down. The whole cycle starts again.

The Menstrual Cycle and Controlling Fertility

*A set of **hormones** controls the **menstrual cycle**. Some of these hormones can be used to **prevent pregnancy**.*

The **Menstrual Cycle** is **Controlled** by **Four Hormones...**

HORMONE	WHAT THE HORMONE DOES
FSH (Follicle-Stimulating Hormone)	Causes an egg to mature in one of the ovaries.
LH (Luteinising Hormone)	Causes the release of an egg (ovulation).
Oestrogen	These hormones are involved in the growth and maintenance of the uterus lining.
Progesterone	

Hormones Can Be Used to **Reduce Fertility**

1) Fertility is how easy it is for a woman to get pregnant.

2) Contraceptives are things that prevent pregnancy.

3) Hormones can be used in contraceptives — these are called hormonal contraceptives.

Oral Contraceptives Contain **Hormones**

1) Oral contraceptives are taken through the mouth as pills.

2) They stop the hormone FSH from being released.

3) This stops eggs maturing.

4) Oral contraceptives are over 99% effective at preventing pregnancy.

5) But they can have bad side effects.
   For example, they can cause headaches and make you feel sick.

The hormones of the menstrual cycle can be controlled

Learn this stuff until you know what hormone does what, and how oral contraceptives work.

Controlling Fertility

Oral contraceptives aren't the only way that hormones can be used to **control fertility**.

Some **Hormonal** Contraceptives **Release Progesterone**

1) Some hormonal contraceptives work by slowly releasing progesterone.

2) This stops eggs from maturing or being released from the ovaries.

3) Examples of contraceptives that work this way are:

Contraceptive patch

1) This is a small patch that is stuck to the skin.

2) It lasts one week.

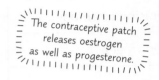

The contraceptive patch releases oestrogen as well as progesterone.

Contraceptive implant

1) This is inserted under the skin of the arm.

2) An implant can last for three years.

Contraceptive injection

Each dose lasts two to three months.

Some **Intrauterine Devices** Contain **Hormones**

1) An intrauterine device (IUD) is a T-shaped device that's inserted into the uterus (womb).

2) It can stop fertilised eggs from implanting in the uterus wall.

3) Some types of IUD release a hormone.

Barriers Stop Egg and Sperm **Meeting**

1) Non-hormonal contraceptives (types that don't use hormones) stop the sperm from getting to the egg.

2) Barrier methods are one type of non-hormonal contraceptive. For example:

Condoms

1) Condoms are worn over the penis during sexual intercourse.

2) Female condoms are worn inside the vagina.

3) Condoms are the only form of contraception that will protect against sexually transmitted diseases.

There are many different types of contraceptives

There are a lot of options when it comes to contraception. There are even more on the next page...

More on Controlling Fertility

*Using condoms isn't the only **barrier** method of contraception — **diaphragms** can also stop the sperm from reaching the egg.*

Diaphragms

1) A <u>diaphragm</u> is a shallow plastic cup that fits over the entrance to the uterus.
2) It has to be used with <u>spermicide</u> (a chemical that <u>disables</u> or <u>kills</u> the sperm).
3) <u>Spermicide</u> can be used alone as a form of contraception. But when used alone, it is <u>not as effective</u> (it's only about 70-80% effective at preventing pregnancy).

There are Other Ways to **Avoid Pregnancy**

Sterilisation

1) In females, <u>sterilisation</u> involves <u>cutting</u> or <u>tying</u> the <u>fallopian tubes</u> (tubes that connect the <u>ovaries</u> to the <u>uterus</u>).
2) In males, it involves <u>cutting</u> or <u>tying</u> the <u>sperm ducts</u> (tubes between the <u>testes</u> and the <u>penis</u>).
3) Sterilisation is <u>permanent</u> (lasts for life).

Natural Methods

1) Pregnancy may be avoided by <u>not having sexual intercourse</u> when a woman is at the stage of the menstrual cycle when she is <u>most likely</u> to get <u>pregnant</u>.
2) It's popular with people who think that hormonal and barrier methods are <u>unnatural</u>.
3) But it's <u>not very effective</u>.

Abstinence

1) The only way to be <u>sure</u> that sperm and egg don't meet is to <u>not have intercourse</u>.
2) This is called <u>abstinence</u>.

Some methods of contraception are more effective than others

You might be asked to <u>evaluate</u> the different <u>hormonal</u> and <u>non-hormonal methods</u> of <u>contraception</u> in your exam. If you do, make sure you weigh up and write about the <u>pros</u> AND the <u>cons</u> of each method.

Warm-Up & Exam Questions

Right then, another lot of pages down. Now there's just the small matter of answering some questions...

Warm-Up Questions

1) Name the hormone that stimulates sperm production in males.
2) Name the hormone that causes an egg to mature in the ovary.
3) What hormones does the contraceptive patch contain?
4) What is spermicide?
5) True or false? Only males can be sterilised to avoid pregnancy?

Exam Questions

1 During puberty, secondary sex characteristics develop. *Grade 1-3*

1.1 Give **one** example of a secondary sex characteristic.

[1 mark]

1.2 In females, ovulation begins to occur at puberty.
How often does ovulation usually occur?

[1 mark]

2 There are several methods that can be used to avoid pregnancy. *Grade 1-3*

Which of the following is a barrier method of contraception?
Tick **one** box.

☐ sterilisation

☐ diaphragm

☐ contraceptive implant

☐ contraceptive injection

[1 mark]

3 The menstrual cycle is controlled by several different hormones. *Grade 4-5*

3.1 What does the hormone oestrogen do?

[1 mark]

3.2 Which hormone causes the release of an egg?

[1 mark]

3.3 Hormones can also be used in contraception.
Explain how oral contraceptives prevent pregnancy.

[2 marks]

DNA

*The first step in understanding **genetics** is getting to grips with **DNA**.*

Chromosomes Are Really Long Molecules of DNA

1) <u>DNA</u> is the <u>chemical</u> that all of the <u>genetic material</u> in a cell is <u>made</u> up from.

2) It contains all the <u>instructions</u> to put an organism together and <u>make it work</u>.

3) A DNA molecule is made up of <u>two strands</u> of DNA coiled together. They make a <u>double helix</u> (a double-stranded spiral).

4) A DNA strand is a <u>polymer</u>. A polymer is something made up of <u>lots of smaller</u> pieces joined <u>together</u>.

5) DNA is found in the <u>nucleus</u> of animal and plant cells.

6) It's found in really long structures called <u>chromosomes</u>.

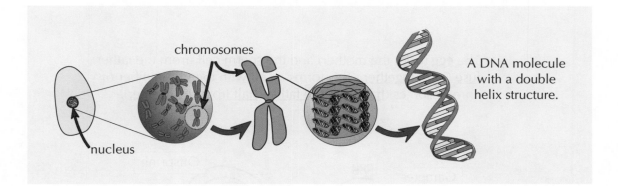

chromosomes

nucleus

A DNA molecule with a double helix structure.

A **Gene** Codes for a **Specific Protein**

1) A <u>gene</u> is a small <u>section</u> of DNA found on a <u>chromosome</u>.

2) Each gene <u>codes for</u> a <u>particular sequence</u> of <u>amino acids</u>.

3) These amino acids are joined together to make a <u>protein</u>.

Every Organism Has a **Genome**

1) <u>Genome</u> is just the fancy term for <u>all</u> of the <u>genetic material</u> in an organism.

2) Scientists have worked out the <u>whole human genome</u>.

3) <u>Understanding</u> the human genome is really important for <u>medicine</u>. This is because:

Inherited diseases are diseases caused by faulty genes and passed from a parent to their offspring.

1) Scientists can <u>find genes</u> in the genome that are <u>linked</u> to different types of <u>disease</u>.

2) If scientists know which genes are linked to <u>inherited diseases</u>, they can <u>understand</u> them better. This could help us to develop <u>treatments</u>.

3) Scientists can look at <u>tiny differences</u> in the genomes of different people. This can help them find out about the <u>migration</u> (movement) of certain populations of people around the world over history.

Sexual Reproduction

*Reproduction is **very important** for all species — it's how they **pass** on their **genes** to the next generation.*

Sexual Reproduction Produces Genetically Different Cells

1) Sexual reproduction is where genes from two organisms (a father and a mother) are mixed.

2) The mother and father produce gametes (sex cells). E.g. egg and sperm cells in animals.

3) The gametes are produced by meiosis (see page 116). Each gamete contains half the number of chromosomes of a normal cell.

4) The egg (from the mother) and the sperm cell (from the father) fuse (join) together. This forms a cell with the full number of chromosomes (half from the father, half from the mother).

5) The offspring receives a mixture of genes, so inherits features from both parents.

6) This mixture of genes produces variation in the offspring.

7) Flowering plants can reproduce in this way too. Their gametes are egg cells and pollen.

Sexual reproduction mixes genes from two organisms...

When you're revising, make sure that you've got your head around sexual reproduction, before moving on to asexual reproduction — that way you don't confuse the two.

Asexual Reproduction

*Some organisms use **asexual** reproduction to **pass** on their **genes**...*

Asexual Reproduction Produces Genetically Identical Cells

1) Asexual reproduction happens by mitosis.

2) One parent cell makes a new cell by dividing in two (see page 28).

3) There's no fusion of gametes.

4) So there's no mixing of genes.

5) This means there's no genetic variation in the new cells.

6) Each new cell is genetically identical to the parent cell
— it has exactly the same genes. The new cell is a clone.

You might need to reproduce these facts in the exam...

The main messages about reproduction are that: 1) sexual reproduction needs two parents and forms cells that are genetically different to the parents, so there's lots of genetic variation. And 2) asexual reproduction needs just one parent to make genetically identical cells, so there's no genetic variation in the offspring.

Meiosis

*Time now to learn about how **sperm** and **egg** cells are made...*

Gametes Are Produced by Meiosis

1) Gametes only have <u>half the number</u> of chromosomes of normal cells.

2) To make gametes, cells divide by <u>meiosis</u>.

3) In humans, meiosis <u>only</u> happens in the <u>reproductive organs</u> (the <u>ovaries</u> in females and <u>testes</u> in males).

4) Here's how <u>meiosis</u> happens:

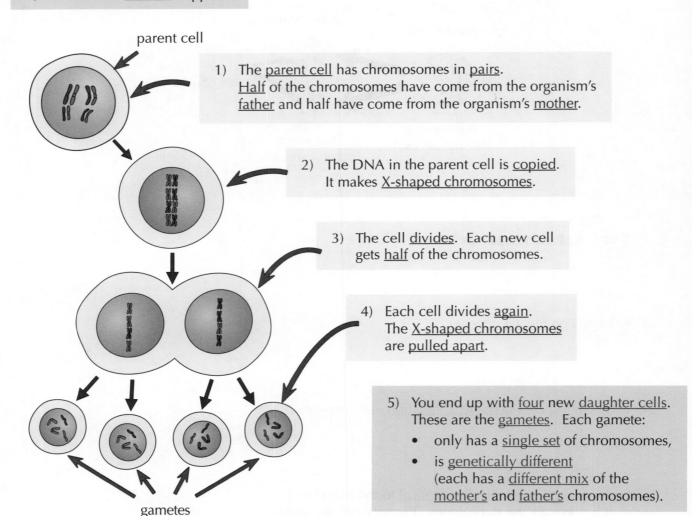

parent cell

1) The <u>parent cell</u> has chromosomes in <u>pairs</u>. <u>Half</u> of the chromosomes have come from the organism's <u>father</u> and half have come from the organism's <u>mother</u>.

2) The DNA in the parent cell is <u>copied</u>. It makes <u>X-shaped chromosomes</u>.

3) The cell <u>divides</u>. Each new cell gets <u>half</u> of the chromosomes.

4) Each cell divides <u>again</u>. The <u>X-shaped chromosomes</u> are <u>pulled apart</u>.

5) You end up with <u>four</u> new <u>daughter cells</u>. These are the <u>gametes</u>. Each gamete:
    *   only has a <u>single set</u> of chromosomes,
    *   is <u>genetically different</u> (each has a <u>different mix</u> of the <u>mother's</u> and <u>father's</u> chromosomes).

gametes

Gametes only have one set of chromosomes...

In humans, <u>meiosis</u> only occurs in <u>reproductive organs</u>, for making <u>gametes</u>.

Q1   Human body cells contain 46 chromosomes each. The graph on the right shows how the mass of DNA per cell changed as some cells divided by meiosis in a human ovary. How many chromosomes were present in each cell when they reached stage 6?   [1 mark]

Topic B6 — Inheritance, Variation and Evolution

Fertilisation and Chromosomes

*Now for a bit more about **gametes** and two **very** important little **chromosomes**...*

Gametes **Fuse** to Make a **New Cell**

1) During fertilisation, two gametes <u>fuse together</u> (see p.114). This makes a <u>new cell</u>.

2) This new cell has the <u>normal number</u> of chromosomes.

3) The new cell <u>divides</u> by <u>mitosis</u> many times to produce <u>lots</u> of new cells. This forms an <u>embryo</u>.

4) As the embryo develops, these cells <u>differentiate</u> (see page 23). The cells become <u>different types</u> of <u>specialised cell</u> that make up a <u>whole organism</u>.

An embryo is an unborn baby at an early stage of growth.

Your **Chromosomes** Control Whether You're **Male** or **Female**

1) There are <u>23 pairs</u> of chromosomes in every human body cell.
2) <u>22</u> are <u>matched pairs</u> of chromosomes that just control your <u>characteristics</u>.
3) The <u>23rd pair</u> are labelled <u>XY</u> or <u>XX</u>.
4) They're the two chromosomes that <u>decide</u> your sex (whether you turn out <u>male</u> or <u>female</u>).

All <u>males</u> have an <u>X</u> and a <u>Y</u> chromosome: XY
The <u>Y chromosome</u> causes <u>male characteristics</u>.

All <u>females</u> have <u>two X chromosomes</u>: XX
The <u>XX combination</u> allows <u>female characteristics</u> to develop.

5) Each sperm has <u>either</u> an X or a Y chromosome.
6) <u>All</u> egg cells have an X chromosome.

Now that I have your undivided attention...

Make sure you know what the <u>X and Y chromosomes</u> are before you head on to the next page...

X and Y Chromosomes

Genetic Diagrams Show the Possible Gamete Combinations

To find the <u>probability</u> (chance) of getting a boy or a girl, you can draw a <u>genetic diagram</u>. This type of genetic diagram is called a <u>Punnett square</u>.

1) Put the <u>possible gametes</u> (eggs or sperm) from <u>one</u> parent down the side. Put those from the <u>other</u> parent along the top.

2) Then in each middle square you <u>fill in</u> the letters from the top and side that line up with that square.

3) The <u>pairs of letters</u> in the middle show the possible combinations of the gametes.

4) There are <u>two XX results</u> and <u>two XY results</u>.

5) This means that there's the <u>same probability</u> of getting a boy or a girl — each one has a <u>1 in 2 chance</u> (which is the same as <u>50%</u>).

female gametes (eggs)

possible combinations of gametes...

male gametes (sperm)

...two males (XY) and two females (XX).

There's More Than One Type of Genetic Diagram

The <u>other type</u> of genetic diagram looks a bit more complicated, but it shows <u>exactly the same</u> thing.

1) At the top are the <u>parents</u>.

2) The middle circles show the <u>possible gametes</u> that are formed. One gamete from the female combines with one gamete from the male (during fertilisation).

3) The criss-cross lines show <u>all</u> the <u>possible</u> ways the X and Y chromosomes <u>could</u> combine.

4) The <u>possible offspring</u> you could get are shown in the bottom circles.

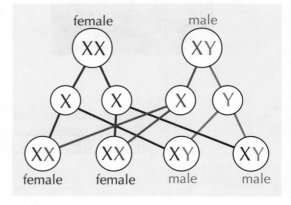

These diagrams aren't as scary as they look...

Most genetic diagrams you'll see in exams concentrate on a <u>gene</u>, instead of a <u>chromosome</u>. But it's pretty much the same. Don't worry — there are loads of other examples on pages 121-122.

Warm-Up & Exam Questions

It's time to see how much you picked up about meiosis, reproduction and sex chromosomes...

Warm-Up Questions

1) True or false? There is variation in the offspring of sexual reproduction.
2) How many cell divisions take place in meiosis?
3) What combination of sex chromosomes do human females have?

Exam Questions

1   Sexual reproduction involves gametes fusing together to form offspring.
This is shown in **Figure 1**. The number of chromosomes in each cell is incomplete.

Figure 1

Chromosomes: ....23............   ....

Complete **Figure 1** to show the number of chromosomes in an egg cell and in a fertilised egg.

[2 marks]

2   An organism's genetic material is made up of a chemical called DNA.

2.1   Which of the following describes the structure of DNA? Tick **one** box.

☐   A protein made up of two strands.   ☐   A polymer made up of two strands.

☐   A protein made up of four strands.   ☐   A polymer made up of four strands.

[1 mark]

2.2   Which of the following contains the largest amount of an organism's DNA? Tick **one** box.

☐   A gene   ☐   Its genome   ☐   A chromosome

[1 mark]

2.3   Explain the relationship between DNA and the proteins produced by an organism.

[3 marks]

3   Some species of worm can produce offspring through a process called fragmentation.
In this process, bits of the parent's body break off and go through cell division
by mitosis, to develop into complete organisms.

3.1   What term is used to describe this form of reproduction?

[1 mark]

3.2   Suggest how the chromosomes in the offspring will compare to those of the parent worm.

[1 mark]

Topic B6 — Inheritance, Variation and Evolution

Genetic Diagrams

*For those of you expecting to see a **diagram** or two on a page called 'Genetic Diagrams', prepare to be disappointed. You need to understand a bit more about what genetic diagrams **show** to start with...*

Different Genes Control Different Characteristics

1) <u>Some</u> characteristics are controlled by a <u>single</u> gene. For example:

- <u>mouse fur colour</u>
- <u>red-green colour blindness</u> in humans.

2) However, <u>most</u> characteristics are controlled by <u>several genes</u>.

All Genes Exist in Different Versions Called Alleles

1) You have <u>two</u> alleles of <u>every gene</u> in your body — <u>one</u> on <u>each chromosome</u> in a pair.

2) If the two alleles are <u>the same</u>, then the organism is <u>homozygous</u> for that characteristic.

3) If the two alleles are <u>different</u>, then the organism is <u>heterozygous</u> for that characteristic.

4) Some alleles are <u>dominant</u> (these are shown with a <u>capital letter</u> on genetic diagrams, e.g. '<u>C</u>'). Some alleles are <u>recessive</u> (these are shown by a <u>small letter</u> on genetic diagrams, e.g. '<u>c</u>').

5) For an organism to show a <u>recessive characteristic</u>, <u>both</u> its alleles must be <u>recessive</u> (e.g. cc). But to show a <u>dominant</u> characteristic, only <u>one</u> allele needs to be dominant (e.g. <u>either CC or Cc</u>).

6) The mix of <u>alleles</u> you have is called your <u>genotype</u>.

7) Your alleles determine your <u>characteristics</u>. The characteristics you have is called your <u>phenotype</u>.

There are lots of fancy words to learn on this page...

Make sure you fully understand what all the <u>different terms</u> on this page mean (i.e. genes, alleles, homozygous, heterozygous, dominant, recessive, genotype and phenotype). You'll feel much more comfortable going into the exam knowing that these words 'aren't going to trip you up.

Genetic Diagrams

*This page is all about how **characteristics** are **inherited** — it involves drawing **genetic diagrams**.*

Genetic Diagrams Can Show How **Characteristics are Inherited**

You can use <u>genetic diagrams</u> to show how <u>single genes</u> for characteristics are <u>inherited</u> (passed from parents to offspring). For example:

1) An allele that causes hamsters to have superpowers is <u>recessive</u> ("b").
2) <u>Normal</u> hamsters don't have superpowers due to a <u>dominant</u> allele ("B").
3) Two <u>homozygous</u> hamsters (<u>BB</u> and <u>bb</u>) are crossed (bred together). A genetic diagram shows what could happen:

A hamster with the genotype BB or Bb will be normal. A hamster with the genotype bb will have superpowers.

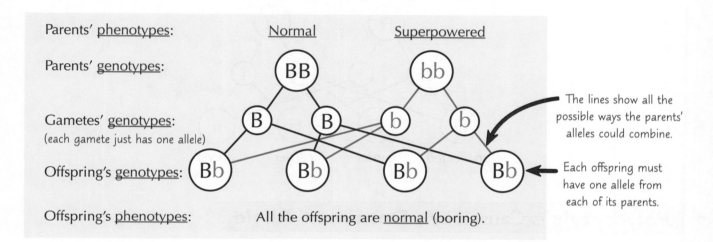

The lines show all the possible ways the parents' alleles could combine.

Each offspring must have one allele from each of its parents.

Punnett Squares are Another **Type** of Genetic Diagram

You can also show genetic crosses in a <u>Punnett square</u>.

This Punnett square shows a cross between <u>two heterozygous</u> hamsters (<u>Bb</u> and <u>Bb</u>):

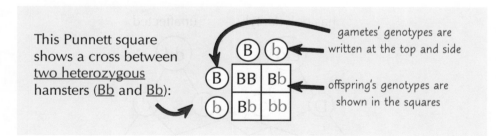

gametes' genotypes are written at the top and side

offspring's genotypes are shown in the squares

1) There's a <u>3 in 4</u> (75%) chance that offspring will be <u>normal</u>.
2) There's a <u>1 in 4</u> (25%) chance that offspring will have <u>superpowers</u>.
3) This gives a 3 normal : 1 superpowers <u>ratio</u> (<u>3:1</u>).

You can master genetic diagrams — you just need to practise them...

You should know how to <u>produce</u> and <u>understand</u> both of these types of genetic diagram before exam day.

Topic B6 — Inheritance, Variation and Evolution

Inherited Disorders

*Inherited disorders are **health conditions**. They are caused by **inheriting** faulty **alleles**.*

Cystic Fibrosis is Caused by a **Recessive Allele**

Cystic fibrosis is an inherited disorder of cell membranes.

1) The allele which causes cystic fibrosis is a recessive allele, 'f'.

2) Because it's recessive, people with only one copy of the allele won't have the disorder — they're known as carriers.

3) For a child to have the disorder, both parents must be either carriers or have the disorder themselves.

4) As the diagram shows, there's a 1 in 4 chance of a child having the disorder if both parents are carriers.

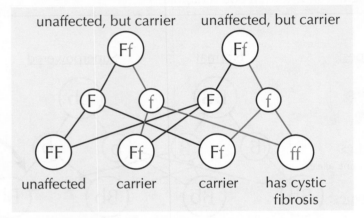

Polydactyly is Caused by a **Dominant Allele**

Polydactyly is an inherited disorder where a baby's born with extra fingers or toes.

1) The disorder is caused by a dominant allele, 'D'.

2) This means that it can be inherited if just one parent carries the faulty allele.

3) The parent that has the faulty allele will have the disorder too since the allele is dominant.

4) As the diagram shows, there's a 50% chance of a child having the disorder if one parent has one D allele.

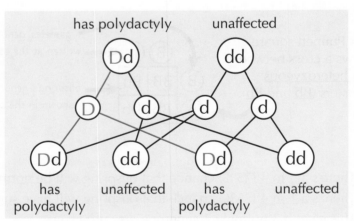

There are no carriers if a dominant allele is the cause...

The important bits to take away from this page are that the allele for cystic fibrosis is recessive and the allele for polydactyly is dominant.

Q1 The Punnett square on the right shows the possible inheritance of polydactyly from two parents. Give the probability that their offspring will have polydactyly. [1 mark]

Family Trees

*Just when you thought you'd finished with **genetic diagrams**, **family trees** show up...*

Family Trees Show the Inheritance of Alleles

1) The diagram below is a <u>family tree</u> for <u>cystic fibrosis</u> (see previous page).

2) From the family tree, you can tell that the allele for cystic fibrosis <u>isn't</u> dominant. This is because plenty of the family <u>carry</u> the allele but <u>don't</u> have the disorder.

3) There is a <u>25% chance</u> that the <u>new baby</u> will have the <u>disorder</u> and a <u>50% chance</u> that it will be a <u>carrier</u>. This is because both of the baby's parents are <u>carriers</u> (Eve and Phil are both Ff).

4) The case of the new baby is just the same as in the genetic diagram on page 122. The baby could be <u>unaffected</u> (FF), a <u>carrier</u> (Ff) or <u>have</u> cystic fibrosis (ff).

It's enough to make you go cross-eyed...

If you're struggling to work out a family tree in the exam, try writing each person's <u>genotype</u> onto it — it might help you to understand it more easily.

Q1 Cystic fibrosis is caused by a recessive allele, f. The dominant allele is F. The family tree on the right shows the inheritance of cystic fibrosis. What is Tamsin's genotype? Use the key above to help you.

[1 mark]

Topic B6 — Inheritance, Variation and Evolution

Embryo Screening

Embryos can be screened for disorders, but not everyone agrees with it...

Embryos Can Be Screened for Inherited Disorders

1) During *in vitro* fertilisation (IVF), embryos are fertilised in a <u>lab</u> and then put in the mother's <u>womb</u>.

2) Before they are put into the mother, scientists can <u>remove a cell</u> from each embryo and <u>look at</u> its <u>genes</u>. This is called <u>embryo screening</u>.

3) Many <u>inherited disorders</u> can be <u>picked up</u> in this way.

4) It's also possible to get DNA from an embryo <u>in the womb</u> and test that for disorders.

5) There are lots of <u>concerns</u> about embryo screening.

6) Some people don't agree with embryonic screening because of the <u>decisions</u> it can lead to.

7) For embryos produced by <u>IVF</u> — after screening, embryos with '<u>bad</u>' alleles would be <u>destroyed</u>.

8) For embryos in the <u>womb</u> — screening could lead to the decision to stop the pregnancy.

9) Here are some more arguments <u>for</u> and <u>against</u> embryo screening:

For Embryonic Screening

1) It will help to stop people <u>suffering</u>.

2) Treating disorders costs a lot of <u>money</u>.

3) There are <u>laws</u> to stop it going too far. At the moment parents cannot even select the sex of their baby (unless it's for health reasons).

Against Embryonic Screening

1) It suggests that <u>people</u> with <u>genetic problems</u> are not wanted. This could lead to them being <u>treated unfairly</u>.

2) There may come a point when people want to screen their embryos so they can pick the <u>features</u> they <u>prefer</u>. E.g. they want a certain eye colour or hair colour.

3) Screening is <u>expensive</u>.

Embryo screening — it's a tricky one...

It's great to think that we might be able to stop people from having inherited disorders that cause suffering, but there are many concerns to think about too. Try writing a <u>balanced argument</u> for and against embryo screening — it's <u>good practice</u>.

Warm-Up & Exam Questions

There's no better preparation for exam questions than doing... err... practice exam questions.
Hang on, what's this I see...

Warm-Up Questions

1) What is a different version of a gene called?
2) What does phenotype mean?
3) What is polydactyly?
4) Give one argument for embryo screening.

Exam Questions

1   Draw **one** line from each genetic term to its definition.

heterozygous		having two of the same allele
homozygous		the mix of alleles in an organism
genotype		having two different alleles

[2 marks]

2   Cystic fibrosis is a genetic disorder caused by recessive alleles.

F = the normal allele   **f** = the faulty allele that causes cystic fibrosis

Figure 1 is an incomplete Punnett square showing the possible inheritance
of cystic fibrosis from one couple.

Figure 1

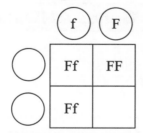

2.1   Complete the Punnett square to show the missing offspring's genotype
and the missing genotypes of the gametes.

[2 marks]

2.2   What proportion of the possible offspring are homozygous?

[1 mark]

2.3   State the phenotypes of the parents.

[2 marks]

Variation

*You'll probably have noticed that not all people are **identical**. There are reasons for this.*

Organisms of the **Same Species** Have **Differences**

1) Different species look... well... different — my dog definitely doesn't look like a daisy.
2) But even organisms of the <u>same species</u> will usually look at least <u>slightly</u> different.
3) These <u>differences</u> are called the <u>variation</u> within a <u>species</u>.
4) Variation can be <u>huge</u> within a <u>population</u>.

Variation Can be **Genetic**

Variation can be <u>genetic</u> — this means it's caused by differences in <u>genes</u> that are <u>inherited</u>.

Variation Can Also be **Environmental**

Variation can also be <u>environmental</u> — this means it's caused by the <u>conditions</u> in which an organism <u>lives</u>. For example:

1) A plant grown on a nice sunny windowsill could grow <u>healthy</u> and <u>green</u>.
2) The same plant grown in darkness would grow <u>tall</u> and <u>spindly</u> and its leaves would turn <u>yellow</u>.

Most Characteristics are Due to **Genes AND** the **Environment**

Most variation in phenotype is caused by a <u>mixture</u> of <u>genes</u> and the <u>environment</u>. For example:

1) The <u>maximum height</u> that an animal or plant could grow to is determined by its <u>genes</u>.
2) But whether it actually grows that tall depends on its <u>environment</u> (e.g. how much food it gets).

You can't blame all of your faults on your parents...

The <u>genes</u> that you inherit from your parents have a really important role in controlling what <u>characteristics</u> you have. However, the <u>conditions</u> in which you live usually affect your characteristics too.

Mutations

*Sometimes the **sequence** of **DNA** can be changed. These changes are called **mutations**. Read on...*

Mutations are Changes to the Genome

1) Sometimes, a gene can <u>mutate</u>.

2) A mutation is a <u>random change</u> in an organism's <u>DNA</u> that can be <u>inherited</u>.

3) Mutations occur <u>continuously</u>.

4) Mutations mean that the gene is <u>changed</u>. This produces a <u>genetic variant</u> (a different form of the gene).

5) Most <u>genetic variants</u> have <u>very little</u> or <u>no effect</u> on an organism's <u>phenotype</u> (its characteristics).

6) <u>Some</u> variants have a <u>small effect</u> on the organism's <u>phenotype</u>. They alter the individual's characteristics but only slightly. For example:

   - Some characteristics (e.g. eye colour) are controlled by <u>more than one gene</u>.
   - A mutation in <u>one</u> of the genes may <u>change</u> the <u>eye colour</u> a bit, but the difference might not be huge.

7) Very <u>rarely</u>, variants can have such a <u>big effect</u> that they lead to a <u>new phenotype</u>, e.g. cystic fibrosis.

8) A new phenotype may be <u>useful</u> if the <u>environment</u> that an organism lives in <u>changes</u>.

9) This is because sometimes a new phenotype makes an individual <u>more suited</u> to a new environment.

10) If this happens, the mutation can become common <u>throughout</u> the species <u>relatively quickly</u>. This happens by <u>natural selection</u> — see the next page.

Evolution

*Evolution is very important. Without it we wouldn't have the great **variety of life** we have on Earth today.*

> **THEORY OF EVOLUTION:** All of today's species have evolved from simple life forms that first started to develop over three billion years ago.

Only the Fittest Survive

1) <u>Charles Darwin</u> came up with a really important theory about <u>evolution</u> — it's called <u>evolution by natural selection</u>. It works like this:

> 1) Organisms in a species show <u>wide variation</u> in their characteristics.
>
> 2) Organisms have to <u>compete</u> for <u>resources</u> in an ecosystem.
>
> 3) This means organisms with <u>characteristics</u> that make them better adapted to their <u>environment</u> will be better at <u>competing</u> with other organisms.
>
> 4) These organisms are <u>more likely to survive</u> and <u>reproduce</u>.
>
> 5) So the <u>genes</u> for the useful characteristics are more likely to be <u>passed on</u> to their <u>offspring</u>.
>
> 6) Over time, <u>useful characteristics</u> become <u>more common</u> in the population and the species <u>changes</u>. This is <u>evolution</u>.

2) Darwin's theory <u>wasn't perfect</u>. At the time he <u>couldn't</u> explain how <u>new</u> characteristics <u>appeared</u> or were <u>passed on</u>. Nowadays we have <u>evidence</u> to back up Darwin's theory, such as:

> 1) The <u>discovery of genetics</u> — it showed that characteristics are passed on in an organism's <u>genes</u>. It also showed that <u>genetic variants</u> (see page 127) produce the characteristics (<u>phenotypes</u>) that are better adapted to the environment.
> 2) <u>Fossils</u> — by looking at fossils of different ages (the <u>fossil record</u>), scientists could see how <u>changes</u> in organisms <u>developed slowly over time</u>.
> 3) <u>Antibiotic resistance</u> — how <u>bacteria</u> are able to evolve to become <u>resistant to antibiotics</u> also further supports <u>evolution</u> by <u>natural selection</u> (see page 130).

Natural selection — the fittest pass on their genes...

Natural selection's all about the organisms with the <u>best characteristics</u> surviving to <u>pass on</u> their <u>genes</u> so that the whole species ends up adapted to its environment.

Q1 The sugary nectar in some orchid flowers is found at the end of a long tube behind the flower. There are moth species with long tongues that can reach the nectar.
Explain how natural selection could have led to the moths developing long tongues. [4 marks]

Q1 Video Solution

Evolution

*Species need to **continue evolving** in order to **survive**. Sometimes this evolution creates a whole **new species**, but if a species can't evolve fast enough it might **die out** completely.*

Evolution Can Lead to **New Species Developing**

1) Over a long period of time, the phenotype of organisms can <u>change</u> a lot because of <u>natural selection</u>.

2) Sometimes, the phenotype can change <u>so much</u> that a completely <u>new species</u> is formed.

3) New species develop when populations of the <u>same</u> species change so much that they <u>can't breed with each other</u> to produce <u>fertile offspring</u>.

Extinction is When **No Individuals** of a Species **Are Left**

Species become extinct for these reasons:

1) The <u>environment changes</u> too quickly (e.g. their habitat is destroyed).

2) A <u>new predator</u> kills them all (e.g. humans hunting them).

3) A <u>new disease</u> kills them all.

4) They can't <u>compete</u> with another (new) species for <u>food</u>.

5) A <u>catastrophic event</u> happens that kills them all (e.g. a volcanic eruption).

Evolution's happening all the time...

Many species evolve so <u>slowly</u> that there are <u>no big changes</u> in them within our lifetime.
However, some species (e.g. bacteria) <u>reproduce really quickly</u>, so we're able to watch <u>evolution in action</u>.

Antibiotic-Resistant Bacteria

*The discovery of **antibiotics** was a huge benefit to medicine — but they might not be a **permanent solution**.*

Bacteria can Evolve and Become Antibiotic-Resistant

1) <u>Antibiotics</u> are drugs that <u>kill bacteria</u>.
2) Bacteria can become <u>resistant</u> to antibiotics by <u>natural selection</u>.
3) Here's what happens:

There's more about natural selection on page 128.

> 1) Bacteria can develop <u>random mutations</u> (changes) in their DNA.
> 2) These can lead to the bacteria being resistant to (<u>not killed by</u>) a particular <u>antibiotic</u>.
> 3) These <u>new strains</u> (types) of bacteria are called <u>antibiotic-resistant bacteria</u>.
> 4) The ability to <u>resist</u> antibiotics is a <u>big advantage</u> for the bacteria.
> 5) It means that the bacteria are able to <u>survive</u> in a host who's being <u>treated</u> to get rid of an infection.
> 6) So the antibiotic-resistant bacteria can <u>reproduce many more times</u>.
> 7) They <u>pass on</u> their gene for antibiotic resistance to their <u>offspring</u>.
> 8) The <u>gene</u> for antibiotic resistance becomes <u>more common</u> in the population over time — the bacteria have <u>evolved</u>.

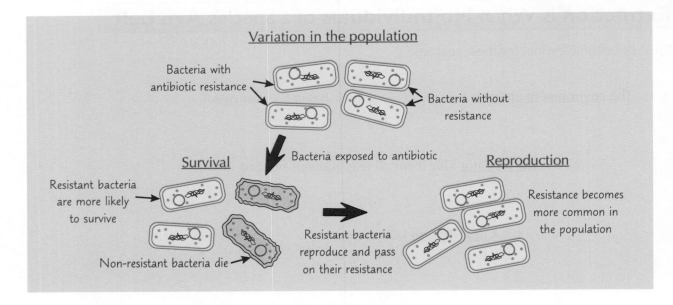

4) Because bacteria are so <u>rapid</u> at <u>reproducing</u>, they can <u>evolve</u> quite <u>quickly</u>.
5) The antibiotic-resistant bacteria <u>keep reproducing</u>.
   This <u>increases</u> the <u>population size</u> of the antibiotic-resistant strain.

Antibiotic Resistant Bacteria Spread Easily

1) <u>Antibiotic-resistant bacteria</u> are a <u>problem</u> because:

> • There is <u>no effective treatment</u> for the infection.
> • People are <u>not immune</u> to the new strain.

2) This means that the antibiotic-resistant strain is able to <u>easily spread</u> between people.

More on Antibiotic-Resistant Bacteria

*Antibiotic-resistance is getting **worse**. But there are ways to **fight it**...*

Antibiotic Resistance is Becoming **More Common**

1) The problem of <u>antibiotic resistance</u> is getting <u>worse</u> because:

- Antibiotics are being <u>overused</u>.
- People <u>aren't</u> using antibiotics <u>correctly</u>.

2) '<u>Superbugs</u>' (bacteria that are resistant to most known antibiotics) are becoming more common.

> E.g. <u>MRSA</u> is a relatively common 'superbug' that's really hard to get rid of.

Antibiotics Need to Be **Used Sensibly**

There are a few things that can be done to <u>avoid</u> antibiotic-resistant bacteria forming:

1) Doctors should <u>only</u> prescribe antibiotics when they <u>really need</u> to.
- They <u>shouldn't be</u> prescribed for <u>non-serious conditions</u> or infections caused by <u>viruses</u>.

Antibiotics don't kill viruses.

2) You should take <u>all</u> the antibiotics a doctor prescribes for you.
- Taking the <u>full course</u> makes sure that <u>all</u> the bacteria are <u>destroyed</u>.
- This means that there are <u>none left</u> to <u>mutate</u> and develop into <u>antibiotic-resistant strains</u>.

3) The use of antibiotics by <u>farmers</u> should be <u>restricted</u> because:
- In farming, antibiotics can be given to animals to prevent them <u>becoming ill</u> and make them <u>grow faster</u>.
- This can lead to the development of <u>antibiotic-resistant strains</u> of bacteria in the animals.
- The antibiotic-resistant bacteria can then <u>spread to humans</u>.

We Can't Make **New** Antibiotics **Fast Enough**

1) Drug companies are working on developing <u>new antibiotics</u> that kill the resistant strains.
2) But there are problems:

- The rate of development is <u>slow</u>.
- The process is really <u>expensive</u>.

3) This means that we're unlikely to be able to <u>keep up</u> with the demand for <u>new drugs</u> to fight new antibiotic-resistant strains.

Warm-Up & Exam Questions

You need to test your knowledge with a few Warm-Up Questions, followed by some Exam Questions...

1) True or false? There is usually only a small amount of variation within a population.
2) True or false? Evolution never leads to new species developing.
3) What is meant by the term 'extinction'?
4) What is an antibiotic?

Exam Questions

1   **Figure 1** shows a type of stingray. The stingray's appearance looks like a flat rock.
It spends most of its time on a rocky sea bed.

1.1   Use words from the box to complete the sentences
about the evolution of the stingray's appearance.

Figure 1

survive	generation	population
die	variation	similarity

The appearance of this stingray's ancestors showed ....

The ancestors that looked like flat rocks were hidden, so were more likely to ....

They were more likely to reproduce and pass their genes on to the next ....

[3 marks]

1.2   Suggest what caused some of the ancestors to look more like flat rocks than others.

[1 mark]

2   Helen and Stephanie are identical twins.
This means they have identical DNA.

2.1   Helen weighs 7 kg more than Stephanie.
Explain whether this is due to genes, environmental factors or both.

[2 marks]

2.2   Stephanie has a birthmark on her shoulder. Helen doesn't.
Explain how this shows that birthmarks are **not** caused by genes.

[1 mark]

Topic B6 — Inheritance, Variation and Evolution

Selective Breeding

'Selective breeding' sounds like it could be a tricky topic, but it's actually quite simple.
*You take the **best** plants or animals and breed them together to get the best possible **offspring**. That's it.*

Selective Breeding is Very Simple

1) <u>Selective breeding</u> is when <u>humans choose</u> which plants or animals are going to <u>breed</u>.

2) Organisms are <u>selectively bred</u> to develop features that are <u>useful</u> or <u>attractive</u>. For example:

Selective breeding is also known as 'artificial selection'.

- Animals that produce more <u>meat</u> or <u>milk</u>.
- Crops with <u>disease resistance</u> (that are not killed by disease).
- Dogs with a <u>good, gentle personality</u>.
- Decorative plants with <u>big</u> or <u>unusual flowers</u>.

3) This is the basic process involved in <u>selective breeding</u>:

1) From your <u>existing plants or animals</u> select the ones which have the <u>feature</u> you're after.
2) <u>Breed them</u> with each other.
3) Select the <u>best</u> of the <u>offspring</u>, and <u>breed them together</u>.
4) Continue this process over <u>several generations</u>. Eventually, <u>all</u> offspring will have the feature you want.

4) Selective breeding is <u>nothing new</u> — people have been doing it for <u>thousands of years</u>.

5) This is how we ended up with <u>edible crops</u> from <u>wild plants</u> and <u>domesticated animals</u> like cows and dogs.

Selective breeding is just breeding the best to get the best...

Different breeds of <u>dog</u> came from <u>selective breeding</u>. E.g. somebody thought 'I like this small, yappy wolf — I'll breed it with this other one'. After thousands of generations, we got <u>poodles</u>.

Q1   Explain how you could selectively breed for floppy ears in rabbits.   [4 marks]

Q1 Video Solution

Selective Breeding

Here's an **Example** of **Selective Breeding**:

A farmer might want his cattle to produce <u>more meat</u>.

1) <u>Genetic variation</u> means some cattle will have <u>better characteristics</u> for producing meat than others, e.g. a <u>larger size</u>.
2) The farmer could select the <u>largest</u> cows and bulls and <u>breed them</u> together.
3) He could then select the <u>largest offspring</u> and breed them together.
4) After <u>several generations</u>, he would get cows with a <u>very high meat yield</u>.

Selective Breeding Has **Disadvantages**

1) The main <u>problem</u> with selective breeding is that it <u>reduces</u> the number of <u>different alleles</u> in a population.

There's more on alleles on page 120.

2) This is because the "<u>best</u>" animals or plants are always used for breeding, and they are all <u>closely related</u> — this is known as <u>inbreeding</u>.

3) This means there's more chance of selectively bred organisms having <u>health problems</u> caused by their <u>genes</u>, e.g. they may inherit harmful <u>genetic defects</u>.

4) There can also be serious problems if a <u>new disease</u> appears.

5) This is because it's less likely that individuals in the population will have <u>alleles</u> that make them <u>resistant</u> to the disease.

6) So, if <u>one</u> individual is affected by the disease, <u>the rest</u> are <u>also</u> likely to be affected.

WORKING SCIENTIFICALLY

Selective breeding has its pros and cons...

Selective breeding has already been producing good results for <u>thousands of years</u>, but it's still important that farmers and other people working in agriculture are aware of the <u>disadvantages</u>. They need to look at the evidence and weigh up the <u>pros</u> and <u>cons</u> before coming to a decision.

Genetic Engineering

*As well as selective breeding, humans can also use **genetic engineering** to **control** an organism's **features**.*

Genetic Engineering Involves Changing an Organism's DNA

1) Genetic engineering is used to give organisms new and useful characteristics.
2) It involves cutting a gene out of one organism and putting it into another organism's cells.
3) Organisms that have had a new gene inserted are called genetically modified (GM) organisms.

Genetic Engineering is Useful in Agriculture and Medicine

In Agriculture:

1) Crops can be genetically engineered — this makes genetically modified (GM) crops.
2) They may be genetically engineered to be resistant to herbicides (chemicals that kill plants). This means that farmers can spray their crops to kill weeds, without affecting the crop itself.
3) Crops can also be genetically engineered to be resistant to insects or disease. Or they can be made to grow bigger and better fruit.
4) These things can increase crop yield (the amount of food produced).

In Medicine:

1) Bacteria can be genetically engineered to produce human insulin. This can be used to treat diabetes (see p.106).
2) Treatments using genetic modification for inherited diseases are being researched.

But There are Some Concerns About Genetic Engineering

There are concerns about using genetic engineering in animals:

1) It can be hard to predict how changing an animal's DNA will affect the animal.
2) Many genetically modified embryos don't survive.
3) Some genetically modified animals also suffer from health problems later in life.

There are also concerns about growing GM crops:

1) Some people say that growing GM crops will affect the number of wild flowers. This could also affect the population of insects.
2) Some people are worried that we might not understand the effects of GM crops on human health.

Warm-Up & Exam Questions

By doing these Warm-Up and Exam Questions, you'll soon find out if you've got the basic facts straight.

Warm-Up Questions

1) True or false? Genetic engineering involves changing an organism's DNA.
2) What is the name given to crops that have been genetically engineered?
3) Name one useful product that humans have genetically modified bacteria to produce.

Exam Questions

1 A farmer wants to use selective breeding to improve disease resistance in her crops.

Use the words from the box to complete the sentences about the disadvantages of selective breeding.

chromosomes	health problems	better characteristics
alleles	more resistant	less resistant

In a population of selectively bred plants, there will be fewer different ....

This means if a new disease appears, the plants may be ....

Due to inbreeding, there's also more chance of selectively bred plants having ....

[3 marks]

2 Organisms can be genetically modified.
This means an organism's genes can be altered to alter its characteristics.

2.1 Plants can be genetically modified to become more resistant to disease.
Suggest **one** other useful way that plants can be genetically modified.

[1 mark]

2.2 Some people think that it is wrong to genetically modify crop plants.
Give **one** objection that a person might have.

[1 mark]

3 Cows can be selectively bred to produce offspring that produce a high milk yield.
Table 1 shows the average milk yield over three generations for a population of cows.

Table 1

Generation	Average milk yield per cow in litres per year
1	5000
2	5375
3	5750

3.1 Calculate the percentage change in average milk yield from generation **2** to generation **3**.

[2 marks]

3.2* Describe the method the farmer used to selectively breed cows to produce a higher milk yield.

[4 marks]

Topic B6 — Inheritance, Variation and Evolution

Fossils

*Fossils are great. If they're **well-preserved**, you can see what really old creatures **looked** like.*

Fossils are the **Remains** of Plants and Animals

1) Fossils are the <u>remains</u> of organisms from <u>many thousands of years ago</u>. They're found in <u>rocks</u>.
2) They provide the <u>evidence</u> that organisms lived ages ago.
3) Fossils can tell us a lot about <u>how much</u> or <u>how little</u> organisms have <u>changed</u> (<u>evolved</u>) over time.
4) Fossils form in rocks in one of <u>three</u> ways:

1. From gradual replacement by minerals

1) Things like <u>teeth</u>, <u>shells</u> and <u>bones</u> don't easily decay.
2) This means they can last a <u>long time</u> when <u>buried</u>.
3) When they do decay, they get <u>replaced by minerals</u>.
4) The minerals form a <u>rock-like substance</u> shaped like the original hard part.

(Most fossils happen this way.)

2. From casts and impressions

1) Fossils can be formed when an organism is <u>buried</u> in a <u>soft</u> material like <u>clay</u>. The clay <u>hardens</u> around it and the organism <u>decays</u>. The organism leaves a <u>cast</u> of itself. An animal's <u>burrow</u> or a plant's <u>roots</u> can also be preserved as casts.
2) Things like <u>footprints</u> are <u>pressed</u> into soft materials. This leaves an <u>impression</u> when they harden.

3. From preservation in places where no decay happens

1) <u>Decay microbes</u> only work if there's <u>oxygen</u>, <u>moisture</u>, <u>warmth</u> and the right <u>pH</u>.
2) In <u>some substances</u> these conditions <u>aren't</u> all <u>present</u>, so decay doesn't happen. For example, there's <u>no oxygen</u> or <u>moisture</u> in <u>amber</u> so decay organisms can't survive.

A preserved organism in amber.

But **No One** Knows How Life Began

1) Fossils show <u>how much</u> or <u>how little</u> different organisms have changed (<u>evolved</u>) as life has developed on Earth over millions of years.
2) There are lots of <u>hypotheses</u> (see p.2) suggesting how life first came into being. For example:

  • Maybe the <u>first life forms</u> appeared in a <u>swamp</u> (or under the <u>sea</u>) here on <u>Earth</u>.
  • Or maybe simple carbon molecules were brought here on <u>comets</u> and developed into simple life forms.

  But no one really knows.

3) These hypotheses can't be supported or disproved because there's a <u>lack</u> of <u>valid</u> evidence.
4) There's a lack of evidence because many early organisms were <u>soft-bodied</u>. Soft tissue tends to decay away <u>completely</u>. So the fossil record is <u>incomplete</u> (unfinished).
5) Plus, fossils that did form millions of years ago may have been <u>destroyed</u> by <u>geological activity</u>. E.g. the movement of tectonic plates may have <u>crushed</u> fossils already formed in the rock.

Classification

*People really seem to like **putting things** into **groups** — biologists certainly do anyway...*

Classification is Organising Living Organisms into Groups

1) In the past, organisms were <u>classified</u> according to <u>characteristics</u> you can see (like number of legs). They were also classified by the <u>structures</u> that make them up (like mitochondria in cells).

2) The more similar two organisms <u>appeared</u>, the more <u>closely related</u> they were thought to be.

3) These characteristics were used to classify organisms in the <u>five kingdom classification system</u>.

4) In this system, living things are divided into <u>five groups</u> called <u>kingdoms</u>. These are:

- <u>Animals</u> — fish, mammals, reptiles, etc.
- <u>Plants</u> — grasses, trees, etc.
- <u>Fungi</u> — mushrooms and toadstools, yeasts, all that mouldy stuff on your loaf of bread.
- <u>Prokaryotes</u> — all <u>single-celled</u> organisms <u>without</u> a nucleus.
- <u>Protists</u> — <u>eukaryotic single-celled</u> organisms.

There's more on prokaryotes and eukaryotes on p.17.

5) The <u>kingdoms</u> are then split into smaller and smaller groups.

6) These groups are <u>phylum</u>, <u>class</u>, <u>order</u>, <u>family</u>, <u>genus</u> and <u>species</u>.

7) The five kingdom classification system was made up by <u>Carl Linnaeus</u>.

Classification Systems Change Over Time

1) Over time, our knowledge of the <u>processes</u> taking place inside organisms has developed.

2) <u>Microscopes</u> have also <u>improved</u> over time. This has allowed us to find out more about the <u>internal structures</u> of organisms.

3) Using this new knowledge, scientists made <u>new</u> models of classification.

4) One of these new models was the <u>three-domain system</u>. It was made up by <u>Carl Woese</u>.

5) He used evidence from <u>analysing chemicals</u> to come up with the system.

6) It showed him that some species were <u>less closely related</u> than first thought.

7) Here's how the three-domain system works:

The three-domain classification system:

All organisms

Domain — Eukaryota, Archaea, Bacteria

All organisms are divided into <u>three big groups</u> called <u>domains</u>:

Kingdom
Phylum
Class
Etc.

- EUKARYOTA — This domain includes a <u>wide range</u> of organisms. E.g. <u>fungi</u>, <u>plants</u>, <u>animals</u> and <u>protists</u>.
- ARCHAEA — These organisms are <u>primitive bacteria</u>. They usually live in <u>extreme places</u> such as hot springs and salt lakes.
- BACTERIA — This domain contains "<u>true bacteria</u>".

The domains are <u>divided</u> into <u>smaller groups</u> — kingdom, phylum, class, order, family, genus, species.

Classification

*A bit of a **Latin** lesson for you now. And a diagram of a **funny-looking tree**.*

Organisms Are **Named** According to the **Binomial System**

1) In the binomial system, every organism is given its own <u>two-part</u> Latin name.
2) The <u>first</u> part refers to the <u>genus</u> that the organism belongs to.
   This gives you information on the organism's <u>ancestry</u> (the organisms it's related to).
3) The <u>second</u> part refers to the <u>species</u>.

E.g. humans are known as *Homo sapiens*.

'*Homo*' is the <u>genus</u>...   ...and '*sapiens*' is the <u>species</u>.

Evolutionary Trees Show **Relationships**

1) Evolutionary trees show how scientists think <u>different species</u> are <u>related</u>.
2) They show <u>common ancestors</u> and relationships between species.
3) The more <u>recent</u> the common ancestor, the more <u>closely related</u> the two species.
   Also, the <u>more characteristics</u> they are likely to <u>share</u>.
4) Scientists look at lots of different types of data to <u>work out</u> these relationships.
   For example:

• For <u>living</u> organisms, they use <u>current classification data</u>.
• For <u>extinct</u> species, they use information from the <u>fossil record</u> (see page 128).

Extinct species are species that don't exist any more.

5) Here's an example of an evolutionary tree:

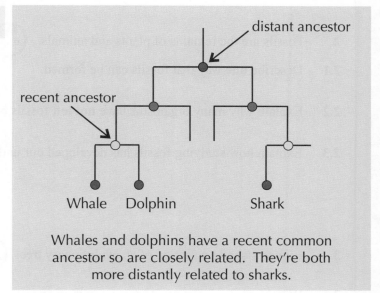

distant ancestor

recent ancestor

Whale   Dolphin   Shark

Whales and dolphins have a recent common ancestor so are closely related. They're both more distantly related to sharks.

Binomial system — uh oh, sounds like maths...

Sometimes, the <u>genus</u> in a binomial name is abbreviated to a <u>capital letter</u> with a <u>full stop after it</u>.

Q1   The evolutionary tree on the right shows the relationship between four species, A-D.
     Which two species shown in the tree are the most closely related?   [1 mark]

Q2   What genus does the Eurasian beaver, *Castor fiber*, belong to?   [1 mark]

Q1 Video Solution

Ⓐ Ⓑ Ⓒ Ⓓ

Warm-Up & Exam Questions

The end of the topic is in sight now — just a few more questions to check you've been paying attention.

Warm-Up Questions

1) True or false? The fossil record is incomplete.
2) True or false? Carl Linnaeus classified organisms based on their characteristics.
3) In the binomial naming system, what does the first part of a name refer to?
4) In the binomial naming system, what does the second part of a name refer to?

Exam Questions

1   Scientists organise living organisms into groups.   *Grade 1-3*

1.1   Which of the following is **not** a domain of the three-domain classification system? Tick **one** box.

☐ Plants   ☐ Eukaryota   ☐ Prokaryotes   ☐ Archaea

[1 mark]

1.2   Which of the following scientists developed the three-domain classification system?
Tick **one** box.

☐ Charles Darwin   ☐ Carl Linnaeus   ☐ Carl Woese

[1 mark]

2   Fossils are the remains of plants and animals.   *Grade 4-5*

2.1   Describe **one** way that fossils can be formed.

[1 mark]

2.2   Explain why many organisms have **not** left fossils behind.

[2 marks]

2.3   Explain how studying fossils has developed our understanding of evolution.

[1 mark]

3   **Figure 1** shows a section of an evolutionary tree.   *Grade 4-5*

3.1   Which species is the most recent common ancestor of
Species **F** and Species **G**?

[1 mark]

3.2   Would you expect Species **D** to look similar to Species **E**?
Give a reason for your answer.

[1 mark]

Figure 1

Competition

*Organisms **interact** with **each other** and their **environment**. This is what **ecology** is all about.*

Learn These Words Before You Start

1) <u>Habitat</u> — the place where an organism <u>lives</u>.
2) <u>Population</u> — <u>all</u> the organisms of <u>one species</u> in a <u>habitat</u>.
3) <u>Community</u> — all the <u>populations</u> of <u>different species</u> in a habitat.
4) <u>Ecosystem</u> — the <u>interaction</u> of a <u>community</u> of organisms with the <u>non-living</u> parts of their environment.

Organisms **Compete** for **Resources** to **Survive**

1) <u>Resources</u> are things that organisms need from their <u>environment</u> and <u>other organisms</u> to <u>survive</u> and <u>reproduce</u>:

- <u>Animals</u> need food, territory (space) and mates.
- <u>Plants</u> need light, water, space and mineral ions.

2) Organisms <u>compete with other species</u> (and members of their <u>own species</u>) for the <u>same resources</u>.

Organisms in a **Community** are **Interdependent**

1) In a community, different species <u>depend</u> on each other for things like <u>food</u>, <u>shelter</u>, <u>pollination</u> and <u>seed dispersal</u>. This is called <u>interdependence</u>.

2) This means that a big change in <u>one part</u> of an ecosystem (e.g. a <u>species</u> being <u>removed</u>) can affect the <u>whole community</u>.

3) The diagram on the right shows part of a <u>food web</u> (a diagram of what eats what) from a <u>stream</u>.

4) If all the stonefly larvae die, then for example:

- There would be <u>less food</u> for <u>water boatmen</u>, so their population might <u>decrease</u>.
- The <u>blackfly larvae</u> would not have to <u>compete</u> with the <u>stonefly larvae</u> for <u>food</u> (algae) so their population might <u>increase</u>.

Part of a <u>food web</u> from a <u>stream</u>:

Frog

Diving beetle   Water boatman

Stonefly larvae   Blackfly larvae

Algae

5) In <u>stable communities</u>, all the species and environmental factors are in <u>balance</u>. This means that the <u>population sizes</u> stay about the <u>same</u>.

Survival — the prize for being a winner

Q1   Give three resources that plants compete for.   [3 marks]

Q2   Look at the food web above. Suggest why the number of water boatmen might increase if all of the diving beetles died.   [2 marks]

Q2 Video Solution

Abiotic and Biotic Factors

*The **environment** in which organisms live **changes** all the time. The **things that change** are either **abiotic** (non-living) or **biotic** (living) factors. These changes can have a big **effect** on a community...*

Abiotic Factors Can **Change** in an **Ecosystem**

<u>Abiotic factors</u> are the <u>non-living</u> factors in an environment. For example:

1) <u>Moisture level</u>

2) <u>Light intensity</u>

3) <u>Temperature</u>

Light intensity can vary within an ecosystem because of shading caused by, e.g. tree cover.

4) <u>Carbon dioxide level</u> (for plants)

5) <u>Wind intensity</u> and <u>direction</u>

6) <u>Oxygen level</u> (for animals that live in water)

7) <u>Soil pH</u> and <u>mineral content</u>

Changes in Abiotic Factors Can **Affect Populations**

1) An <u>increase</u> or <u>decrease</u> in an abiotic factor is a <u>change</u> in the environment.

2) This can affect the <u>size</u> of <u>populations</u> in a <u>community</u>.

3) A change in an abiotic factor that affects one species could also affect the population sizes of <u>other</u> species that <u>depend on them</u> (see previous page). For example:

- A <u>decrease</u> in the <u>mineral content</u> of the soil could affect the <u>growth</u> of a plant species.
- This could cause a <u>decrease</u> in the <u>population size</u> of the plant species.
- A decrease in the plant population could <u>affect</u> any <u>animal species</u> that <u>depend</u> on it for <u>food</u>.

A = not, biotic = living, so abiotic means non-living

Some <u>human activities</u> can affect the <u>abiotic factors</u> of <u>ecosystems</u> — see pages 153, 156 and 157 for more. As you can see from this page, this can affect some organisms <u>directly</u> and other organisms <u>indirectly</u>.

Abiotic and Biotic Factors

*The previous page shows how abiotic factors can affect the **populations** in an ecosystem, but changes in **biotic factors** can also have big consequences. This page has a few examples to show you how.*

Biotic Factors Can Also Change in an Ecosystem

1) Biotic factors are the living factors in an environment.
2) A change in a biotic factor could affect the population size of some species. This could then affect species that depend on them (see page 141).
3) Biotic factors include:

1. Competition

One species may outcompete another so that numbers are too low to breed.

- Red and grey squirrels live in the same habitat and eat the same food.
- Grey squirrels outcompete the red squirrels for food and shelter.
- So the population of red squirrels is decreasing.

'Outcompete' means they're better at getting the resources they need to survive.

2. Availability of Food

If there is less food available, the population size will decrease.

3. New Predators

Predators are animals that kill other animals

A new predator could cause a decrease in the prey population. There's more about predator-prey populations on page 145.

4. New Pathogens

Pathogens are microorganisms that cause disease.

A new pathogen could quickly decrease the population of an affected species.

REVISION TIP

Changing biotic factors — it's like dominoes...

Learn the list of factors here, as well as on the previous page. I reckon this is a prime time for shutting the book, scribbling them all down and then checking how you did.

Adaptations

*Life exists in so many **different environments**. It's all because of the **adaptations** that organisms have...*

Adaptations Allow Organisms to Survive

1) <u>Organisms</u>, including <u>microorganisms</u>, are <u>adapted</u> to survive in the <u>conditions</u> of their <u>environment</u>.
2) This means they have <u>special features</u> that <u>suit</u> their environment.
3) These <u>features</u> are called <u>adaptations</u>. Adaptations can be:

1. Structural

These are <u>features</u> of an organism's <u>body structure</u> — such as <u>shape</u> or <u>colour</u>. For example:

Animals that live in <u>hot</u> places (like <u>camels</u>) have a <u>thin layer</u> of <u>fat</u> and a <u>large surface area</u> compared to their <u>volume</u>. This helps them <u>lose heat</u>.

Arctic animals (like the <u>Arctic fox</u>) have <u>white fur</u> so they <u>can't be seen</u> against the snow.
This helps them <u>avoid predators</u> and <u>sneak up on prey</u>.

2. Behavioural

These are ways that organisms <u>behave</u>.

E.g. many species (e.g. <u>swallows</u>) <u>migrate</u> (move away) to <u>warmer climates</u> during the <u>winter</u>. So they <u>avoid</u> the problems of living in <u>cold conditions</u>.

3. Functional

These are things that go on <u>inside</u> an organism's <u>body</u>.
They can be related to <u>processes</u> like <u>metabolism</u> (all the chemical reactions happening in the body).

E.g. <u>desert</u> animals make sure they don't <u>lose</u> too much <u>water</u>. They produce <u>very little sweat</u> and <u>small amounts</u> of <u>concentrated urine</u> (wee without much water in it).

Extremophiles Live in Extreme Places

Some <u>microorganisms</u> (e.g. bacteria) are <u>extremophiles</u> — they're adapted to live in <u>extreme conditions</u>.
For example:

- at <u>high temperatures</u> (e.g. in super hot volcanic vents)
- in places with a <u>high salt concentration</u> (e.g. very salty lakes)
- at <u>high pressure</u> (e.g. in deep sea vents).

Organisms can adapt to life in really extreme environments

Q1   The diagram on the right shows a penguin. Some of its adaptations are labelled. Penguins live in the cold, icy environment of the Antarctic. They swim in the sea to hunt for fish to eat. Some penguins huddle together in groups to keep warm.

thick layer of fat

flippers

webbed feet

    a) What type of adaptation is being described when penguins 'huddle together'? [1 mark]
    b) Use the labels on the diagram to explain one way that the penguin is adapted to its environment. [2 marks]

Food Chains

*Remember **food webs** from page 141? Well, **food chains** are a similar idea — read on to find out more...*

Food Chains Show **What's Eaten by What**

1) <u>Food chains</u> always start with a <u>producer</u>.

2) Producers <u>make</u> (produce) <u>their own food</u> using energy from the Sun.

3) Producers are usually <u>green plants</u> or <u>algae</u> — they make <u>glucose</u> by <u>photosynthesis</u> (see page 85).

4) Some of this glucose is used to make the plant's <u>biomass</u> — its <u>mass</u> of <u>living material</u>.

5) Biomass is <u>passed along</u> a food chain when an organism <u>eats</u> another organism.

6) <u>Consumers</u> are organisms that <u>eat other organisms</u>:

   - <u>Primary</u> consumers eat <u>producers</u>.
   - <u>Secondary</u> consumers eat <u>primary</u> consumers.
   - <u>Tertiary</u> consumers eat <u>secondary</u> consumers.

7) Here's an example of a <u>food chain</u>:

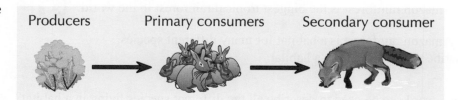

Producers   Primary consumers   Secondary consumer

Populations of **Prey** and **Predators** Go in **Cycles**

1) Consumers that <u>hunt and kill</u> other animals are called <u>predators</u>.

2) The animals they eat are called <u>prey</u>.

3) In a <u>stable community</u>, the <u>population size</u> of a species is <u>limited</u> by the amount of <u>food</u> it has. So the population size of <u>predators</u> is <u>affected</u> by the number of their <u>prey</u>.

For more about a stable community see page 141.

1) Foxes are <u>predators</u>. Rabbits are their <u>prey</u>.

2) If the <u>number of rabbits increases</u>, then the number of <u>foxes</u> will <u>increase</u>.

3) This is because there is <u>more food</u> for the foxes.

4) But as the number of foxes <u>increases</u>, then the number of rabbits will <u>decrease</u>.

5) This is because <u>more</u> rabbits will be <u>eaten</u> by the foxes.

A peak in rabbit numbers is followed by a peak in foxes

4) It <u>takes a while</u> for one population to <u>respond</u> to changes in the other one.

E.g. the number of foxes goes up <u>after</u> the number of rabbits goes up. This is because it <u>takes time</u> for the foxes to <u>reproduce</u>.

A food chain shows part of a food web

Q1   Look at the following food chain for a particular area: grass → grasshopper → rat → snake

    a) Name the producer in the food chain.   [1 mark]

    b) How many consumers are there in the food chain?   [1 mark]

    c) Name the primary consumer in the food chain.   [1 mark]

    d) All the rats in the area are killed.
       Explain two effects that this could have on the food chain.   [4 marks]

Q1 Video Solution

Warm-Up & Exam Questions

This ecology topic's a long one — so make sure you've really got these first few pages stuck in your head before moving on and learning the rest. These questions should help you out.

Warm-Up Questions

1) Animals compete with one another for food. Give one other factor that animals compete for.
2) Name two abiotic factors.
3) True or false? Food chains always start with a primary consumer.
4) What would happen to the size of a predator population if there was less prey available?

Exam Questions

1 The Amazon rainforest is the biggest tropical rainforest in the world. **(Grade 3-4)**

1.1 The Amazon rainforest is a habitat for many different species.
Describe what is meant by a habitat.

[1 mark]

1.2 Which word can be used to describe all the different species living in a habitat?
Tick **one** box.

☐ population   ☐ community   ☐ ecosystem   ☐ distribution

[1 mark]

2 **Figure 1** shows a food chain for a particular area: **(Grade 4-5)**

Figure 1

algae → shrimp → sea turtle → tiger shark

2.1 What term is used to describe the tiger shark in **Figure 1**?
Tick **one** box.

☐ producer   ☐ primary consumer   ☐ secondary consumer   ☐ tertiary consumer

[1 mark]

2.2 Explain the importance of the algae in **Figure 1**.

[2 marks]

3 The Harris's antelope squirrel lives in hot deserts in parts of the USA and Mexico. **(Grade 4-5)**
It has grey fur, small ears and does not sweat.
It has sharp claws which enable it to dig burrows, in which it lives.
Above ground, during the hottest parts of the day it often holds its large tail over its head,
or lies in the shade with its limbs spread out wide.

3.1 Give **one** functional adaptation the Harris's antelope squirrel has to its environment.

[1 mark]

3.2 Give **two** behavioural adaptations the Harris's antelope squirrel has to its environment.

[2 marks]

Using Quadrats

*This is where the **fun** starts. Studying **ecology** gives you the chance to **rummage around** in bushes, get your hands **dirty** and look at some **real organisms**, living in the wild.*

Differences in the Environment Affect Where Organisms Live

1) The <u>distribution</u> of an organism is <u>where</u> an organism is <u>found</u>.

2) Where an organism is found is affected by <u>biotic and abiotic factors</u> (see pages 142-143).

3) An organism might be <u>more common</u> in <u>one area</u> than another due to <u>differences</u> in <u>factors</u> between the two areas. For example, in a field, you might find daisies are more common in the <u>open</u> than <u>under trees</u>, because there's <u>more light</u>.

4) To <u>study</u> the distribution of an organism you can use <u>quadrats</u> or <u>transects</u> (see next page).

Use Quadrats to Study The Distribution of Small Organisms

Here's how to compare <u>how common</u> an organism is in <u>two different areas</u> — these are called <u>sample areas</u>.

A quadrat (square frame)

1) Place a <u>quadrat</u> on the ground in the <u>first</u> sample area. It needs to be placed at <u>random</u> (see p.400).

2) <u>Count</u> all the organisms you're interested in <u>within</u> the quadrat.

3) <u>Repeat</u> steps 1 and 2 as many times as you can.

4) <u>Work out</u> the <u>mean</u> number of organisms per quadrat within the first sample area.

> **EXAMPLE** **Fatima counted the number of daisies in 7 quadrats within her first sample area. She recorded the following results: 18, 20, 22, 23, 23, 23, 25**
>
> Here the MEAN is: $\dfrac{\text{TOTAL number of organisms}}{\text{NUMBER of quadrats}} = \dfrac{154}{7} = 22$ daisies per quadrat

5) <u>Repeat</u> steps 1 to 4 in the <u>second</u> sample area.

6) Finally <u>compare</u> the two means. E.g. you might find 2 daisies per quadrat in a shady area, and 22 daisies per quadrat (lots more) in a sunny area.

The population size of an organism is sometimes called its abundance.

You Can Work Out the Population Size of an Organism

> **EXAMPLE** **Students used quadrats, each with an area of 0.25 m², to randomly sample daisies in a field. They found a mean of 10 daisies per quadrat. The field's area was 800 m². Estimate the population of daisies in the field.**
>
> 1) Divide the area of the habitat by the quadrat size. $800 \div 0.25 = 3200$
>
> 2) Multiply this by the mean number of organisms per quadrat. $3200 \times 10 = 32\,000$ daisies in the field

---

Don't try to study elephants using a quadrat

Q1 A field was randomly sampled for tulips using a quadrat with an area of 0.25 m². The field had an area of 1200 m². A mean of 0.75 tulips was found per quadrat. Estimate the total population of tulips. [2 marks]

Q1 Video Solution

Using Quadrats

*So, now you think you've learnt **all about** distribution. Well **hold on** — there's more **ecology fun** to be had.*

Use **Transects** to **Study** The **Distribution** of Organisms

You can use lines called <u>transects</u> to help find out how organisms are <u>distributed</u> across an area.
E.g. if an organism becomes <u>more or less common</u> as you move from a hedge towards the middle of a field.
Here's what to do:

1) <u>Mark out a line</u> in the area you want to study using a tape measure.

2) <u>Collect data</u> along the line by either:

- <u>Counting</u> all the organisms you're interested in that <u>touch</u> the line.

- Or by using <u>quadrats</u> (see previous page) placed along the line.

tape measure

quadrat

You Can **Estimate** the **Percentage Cover** of a **Quadrat**

1) Sometimes it can be difficult to count <u>all</u> of the organisms in a quadrat (e.g. if they're grass).

2) In this case, you can find the <u>percentage cover</u> instead.

3) This means <u>estimating</u> the percentage <u>area</u> of the quadrat that the organisms <u>cover</u>.

4) You can do this by <u>counting</u> the number of <u>little squares</u> they cover.

EXAMPLE

Some students were measuring the distribution of an organism across a school playing field. They placed quadrats at regular intervals along a transect.
Below is a picture of one of the quadrats.
Calculate the percentage cover of the organism in this quadrat.

<u>One quadrat</u>

Area covered by organism

1) <u>Count</u> the <u>number of squares</u> covered by the organism. You count a square if it's <u>more than half</u> covered.

47 squares are covered by the organism.

2) Make this into a <u>percentage</u>:

- Divide the number of squares covered by the organism by the total number of squares in the quadrat (100).

- Multiply the result by 100.

(47/100) × 100
= 0.47 × 100 = 47%

PRACTICAL TIP

You don't need fancy kit to study the distribution of organisms

So if you want to measure the distribution of a organism <u>across</u> an area, you could use a <u>transect</u>. You can use them <u>alone</u> or along with <u>quadrats</u>. Using <u>percentage cover</u> instead of <u>number</u> of organisms is a good way of studying the distribution of plants, as there may be <u>too many</u> to count.

The Water Cycle

*The **amount** of water on Earth is pretty much **constant** — but **where** it is changes.*
*Water moves between **rivers**, **lakes**, **oceans** and the **atmosphere** in what's known as the **water cycle**.*

The **Water Cycle** Means Water is **Constantly Recycled**

1) <u>Energy</u> from the <u>Sun</u> makes water <u>evaporate</u> from the land and sea. This turns the water into <u>water vapour</u>.

2) Water also evaporates from <u>plants</u> — this is called <u>transpiration</u> (see p.68).

3) The warm water vapour is <u>carried upwards</u>. When it gets higher up, the water vapour <u>cools</u>. It <u>condenses</u> to form <u>clouds</u>.

As warm water vapour rises it cools down and forms clouds.

4) Water falls from the clouds as <u>precipitation</u> (usually rain, but sometimes snow or hail). <u>Precipitation</u> provides <u>fresh water</u> for <u>plants</u> and <u>animals</u>:

Plants

1) Some water is <u>absorbed</u> by the <u>soil</u>. Plants <u>take up</u> the water through their <u>roots</u>.
2) Plants <u>need</u> water for things like <u>photosynthesis</u> (p.85).
3) Some water becomes part of the plants' <u>tissues</u>. It's passed to <u>animals</u> when plants are <u>eaten</u>.

Animals

1) Animals need water for the <u>chemical reactions</u> in their bodies.
2) They <u>return</u> water to the <u>soil</u> and <u>atmosphere</u> in their <u>waste</u> (e.g. sweat and urine).

5) Water that doesn't get absorbed by the soil will <u>run off</u> into <u>streams</u> and <u>rivers</u>.

6) The water <u>drains</u> back into the <u>sea</u>. Then it <u>evaporates</u> all over <u>again</u>.

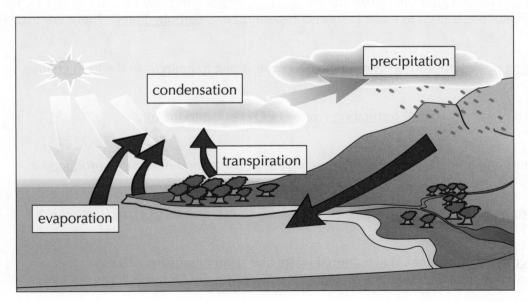

The Carbon Cycle

*All the **nutrients** in our environment get **recycled** — there's a balance between what **goes in** and what **goes out**.*

Materials are Recycled by Decay

1) <u>Living things</u> are made of <u>materials</u> they <u>take</u> from the world around them.

> E.g. plants take up <u>mineral ions</u> from the soil.
> * These are used to make <u>molecules</u> that make up the plant.
> * The molecules are <u>passed up the food chain</u> when the plant is <u>eaten</u>.

2) These materials are <u>returned</u> to the environment in <u>waste products</u>, or when <u>dead</u> organisms <u>decay</u>.

3) Materials decay because they're <u>broken down</u> by <u>microorganisms</u>.

4) <u>Decay</u> puts stuff that plants need to <u>grow</u> (e.g. mineral ions) <u>back</u> into the <u>soil</u> — they are <u>recycled</u>.

The **Constant Cycling** of **Carbon** is called the **Carbon Cycle**

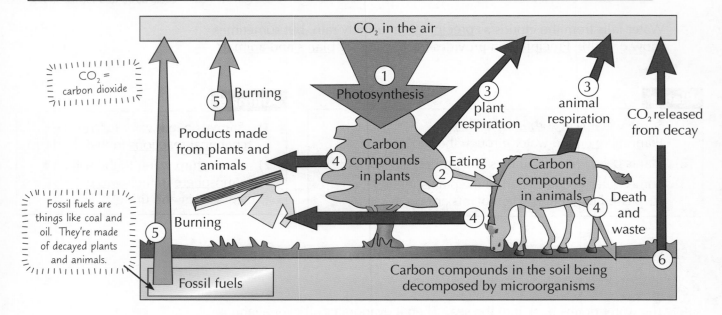

① <u>Plants</u> take in CO_2 from the air during <u>photosynthesis</u>. They use the carbon in CO_2 to make <u>glucose</u>. This glucose is used to make carbon compounds, e.g. <u>carbohydrates</u>. These are used for <u>growth</u>.

② <u>Eating</u> passes the carbon compounds in plants along to <u>animals</u> in the <u>food chain</u>.

③ Both plant and animal <u>respiration</u> releases CO_2 back into the <u>air</u>.

See p.91-92 for more on respiration.

④ Plants and animals eventually <u>die</u>, or are killed and turned into <u>useful products</u>.

⑤ <u>Burning</u> plant and animal products (and fossil fuels) releases CO_2 back into the air.

⑥ <u>Microorganisms</u> break down <u>animal waste</u> and <u>dead organisms</u>. As they break down the material, they <u>release CO_2</u> back into the air through <u>respiration</u>.

Warm-Up & Exam Questions

You can't just stare at these pages and expect all of the information to go in. Especially the practical pages with the maths examples. Do these questions to see how well you really know the stuff.

Warm-Up Questions

1) Give one piece of equipment that you could use to study the distribution of an organism.
2) Name one type of precipitation.
3) What is the role of microorganisms in the carbon cycle?
4) How is the carbon in fossil fuels returned to the atmosphere?

Exam Questions

1   The water cycle describes the constant movement of water molecules on the Earth.

Use words from the box below to complete the sentences about the water cycle.

| condenses   precipitation   transpiration   evaporate   condensation   condense   evaporates |

Energy from the sun makes water ....

When warm water vapour gets higher up, the water vapour cools and ....

Water falls from the clouds as ....

[3 marks]

PRACTICAL

2   Some students studied the distribution of poppies across a field
next to a wood. A sketch of the area is shown in **Figure 1**.

Figure 1

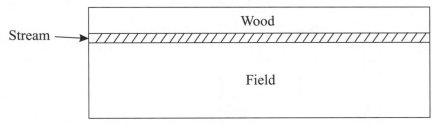

The students' results are shown in **Table 1**.

Table 1

| Number of poppies per m² | 5 | 9 | 14 | 19 | 26 |
| Distance from wood (m) | 2 | 4 | 6 | 8 | 10 |

2.1   Describe the trend shown in **Table 1**.

[1 mark]

2.2   The students suggest that light intensity may affect the distribution of the poppies.
Give **one** other factor that could affect the distribution of the poppies.

[1 mark]

Exam Questions

3   **Figure 2** shows a simplified version of the carbon cycle.

Figure 2

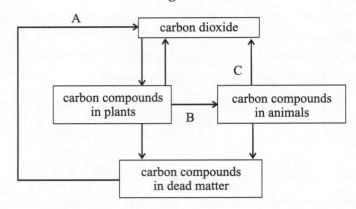

3.1   Name the process that is occurring at stage **B**.

[1 mark]

3.2   Name the process that is occurring at stage **C**.

[1 mark]

3.3   Explain how carbon is released from dead matter in the soil (stage **A**).

[2 marks]

3.4   Name the only process in the carbon cycle that removes carbon dioxide from the air.

[1 mark]

PRACTICAL

4   A group of students decided to study the distribution of a grass species in a field.
Figure 3 shows a sketch of the grass species in one of their quadrats.

Figure 3

4.1   Use **Figure 3** to estimate the percentage cover of the grass species in the quadrat.

[1 mark]

4.2   Give **one** reason why the students may have decided to estimate the percentage cover of the grass.

[1 mark]

Biodiversity and Waste Management

*Unfortunately, human activity can **negatively affect** the **planet** and its **variety of life**.*

Earth's **Biodiversity** is Important

> Biodiversity is the <u>variety of different species</u> of organisms on Earth, or within an ecosystem.

1) Different species <u>depend</u> on each other for different things in an ecosystem (see page 141).
2) Different species can also help keep the <u>conditions</u> in their <u>environment</u> right for each other, e.g. they can help keep the soil at the right pH.
3) So having a <u>high biodiversity</u> can mean that an ecosystem is more <u>stable</u>.
4) For the human species to <u>survive</u>, it's important that a good level of biodiversity is maintained.
5) Lots of human actions are <u>reducing</u> biodiversity (see below, and pages 155-157).
6) It's only <u>recently</u> that we've started <u>taking measures</u> to <u>stop</u> biodiversity decreasing.

More People Means Greater Demands on the **Environment**

1) The <u>population</u> of the world is <u>increasing</u> very quickly.
2) <u>More people</u> need <u>more resources</u> to survive.
3) People are also demanding a <u>higher standard of living</u>. This means that more people want <u>luxuries</u> that make life more comfortable, e.g. cars, computers, etc.
4) This means that we use <u>more raw materials</u> and <u>more energy</u> to make things.
5) So resources are being <u>used</u> more quickly than they are being <u>replaced</u>.

We're Also Producing **More Waste**

1) As we make more things, we produce more <u>waste</u>. This includes <u>waste chemicals</u>.
2) This waste can cause <u>harmful pollution</u> if it's not <u>handled properly</u>.
3) Pollution <u>kills</u> plants and animals. This <u>reduces biodiversity</u>.
4) <u>Pollution</u> can affect:

Water

- <u>Sewage</u> and <u>toxic chemicals</u> from industry can pollute lakes, rivers and oceans.
- <u>Fertilisers</u> (and other chemicals) used on land can be washed into water.
- This will affect the plants and animals that rely on these sources of water for survival.

Land

- We use <u>toxic chemicals</u> for farming (e.g. pesticides and herbicides).
- We dump a lot of <u>household waste</u> in landfill sites.

Air

- <u>Smoke</u> and <u>acidic gases</u> can pollute the air if they are released into the atmosphere.

Global Warming

*You might remember the **carbon cycle** from p.150. Well, carbon dioxide has an important role in keeping the Earth **warm enough** for life. It's not so good when there's **too much** of it in the atmosphere though...*

Carbon Dioxide and Methane Trap Energy from the Sun

1) Gases in the Earth's atmosphere trap energy from the Sun.

2) These gases mean that <u>not all</u> of the <u>energy</u> is <u>lost</u> into space. This helps to keep the Earth <u>warm</u>.

3) These gases are called <u>greenhouse gases</u>. Without them the Earth would be <u>very cold</u>.

4) But the levels of two greenhouse gases are <u>increasing</u> — <u>carbon dioxide</u> (CO_2) and <u>methane</u>.

5) The increasing <u>levels</u> of greenhouse gases are causing the Earth to <u>heat up</u> — this is <u>global warming</u>.

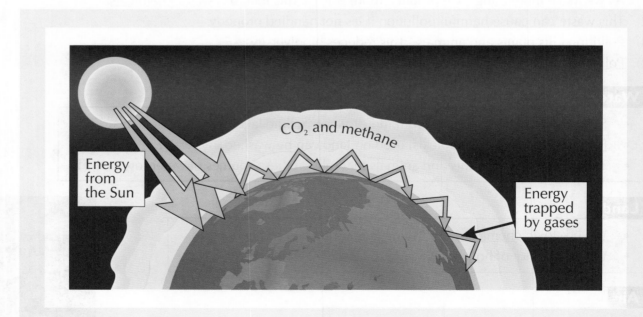

Global Warming

*The Earth is getting **warmer**. Climate scientists are now trying to work out what the **effects** of global warming might be — sadly, it's not as simple as everyone having nicer summers.*

The **Results** of **Global Warming** Could be Pretty **Serious**

There are several reasons to be <u>worried</u> about global warming. Here are a few:

Flooding

1) Higher temperatures cause <u>seawater</u> to <u>expand</u> and <u>ice</u> to <u>melt</u>. This causes the sea level to <u>rise</u>.
2) If it keeps rising it'll lead to <u>flooding</u> of low-lying land.
3) This will result in the loss of <u>habitats</u> (where organisms live).

Changes in the distribution of species

1) Global warming may lead to changes in <u>rainfall</u> and <u>temperature</u> in many areas.
2) This could cause the <u>distribution</u> (spread) of many <u>animal</u> and <u>plant species</u> to change.
3) E.g. if some areas become <u>warmer</u>:
   - Species that <u>do well</u> in <u>warm</u> conditions may spread <u>further</u>.
   - Species that need <u>cooler temperatures</u> may have a <u>smaller</u> area to live in.

Less biodiversity

1) Some species may not be able to <u>survive</u> a <u>change</u> in the climate.
2) These species might become <u>extinct</u>.
3) This could <u>reduce biodiversity</u> (see p.153).

Changes in migration patterns

1) There could be <u>changes in migration patterns</u> (where animals move to during different seasons).
2) E.g. some birds may migrate <u>further north</u>, as more northern areas are getting <u>warmer</u>.

We need to act fast, before the worst effects of climate change

Global warming is rarely out of the news. <u>Most scientists</u> accept that it's happening and that <u>human activity</u> has caused most of the recent warming, based on the evidence that has so far been collected. However, they don't know exactly what the <u>effects</u> will be and scientists will have to collect more data before these questions can really be answered.

Deforestation and Land Use

Trees and ***peat bogs*** trap carbon dioxide and ***lock it up***. *The problems start when it **escapes**...*

Humans Use **Lots of Land** for **Lots of Purposes**

1) We use land for things like <u>building</u>, <u>quarrying</u>, <u>farming</u> and <u>dumping waste</u>.
2) This means that there's <u>less land</u> available for <u>other organisms</u>.
3) Sometimes, the way we use land has a <u>bad effect</u> on the environment.

Destroying Peat Bogs Adds **More CO₂** to the Atmosphere

1) <u>Bogs</u> are areas of land that are <u>acidic</u> and <u>waterlogged</u>.

2) Plants that live in bogs <u>don't fully decay</u> when they die. The partly-rotted plants <u>build up</u> to form <u>peat</u>.

3) So the <u>carbon</u> in the plants is <u>stored</u> in the <u>peat</u>.

4) Peat bogs can be <u>drained</u>, so the peat can be sold to gardeners as <u>compost</u>.

5) When the peat is drained, <u>microorganisms</u> can break it down. They <u>release carbon dioxide (CO₂)</u> when they <u>respire</u>.

6) Peat can also be sold as a <u>fuel</u>. CO₂ is released when the peat is <u>burned</u>.

7) Destroying the bogs <u>reduces</u> the area of the <u>habitat</u>.

8) This reduces the number of <u>animals</u>, <u>plants</u> and <u>microorganisms</u> that live there. So it <u>reduces biodiversity</u>.

We need to use land, but we also need a healthy environment

We can't really <u>avoid</u> using land — we need it to grow enough food or build enough houses for people. The human population is <u>increasing</u> so it's likely that we'll use <u>even more</u> land in the future. We'll have to find a way to manage land use to <u>reduce</u> the negative effects on the environment.

Deforestation and Land Use

*Many parts of the world have **already** been changed lots by deforestation. For example, much of the **UK** used to be covered in forests. Deforestation can be **bad news** for several reasons.*

Deforestation Means **Chopping Down Trees**

<u>Deforestation</u> is the <u>cutting down</u> of <u>forests</u>. It is done for many <u>reasons</u>, like:

- To <u>clear land</u> for farming (e.g. cattle or rice crops) to provide <u>more food</u>.
- To grow <u>crops</u> to make <u>biofuels</u>.

Deforestation Can Cause Many **Problems**

Deforestation causes big problems when it's done on a <u>large-scale</u>, e.g. cutting down rainforests in <u>tropical areas</u>. These are:

Less carbon dioxide taken in

- Trees take in carbon dioxide from the atmosphere during <u>photosynthesis</u> (page 85).
- So <u>cutting down</u> trees means that less carbon dioxide is <u>removed</u> from the atmosphere.
- Trees '<u>lock up</u>' some of the <u>carbon</u> in their wood. Removing trees means that less is locked up.

More carbon dioxide released

- Carbon dioxide is <u>released</u> when trees are <u>burnt</u> to clear land.
- <u>Microorganisms</u> feeding on <u>dead wood</u> release carbon dioxide through <u>respiration</u> (p.91).

More CO_2 in the atmosphere causes global warming (see p.154).

Less biodiversity

- Habitats like forests can contain many species of <u>plants</u> and <u>animals</u> — they have <u>high biodiversity</u>.
- When forests are destroyed, many species may become <u>extinct</u> (p.129). This <u>reduces</u> biodiversity.

Not a very cheerful page, I know...

Make sure you can link together all the information on pages 154-157 — for example, how <u>deforestation</u> and <u>peat burning</u> can contribute to <u>global warming</u>, and how this might affect <u>biodiversity</u>. In the exam, you might get an extended response question that requires you to draw on several different areas of knowledge like this.

Maintaining Ecosystems and Biodiversity

*It's really important that biodiversity is **maintained** as damage to ecosystems or populations of species can be **hard to undo**. This page is about some of the different **methods** that can be used to maintain biodiversity.*

There are **Programmes** to **Protect Ecosystems** and **Biodiversity**

1) Human activities can <u>reduce biodiversity</u> and <u>damage ecosystems</u>.
2) In some areas, <u>programmes</u> to <u>minimise the damage</u> have been set up by <u>concerned citizens</u> and <u>scientists</u>. Here are a few examples:

1. Breeding Programmes

1) Animal species that are at <u>risk</u> of dying out are called <u>endangered species</u>.
2) They can be bred in <u>captivity</u>.
3) This makes sure some individuals will <u>survive</u> if the species <u>dies out</u> in the wild.
4) Individuals can sometimes be <u>released</u> into the <u>wild</u>. This can be to <u>boost</u> a population or <u>replace</u> one that's been wiped out.

Pandas are an endangered species. Many efforts have been made to breed pandas in captivity.

2. Habitat Protection

<u>Protecting</u> and <u>regenerating</u> (rebuilding) <u>rare habitats</u> helps to protect the <u>species</u> that live there.

3. Reintroducing **Hedgerows** and **Field Margins**

1) Field margins are areas of land around the <u>edges</u> of fields where wild flowers and grasses are left to <u>grow</u>.
2) <u>Hedges</u> can be planted around fields to form <u>hedgerows</u>.
3) Hedgerows and field margins provide a <u>habitat</u> for <u>lots of types</u> of organisms.
4) This is very useful for fields that only have <u>one type of crop</u>. This is because these fields have <u>very low biodiversity</u>.

4. Recycling

1) This <u>reduces</u> the amount of <u>waste</u> that gets dumped in <u>landfill</u> sites.
2) This could <u>reduce</u> the amount of <u>land</u> taken over for landfill. So <u>ecosystems</u> can be left alone.

5. **Government** Programmes

1) Deforestation <u>increases</u> the amount of <u>carbon dioxide</u> in the atmosphere (see previous page).
2) Some governments have made <u>rules</u> to <u>reduce deforestation</u>.
3) They have also made rules to reduce the amount of <u>carbon dioxide</u> released by <u>businesses</u>.
4) This could help to <u>stop global warming increasing</u> (see page 154).

Warm-Up & Exam Questions

I hope you've got all of that important information in your head. There's a lot to remember here, so have a flick back when you're doing these questions in case you've forgotten any little details.

Warm-Up Questions

1) What is meant by 'biodiversity'?
2) Give one way in which land can become polluted.
3) Give two greenhouse gases.
4) True or false? Destroying peat bogs adds more CO_2 to the atmosphere.
5) What is meant by the term 'deforestation'?

Exam Questions

1 Ecosystems and biodiversity can be protected by programmes set up by scientists.

1.1 Hedgerows can be reintroduced around fields in order to protect biodiversity.

Give **one** reason why reintroducing hedgerows around fields is important for biodiversity.

[1 mark]

1.2 Breeding programmes can be used to protect endangered species.

Explain how breeding programmes can be used to prevent an endangered species from dying out.

[3 marks]

2 Humans are producing increasing amounts of waste.
This has negative impacts for biodiversity and the environment.

2.1 Give **two** types of waste that pollute the air.

[2 marks]

2.2 Describe **one** way in which waste produced by humans pollutes water.

[1 mark]

2.3 Give **two** reasons why humans are producing increasingly more waste.

[2 marks]

2.4 Recycling reduces the amount of waste that gets dumped at landfill sites.
Explain how this helps to protect biodiversity.

[1 mark]

3* Most scientists accept that global warming is happening.
They believe that it could cause major changes to our environment.

Explain why deforestation contributes to global warming.

[6 marks]

Revision Summary for Topics B5-7

That's Topics B5-7 done. I bet you're in the mood for a list of revision questions now. You're in luck.

For even more practice, try the Retrieval Quizzes for Topics B5-7 — just scan the QR codes!

- Try these questions and tick off each one when you get it right.
- When you're completely happy with a topic, tick it off.

Topic B5 — Homeostasis and Response (p.97-111) ☐

1) What is homeostasis?
2) What makes up the central nervous system?
3) What is the purpose of a reflex reaction?
4) Name one factor that can affect reaction time.
5) Give two differences between nervous and hormonal responses.
6) What does luteinising hormone (LH) do?
7) What hormone does the contraceptive injection contain?
8) Which of the following is a hormonal contraceptive — condom, implant or diaphragm?

Topic B6 — Inheritance, Variation and Evolution (p.113-139) ☐

9) What do genes code for?
10) What is the name for all of the genetic material in an organism?
11) Name the male and female gametes of animals.
12) What is the probability that offspring will have the XX combination of sex chromosomes?
13) Which of these genotypes is heterozygous — FF, Ff or ff?
14) Name one inherited disorder.
15) Give one argument against screening embryos for inherited disorders.
16) What is variation?
17) Name the process by which evolution happens.
18) What leads to the formation of antibiotic-resistant strains of bacteria?
19) What is selective breeding?
20) What is genetic engineering?
21) What are fossils?
22) What is the smallest group in the Linnaean system of classification?

Topic B7 — Ecology (p.141-158) ☐

23) Define 'ecosystem'.
24) What things do plants compete for in an ecosystem?
25) What are biotic factors?
26) What is meant by the term 'biomass'?
27) What do primary consumers eat?
28) Explain how a quadrat can be used to investigate the distribution of clover plants in two areas.
29) What role do plants have in the carbon cycle?
30) Suggest why it's important to have high biodiversity in an ecosystem.
31) Give one way global warming could reduce biodiversity.
32) Explain why the destruction of peat bogs adds more carbon dioxide to the atmosphere.

Topics B5-7 — Revision Summary

Atoms

*All substances are made of **atoms**. They're really **tiny** — too small to see, even with your microscope. Atoms are so tiny that a **50p piece** contains about 77 400 000 000 000 000 000 000 of them.*

Atoms Contain **Protons**, **Neutrons** and **Electrons**

Atoms have a radius of about 0.1 nanometres (that's 1×10^{-10} m). There are a few different modern models of the atom — but chemists tend to like the model on the right best.

The **Nucleus**

1) It's in the middle of the atom.
2) It contains protons and neutrons.
3) The nucleus has a radius of around 1×10^{-14} m (that's around 1/10 000 of the atomic radius).
4) It has a positive charge because of the protons.
5) Almost the whole mass of the atom is in the nucleus.

atomic radius

> A nanometre (nm) is 0.000000001 m. Shown in standard form, that's 1×10^{-9} m. Standard form is used for showing really large or really small numbers.

The **Electrons**

1) Move around the nucleus in electron shells (levels).
2) They're negatively charged.
3) Electrons have almost no mass.

Particle	Relative Mass	Relative Charge
Proton	1	+1
Neutron	1	O
Electron	Very small	−1

You need to know the charges of protons, neutrons and electrons.

You also need to know how heavy they are compared to each other (their relative masses).

- Protons are heavy (compared to electrons) and positively charged.
- Neutrons are heavy (compared to electrons) and neutral.
- Electrons are tiny and negatively charged.

Atomic Number and **Mass Number** Describe an Atom

1) The nuclear symbol of an atom tells you its atomic (proton) number and mass number.

> atomic number = number of protons
> mass number = number of protons + number of neutrons
> number of neutrons = mass number − atomic number

Nuclear symbol for sodium

Mass number → 23
Atomic number → 11 Na   Element symbol (see next page).

Number of protons = 11
Number of neutrons = 23 − 11 = 12
Number of electrons = 11

2) Atoms have no charge overall. They're neutral.
3) This is because they have the same number of protons as electrons. So, in an atom...

> number of electrons = atomic number

4) The charge on the electrons is the same size as the charge on the protons, but opposite. So they cancel out.
5) In an ion, the number of protons doesn't equal the number of electrons. This means it has an overall charge. For example, an ion with a 2− charge, has two more electrons than protons.

> In a positive ion: number of electrons = atomic number − charge
> In a negative ion: number of electrons = atomic number + charge

> An ion is an atom or group of atoms that has lost or gained electrons.

The charges of the protons and electrons cancel out in an atom

Q1   An atom of gallium has an atomic number of 31 and a mass number of 70.
      Give the number of electrons, protons and neutrons in the atom.

[3 marks]

Q1 Video Solution

Elements

*An **element** is a substance made up of atoms that all have the **same** number of **protons** in their nucleus.*

Elements are Made Up of Atoms With the Same Atomic Number

1) The smallest part of an element that you can have is a single atom of that element.

2) The number of protons in the nucleus decides what type of atom it is.

> For example, an atom with one proton in its nucleus is hydrogen.
> An atom with two protons is helium.

3) If a substance only contains atoms with the same number of protons it's called an element.

4) So all the atoms of a particular element have the same number of protons.
   And different elements have atoms with different numbers of protons.

5) There are about 100 different elements.
   Each element is made up of only one type of atom — some examples are shown in the diagram below.

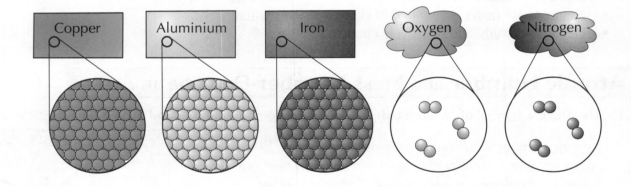

Atoms Can be Represented by Symbols

1) Atoms of each element can be represented by a one or two letter symbol.
2) You'll see these symbols on the periodic table (see page 180).
3) For example:

| C = carbon | O = oxygen | Na = sodium | Mg = magnesium | Fe = iron |

All atoms in an element have the same number of protons

Atoms and elements — make sure you know what they are and the differences between them. You don't need to learn all the symbols as you can use a periodic table, but it's handy to know the common ones.

Isotopes

*What's inside different atoms of the **same element** can vary. Read on to find out how...*

Isotopes are the Same Except for Extra **Neutrons**

1) Isotopes are:

> Atoms with the <u>same</u> number of <u>protons</u> but a <u>different</u> number of <u>neutrons</u>

2) So they have the <u>same atomic number</u> but <u>different mass numbers</u>.

The number of neutrons is the mass number minus the atomic number.

3) Carbon-12 and carbon-13 are isotopes of <u>carbon</u>.

Carbon-12

6 PROTONS
6 ELECTRONS
6 NEUTRONS

$^{12}_{6}\text{C}$

Carbon-13

6 PROTONS
6 ELECTRONS
7 NEUTRONS

$^{13}_{6}\text{C}$

4) If an element has a number of isotopes, you can describe it using <u>relative atomic mass</u> (A_r) instead of mass number. This is an <u>average</u> mass.

> You can work out the 'sum of' two or more amounts by adding them together.

5) A_r is worked out from the <u>different masses</u> and <u>abundances</u> (amounts) of each isotope.

$$\text{relative atomic mass } (A_r) = \frac{\text{sum of (isotope abundance} \times \text{isotope mass number)}}{\text{sum of abundances of all the isotopes}}$$

6) You can use this <u>formula</u> to work out the <u>relative atomic mass</u> of an element:

EXAMPLE   **Copper has two stable isotopes. Cu-63 has an abundance of 69.2% and Cu-65 has an abundance of 30.8%. Calculate the relative atomic mass of copper to 1 decimal place.**

abundance × mass number of Cu-63   abundance × mass number of Cu-65

$$\text{Relative atomic mass} = \frac{(69.2 \times 63) + (30.8 \times 65)}{69.2 + 30.8} = \frac{4359.6 + 2002}{100} = \frac{6361.6}{100} = 63.616 = 63.6$$

abundance of Cu-63 + abundance of Cu-65

Relative atomic mass is the average atomic mass of an element

Make sure you <u>understand</u> and know <u>how to use</u> the formula to find the A_r of an element.

Q1   What are isotopes?   [1 mark]

Q2 Video Solution

Q2   Silicon, Si, has three stable isotopes. Si-28 has an abundance of 92.2%,
Si-29 has an abundance of 4.7% and Si-30 has an abundance of 3.1%.
Calculate silicon's relative atomic mass to 1 decimal place.   [2 marks]

Compounds

*It would be great if we only had to deal with elements. But unluckily for you, elements can mix and match to make lots of new substances called **compounds**. And this makes things a little bit more complicated...*

Atoms **Join Together** to Make **Compounds**

1) During a chemical reaction, at least one <u>new</u> substance is made.
You can usually measure a <u>change in energy</u> such as a temperature change, as well.

2) When <u>two or more elements react</u>, they form <u>compounds</u>.
<u>Compounds</u> are substances that contain atoms of different elements.

3) The atoms of each element are in <u>fixed proportions</u>
(amounts) in the compound.

4) The atoms are held together by <u>chemical bonds</u>.

5) The only way to <u>separate</u> a compound into its elements is by using a <u>chemical reaction</u>.

> There are different types of compound. For example, ionic compounds (see p.192-194) and covalent compounds (see p.196-198).

A **Formula** Shows What **Atoms** are in a **Compound**

1) Compounds can be represented by <u>formulas</u>.

2) The formulas are made up of element symbols in the <u>same proportions</u> as the elements in the compound.

3) The <u>number</u> of different element symbols tells you <u>how many</u> elements are in the compound.

- For example, carbon dioxide, CO_2, is a <u>compound</u> made from a <u>reaction</u> between carbon and oxygen.
- It contains <u>1 carbon atom</u> and <u>2 oxygen atoms</u>.

carbon + oxygen → carbon dioxide

- Here's another example: the formula of <u>sulfuric acid</u> is H_2SO_4.
- So, each molecule contains <u>2 hydrogen atoms</u>, <u>1 sulfur atom</u> and <u>4 oxygen atoms</u>.

> As an element, oxygen goes around in pairs of atoms (so it's O_2).

- There might be <u>brackets</u> in a formula, e.g. calcium hydroxide is $Ca(OH)_2$.
- The little number <u>2</u> outside the bracket means there's <u>two of everything</u> inside the brackets.
- So in $Ca(OH)_2$ there's <u>1 calcium atom</u>, <u>2 oxygen atoms</u> and <u>2 hydrogen atoms</u>.

4) Here are some examples of formulas which might come in handy:

Carbon dioxide — CO_2	Sodium chloride — $NaCl$	Calcium chloride — $CaCl_2$
Ammonia — NH_3	Carbon monoxide — CO	Sodium carbonate — Na_2CO_3
Water — H_2O	Hydrochloric acid — HCl	Sulfuric acid — H_2SO_4

The atoms in compounds are chemically joined

In your exams, you could be asked to give the name of a compound from its formula. Make sure you get lots of <u>practice</u> using the <u>periodic table</u> to find which elements the different <u>symbols</u> stand for — you'll save a lot of time if you <u>already know</u> where to look.

Q2 Video Solution

Q1 How many atoms are in one particle of Na_2CO_3? [1 mark]

Q2 A compound has the formula $Al_2(SO_4)_3$. Name the elements and state how many atoms of each element are represented in its formula. [1 mark]

Chemical Equations

Chemical equations are used to show what is happening to substances involved in **chemical reactions**. They tell us what **atoms** are involved and how the substances change during a reaction.

Chemical Reactions are Shown Using Chemical Equations

1) One way to show a chemical reaction is to write a <u>word equation</u>.

2) Word equations show the <u>names</u> of the chemicals that are reacting and being produced.

Here's an example — <u>methane</u> reacts with <u>oxygen</u> to make <u>carbon dioxide</u> and <u>water</u>:

methane + oxygen → carbon dioxide + water

The chemicals on the <u>left-hand side</u> of the equation are called the <u>reactants</u> (because they react with each other).

The chemicals on the <u>right-hand side</u> are called the <u>products</u> (because they've been produced from the reactants).

Symbol Equations Show the Atoms on Both Sides

1) Chemical <u>reactions</u> can be shown using symbol equations.

2) Symbol equations just show the <u>symbols or formulas</u> of the <u>reactants</u> and <u>products</u>.

magnesium + oxygen → magnesium oxide
$$2Mg + O_2 \rightarrow 2MgO$$

You'll have spotted that there's a '2' in front of the Mg and the MgO. The reason for this is explained on the next page...

Symbol equations give you extra information

Writing symbol equations makes it easier to see <u>how many atoms</u> are involved in a <u>reaction</u>, and where they all <u>end up</u>. It also saves quite a lot of time, so it's no wonder scientists prefer them to word equations. You'll need to make sure you're <u>comfortable using both</u> for your exams though.

Chemical Equations

Symbol Equations Need to be Balanced

1) There must always be the <u>same</u> number of atoms on <u>both sides</u> — they can't just <u>disappear</u>.

2) You <u>balance</u> the equation by putting numbers <u>in front</u> of the formulas.
Take this equation for reacting sulfuric acid with sodium hydroxide:

$$H_2SO_4 + NaOH \rightarrow Na_2SO_4 + H_2O$$

Left-hand side	Right-hand side
H = 3	H = 2
S = 1	S = 1
O = 5	O = 5
Na = 1	Na = 2

3) The <u>formulas</u> are all correct but the numbers of some atoms <u>don't match up</u> on both sides.

4) This equation needs <u>balancing</u> — see below for how to do this.

Here's How to Balance an Equation

The more you <u>practise</u>, the <u>quicker</u> you get, but all you do is this:

1) Find an element that <u>doesn't balance</u> and <u>pencil in a number</u> in front of one of the substances to try and sort it out.

2) <u>See where it gets you</u>. The equation may still <u>not</u> be balanced. Don't worry, just pencil in <u>another number</u> and see where that gets you.

3) Keep doing this until the equation is <u>completely balanced</u>.

> You can't change formulas like H_2SO_4 to H_2SO_5. You can only put numbers in front of them.

EXAMPLE

In the equation above you'll notice we're short of <u>Na atoms</u> on the LHS (Left-Hand Side).

1) The only thing you can do about that is make it <u>2NaOH</u> instead of just NaOH:

$$H_2SO_4 + 2NaOH \rightarrow Na_2SO_4 + H_2O$$

	LHS	RHS
	H = 4	H = 2
	S = 1	S = 1
	O = 6	O = 5
	Na = 2	Na = 2

2) But that now gives <u>too many</u> H atoms and O atoms on the LHS. So to balance that up you could try putting <u>2H₂O</u> on the RHS (Right-Hand Side):

$$H_2SO_4 + 2NaOH \rightarrow Na_2SO_4 + 2H_2O$$

3) And suddenly there it is — <u>everything balances</u>.

Getting good at balancing equations takes patience and practice

Remember, a number <u>in front</u> of a formula applies to the <u>entire formula</u> — so, $3CH_4$ means three lots of CH_4. The little numbers <u>within or at the end</u> of a formula only apply to the <u>atom</u> or <u>brackets</u> immediately before. So the 4 in CH_4 means there are 4 Hs, but there's just 1 C, not 4.

Q2 Video Solution

Q1   Balance the equation: $Fe + Cl_2 \rightarrow FeCl_3$ [1 mark]

Q2   Hydrogen and oxygen molecules are formed in a reaction where water splits apart.
For this reaction: a) State the word equation.
b) Give a balanced symbol equation.   [3 marks]

Warm-Up & Exam Questions

So, you reckon you know your elements from your compounds? Have a go at these questions and see how you do. If you get stuck on something, just flick back and give it another read through.

Warm-Up Questions

1) What does the mass number tell you about an atom?

2) What is the definition of an element?

3) True or false? A compound may contain atoms of only one element.

4) Name the compound that has the formula $CaCl_2$.

5) Balance this equation for the reaction of potassium (K) and water (H_2O):
$$K + H_2O \rightarrow KOH + H_2$$

Exam Questions

1 This question is about atomic structure.

1.1 Which row of **Table 1** correctly shows the relative charges of a proton and a neutron?
Tick **one** box.

Table 1

Relative charge of a proton	Relative charge of a neutron	
+1	−1	☐
+1	0	☐
0	+1	☐
−1	0	☐

[1 mark]

1.2 Where are protons and neutrons found in an atom?
Tick **one** box.

☐ spread around the atom ☐ in shells around the nucleus ☐ in the nucleus ☐ in the electrons

[1 mark]

1.3 An atom has 8 electrons. How many protons does the atom have?

[1 mark]

1.4 What is the relative mass of a proton?

[1 mark]

2 **Table 2** gives some information about sodium.

Table 2

Element	Number of protons	Mass number
sodium	11	23

2.1 How many neutrons does sodium have?

[1 mark]

2.2 Give the atomic number of sodium.

[1 mark]

2.3 What is the chemical symbol for sodium?

[1 mark]

Exam Questions

3 Methane (CH_4) reacts with oxygen (O_2) to make carbon dioxide (CO_2) and water (H_2O). *(Grade 3-4)*

3.1 Give the names of the reactants in this reaction.

[1 mark]

3.2 Give the names of the products in this reaction.

[1 mark]

3.3 Which molecule involved in the reaction is composed of only one element?

[1 mark]

3.4 Balance the symbol equation for the reaction below.

$$CH_4 + ...O_2 \rightarrow CO_2 + ...H_2O$$

[1 mark]

4 Sulfuric acid (H_2SO_4) reacts with ammonia (NH_3) to form ammonium sulfate, $(NH_4)_2SO_4$. *(Grade 4-5)*

4.1 Complete and balance the symbol equation below.

$$................. + ... \rightarrow (NH_4)_2SO_4$$

[2 marks]

4.2 How many different elements are there in this reaction?

[1 mark]

4.3 How many hydrogen atoms are there in the formula of ammonium sulfate?

[1 mark]

5 The element boron has two isotopes, boron-10 and boron-11. *(Grade 4-5)*
Details about the boron-11 isotope are shown below.

$$^{11}_{5}B$$

5.1 Complete the sentence below explaining what an isotope is. Use words from the box.

protons	shells	neutrons	nuclei	electrons

Isotopes are different forms of the same element, which have the

same number of .... but different numbers of ....

[2 marks]

5.2 How many protons are there in an atom of boron-11?

[1 mark]

5.3 Boron-10 has a mass number of 10 and a percentage abundance of 20%.
Boron-11 has a mass number of 11 and a percentage abundance of 80%.
Use the equation below to calculate the relative atomic mass of boron.

$$\text{relative atomic mass} = \frac{\text{sum of (isotope abundance} \times \text{isotope mass number)}}{\text{sum of abundances of all the isotopes}}$$

[3 marks]

Mixtures

*Mixtures in **chemistry** are just like mixtures in everyday life, lots of **separate** things all mixed together.*

Mixtures are Easily Separated — Not Like Compounds

1) Mixtures contain <u>at least two</u> different <u>elements</u> or <u>compounds</u>.

2) There <u>aren't</u> any <u>chemical bonds</u> between the different parts of a mixture.

<u>Air</u> is a <u>mixture</u> of gases, mainly nitrogen, oxygen, carbon dioxide and argon.
The gases can all be <u>separated out</u> fairly easily.

<u>Crude oil</u> is a <u>mixture</u> of different length hydrocarbon molecules (see p.248).

3) The different parts of a mixture can be <u>separated</u> out by <u>methods</u> such as:

- filtration (p.171)
- crystallisation (p.171)
- simple distillation (p.173)
- fractional distillation (p.174)
- chromatography (p.170)

4) The methods are all <u>physical methods</u>.
This means they <u>don't</u> involve any chemical reactions, and don't form any new substances.

Each Part of a Mixture Keeps Its Own Properties

1) Properties describe what a substance is <u>like</u> and how it <u>behaves</u>, such as hardness or boiling point.

2) The <u>properties</u> of a mixture are just a <u>mixture</u> of the properties of the <u>separate parts</u>.
The chemical properties of a substance <u>aren't</u> changed by it being part of a mixture.

For example, a <u>mixture</u> of <u>iron powder</u> and <u>sulfur powder</u> will show the <u>properties</u> of <u>both</u> iron and sulfur. It will contain grey magnetic bits of iron and bright yellow bits of sulfur.

Iron and sulfur, mixed together but not reacted.

Mixtures can be separated without a chemical reaction

Remember that the different parts of mixtures <u>aren't joined together chemically</u>. This means their chemical properties are <u>not changed</u> and the compounds or elements can be separated by <u>physical methods</u>.

PRACTICAL

Chromatography

Paper chromatography is a really useful technique to separate the compounds in a mixture.

You Need to Know How to Do **Paper Chromatography**

One method of separating substances in a mixture is <u>chromatography</u>.
Chromatography can be used to separate different <u>dyes</u> in an <u>ink</u>. Here's how you can do it:

filter paper

spot of ink

pencil line

1) Draw a <u>line</u> near the bottom of a sheet of <u>filter paper</u>.
(Use a <u>pencil</u> to do this — pencil marks won't dissolve in the solvent.)

> A solvent is a liquid which dissolves another substance.

2) Add a <u>spot</u> of the ink to the line.

3) Pour a small amount of <u>solvent</u> into a beaker so it forms a <u>shallow layer</u>.

4) The <u>solvent</u> used depends on what's being tested. Some compounds <u>dissolve</u> well in <u>water</u>, but sometimes other solvents, like ethanol, are needed.

5) Place the sheet in the beaker of <u>solvent</u>. Make sure the ink isn't touching the solvent — you don't want it to <u>dissolve</u> into it.

6) Place a <u>lid</u> on top of the container to stop the solvent <u>evaporating</u>.

7) The solvent <u>seeps</u> up the paper, carrying the ink with it.

 shallow solvent

8) When the <u>solvent</u> has nearly reached the <u>top</u> of the paper, take the paper out of the beaker and leave it to <u>dry</u>.

> The point the solvent has reached as it moves up the paper is the solvent front.

9) The end result is a pattern of spots called a <u>chromatogram</u>.

Chromatography **Separates** the Parts of a Mixture

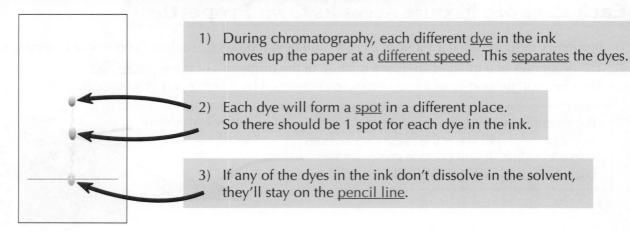

1) During chromatography, each different <u>dye</u> in the ink moves up the paper at a <u>different speed</u>. This <u>separates</u> the dyes.

2) Each dye will form a <u>spot</u> in a different place. So there should be 1 spot for each dye in the ink.

3) If any of the dyes in the ink don't dissolve in the solvent, they'll stay on the <u>pencil line</u>.

 PRACTICAL TIP

Chromatography separates the different dyes in inks

Make sure you use a <u>pencil</u> to draw your <u>baseline</u> on the sheet of paper for your <u>chromatogram</u>. If you use a <u>pen</u>, all the components of the ink in the pen will get separated, along with the substance you're analysing, which will make your results very <u>confusing</u>.

Filtration and Crystallisation PRACTICAL

*Filtration and crystallisation are **methods** of **separating mixtures**. Chemists use these methods all the time to separate **solids** from **liquids**, so it's worth making sure you know how to do them.*

Filtration Separates Insoluble Solids from Liquids

Filtration can be used to separate an insoluble solid from a liquid reaction mixture (insoluble solids can't be dissolved in the liquid). This can help make substances pure.

1) Put some filter paper in a funnel.
2) Pour the mixture into the filter paper.
3) Make sure the mixture doesn't go above the filter paper.
4) The liquid passes through the paper into the beaker.
   The solid is left behind in the filter paper.

Filter paper folded into a cone shape — the solid is left in the filter paper.

Two Ways to Separate Soluble Solids from Solutions

If a solid can be dissolved we say it's soluble. There are two methods you can use to separate a soluble salt from a solution — evaporation and crystallisation.

Evaporation

1) Slowly heat the solution in an evaporating dish.
   The solvent will evaporate.
2) Eventually, crystals will start to form.
3) Keep heating until all you have left are dry crystals.

You could also use a water bath, or an electric heater.

evaporating dish

Bunsen burner

Evaporation is a really quick way of separating a soluble salt from a solution. But, you can only use it if the salt doesn't break down when it's heated. Otherwise, you'll have to use crystallisation.

Crystallisation

1) Gently heat the solution in an evaporating dish.
   Some of the solvent will evaporate.
2) Once some of the solvent has evaporated, or when you see crystals start to form, stop heating.
   Leave the solution to cool.
3) The salt should start to form crystals.
4) Filter the crystals out of the solution.
   Leave them in a warm place to dry.

You should also use crystallisation if you want to make nice big crystals of your salt.

Salt crystallising out of solution.

Remember — soluble solids will dissolve in a solvent...

...but insoluble solids won't. The method you use to separate a solid from a solution depends on whether it's soluble or insoluble, so make sure you know the difference between the two.

PRACTICAL Filtration and Crystallisation

*Here's how you can put filtration and crystallisation to **good use**. Separating rock salt...*

Filtration and Crystallisation can be Used to Separate Rock Salt

1) Rock salt is a mixture of salt and sand. Salt dissolves in water and sand doesn't.
2) This difference in physical properties means we can separate them. Here's what to do...

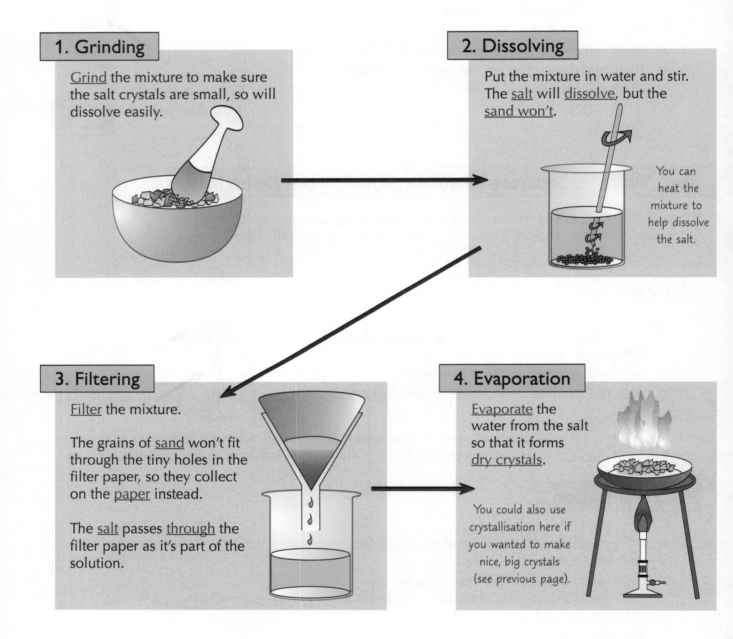

1. Grinding

Grind the mixture to make sure the salt crystals are small, so will dissolve easily.

2. Dissolving

Put the mixture in water and stir. The salt will dissolve, but the sand won't.

You can heat the mixture to help dissolve the salt.

3. Filtering

Filter the mixture.

The grains of sand won't fit through the tiny holes in the filter paper, so they collect on the paper instead.

The salt passes through the filter paper as it's part of the solution.

4. Evaporation

Evaporate the water from the salt so that it forms dry crystals.

You could also use crystallisation here if you wanted to make nice, big crystals (see previous page).

 EXAM TIP

Separating rock salt requires filtration and evaporation

You may be asked how to separate another type of mixture containing insoluble and soluble solids — just apply the same method and think through what is happening in each stage.

Simple Distillation

*Distillation is used to separate mixtures which contain **liquids**. This first page looks at simple distillation.*

Simple Distillation is Used to Separate Solutions

1) <u>Simple distillation</u> is used to separate a <u>liquid</u> from a <u>solution</u>.
2) First, the solution is <u>heated</u>.
3) The part of the solution that has the lowest boiling point <u>evaporates</u> first and turns into a <u>gas</u>.
4) The gas travels into the <u>condenser</u>.
5) In the condenser, the gas is <u>cooled</u> and <u>condenses</u> (turns back into a liquid).
6) The liquid drips out of the condenser and can be <u>collected</u>.
7) The rest of the <u>solution</u> is left behind in the flask.

You can use simple distillation to get <u>pure water</u> from <u>seawater</u>. The <u>water</u> evaporates. It is then condensed and collected. This leaves the <u>salt</u> behind in the flask.

thermometer

Make sure the water goes in at the bottom of the condenser and out at the top.

When the water is being distilled, the thermometer will read 100 °C.

Condenser — the gas turns back into a liquid here.

water out

flask

seawater

heat

water in

pure distilled water

8) Simple distillation can't be used to separate mixtures of liquids with <u>similar boiling points</u>. So, you need to use another method instead — like fractional distillation (see next page).

Only gas should leave the flask during simple distillation

Make sure you don't put <u>too much</u> liquid in the flask, or heat it <u>too vigorously</u> — some of the unseparated solution could get into the condenser, meaning your product <u>won't be pure</u>.

Topic C1 — Atomic Structure and the Periodic Table

Fractional Distillation

*Another type of distillation is **fractional distillation**. This is trickier to carry out than simple distillation, but it can separate out **mixtures of liquids** even if their **boiling points** are close together.*

Fractional Distillation is Used to Separate a Mixture of Liquids

1) If you've got a <u>mixture of liquids</u> you can separate it using <u>fractional distillation</u>.

2) You put your <u>mixture</u> in a flask and stick a <u>fractionating column</u> on top, as shown below. Then you heat it.

3) The <u>different liquids</u> will have <u>different boiling points</u>.

4) So, they will evaporate at <u>different temperatures</u>.

5) The substance with the <u>lowest boiling point</u> evaporates first.

6) When the temperature on the thermometer matches the boiling point of this substance, it will reach the <u>top</u> of the column.

7) The substance will then enter the condenser, where it cools and <u>condenses</u>.

8) You can <u>collect</u> the liquid as it drips out of the condenser.

9) When the first liquid has been collected, you <u>raise</u> the <u>temperature</u> until the <u>next one</u> reaches the top.

> The diagram shows an experiment that can be used to show how fractional distillation of <u>crude oil</u> at a refinery works (see p.249).

For safety reasons this experiment uses a substitute for real crude oil.

thermometer

water out

coolest bit of column

condenser

fractionating column filled with glass rods

water in

hottest bit of column

crude oil substitute

fractions collected at lower temperatures

heat

Fractional distillation is used in the lab and industry

You've made it to the end of the pages on <u>separation techniques</u>, so make sure you understand what each of the methods can be used to separate and the <u>apparatus</u> set-up for each technique.

Q1   Propan-1-ol, methanol and ethanol have boiling points of 97 °C, 65 °C and 78 °C respectively. A student uses fractional distillation to separate a mixture of these compounds. State which liquid will be collected in the second fraction and explain why.   [2 marks]

Q1 Video Solution

Warm-Up & Exam Questions

So the last few pages have all been about mixtures and how to separate them. Here are some questions to get stuck into and make sure you know your filtration from your distillation...

Warm-Up Questions

1) True or False? The chemical properties of a substance are changed by it being part of a mixture.
2) Give the name of a method to separate a soluble solid from a solution.
3) Which part of the fractionating column is coolest during fractional distillation?

Exam Questions

1   A scientist is using paper chromatography to compare two different compounds.
He draws a pencil line near the bottom of a sheet of filter paper and adds a spot of
each of the different compounds to the line, leaving gaps between each spot.

1.1   Describe the next thing that the scientist should do with the filter paper.

[1 mark]

1.2   Why is pencil used to draw the line on the filter paper?

[1 mark]

2   A gardener uses a mixture of insoluble sharp sand and
soluble ammonium sulfate fertiliser to treat his lawn.

A student plans to use the method below to separate the
gardener's mixture into sharp sand and ammonium sulfate.

1.   Mix the lawn sand with water and stir.
2.   Filter the mixture using filter paper.
3.   Pour the remaining solution into an evaporating dish and slowly heat it.

Explain the purpose of **each** of the steps in the student's method.

[3 marks]

3   Simple distillation can be used to separate mixtures of
liquids. **Table 1** gives the boiling points of three liquids.

Figure 1

<table>
<tr><td colspan="2" align="center">Table 1</td></tr>
<tr><th>Liquid</th><th>Boiling point (°C)</th></tr>
<tr><td>Methanoic acid</td><td>101</td></tr>
<tr><td>Propanone</td><td>56</td></tr>
<tr><td>Water</td><td>100</td></tr>
</table>

3.1   **Figure 1** shows the apparatus needed for simple distillation.
Describe how the apparatus shown in **Figure 1** could be
used to separate propanone from a solution of propanone
and water. Propanone is highly flammable.
Include any relevant safety precautions in your answer.

[6 marks]

3.2   Simple distillation can **not** be used to separate water from a solution of water and methanoic acid.
Give a technique that **would** be suitable for separating water and methanoic acid.

[1 mark]

The History of the Atom

*You may have thought you were done with the **atom** after page 161. Unfortunately, you don't get away that easily. The next couple of pages are all about how **scientists** came to understand the atom as we do today.*

Ideas About What Atoms Look Like Have Changed Over Time

1) Scientists used to think that atoms were <u>solid spheres</u>.

2) They then found atoms contain even smaller, negatively charged particles — <u>electrons</u>.

3) This led to a model called the '<u>plum pudding model</u>' being created.

4) The plum pudding model showed the atom as a <u>ball</u> of <u>positive charge</u> with <u>electrons scattered</u> in this ball.

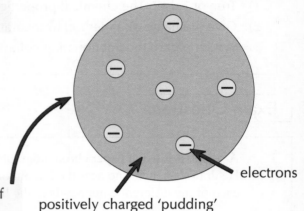

electrons

positively charged 'pudding'

Experiments Showed that the Plum Pudding Model Was Wrong

1) Later, scientists carried out <u>alpha particle scattering experiments</u>. They fired positively charged <u>alpha particles</u> at a very thin sheet of gold.

2) From the plum pudding model, they <u>expected</u> most of the particles to <u>go straight through</u> the sheet. They predicted that a few particles would <u>change direction</u> by a <u>small</u> amount.

3) But instead, some particles changed direction <u>more than expected</u>. A small number even went <u>backwards</u>.

4) This meant the plum pudding model <u>couldn't</u> be right.

5) So, scientists came up with the <u>nuclear model</u> of the atom:

- There's a tiny, positively charged <u>nucleus</u> at the centre of the atom.
- Most of the <u>mass</u> is in the nucleus.
- The nucleus is surrounded by 'cloud' of negative <u>electrons</u>.
- Most of the atom is <u>empty space</u>.

A few particles go backwards.

Most of the particles pass through empty space, but a few change direction.

Topic C1 — Atomic Structure and the Periodic Table

The History of the Atom

Bohr's **Nuclear Model** Explains a Lot

1) <u>Niels Bohr</u> changed the nuclear model of the atom.
   (See previous page for more information on the nuclear model).

2) He suggested that the electrons <u>orbit</u> (go around) the nucleus in <u>shells</u> (levels).

3) Each shell is a <u>fixed distance</u> from the nucleus.

4) Bohr's theory was supported by many <u>experiments</u>.
   Experiments later showed that Bohr's theory was correct.

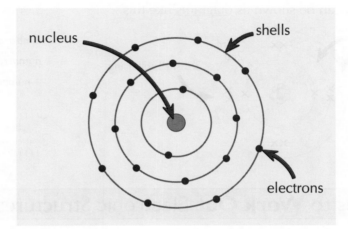

Later Experiments Found **Protons** and **Neutrons**

1) More experiments by scientists showed that the nucleus can be <u>divided</u> into smaller particles.
   Each particle has the <u>same positive charge</u>. These particles were named <u>protons</u>.

2) Experiments by <u>James Chadwick</u> showed that the nucleus also contained <u>neutral particles</u> — <u>neutrons</u>.
   This happened about 20 years after scientists agreed that atoms have nuclei.

3) This led to a model of the atom which was <u>pretty close</u> to the one we have today (see page 161).

Our understanding of what an atom looks like has changed

The history of the atom is a fine example of the scientific method. It shows how our understanding of science can go through <u>many stages</u>, as scientists built upon other people's work with <u>new evidence</u>. And new evidence allows <u>new predictions</u> to be made, so the progress <u>continues</u>.

Electronic Structure

Electrons don't just float around the nucleus randomly. They move in areas called **shells**.

Electron Shell **Rules**:

1) Electrons always move in <u>shells</u> (sometimes called <u>energy levels</u>).

2) The <u>inner</u> shells are <u>always filled up first</u>. These are the ones closest to the nucleus.

3) Only a <u>certain number</u> of electrons are allowed in each shell:

> **1st shell: 2   2nd shell: 8   3rd shell: 8**

4) Atoms are a lot <u>more stable</u> when they have <u>full electron shells</u>.

5) In most atoms, the <u>outer shell</u> is <u>not full</u>. These atoms will <u>react</u> to fill it.

Electron structures can be shown as <u>diagrams</u> like this...

The first two shells are full.
3rd
2nd
1st
3rd shell still filling

...or as <u>numbers</u> like this: 2, 8, 1

number of electrons in 1st shell
number of electrons in 2nd shell
number of electrons in 3rd shell

Both of these show the electron structure of sodium.

Follow the Rules to **Work Out** Electronic Structures

You can easily work out the <u>electronic structures</u> for the first <u>20</u> elements of the periodic table (things get a bit more complicated after that).

EXAMPLE   **What is the electronic structure of magnesium?**

1) From the periodic table, you can see that magnesium's <u>atomic number</u> is 12. This means it has 12 protons. So it must have 12 electrons.

2) Follow the 'Electron Shell Rules' above. The first shell can only take <u>2 electrons</u>.   2...

3) The second shell can take <u>up to 8 electrons</u>.   2, 8...

4) So far we have a total of 10 electrons (2 + 8). So the third shell must also be <u>partly filled</u> with 2 electrons. This makes 12 electrons in total (2 + 8 + 2).

So the electronic structure for magnesium must be 2, 8, 2.

Here are some more examples of electronic structures:

H Hydrogen

1
Atomic no. = 1

He Helium

2
Atomic no. = 2

Li Lithium

2,1
Atomic no. = 3

C Carbon

2,4
Atomic no. = 6

Ne Neon

2,8
Atomic no. = 10

Ca Calcium

2,8,8,2
Atomic no. = 20

The first electron shell can only hold two electrons

Q1   Describe the order in which electron shells are filled up.   [1 mark]

Q2   Give the electronic structure of argon (atomic number = 18).   [1 mark]

Q2 Video Solution

Topic C1 — Atomic Structure and the Periodic Table

Development of the Periodic Table

We haven't always known as much about chemistry as we do now.
*Early chemists looked at **patterns** in the elements' properties to help them understand chemistry better.*

In the **Early 1800s** Elements Were **Arranged** By **Atomic Weight**

1) Until quite recently, scientists hadn't discovered protons, neutrons or electrons. So they had <u>no idea</u> of <u>atomic number</u>.

2) So scientists used <u>atomic weight</u> to arrange the elements into a <u>periodic table</u>.

3) These early periodic tables were <u>not complete</u>.

4) This is because <u>not all</u> of the elements had been <u>found</u> yet.

5) And putting the elements in order of atomic weight meant that some elements were also put in the <u>wrong group</u> (column).

Dmitri Mendeleev Left Gaps and **Predicted** New Elements

1) In <u>1869</u>, a scientist called <u>Mendeleev</u> took all of the known elements and arranged them into a table.

<u>Mendeleev's Table of the Elements</u>

```
H
Li Be                              B  C  N  O  F
Na Mg                              Al Si P  S  Cl
K  Ca *  Ti V  Cr Mn Fe Co Ni Cu Zn *  *  As Se Br
Rb Sr Y  Zr Nb Mo *  Ru Rh Pd Ag Cd In Sn Sb Te I
Cs Ba *  *  Ta W  *  Os Ir Pt Au Hg Tl Pb Bi
```

2) He ordered them <u>mainly</u> by their <u>atomic weight</u>.

3) Sometimes he <u>switched</u> their positions or left <u>gaps</u> in the table.

4) This was so he could make sure that elements with <u>similar properties</u> stayed in the <u>same groups</u>.

5) Some of the <u>gaps</u> left space for elements that hadn't been found yet. Mendeleev used the position of the gaps to <u>predict the properties</u> of these elements.

6) <u>New elements</u> have been found since which <u>fit</u> into these gaps. This shows that Mendeleev's ideas were right.

- <u>Isotopes</u> were discovered a while after Mendeleev made his Table of Elements.
- Isotopes have different masses but share the same properties. This means they have the <u>same position</u> on the periodic table.
- So, Mendeleev was <u>right</u> to swap some elements around to keep properties together — even if it meant they weren't in order of atomic weight.

By leaving gaps in the table Mendeleev had the right idea

Make sure you can <u>describe</u> what Mendeleev did to <u>fix the problems</u> with early periodic tables.

The Modern Periodic Table

*Mendeleev got pretty close to producing something that you might **recognise** as a periodic table. The big breakthrough came when the **structure** of the **atom** was understood a bit better.*

The Periodic Table Helps you to See Patterns in Properties

1) There are about 100 elements.

2) In the periodic table the elements are laid out in order of increasing atomic number.

3) There are repeating (periodic) patterns in the properties of the elements.
   These periodic properties give the periodic table its name.

4) Metals are found to the left of the periodic table and non-metals are found to the right.

alkali metals
(see pages 183-184)

halogens
(see pages 185-186)

noble gases
(see page 187)

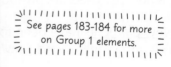 (pink line separates metals and non-metals)

5) Elements with similar properties are arranged to form columns. These columns are called groups.

6) The group number of an element is the same as the number of outer shell electrons it has.
   (Except for Group 0 — helium has two electrons in its outer shell and the rest have eight.)

7) So, all the elements in a group have the same number of electrons in their outer shell.
   This means that elements in a group react in similar ways.

> • The Group 1 elements are Li, Na, K, Rb, Cs and Fr.
> • They all have one electron in their outer shells.
> • They're all metals and they react in a similar way.

See pages 183-184 for more on Group 1 elements.

8) If you know the properties of one element, you can predict properties of other elements in that group.

9) You can also make predictions about trends in reactivity.
   E.g. in Group 1, the elements react more violently as you go down the group.

10) The rows in the periodic table are called periods. Each new period represents another shell of electrons.

The periodic table really helps with understanding chemistry

The periodic table is organised into groups and periods. This lets you see patterns in reactivity and properties. And this means you can make predictions on how reactions will occur.

Warm-Up & Exam Questions

The last few pages have been tough with lots of information to learn. Luckily, here are some questions to get your head around to help you test your understanding.

Warm-Up Questions

1) Describe the 'plum pudding' model of the atom.
2) How many electrons can be held in the following:
   a) the first shell of an atom?
   b) the second shell of an atom?
3) Why did Mendeleev leave gaps in his table of the elements?

Exam Questions

1 The periodic table contains all the known elements arranged in order. *(Grade 3-4)*

1.1 How were elements generally ordered in early periodic tables?
Tick **one** box.

☐ alphabetically   ☐ by atomic number   ☐ by abundance   ☐ by atomic weight

[1 mark]

1.2 How are the elements arranged in the modern periodic table?
Tick **one** box.

☐ alphabetically   ☐ by atomic number   ☐ by abundance   ☐ by atomic weight

[1 mark]

1.3 Explain why elements in the same group of the periodic table have similar chemical properties.

[1 mark]

2 The atomic number of sulfur is 16. *(Grade 4-5)*

2.1 Complete **Figure 1** to show the electronic structure of sulfur.

Figure 1

[1 mark]

2.2 Which group of the periodic table is sulfur in?

[1 mark]

2.3 Name another element that has the same number of electrons in its outer shell as sulfur.

[1 mark]

2.4 How many electrons does sulfur need to gain to have a full outer shell?

[1 mark]

Topic C1 — Atomic Structure and the Periodic Table

Metals and Non-Metals

*Metals are used for all sorts of things so they're **really important** in modern life.*

Most Elements are Metals

1) Metals are elements which can <u>form positive ions</u> when they react.
2) They're towards the <u>bottom</u> and to the <u>left</u> of the periodic table.
3) <u>Most elements</u> in the periodic table are metals.
4) <u>Non-metals</u> are at the far <u>right</u> and <u>top</u> of the periodic table.
5) Non-metals <u>don't</u> usually <u>form positive ions</u> when they react.

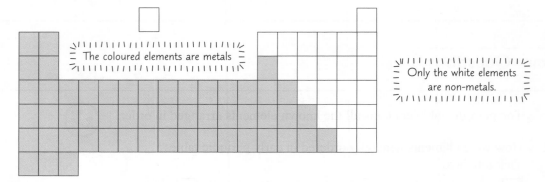

The coloured elements are metals

Only the white elements are non-metals.

The **Electronic Structure** of Atoms Affects How They Will React

1) Atoms are more <u>stable</u> with a full outer shell. So, they react by <u>losing</u>, <u>gaining</u> or <u>sharing</u> electrons.
2) Metal elements are to the <u>left</u> and towards the <u>bottom</u> of the periodic table so they lose electrons quite easily. When this happens, they <u>form positive ions</u>, with a full outer shell.
3) <u>Non-metals</u> are to the right of the periodic table or towards the top, so it's easier for them to <u>share</u> or <u>gain</u> electrons to get a full outer shell.

Metals and **Non-Metals** Have **Different Physical Properties**

1) All metals have <u>similar</u> physical properties.

   - They're <u>strong</u> (hard to break), but can be <u>bent</u> or <u>hammered</u> into different shapes (malleable).
   - They're great at <u>conducting heat</u> and <u>electricity</u>.
   - They have high <u>boiling and melting points</u>.

2) Non-metals <u>don't</u> tend to show the same properties as metals.

   - They tend to be <u>dull looking</u>.
   - They're more <u>brittle</u>. This means they'll <u>break</u> more easily if you try to <u>bend</u> them.
   - They're <u>not always solids</u> at room temperature.
   - They <u>don't</u> usually <u>conduct electricity</u>.
   - They often have a <u>lower density</u>.

Metals have quite different properties from non-metals

And you'll need to make sure you can remember them. Try <u>covering up</u> the lists of properties of metals and non-metals above and <u>writing down</u> as many as you can from memory.

Group 1 Elements

*Group 1 elements are known as the **alkali metals**. As metals go, they're pretty **reactive**.*

The **Group 1** Elements are **Reactive, Soft** Metals

1) The alkali metals are lithium, sodium, potassium, rubidium, caesium and francium.

2) They all have <u>one electron</u> in their outer shell.
   This makes them <u>very reactive</u>. It also gives them <u>similar properties</u>.

3) The alkali metals are all <u>soft</u>.

4) They all have <u>low density</u> (they're quite <u>light</u>).

There are **Patterns** in the **Properties** of Group 1 Metals

1) As you go down Group 1, the properties of the alkali metals change.
   For example:

- <u>Reactivity increases</u> — the outer electron is
  <u>more easily lost</u> as it gets <u>further</u> from the nucleus.
  This is because it's <u>less attracted</u> to the nucleus.

- <u>Melting</u> and <u>boiling</u> points get lower.

- <u>Relative atomic mass</u> goes up.

Group 1	Group 2
7 **Li** Lithium 3	
23 **Na** Sodium 11	
39 **K** Potassium 19	
85.5 **Rb** Rubidium 37	
133 **Cs** Caesium 55	
223 **Fr** Francium 87	

2) These patterns in the properties are called <u>trends</u>.

The properties of Group 1 metals change as you go down the group

In the exam you might be given a <u>trend</u> and then asked to <u>predict properties</u> of other Group 1 metals.
For example, the <u>reactivity</u> of Group 1 metals <u>increases</u> as you go <u>down the group</u>,
so you know that potassium will react more vigorously than sodium.

Group 1 Elements

*You met **Group 1 metals** on the previous page, so now it's time to learn about some of their **reactions**...*

Alkali Metals Form **Ionic Compounds** with **Non-Metals**

The Group 1 elements <u>easily</u> lose their one outer electron to form a full outer shell.
So they form <u>1+ ions</u> easily.

Reaction With **Water**

1) The reactions are <u>vigorous</u> and produce a <u>metal hydroxide</u> and <u>hydrogen gas</u>:

> **alkali metal + water → metal hydroxide + hydrogen**

For example:

> **sodium + water → sodium hydroxide + hydrogen**
> $$2Na_{(s)} + 2H_2O_{(l)} \rightarrow 2NaOH_{(aq)} + H_{2(g)}$$

2) The <u>metal hydroxides</u> are compounds that <u>dissolve</u> in the <u>water</u>.

The little letters in brackets after each substance in the reaction show what state the substance is in — see p.207.

3) The <u>more reactive</u> (lower down in the group) an alkali metal is, the more <u>violent</u> the reaction.
4) Lithium, sodium and potassium <u>float</u> and <u>move</u> around the surface, <u>fizzing</u> furiously.
5) The reaction with potassium gives out enough energy to <u>ignite</u> the hydrogen (set it on fire).

Reaction With **Chlorine**

1) Group 1 metals react <u>vigorously</u> when heated in <u>chlorine gas</u> to form <u>white salts</u> called <u>metal chlorides</u>.

> **alkali metal + chlorine → metal chloride**

For example:

> **sodium + chlorine → sodium chloride**
> $$2Na_{(s)} + Cl_{2(g)} \rightarrow 2NaCl_{(s)}$$

2) As you go down the group, the reaction gets <u>more vigorous</u>.

Reaction With **Oxygen**

1) Group 1 metals can react with <u>oxygen</u> to form a <u>metal oxide</u>.
2) Different types of <u>oxide</u> will form depending on the Group 1 metal.
3) Group 1 metals are <u>shiny</u> but when they react with oxygen in the air they turn a <u>dull grey</u> (they <u>tarnish</u>). This is because a layer of <u>metal oxide</u> is formed on the surface.

Alkali metals all react in a similar way...

...which is handy for you, because it means you don't need to learn the <u>reaction products</u> for each metal separately. You just need to remember the <u>types of product</u> that are formed during each reaction, then switch 'metal' for whichever <u>Group 1 element</u> you're interested in.

Q1 Video Solution

Q1   Write a word equation for the reaction between lithium and water.   [1 mark]

Group 7 Elements

*The **Group 7** elements are known as the halogens. Like the **alkali metals**, **halogens** also show trends down the group. However, these trends are a bit different...*

The **Halogens** Show Patterns in their **Properties**

1) The halogens are fluorine, chlorine, bromine, iodine and astatine.

2) As elements, the halogens form molecules that contain two atoms. For example, chlorine (Cl_2) is a fairly reactive, poisonous green gas.

3) As you go down Group 7, the halogens:

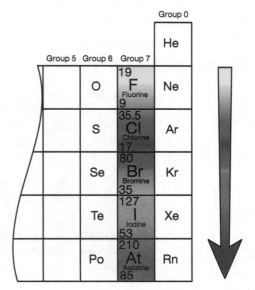

- become less reactive — it's harder to gain an extra electron as the outer shell is further from the nucleus.

- have higher melting and boiling points.

- have higher relative atomic masses.

You can use these trends to predict properties of halogens. E.g. iodine will have a higher boiling point than chlorine as it's further down the group.

4) All the Group 7 elements react in similar ways. This is because they all have seven electrons in their outer shell.

Halogens can Form **Molecular Compounds**

1) When halogen atoms react with other non-metals, they share electrons and form covalent bonds (see page 196). This is so they can get a full outer shell.

2) These reactions form compounds with simple molecular structures (see p.197-198).

Bonding in hydrogen chloride, HCl.

Halogens all exist as molecules with two atoms

Just like alkali metals, you may be asked to predict the properties of a halogen from a given trend down the group. Make sure you understand why the halogens' electronic structures mean they react in similar ways.

Group 7 Elements

*You also need to know all about how the halogens **react** with **metals** and **halide salts**, so get reading this page...*

Halogens Form **Ionic Bonds** with **Metals**

1) The halogens form <u>1– ions</u> called <u>halides</u>:

- <u>fluoride</u>, F^-
- <u>bromide</u>, Br^-
- <u>chloride</u>, Cl^-
- <u>iodide</u>, I^-

2) Halides form when halogens bond with <u>metals</u>.
For example Na^+Cl^- or $Ca^{2+}Br_2^-$.

3) The compounds (halide salts) that form have <u>ionic structures</u>.

4) The diagram shows the bonding in sodium chloride, NaCl.

<u>Sodium</u> loses an electron and forms a +1 ion and <u>chlorine</u> gains an electron forming a –1 ion.

More Reactive Halogens **Displace Less Reactive** Halogens

1) A reaction can take place between a <u>halogen</u> and the <u>halide salt</u> of a <u>less reactive</u> halogen.

2) These are called <u>displacement reactions</u>.

3) When this happens, the <u>less reactive</u> halogen changes from a halide (1– ion) to a <u>halogen</u>.
The <u>more reactive</u> halogen changes from a halogen into a <u>halide ion</u> and becomes part of the <u>salt</u>.

For example, chlorine is <u>more reactive</u> than bromine.
So if you add <u>chlorine</u> to a solution containing a <u>bromide salt</u>, bromine will be <u>displaced</u>.

$$Cl_{2(g)} + 2KBr_{(aq)} \rightarrow Br_{2(aq)} + 2KCl_{(aq)}$$
Pale green · · · · · · · · · · · · · · Orange

Halogens higher up the group will displace the ones lower down

The halogens get <u>less reactive</u> as you go down the group. So a halogen will only be able to displace another halogen if it's <u>higher up</u> in Group 7. If it's lower down Group 7, <u>no reaction</u> will happen.

Q1 Give the balanced symbol equation for the displacement reaction between bromine and sodium iodide.

[1 mark]

Topic C1 — Atomic Structure and the Periodic Table

Group 0 Elements

*The **noble gases don't react** with very much and you can't even see them — makes them a bit **dull** really.*

Group 0 Elements are All **Unreactive, Colourless Gases**

1) Group 0 elements are called the noble gases.
   They include the elements helium, neon and argon (plus a few others).

2) All elements in Group 0 are colourless gases at room temperature.

3) They all have eight outer shell electrons,
   apart from helium which has two.
   This means they have a stable full outer shell.

   Helium only has electrons in the first shell, which only needs 2 to be filled.

4) This stability makes them very unreactive (inert).
   This means they don't form molecules easily.
   So the elements are single atoms.

5) Because noble gases are unreactive, some reactions are carried
   out in an atmosphere that only contains a noble gas, instead of air.

6) This is done if the reactants could react with things in the air (e.g. oxygen or water) instead of taking
   part in the reaction you're trying to do. It's also done if the products react with things in the air.

There are **Patterns** in the **Properties** of the Noble Gases

1) As you go down Group 0, the relative atomic masses of the elements increase.

2) This means that as you go down the group,
   the elements have more electrons.

3) More electrons means stronger forces between atoms.

4) The stronger the forces, the higher the boiling point.
   So as you go down Group 0, the boiling points increase.

5) If you're given the boiling point of one noble gas you
   can predict the boiling point for another one.
   So make sure you know the pattern.

Noble Gas
helium
neon
argon
krypton
xenon
radon

Increasing boiling point

EXAMPLE   **Neon is a gas at 25 °C. Predict what state helium is at this temperature.**

Helium has a lower boiling point than neon as it is further up the group.

So, helium must also be a gas at 25 °C.

EXAMPLE   **Radon has a boiling point of –62 °C and krypton has a
boiling point of –153 °C. Predict the boiling point of xenon.**

Xenon comes in between radon and krypton in the group.
So, you can predict that its boiling point would be between their boiling points.

E.g. xenon has a boiling point of –100 °C.

The actual boiling point of xenon is –108 °C — which is between –62 °C and –153 °C. Just as predicted.

Just like other groups of elements, the noble gases follow patterns...

Although they're unreactive and hard to see, they're actually pretty useful. It took a while to discover them,
but we now know all about them, including the trend in their boiling points.

Warm-Up & Exam Questions

These questions are all about the groups of the periodic table that you need to know about. Treat the exam questions like the real thing — don't look back through the book until you've finished.

Warm-Up Questions

1) Do metals form positive or negative ions?
2) Give two physical properties of most metals.
3) What is the product formed when lithium reacts with chlorine?
4) Do halide ions have a positive or a negative charge?
5) Which group of the periodic table are the noble gases in?

Exam Questions

1   **Table 1** shows some of the physical properties of four of the halogens.

Table 1

Halogen	Physical state at room temperature
Fluorine	gas
Chlorine	gas
Bromine	liquid
Iodine	solid

1.1   Which halogen in **Table 1** is the most reactive?

[1 mark]

1.2   Which halogen in **Table 1** has the highest melting point?

[1 mark]

2   **Figure 1** shows the periodic table.

Figure 1

2.1   Element **X** is found in the first column of the periodic table.
What name is given to the elements found in the first column of the periodic table?
Tick **one** box.

☐ halogens   ☐ alkali metals   ☐ noble gases   ☐ non-metals

[1 mark]

2.2   Element **Y** does not conduct electricity.
Predict whether element **Y** will be found to the left or the right of line **A** in **Figure 1**.
Explain your answer.

[2 marks]

Topic C1 — Atomic Structure and the Periodic Table

Exam Questions

3   Group 1 elements include lithium, sodium and potassium.

3.1   Explain why the Group 1 elements react vigorously with water.

[1 mark]

3.2   The equation for the reaction of potassium with water is:

$$2K + 2H_2O \rightarrow 2KOH + H_2$$

Name the **two** products of the reaction.

[2 marks]

3.3   Potassium is more reactive than lithium and sodium.
Why do the Group 1 elements become more reactive as you go down Group 1?
Tick **one** box.

☐   The outer electron is closer to the nucleus and so more attracted to the nucleus.

☐   The outer electron is closer to the nucleus and so less attracted to the nucleus.

☐   The outer electron is further from the nucleus and so less attracted to the nucleus.

☐   The outer electron is further from the nucleus and so more attracted to the nucleus.

[1 mark]

4   Chlorine is a Group 7 element.
Chlorine's electron arrangement is shown in **Figure 2**.

Figure 2

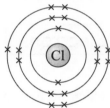

4.1   Chlorine is very reactive and forms compounds with metals.
What type of bonds form between chlorine and metals?

[1 mark]

When chlorine is bubbled through potassium iodide solution a reaction occurs.
The equation below shows the reaction.

$$Cl_{2(g)} + 2KI_{(aq)} \rightarrow I_{2(aq)} + 2KCl_{(aq)}$$

4.2   Identify the type of reaction that occurs.

[1 mark]

4.3   What does the reaction show about the relative reactivities of Cl_2 and I_2? Give a reason for your answer.

[2 marks]

4.4   None of the elements in Group 0 will react with potassium iodide or potassium bromide.
Using your knowledge of the electronic structure of the Group 0 elements,
explain why no reaction occurs.

[1 mark]

Ions

*Ions crop up all over the place in chemistry. You need to know **what** they are and **how** they form. Luckily for you, this page has got that covered. So crack on with it.*

Ions are Made When **Electrons** are Transferred

1) <u>Ions</u> are <u>charged</u> particles — for example Cl^- or Mg^{2+}.

> Ions will always have a '+' or '−' sign after the formula. A '+' tells you the ion is positive. A '−' sign tells you the ion is negative.

2) Ions are formed when atoms <u>gain</u> or <u>lose</u> electrons.

3) They do this to get a <u>full outer shell</u> — like a noble gas. This is because a full outer shell is very <u>stable</u>.

> The noble gases are in Group O of the periodic table.

4) <u>Metal</u> atoms <u>lose</u> electrons from their <u>outer shell</u> to form <u>positive ions</u>.

5) <u>Non-metal</u> atoms <u>gain</u> electrons into their <u>outer shell</u> to form <u>negative ions</u>.

6) The <u>number</u> of electrons lost or gained is the same as the <u>charge</u> on the ion. For <u>example</u>:

> If 2 electrons are <u>lost</u>, the particle now has two more protons than electrons. So the charge is <u>2+</u>.
>
> If 3 electrons are <u>gained</u>, the particle now has three more electrons than protons. So the charge is <u>3−</u>.

Ionic Bonding — **Transfer** of Electrons

1) <u>Metals</u> and <u>non-metals</u> can react together.
2) When this happens, the <u>metal</u> atoms <u>lose</u> electrons to form <u>positively charged ions</u>.
3) The <u>non-metal atoms gain</u> these <u>electrons</u> to form <u>negatively charged ions</u>.
4) These oppositely charged ions are <u>strongly attracted</u> to one another by <u>electrostatic forces</u>.
5) This attraction is called an <u>ionic bond</u>. It holds the ions together to make an <u>ionic compound</u>.

Metal atoms will form positively charged ions

Some atoms <u>gain</u> electrons and some atoms <u>lose</u> electrons. An ionic bond is just the <u>attraction</u> between the electrostatic charges of the newly formed ions.

Q1 Explain why simple ions often have noble gas electronic structures. [2 marks]

Q1 Video Solution

Ions

You need to be able to predict the ions that the atoms in Groups 1, 2, 6 and 7 will form.
*Don't worry, though — the **periodic table** is here to help you.*

You can **Work Out** What Ions are Formed by Groups **1, 2, 6 and 7**

1) <u>Group 1 and 2 elements</u> are <u>metals</u>. They <u>lose</u> electrons to form <u>positive ions</u>.

2) <u>Group 6 and 7 elements</u> are <u>non-metals</u>. They <u>gain</u> electrons to form <u>negative ions</u>.

3) Elements in the same <u>group</u> all have the same number of <u>outer electrons</u>.
   So they have to <u>lose or gain</u> the same number to get a full outer shell.
   And this means that they form ions with the <u>same charges</u>.

4) You <u>don't</u> have to <u>remember</u> what ions <u>most elements</u> form. You can just look at the periodic table.

Group 1 elements form ions by <u>losing</u> one electron. They form <u>1+</u> ions.

Group 2 elements form ions by <u>losing</u> two electrons. They form <u>2+</u> ions.

Group 6 elements form ions by <u>gaining</u> two electrons. They form <u>2–</u> ions.

Group 7 elements form ions by <u>gaining</u> one electron. They form <u>1–</u> ions.

Noble gases

A sodium atom (Na) is in <u>Group 1</u> so it <u>loses</u> 1 electron to form a sodium ion (Na$^+$).

A '+' by itself means the ion has a 1+ charge. A '–' by itself means the ion has a 1– charge.

A magnesium atom (Mg) is in <u>Group 2</u> so it <u>loses</u> 2 electrons to form a magnesium ion (Mg^{2+}).

A chlorine atom (Cl) is in <u>Group 7</u> so it <u>gains</u> 1 electron to form a chloride ion (Cl$^-$).

An oxygen atom (O) is in <u>Group 6</u> so it <u>gains</u> 2 electrons to form an oxide ion (O^{2-}).

Ionic Bonding

Dot and Cross Diagrams Show How Ionic Compounds are Formed

1) <u>Dot and cross diagrams</u> show how electrons are <u>arranged</u> in an atom or ion.

2) Each electron is represented by a <u>dot</u> or a <u>cross</u>.

3) So these diagrams can show which <u>atom</u> the electrons in an <u>ion</u> originally came from.

Sodium Chloride (NaCl)

The <u>sodium</u> (Na) atom loses its outer electron. It forms an <u>Na^+</u> ion.

The <u>chlorine</u> (Cl) atom gains the electron.

It forms a <u>Cl^-</u> (<u>chloride</u>) ion.

Here, the dots represent the Na electrons and the crosses represent the Cl electrons.

Na
sodium atom

Cl
chlorine atom

Na^+
sodium ion

Cl^-
chloride ion

Magnesium Oxide (MgO)

The <u>magnesium</u> (Mg) atom loses its <u>two</u> outer electrons.
It forms an <u>Mg^{2+}</u> ion.

The <u>oxygen</u> (O) atom gains the electrons.
It forms an <u>O^{2-}</u> (<u>oxide</u>) ion.

Mg
magnesium atom

O
oxygen atom

Mg^{2+}
magnesium ion

O^{2-}
oxygen ion

We've only shown the outer shells of electrons in these two dot and cross diagrams. It makes it easier to see what's going on.

Magnesium Chloride (MgCl₂)

The <u>magnesium</u> (Mg) atom loses its <u>two</u> outer electrons. It forms an <u>Mg^{2+}</u> ion.
The two <u>chlorine</u> (Cl) atoms gain <u>one electron each</u>. They form <u>two Cl^-</u> (chloride) ions.

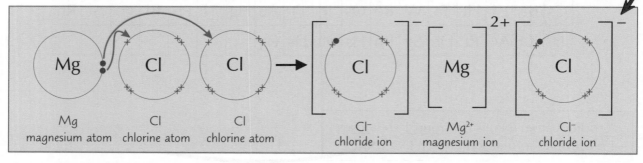

Mg
magnesium atom

Cl
chlorine atom

Cl
chlorine atom

Cl^-
chloride ion

Mg^{2+}
magnesium ion

Cl^-
chloride ion

4) Dot and cross diagrams are useful for showing <u>how</u> ionic compounds are formed.

5) But they <u>don't</u> show the <u>structure</u> of the compound, the <u>size</u> of the ions or how they're <u>arranged</u>.

6) They also make it look like the electrons that are <u>crosses</u> might be <u>different</u> from the electrons that are <u>dots</u>. Really, they're all the same.

Dot and cross diagrams show the arrangement of electrons

Electrons can't just disappear, so there should always be the <u>same number</u> on each side of the dot and cross diagram. If you're asked to draw one in the exam, remember to <u>count and check</u>.

Q2 Video
Solution

Q1 Describe what is represented on a dot and cross diagram by an arrow pointing from an electron shell of one atom to an electron shell of another atom.
[1 mark]

Q2 Draw a dot and cross diagram to show how potassium (a Group 1 metal) and bromine (a Group 7 non-metal) form potassium bromide (KBr).
[3 marks]

Ionic Compounds

Ionic compounds are just compounds that **only** contain **ionic bonds**. One of the main ionic compounds you need to know about is **sodium chloride**. And that's just **salt**. Nothing scary about that.

Ionic Compounds Have A Giant Ionic Lattice Structure

1) In ionic compounds, the ions are arranged in a <u>pattern</u>. This is called a <u>giant ionic lattice</u>.

2) There are strong <u>electrostatic forces of attraction</u> between <u>oppositely charged</u> ions.

3) These forces are called <u>ionic bonds</u> and they act in <u>all directions</u>.

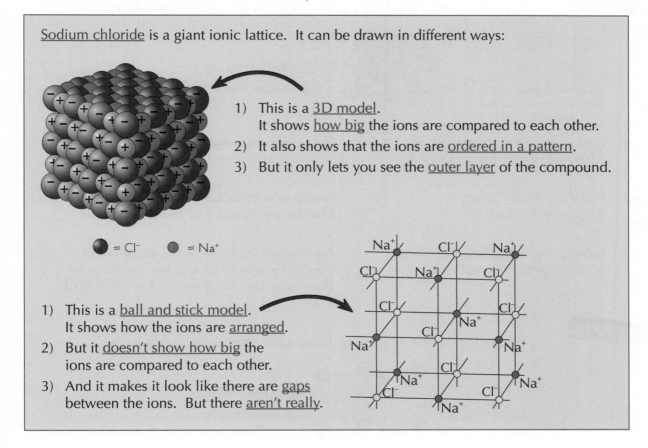

<u>Sodium chloride</u> is a giant ionic lattice. It can be drawn in different ways:

1) This is a <u>3D model</u>.
It shows <u>how big</u> the ions are compared to each other.

2) It also shows that the ions are <u>ordered in a pattern</u>.

3) But it only lets you see the <u>outer layer</u> of the compound.

● = Cl⁻   ● = Na⁺

1) This is a <u>ball and stick model</u>.
It shows how the ions are <u>arranged</u>.

2) But it <u>doesn't show how big</u> the ions are compared to each other.

3) And it makes it look like there are <u>gaps</u> between the ions. But there <u>aren't really</u>.

Ionic Compounds All Have Similar Properties

1) They all have <u>high melting points</u> and <u>high boiling points</u>.
This is because lots of <u>energy</u> is needed to break all the <u>strong ionic bonds</u>.

2) When they're <u>solid</u>, the ions are held in place, so the solid compounds <u>can't conduct</u> electricity.

3) When ionic compounds <u>melt</u>, the ions are <u>free to move</u> and they <u>can conduct</u> electricity.

4) Some ionic compounds <u>dissolve</u> in water.
The ions can <u>move</u> in the solution, so they <u>can conduct</u> electricity.

Ionic Compounds

*You might need to work out the **empirical formula** of an **ionic compound** from a **diagram** — here's how.*

Use **Charges** to Find the **Empirical Formula** of an Ionic Compound

1) For a <u>dot and cross</u> diagram, just <u>count up</u> and write down how <u>many</u> ions there are of <u>each element</u>.
2) For a 3D diagram, <u>use</u> the diagram to work out <u>what ions</u> are in the compound.
3) Then <u>balance</u> the charges of the ions so that the overall charge on the compound is zero.

EXAMPLE

What's the empirical formula of the ionic compound shown below?

⊙⃝⃝ *The empirical formula shows the smallest ratio of particles.*

○ = **Potassium ion**

● = **Oxide ion**

1) Look at the diagram to work out what ions are in the compound.

The compound contains potassium and oxide ions.

2) Work out what <u>charges</u> the ions will form.

Potassium is in Group 1 so forms 1+ ions. Oxygen is in Group 6 so forms 2− ions.

3) <u>Balance</u> the charges so the charge of the empirical formula is <u>zero</u>.

A potassium ion has a 1+ charge, so two of them are needed to balance the 2− charge of an oxide ion. The empirical formula is K_2O.

EXAMPLE

What's the empirical formula of the ionic compound shown below?

● = **Chloride ion**

○ = **Caesium ion**

1) Look at the diagram to work out what ions are in the compound.

The compound contains caesium ions and chloride ions.

2) Work out what <u>charges</u> the ions will form.

Caesium is in Group 1 so forms 1+ ions. Chlorine is in Group 7 so forms 1− ions.

3) <u>Balance</u> the charges so the charge of the empirical formula is <u>zero</u>.

A caesium ion has a 1+ charge, so you only need one to balance out the 1− charge of the chloride ion. The empirical formula is CsCl.

Ionic compounds have regular lattice structures

● = sulfide ion
● = magnesium ion

Q1 Video Solution

As long as you can find the <u>charge</u> of the ions in an ionic compound, you can work out the <u>empirical formula</u>. Try practising with different ionic compounds.

Q1 The structure of an ionic compound is shown on the right.
  a) Predict, with reasoning, whether the compound
     has a high or a low melting point. [2 marks]
  b) Explain why the compound can conduct electricity when molten. [1 mark]
  c) Use the diagram to find the empirical formula of the compound. [3 marks]

Warm-Up & Exam Questions

Congratulations, you got to the end of the pages on ions. Now test yourself with these questions...

Warm-Up Questions

1) What is an ion?
2) What is the charge on a ion formed from a Group 7 element?
3) Sodium chloride has a giant ionic structure. Does it have a high or a low boiling point?
4) True or false? Ionic compounds conduct electricity when dissolved in water.
5) What is the empirical formula of the compound containing Al^{3+} and OH^- ions only?
   A. $Al_3(OH)$ B. $Al(OH)_4$ C. $Al(OH)_3$ D. $Al(OH)_2$

Exam Questions

1   When lithium reacts with oxygen it forms the ionic compound Li_2O.

1.1   Complete **Figure 1** to show the electron arrangements and the charges on the ions when Li_2O is formed.

Figure 1

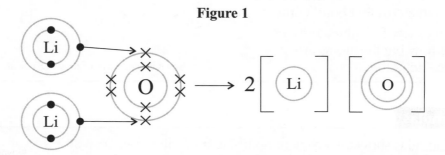

[2 marks]

1.2   What is the formula of the compound lithium forms with chlorine?
Tick **one** box.

☐ $LiCl_2$ ☐ $LiCl$ ☐ Li_2Cl ☐ $LiCl_3$

[1 mark]

2   Sodium and chlorine react to form sodium chloride, an ionic compound.

2.1   Explain how you can use the charges on the sodium and chloride ions to
determine the empirical formula of sodium chloride.

[2 marks]

2.2   Explain why sodium chloride has a high melting point.

[2 marks]

2.3   Explain why solid sodium chloride does not conduct electricity, but molten sodium chloride does.

[2 marks]

2.4   Give **one** other way, besides melting, of making sodium chloride conduct electricity.

[1 mark]

Covalent Bonding

*Some elements form **covalent** bonds — they **share** electrons with each other in order to have full outer shells.*

Covalent Bonds — **Sharing** Electrons

1) When <u>non-metal</u> atoms bond together, they <u>share</u> pairs of electrons to make <u>covalent bonds</u>.
2) Covalent bonds are <u>electrostatic forces</u> and are very <u>strong</u>.
3) Atoms only share electrons in their <u>outer shells</u>.
4) Atoms get one <u>extra</u> shared electron for each single <u>covalent bond</u> that they form.
5) Each atom usually makes <u>enough</u> covalent bonds to <u>fill up</u> its outer shell. This makes them very <u>stable</u>.

There are **Different Ways** of **Drawing** Covalent Bonds

Nitrogen has five outer electrons. To form <u>ammonia</u> (NH_3) it forms <u>three covalent bonds</u> to get the extra 3 electrons it needs for a <u>full outer shell</u>. Here are different ways the bonding can be <u>shown</u>:

Dot and Cross Diagrams

1) Electrons shown in the <u>overlap</u> between two atoms are <u>shared electrons</u>.
2) Dot and cross diagrams show <u>which atoms</u> the electrons in a covalent bond come from.
3) But they <u>don't</u> show how the atoms are <u>arranged</u>, or how <u>big</u> the atoms are compared to each other.

Strong covalent bond.

Two different ways of drawing dot and cross diagrams.

Displayed Formulas

1) <u>Displayed formulas</u> show the covalent bonds as single lines between atoms.
2) If it's a <u>single</u> covalent bond, there'll be <u>one</u> line. If it's a <u>double</u> covalent bond, there'll be <u>two</u> lines.
3) They're good for showing <u>how</u> atoms are connected in <u>large</u> molecules.
4) But they <u>don't</u> show the <u>3D structure</u> of the molecule. They also don't show <u>which atoms</u> the electrons in the covalent bond have come from.

Covalent bond

3D Models

1) 3D models show the <u>atoms</u>, the <u>covalent bonds</u> and how they're <u>arranged</u>.
2) But 3D models can be <u>confusing</u> for large molecules.
3) And they don't show <u>where</u> the electrons in the bonds have <u>come from</u>.

You can find the <u>molecular formula</u> of a simple molecular compound from these diagrams by <u>counting up</u> how many atoms of each element there are.

A molecular formula shows you how many atoms of each element are in a molecule.

 EXAMPLE   **Find the molecular formula of ethane from the diagram of ethane.**

In the diagram, there are two carbon atoms and six hydrogen atoms. So the molecular formula is C_2H_6.

Covalent Bonding

*It's always handy to have an assortment of **examples** up your sleeve when you go into a chemistry exam. You've already seen ammonia, so use this page to familiarise yourself with a **few more** important molecules.*

Learn These Examples of Simple Molecular Substances

1) <u>Simple molecular substances</u> are made up of molecules that contain a <u>few atoms</u> joined together by <u>covalent bonds</u>.

2) Here are some <u>common examples</u> that you should know...

Make sure you can also draw the dot and cross diagram of ammonia, NH_3, which is on the previous page.

Hydrogen, H_2

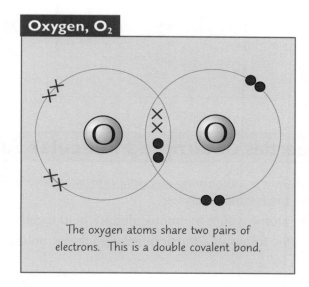

Oxygen, O_2

The oxygen atoms share two pairs of electrons. This is a double covalent bond.

Chlorine, Cl_2

Hydrogen chloride, HCl

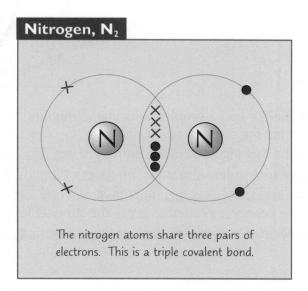

Nitrogen, N_2

The nitrogen atoms share three pairs of electrons. This is a triple covalent bond.

Covalent bonding involves sharing electrons

You might be asked to draw a <u>dot and cross diagram</u> for a simple molecule in the exam. The ones you need to know are shown on this page and the next page (oh, and don't forget to learn ammonia too).

Covalent Bonding

*Just in case you can't get enough of **simple molecular substances**, here's another **whole page** on them...*

Some More Examples of **Simple Molecular** Substances

Properties of **Simple Molecular** Substances

1) Substances containing <u>covalent bonds</u> usually have <u>simple molecular structures</u>, like the examples above.

2) The atoms <u>within</u> the molecules are held together by <u>very strong covalent bonds</u>.

3) But the forces of attraction <u>between</u> these molecules are <u>very weak</u>.

Weak intermolecular forces

Oxygen

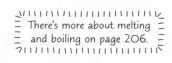

There's more about melting and boiling on page 206.

4) To melt or boil a simple molecular compound, you only need to break the <u>weak intermolecular forces</u> and <u>not</u> the covalent bonds.

5) So the melting and boiling points are <u>very low</u>, because it's <u>easy</u> to <u>break</u> the intermolecular forces.

6) Most molecular substances are <u>gases or liquids</u> at room temperature.

7) As molecules get <u>bigger</u>, the intermolecular forces get <u>stronger</u>.
More energy is needed to <u>break</u> the stronger forces, so the melting and boiling points <u>increase</u>.

8) Molecular compounds <u>don't conduct electricity</u> because they <u>aren't charged</u>.

Simple molecular substances are easy to melt

Remember, it's the weak forces <u>between molecules</u> that are broken when a simple molecular substance melts — <u>not</u> the strong covalent bonds between the atoms in the molecules. It's easy to get the two mixed up, so get your head around it now before moving on.

Q1 Video Solution

Q1   Draw a dot and cross diagram to show the bonding in a molecule of ammonia (NH_3). [2 marks]

Warm-Up & Exam Questions

The questions on this page are all about covalent bonding. Go through them and if you have any problems, make sure you look back at the relevant pages again until you've got to grips with it all.

Warm-Up Questions

1) What is a covalent bond?

2) How many triple covalent bonds does a molecule of nitrogen have?

3) True or false? Most simple molecular substances are solids at room temperature.

4) Which forces are stronger in simple molecular substances — covalent bonds (between atoms) or intermolecular forces (between molecules)?

Exam Questions

1 The bonding in phosphorus trichloride (PCl_3) is shown in **Figure 1**. Only the outer electrons are shown.

Figure 1

How many electrons are there in the outer shell of each atom in PCl_3?

[1 mark]

1.2 How many shared pairs of electrons are there in a molecule of PCl_3?

[1 mark]

1.3 How many double covalent bonds are there in a molecule of PCl_3?

☐ 0 ☐ 1 ☐ 2 ☐ 3

[1 mark]

2 Draw a dot and cross diagram for a molecule of hydrogen (H_2). **Grade 3-4**

[1 mark]

3 Hydrogen chloride is a simple molecular substance. **Grade 4-5**

3.1 How many single covalent bonds are there in a molecule of hydrogen chloride?

[1 mark]

3.2 Explain why hydrogen chloride has a low boiling point.

[1 mark]

3.3 Explain why hydrogen chloride gas has poor electrical conductivity.

[1 mark]

Polymers

*Simple molecular substances aren't the only covalent compounds you need to know about — **polymers** are also made up of **covalent bonds**. Their properties are a bit different to simple molecular compounds, though.*

Polymers Have **Very Large** Molecules

1) In a polymer, lots of <u>small units</u> are joined together to form a <u>long molecule</u>.

2) All the atoms in a polymer are joined by strong <u>covalent bonds</u>.

Instead of drawing out a whole polymer, you can draw a small part of it, called the <u>repeating unit</u>. The polymer is made up of this unit <u>repeated</u> over and over again.

The names of polymers usually have 'poly' followed by something in brackets. E.g. this is poly(ethene).

The bonds through the brackets join up to the next repeating unit.

'n' is a large number. It tells you that the unit's repeated lots of times.

The bit in brackets is the repeating unit.

To find the <u>molecular formula</u> of a polymer...

- Write down the molecular formula of the <u>repeating unit</u>. Put <u>brackets</u> around it. Then put an '<u>n</u>' outside.
- So for the polymer above, the molecular formula of the polymer is $(C_2H_4)_n$.

3) The intermolecular forces between polymer molecules are <u>larger</u> than between simple covalent molecules. This means <u>more energy</u> is needed to break them. So most polymers are <u>solid</u> at room temperature.

4) The intermolecular forces are still <u>weaker</u> than ionic or covalent bonds. This means they generally have <u>lower</u> melting and boiling points than <u>ionic</u> or <u>giant covalent</u> (see next page) compounds.

Polymers contain lots of strong covalent bonds

You've probably heard of a few <u>polymers</u> before — polyesters and polystyrene are used a lot in our day-to-day lives. Polymers are <u>really useful</u> materials, so you need to be able to recognise them.

Q1   The repeating unit of poly(chloroethene) is shown on the right.
      What's the molecular formula of poly(chloroethene)?   [1 mark]

Q1 Video Solution

Giant Covalent Structures

*That's right — there's another class of **covalent structures** you need to know about. Here we go...*

Giant Covalent Structures Include Diamond, Graphite and Silica

1) In <u>giant covalent</u> structures, <u>all</u> the atoms are <u>bonded</u> to <u>each other</u> by <u>strong</u> covalent bonds.

2) They have <u>very high</u> melting and boiling points.
This is because lots of energy is needed to break the covalent bonds between the atoms.

3) They <u>don't</u> contain charged particles, so they <u>don't conduct electricity</u> (except for a few weird exceptions such as graphite, see below).

4) The examples you should know about are <u>diamond</u> and <u>graphite</u>, which are both made from <u>carbon atoms</u> only, and <u>silicon dioxide</u> (silica).

Silicon dioxide
(silica)

Diamond is Very Hard

1) In diamond, each carbon atom forms <u>four covalent bonds</u>.

2) This makes diamond <u>really hard</u>.

3) It takes a lot of energy to <u>break</u> the covalent bonds. So diamond has a <u>very high melting point</u>.

4) Diamond <u>doesn't conduct electricity</u> because it has <u>no free electrons</u> or ions.

The structures are really much larger than we've shown on this page. The rest of the substance looks the same, so we've just drawn a section.

Graphite Contains Layers of Hexagons

1) Graphite contains <u>layers</u> of <u>carbon atoms</u>. The carbon atoms are arranged in <u>hexagons</u> (rings of six carbon atoms).

2) Each carbon atom forms <u>three covalent bonds</u>.

3) There <u>aren't</u> any covalent bonds <u>between</u> the layers. So the layers can move over each other. This makes graphite <u>soft</u> and <u>slippery</u>.

4) <u>Lots of energy</u> is needed to break the covalent bonds in the layers. So graphite has a <u>high melting point</u>.

5) Each carbon atom has <u>one</u> electron that's <u>free to move</u> (delocalised). So graphite <u>conducts electricity</u> and <u>thermal energy</u> (heat) — a bit like a metal does (see p.203).

Giant covalent structures have high melting and boiling points

You <u>do</u> have to break the <u>very strong</u> covalent bonds between atoms in order to melt or boil a <u>giant covalent structure</u>. This gives them very high melting and boiling points.

Q1   Describe the structure and bonding of graphite.   [4 marks]

Q1 Video Solution

Topic C2 — Bonding, Structure and Properties of Matter

Giant Covalent Structures

*Along with diamond and graphite, carbon atoms also make up **graphene** and **fullerenes**.*

Graphene is **One Layer** of Graphite

1) Graphene is a <u>sheet</u> of carbon atoms joined together in <u>hexagons</u>. You can think of it as <u>one layer</u> of graphite.

2) The covalent bonds make it very <u>strong</u>. It's also very <u>light</u>.

3) It can be added to <u>other materials</u> to make <u>composites</u>. The graphene makes the materials <u>stronger</u> but not much <u>heavier</u>.

4) Graphene contains <u>electrons</u> that are <u>free to move</u>. So it <u>conducts electricity</u>. This means it could be used in <u>electronics</u>.

Fullerenes Form **Spheres** and **Tubes**

1) <u>Fullerenes</u> are molecules of <u>carbon</u>, shaped like <u>closed tubes</u> or <u>hollow balls</u>.

2) The carbon atoms are mainly arranged in <u>hexagons</u>. They can also form rings of <u>five</u> carbon atoms or rings of <u>seven</u> carbon atoms.

3) Fullerenes can be used to <u>deliver drugs</u> into the body. They also make great <u>catalysts</u> (see p.235).

4) <u>Buckminsterfullerene</u> (C_{60}) was the first fullerene to be found. It's shaped like a <u>hollow sphere</u> (ball).

5) Fullerenes can form <u>nanotubes</u> — tiny carbon <u>cylinders</u>.

6) The ratio between the length and the diameter of nanotubes is very <u>high</u> (they're very <u>long</u> compared to their <u>width</u>).

7) Nanotubes have properties that make them useful in <u>electronics</u>. They can also be used to <u>strengthen materials</u> without adding much <u>weight</u>.

Technology that uses very small particles is called nanotechnology.

Carbon comes in many different forms

There's been quite a bit of information on the last two pages. Before you go on, make sure you can explain the <u>properties</u> of all these forms of carbon. Remember, just because they all contain carbon doesn't mean they're all the same — it all comes down to how the carbon atoms are <u>arranged</u> in the structure.

Metallic Bonding

Ever wondered what gives a metal its properties? Most of it comes down to bonding...

Metallic Bonding Involves Delocalised Electrons

1) <u>Metals</u> are <u>giant structures</u> of atoms.
   This means they contain <u>lots and lots</u> of metal atoms bonded together.

2) The electrons in the <u>outer shell</u> of the metal atoms are <u>free to move around</u> (delocalised).

3) There are strong forces of <u>electrostatic attraction</u> between
   the <u>positive metal ions</u> and the shared <u>negative electrons</u>.

4) These forces of attraction are known as <u>metallic bonds</u>.
   They <u>hold</u> the <u>atoms</u> together in a <u>regular pattern</u>.

Metal atoms

Delocalised electrons

The Bonding in Metals Affects their Properties

1) Metallic bonds are very <u>strong</u>, so <u>lots of energy</u> is needed to break them.

2) This means that most substances with metallic bonds have very <u>high</u> melting and boiling points.

3) They're usually <u>solids</u> at room temperature.

4) The <u>delocalised electrons</u> in the metal are <u>free to move</u>.

5) These electrons can carry <u>electrical charge</u> and <u>thermal</u> (heat) energy through the whole structure.

6) This means metals are good <u>conductors</u> of <u>electricity</u> and <u>heat</u>.

7) The layers of atoms in a metal can <u>slide</u> over each other.

8) Because of this, metals can be <u>bent</u> or <u>formed</u> into different shapes.

Metallic Bonding is Found in Alloys

1) <u>Pure metals</u> are often quite <u>soft</u>.

2) Most of the metals we use are <u>alloys</u>.
   An alloy is a <u>mixture</u> of <u>two or more metals</u> or a <u>metal and another element</u>.

3) Mixing another element with a pure metal causes the layers of metal atoms to
   <u>lose their shape</u>. This is because different elements have <u>different sized atoms</u>.

4) It becomes more <u>difficult</u> for the atoms to <u>slide</u> over each other.

5) This makes alloys <u>harder</u> and so <u>more useful</u> than pure metals.

Metallic bonding is what makes metals, well... metals

The bonding between atoms is the key to understanding the <u>structure</u> and <u>properties</u> of any
substance — metals included. Take a moment to check you can <u>explain</u> how they are related.

Warm-Up & Exam Questions

Lots of information to learn on the previous few pages — here are some questions to test yourself on.

Warm-Up Questions

1) True or False? The repeating units in a polymer are held together with covalent bonds.
2) At room temperature, what state are most polymers in?
3) Describe the differences in the hardness and electrical conductivity of diamond and graphite.
4) Why can most metals be bent into different shapes?

Exam Questions

1 Draw one line from each carbon structure to its description.

Carbon structure	**Description**

Diamond

A structure of carbon in which each carbon atom forms four covalent bonds.

A carbon structure shaped like a closed tube or hollow ball.

Graphite

A layered structure in which each carbon atom forms three covalent bonds.

[2 marks]

2 Silicon carbide has a giant covalent structure and is a solid at room temperature.

2.1 Explain, in terms of its bonding and structure, why silicon carbide has a high melting point.

[2 marks]

2.2 Give **one** other example of a substance with a giant covalent structure.

[1 mark]

3 **Figure 1** shows the arrangement of atoms in two different materials.
A is a metal and **B** is an alloy.

Figure 1

A   B

3.1 Define the term 'alloy'.

[1 mark]

3.2 Explain how delocalised electrons make metals good conductors of heat.

[2 marks]

3.3 Iron is a metal. Steel is an alloy of iron and carbon.
Explain why steel is harder than iron.

[4 marks]

States of Matter

*You can explain quite a bit of stuff in **chemistry** if you can get your head around this lot.*

The **Three States of Matter** — Solid, Liquid and Gas

1) Materials come in <u>three</u> different forms — <u>solid</u>, <u>liquid</u> and <u>gas</u>. These are the <u>three states of matter</u>.
2) <u>Particle theory</u> is a <u>model</u> where each particle is seen as a <u>small</u>, <u>solid sphere</u> (ball).
3) You can use <u>particle theory</u> to show what solids, liquids and gases are like. It can be used to explain how the particles in solids, liquids and gases <u>behave</u>.

> The particles could be atoms, ions or molecules.

Solids

1) In solids, there are <u>strong forces</u> of attraction between particles.
2) The particles are held <u>close together</u> in <u>fixed positions</u> to form a <u>pattern</u>.
3) Solids have a <u>fixed shape</u> and <u>volume</u>.

Liquids

1) In liquids, there are <u>weak forces</u> of attraction between the particles.
2) They're randomly arranged and <u>free</u> to <u>move</u> past each other, but they tend to <u>stick closely together</u>.
3) Liquids have a fixed volume but <u>don't</u> keep a <u>fixed shape</u>. So they flow to fill the bottom of a container.

Gases

1) In gases, the forces of attraction between the particles are <u>very weak</u>.
2) The particles are <u>free</u> to <u>move</u> and are spaced <u>far apart</u>.
3) The particles in gases travel in <u>straight lines</u>.
4) Gases <u>don't</u> have a fixed <u>shape</u> or <u>volume</u>. They will always <u>fill</u> containers.

> If you ever see something described as 'gaseous', it just means that it's a gas.

Particle theory explains solids, liquids and gases

Particle theory imagines all particles as small snooker ball-like spheres. It's not quite like that in real life, of course, but it's a good theory for understanding the <u>properties</u> and <u>behaviour</u> of the three states of matter.

States of Matter

Substances Can **Change** from **One State to Another**

Solid → Liquid → Gas

1) When a solid is <u>heated</u>, its particles gain <u>energy</u> and start to <u>move about</u>.

2) Some of the forces between the particles <u>break</u>.

3) At a <u>temperature</u> called the <u>melting point</u>, the particles have enough energy to <u>break free</u> from their positions. This is <u>MELTING</u>. The <u>solid</u> turns into a <u>liquid</u>.

4) When a liquid is <u>heated</u>, the particles get even <u>more</u> energy.

5) The forces holding the liquid together <u>weaken</u> and <u>break</u>.

6) At a temperature called the <u>boiling point</u>, the particles have <u>enough</u> energy to <u>break</u> the forces. This is <u>BOILING</u>. The <u>liquid</u> becomes a <u>gas</u>.

Gas → Liquid → Solid

1) As a gas <u>cools</u>, the particles have <u>less energy</u>.

2) <u>Forces form</u> between the particles.

3) At the <u>boiling point</u>, the forces between the particles are strong enough that the <u>gas</u> becomes a <u>liquid</u>. This is <u>CONDENSING</u>.

4) When a <u>liquid cools</u>, the particles have <u>less energy</u>, so move around less.

5) The <u>forces</u> between the particles become stronger.

6) At the <u>melting point</u>, the forces between the particles are so strong that they're <u>held in place</u>. The <u>liquid</u> becomes a <u>solid</u>. This is <u>FREEZING</u>.

The <u>amount</u> of energy needed for a substance to <u>change state</u> depends on <u>how strong</u> the forces between particles are. The <u>stronger</u> the forces, the <u>more energy</u> is needed to break them, and so the <u>higher</u> the melting and boiling points of the substance.

States of Matter

*The **state** a substance is in can be really important in working out **how it will react**. This page is all about how chemists **show** what the state of a substance is and how they **predict** what state a substance will be in.*

State Symbols Tell You the State of a Substance in an Equation

1) You saw on page 165 how a chemical reaction can be shown using a <u>symbol equation</u>.
2) Symbol equations can include <u>state symbols</u> next to each substance. They're always shown in <u>brackets</u>, and they're normally <u>subscripts</u> (slightly smaller and below the rest of the letters).
3) They tell you whether each substance is a <u>solid</u>, a <u>liquid</u>, a <u>gas</u> or <u>dissolved in water</u>:

(s) — solid   (l) — liquid   (g) — gas   (aq) — aqueous

'Aqueous' means 'dissolved in water'.

For <u>example</u>:

$$2HCl_{(aq)} + CaCO_{3(s)} \rightarrow CaCl_{2(aq)} + H_2O_{(l)} + CO_{2(g)}$$

dissolved in water   solid   dissolved in water   liquid   gas

You Have to be Able to Predict the State of a Substance

1) You can predict <u>what state</u> a substance is in at a <u>certain temperature</u>.
2) If the temperature's <u>below</u> the <u>melting point</u> of substance, it'll be a <u>solid</u>.
3) If it's <u>above</u> the <u>boiling point</u>, it'll be a <u>gas</u>.
4) If it's <u>in between</u> the two points, then it's a <u>liquid</u>.

The bulk properties such as the melting point of a material depend on how lots of atoms interact together. An atom on its own doesn't have these properties.

EXAMPLE   **Which of the substances in the table is a liquid at room temperature (25 °C)?**

	melting point	boiling point
oxygen	–219 °C	–183 °C
nitrogen	–210 °C	–196 °C
bromine	–7 °C	59 °C

Oxygen and nitrogen have boiling points below 25 °C, so will both be gases at room temperature.

The answer's bromine.
It melts at –7 °C and boils at 59 °C.
So, it'll be a liquid at room temperature.

Changing between states is reversible

Make sure you can describe what happens to particles, and the forces between them, as a substance is <u>heated</u> and <u>cooled</u>. Don't forget to learn the technical terms for each <u>state change</u>.

Q1   Ethanol melts at –114 °C and boils at 78 °C. Predict the state that ethanol is in at:
    a) –150 °C   b) 0 °C   c) 25 °C   d) 100 °C   [4 marks]

Q1 Video Solution

Warm-Up & Exam Questions

Reckon you know all there is to know about this section? Have a go at these questions and see how you get on. If you get stuck on something — just flick back and give it another read through.

Warm-Up Questions

1) What state of matter has a fixed arrangement of particles?
2) True or false? There are only weak forces of attraction between particles in a gas.
3) Describe what happens to the bonding in a substance when it condenses.
4) How you would show that sodium ions (Na^+) are dissolved in water in a symbol equation.
   A. $Na^{+(aq)}$ B. $Na^+_{(l)}$ C. $Na^+_{(aq)}$ D. $Na^+_{(s)}$

Exam Questions

1   **Figure 1** shows a vessel in a distillery. The walls of the vessel are solid copper.

Grade 3-4

Figure 1

Complete the sentences about solids using words from the box.
Each word may be used once, more than once or not at all.

weak	move	colder	hotter	random
strong	expand	heavier	dissolve	regular

In solids, there are .... forces of attraction between particles,

which hold them in fixed positions in a .... arrangement.

The particles don't .... from their positions, so solids keep their shape.

The .... the solid becomes, the more the particles in the solid vibrate.

[4 marks]

2   **Figure 2** shows a substance changing between solid, liquid and gas states.

Grade 4-5

Figure 2

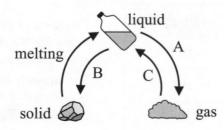

liquid

melting

A

B   C

solid   gas

2.1   Give the letter of the arrow that represents **condensing**.

[1 mark]

2.2   Give the name of the process represented by arrow **A**.

[1 mark]

2.3   Use particle theory to explain why gases fill their containers.

[2 marks]

Relative Formula Mass

*Calculating **relative formula mass** is important for lots of calculations in chemistry.*
*It might sound a bit hard to begin with, but it gets easier with **practice**. We'd better get cracking...*

Compounds Have a Relative Formula Mass, M_r

To find the <u>relative formula mass</u>, M_r, of a compound, add together the relative atomic masses of all the atoms in the <u>molecular formula</u>.

> The relative atomic mass (A_r) of an element is on the periodic table. See page 163 for more.

EXAMPLES

a) Find the relative formula mass of $MgCl_2$.

> In the exams, you might be given the relative atomic masses you need in the question.

1) Look up the <u>relative atomic masses</u> of all the elements in the compound on the periodic table.

A_r of Mg = 24 A_r of Cl = 35.5

2) <u>Add up</u> all the relative atomic masses of the atoms in the compound.

> There are two chlorine atoms in $MgCl_2$, so the relative atomic mass of chlorine needs to be multiplied by 2.

$Mg + (2 \times Cl) = 24 + (2 \times 35.5) = 24 + 71 = 95$
M_r of $MgCl_2$ = 95

b) Find the relative formula mass of $Ca(OH)_2$.

1) Look up the <u>relative atomic masses</u> of all the elements in the compound on the periodic table.

A_r of Ca = 40 A_r of O = 16 A_r of H = 1

2) <u>Add up</u> all the relative atomic masses of the atoms in the compound.

> The small number 2 after the bracket in the formula $Ca(OH)_2$ means that there's two of everything inside the brackets.

$Ca + [(O + H) \times 2] = 40 + [(16 + 1) \times 2] = 40 + 34 = 74$
M_r of $Ca(OH)_2$ = 74

You Can Calculate the % Mass of an Element in a Compound

To work out the <u>percentage mass</u> of an element in a compound, you need to use this <u>formula</u>:

$$\text{Percentage mass of an element in a compound} = \frac{A_r \times \text{number of atoms of that element}}{M_r \text{ of the compound}} \times 100$$

EXAMPLE

Find the percentage mass of sodium (Na) in sodium bromide (NaBr).

1) Look up the <u>relative atomic masses</u> of all the elements in the compound on the periodic table.

A_r of Na = 23 A_r of Br = 80

2) Add up the relative atomic masses of all the atoms in the compound to find the <u>relative formula mass</u>.

M_r of NaBr = 23 + 80 = 103

3) Use the formula to calculate the percentage mass.

$$\text{Percentage mass of sodium} = \frac{A_r \times \text{number of atoms of that element}}{M_r \text{ of the compound}} \times 100$$
$$= \frac{23 \times 1}{103} \times 100 = 22\%$$

Relative formula mass — add up all the relative atomic masses

You'll get a <u>periodic table</u> in the exams, which could be handy for these sorts of calculations — the <u>relative atomic mass</u> of an element is the <u>bigger number</u> next to the element's symbol.

Q1   Calculate the relative formula mass (M_r) of: a) CO_2 b) LiOH   c) H_2SO_4 [3 marks]

Q2   Calculate the percentage composition by mass of potassium in potassium hydroxide (KOH).   [2 marks]

Q2 Video Solution

Conservation of Mass

*You've probably realised by now that you can't **magic** stuff out of thin air. It can't magically **disappear**, either.*

In a Chemical Reaction, **Mass Always Stays** the **Same**

1) During a chemical reaction <u>no atoms are lost</u> and <u>no atoms are made</u>.

2) This means there are the <u>same number and types of atoms</u> on each side of a reaction equation.

3) Because of this, no mass is lost or gained — we say that mass is <u>conserved</u> (stays the same) in a reaction.

> For example: $2Li + F_2 \rightarrow 2LiF$
> In this reaction, there are <u>2 lithium atoms</u> and <u>2 fluorine atoms</u> on <u>each side</u> of the equation.

4) You can see that mass stays the same if you <u>add up</u> the relative formula masses of the substances on each side of a <u>balanced symbol equation</u>.

5) The total M_r of all the reactants will be the <u>same</u> as the total M_r of the products.

If you're not sure what the big numbers and the little numbers in reaction equations mean, see pages 164-166.

EXAMPLE

Show that mass is conserved in this reaction: $2Li + F_2 \rightarrow 2LiF$.
Relative atomic masses (A_r): Li = 7, F = 19

1) Add up the relative formula masses on the <u>left-hand side</u> of the equation.

$2 \times A_r(Li) + M_r(F_2) = (2 \times 7) + (2 \times 19)$
$= 14 + 38$
$= 52$

2) Add up the relative formula masses on the <u>right-hand side</u> of the equation.

$2 \times M_r(LiF) = 2 \times (7 + 19)$
$= 2 \times 26$
$= 52$

The total M_r on the left-hand side of the equation is the same as the total M_r on the right-hand side, so mass is conserved.

You can **Calculate** the Mass of a Reactant or Product

1) You can use the idea of conservation of mass to <u>work out</u> the mass of a reactant or product in a reaction.

2) You need to know the masses of <u>all</u> the reactants and products except for <u>one</u>.

3) You can work out the <u>total mass</u> of everything on one side of the equation.

4) You can also work out the total mass of everything on the other side of the equation, <u>except</u> for the thing you don't know the mass of.

5) The mass of the thing you <u>don't</u> know is the <u>difference</u> between these two totals.

EXAMPLE

6 g of magnesium completely reacts with 4 g of oxygen in the following reaction:
$$2Mg + O_2 \rightarrow 2MgO$$
What mass of magnesium oxide is formed?

1) Find the total mass of reactants. $4 + 6 = 10 \ g$

2) Magnesium oxide is the only product. So the mass of products you do know is 0 g.

Mass of magnesium oxide = $10 - 0 = 10 \ g$

The M_r of the reactants will always equal the M_r of the products

Don't forget that, in a reaction, the <u>total mass of reactants</u> is the same as the <u>total mass of products</u>.

Q1 Show that mass is conserved in the reaction: $H_2SO_{4(aq)} + 2NaOH_{(aq)} \rightarrow Na_2SO_{4(aq)} + 2H_2O_{(l)}$
$A_r(H) = 1, A_r(O) = 16, A_r(Na) = 23, A_r(S) = 32$ **[5 marks]**

Q1 Video Solution

Conservation of Mass

*Even though mass is always (always) conserved in a reaction, sometimes you can carry out an experiment where the mass of the **reaction container** changes. Time to find out why...*

If the Mass **Seems to Change**, There's Usually a **Gas** Involved

In some experiments, the <u>mass</u> of an <u>unsealed reaction container</u> might <u>change</u> during a reaction. This usually happens for one of two reasons...

1) If One of the Reactants is a **Gas**, the Mass Could **Go Up**

If the mass <u>goes up</u>, it's probably because one of the things that <u>reacts</u> is a <u>gas</u> that's found in air (e.g. oxygen) and all the things that are <u>made</u> are solids, liquids or in solution.

1) <u>Before</u> the reaction, the gas is floating around in the air.
   It's there, but it's not trapped in the reaction container.
   This means you <u>can't</u> measure its <u>mass</u>.

2) When the gas <u>reacts</u>, its atoms become part of the product,
   which is held inside the reaction container.

3) So the <u>total mass</u> of the stuff <u>inside</u> the reaction container <u>goes up</u>.

> • When a <u>metal</u> reacts with <u>oxygen</u> in an unsealed container, the mass of the container <u>goes up</u>.
> • This is because the mass of the oxygen atoms <u>isn't measured</u> when they're part of the <u>gas</u>, but it is when they're in the <u>metal oxide</u>.
> $$metal_{(s)} + oxygen_{(g)} \rightarrow metal\ oxide_{(s)}$$

2) If One of the Products is a **Gas**, the Mass Could **Go Down**

If the mass <u>goes down</u>, it's probably because one of the <u>products</u> is a <u>gas</u> and all the things that <u>react</u> are solids, liquids or in solution.

1) <u>Before</u> the reaction, all the reactants are held in the reaction container.

2) If the container <u>isn't sealed</u>, then the gas can <u>escape</u> from the reaction container as it's formed.

3) It's no longer trapped in the reaction container, so you <u>can't</u> measure its <u>mass</u>.

4) This means the total mass of the stuff <u>inside</u> the reaction container <u>goes down</u>.

Remember from the particle model on page 205 that a gas will spread out to fill any container it's in. So if the reaction container isn't sealed, the gas will escape into the air.

> • When a <u>metal carbonate</u> is heated, it can break down to form a <u>metal oxide</u> and <u>carbon dioxide</u> gas.
> *Reactions where substances are heated and break down are called thermal decomposition reactions.*
> • When this happens, the mass of the reaction container will <u>go down</u> if it isn't sealed.
> • But really, the mass of the <u>metal oxide</u> and the <u>carbon dioxide</u> formed will be the <u>same as</u> the mass of the <u>metal carbonate</u>.
> $$metal\ carbonate_{(s)} \rightarrow metal\ oxide_{(s)} + carbon\ dioxide_{(g)}$$

Mass is ALWAYS conserved in a reaction...

Everything has to be the same on <u>both sides</u> of a <u>reaction equation</u>. If it seems like it's not, the chances are there's a <u>gas</u> involved. So check those <u>state symbols</u> for the little $_{(g)}$.

Q1 Video Solution

Q1   During a reaction, the mass in a reaction container increases.
      What does this tell you about the states of matter of the products and reactants?   [2 marks]

Q2   A scientist carries out the reaction below. He does it in an unsealed reaction container:
      $2Na_{(s)} + 2HCl_{(aq)} \rightarrow 2NaCl_{(aq)} + H_{2(g)}$. Predict how the mass of the reaction container
      will change as the reaction takes place.   [1 mark]

Concentrations of Solutions

*Lots of reactions take place between substances that are dissolved in a **solution**. And sometimes it's useful to find out the **mass** of a substance that's dissolved in a **solution**. Hold onto your hats and concentrate...*

Concentration is a Measure of How **Crowded** Things Are

1) The <u>amount</u> of a substance (e.g. the mass) in a certain <u>volume</u> of a solution is called its <u>concentration</u>.

2) The <u>more</u> substance that's dissolved in a certain volume, the <u>more concentrated</u> the solution.

Concentration can be Measured in g/dm³

1) You can find the concentration of a solution if you know the <u>mass</u> of the substance dissolved and the <u>volume</u> of the solution.

The thing that dissolves the solid is called a 'solvent'. The solid that dissolves in the solvent is called a 'solute'.

2) The units will be <u>units of mass/units of volume</u>. For example, g/dm³.

3) Here's how to calculate the concentration of a solution in <u>grams per decimetre cubed</u> (g/dm³):

in g/dm³ ← $$\text{concentration} = \frac{\text{mass of dissolved substance}}{\text{volume of solvent}}$$ → in g, → in dm³

EXAMPLES

a) **30 g of sodium chloride is dissolved in 0.2 dm³ of water. What's the concentration of this solution in g/dm³?**

1 dm³ = 1000 cm³

Put the numbers into the formula to calculate the concentration. $\text{concentration} = \frac{30}{0.2} = 150 \text{ g/dm}^3$

b) **15 g of salt is dissolved in 500 cm³ of water. What's the concentration of this solution in g/dm³?**

1) The units of the volume need to be dm³ so that the units of concentration are in g/dm³. So make the units of volume <u>dm³</u> by dividing by 1000: $500 \div 1000 = 0.5 \text{ dm}^3$

2) Now you've got the mass and the volume in the right units, just stick them in the formula: $\text{concentration} = \frac{15}{0.5} = 30 \text{ g/dm}^3$

4) You can rearrange the equation above to find the <u>mass</u> of substance dissolved in a certain <u>volume</u> of solution if you know its concentration.

5) Here's a formula triangle to help with rearranging the equation: →

6) To use the formula triangle, just <u>cover up</u> the thing you want to find with your finger and write down what's left showing.

in g/dm³, **mass**, in g, **conc. × volume**, in dm³

EXAMPLE

A solution of magnesium chloride has a concentration of 24 g/dm³. What mass of magnesium chloride is there in 0.40 dm³ of this solution?

1) You want to find the mass. So cover up 'mass' in the formula triangle. This leaves 'concentration × volume'. $\text{mass} = \text{conc.} \times \text{volume}$

2) Use this equation to calculate the mass: $\text{mass} = 24 \times 0.40 = 9.6 \text{ g}$

When you measure something like the mass of a substance or the volume of a solution, there's always some uncertainty to the measurement. You can calculate this uncertainty from a range — see pages 9 and 15 for more.

That formula triangle is very useful...

Make sure you know the equation for <u>concentration</u>. And make sure you can <u>rearrange</u> it to find the mass of solute or the volume of the solution. Practising using the <u>formula triangle</u> should help.

Q1 Video Solution

Q1 Calculate the concentration, in g/dm³, of a solution that contains 0.6 g of salt in 15 cm³ of solvent. **[2 marks]**

Warm-Up & Exam Questions

There's no getting around it — there's quite a bit of maths in Topic 3. But the best way to get good at maths questions is lots of practice. So here are some questions to help you do just that...

Warm-Up Questions

1) What is meant by the relative formula mass of a compound?

2) The A_r of hydrogen (H) is 1 and the A_r of oxygen (O) is 16. Calculate the M_r of water (H_2O).

3) True or false? Conservation of mass means that no mass is lost or gained during a reaction.

4) What does it usually mean if the mass of a container increases during a reaction?

5) A student is calculating the concentration of a solution.
The mass of the dissolved substance is in grams and the volume of the solvent is in dm³.
What units should the student use for the concentration?

Exam Questions

1 Which of the following is the M_r of calcium chloride ($CaCl_2$)? **Grade 1-3**
Tick **one** box.
Relative atomic masses (A_r): Cl = 35.5, Ca = 40

☐ 54 ☐ 75.5 ☐ 111 ☐ 71

[1 mark]

2 Which of the following compounds has a relative formula mass of 62? **Grade 3-4**
Tick **one** box.
Relative atomic masses (A_r): F = 19, Na = 23, Mg = 24, Cl = 35.5, K = 39, Br = 80

☐ sodium chloride, NaCl ☐ potassium bromide, KBr

☐ magnesium fluoride, MgF_2 ☐ sodium bromide, NaBr

[1 mark]

3 Zinc carbonate decomposes when it is heated. The equation for this reaction is: **Grade 3-4**

$$ZnCO_{3(s)} \rightarrow ZnO_{(s)} + CO_{2(g)}$$
zinc carbonate → zinc oxide + carbon dioxide

In one reaction, a sample of zinc carbonate completely decomposed.
The decomposition produced 48.6 kg of zinc oxide and 26.4 kg of carbon dioxide.
Calculate the mass of zinc carbonate that decomposed.

[1 mark]

4 The formula of the compound zinc cyanide is $Zn(CN)_2$. **Grade 4-5**
Calculate the relative formula mass of zinc cyanide.

[2 marks]

Exam Questions

5   A solution of calcium hydroxide, $Ca(OH)_2$, can be known as limewater.   *Grade 4-5*

5.1   Calculate the relative formula mass of calcium hydroxide, $Ca(OH)_2$.
Relative atomic masses (A_r): H = 1, O = 16, Ca = 40

[1 mark]

Calcium hydroxide reacts with nitric acid. The word equation for this reaction is:

calcium hydroxide + nitric acid → calcium nitrate + water

5.2   In one experiment, 18.5 g of calcium hydroxide reacted completely with 31.5 g of nitric acid.
9 g of water was produced in the reaction. What mass of calcium nitrate was formed?

[1 mark]

6   A student carries out the following reaction in an unsealed container: *Grade 4-5*

$$2HCl_{(aq)} + MgCO_{3(s)} \rightarrow MgCl_{2(aq)} + H_2O_{(l)} + CO_{2(g)}$$

6.1   Calculate the relative formula mass of $MgCO_3$.
Relative atomic masses (A_r): C = 12, O = 16, Mg = 24

[1 mark]

6.2   How will the mass of the reaction vessel and its contents change during the reaction?
Tick **one** box.

☐ The mass will decrease   ☐ The mass will stay the same

☐ The mass will increase   ☐ It is impossible to tell from the information given

[1 mark]

7   A teacher makes up a solution of copper sulfate to use in an experiment.   *Grade 4-5*
She dissolves copper sulfate powder in 1500 cm³ of water.
The concentration of copper sulfate in the solution is 12 g/dm³.

7.1   Convert 1500 cm³ to dm³.

[1 mark]

7.2   Calculate the mass of copper sulfate the teacher used.

[2 marks]

8   The compound potassium hydroxide has the formula KOH.   *Grade 4-5*
Potassium hydroxide dissolves easily in water.

8.1   A scientist dissolved 40 g of potassium hydroxide in 0.25 dm³ of water.
Calculate the concentration of the solution formed in g/dm³.

[2 marks]

8.2   Calculate the percentage by mass of potassium in potassium hydroxide.
Give your answer to 3 significant figures.
Relative atomic masses (A_r): H = 1, O = 16, K = 39

[3 marks]

Acids, Bases and Their Reactions

Acids and *bases* crop up everywhere in chemistry — so here's the lowdown on the basics of pH...

The pH Scale Goes From 0 to 14

1) The pH scale is a measure of how acidic or alkaline a solution is.
2) The lower the pH of a solution, the more acidic it is.
3) The higher the pH of a solution, the more alkaline it is.
4) A neutral substance (e.g. pure water) has pH 7.

Acids and Bases Neutralise Each Other

1) When acids dissolve in water, they form solutions with a pH of less than 7.
   Acids form H^+ ions in water.
2) Bases have pHs greater than 7.
3) Alkalis are bases that dissolve in water to form solutions with a pH greater than 7.
   Alkalis form OH^- ions in water. For example, soluble metal hydroxides are alkalis.

> The reaction between acids and bases is called neutralisation:
>
> $$Acid + Base \rightarrow Salt + Water$$
>
> Neutralisation between acids and alkalis can be shown using H^+ and OH^- ions like this:
>
> $$H^+_{(aq)} + OH^-_{(aq)} \rightarrow H_2O_{(l)}$$
>
> Hydrogen (H^+) ions react with hydroxide (OH^-) ions to produce water.
>
> The products of neutralisation reactions have a pH of 7.
> This means they're neutral.

4) You can use a chemical called an indicator to tell when a neutralisation reaction is over.
5) An indicator is a dye that changes colour depending on whether it's above or below a certain pH.
6) The indicator is added to the acid or alkali you're neutralising. Then the other substance is gradually added. The indicator will change colour when the neutralisation reaction is over.
7) Universal indicator is an indicator that gives the colours shown on the pH scale above.
   It turns green when the pH of a solution is neutral.

There's more on indicators on page 394.

Interesting fact — your skin is slightly acidic (pH 5.5)

When you mix an acid with an alkali, hydrogen ions from the acid react with hydroxide ions from the alkali to make water. The leftover bits of the acid and alkali make a salt.

Acids, Bases and Their Reactions

*There's more about **neutralisation reactions** coming up on this page...*

Metal **Oxides** and Metal **Hydroxides** are **Bases**

1) Metal oxides and metal hydroxides react with acids in neutralisation reactions to form a salt and water.

2) The salt that forms depends upon the acid and the metal ion in the oxide or hydroxide.

3) HCl reacts to form chlorides, H_2SO_4 reacts to form sulfates and HNO_3 reacts to form nitrates.

hydrochloric acid	+	copper oxide	→	copper chloride	+ water
2HCl	+	CuO	→	$CuCl_2$	+ H_2O

sulfuric acid	+ potassium hydroxide	→	potassium sulfate	+ water
H_2SO_4	+ 2KOH	→	K_2SO_4	+ $2H_2O$

nitric acid	+ sodium hydroxide	→	sodium nitrate	+ water
HNO_3	+ NaOH	→	$NaNO_3$	+ H_2O

Acids and Metal **Carbonates** Produce **Carbon Dioxide**

Metal carbonates are also bases. They react with acids to produce a salt, water and carbon dioxide.

sulfuric acid	+	calcium carbonate	→	calcium sulfate	+ water	+	carbon dioxide
H_2SO_4	+	$CaCO_3$	→	$CaSO_4$	+ H_2O	+	CO_2

hydrochloric acid	+	sodium carbonate	→	sodium chloride	+ water	+	carbon dioxide
2HCl	+	Na_2CO_3	→	2NaCl	+ H_2O	+	CO_2

Acid + Base → Salt + Water (and sometimes carbon dioxide)

There's a whole lot of chemical symbols and equations in this section, so now is a good time to make sure you're comfortable using them. Look back at pages 164-166 if you need more help.

Q1 Video Solution

Q1 Calcium carbonate is added to hydrochloric acid. Write the word equation and the balanced symbol equation for the reaction that occurs. [3 marks]

Acids, Bases and Their Reactions

*Talking about **acids** and **bases** is all well and good, but you need to know how to measure their **pH** too. You also need to know the correct method for making **soluble salts** from an acid and an insoluble base.*

You Can **Measure** the pH of a Solution

1) As you saw on page 215, an <u>indicator</u> is a <u>dye</u> that <u>changes colour</u> depending on whether it's <u>above or below a certain pH</u>.

2) <u>Wide range indicators</u> are substances that <u>gradually change colour</u> as pH changes.

3) They're useful for <u>estimating</u> the pH of a solution.

4) For example, <u>Universal indicator</u> is a wide range indicator. See page 215 for a reminder of its colours.

5) A <u>pH probe</u> attached to a <u>pH meter</u> can also be used to measure pH <u>electronically</u>.

6) The probe is put in the solution and the pH is shown as a <u>number</u>. This means it's more accurate than an indicator.

Remember, acids have a pH of less than 7. Bases have a pH of more than 7.

You can Make **Soluble Salts** Using an **Insoluble Base**

1) If you react an <u>acid</u> with an <u>insoluble base</u> or a <u>metal</u>, you can make a <u>soluble salt</u>.

2) First, pick the <u>acid</u> that contains the same <u>negative ion</u> as the salt you want to make. For example, to make <u>copper chloride</u>, you'd choose <u>hydrochloric acid</u>.

3) Then pick an <u>insoluble base</u> with the same <u>positive ion</u> as the salt you want to make. You could use an <u>insoluble metal oxide</u>, <u>hydroxide</u>, or <u>carbonate</u>.

4) So to make <u>copper chloride</u>, you'd choose <u>copper oxide</u>, <u>copper hydroxide</u> or <u>copper carbonate</u>. Here's the equation for making copper chloride from <u>hydrochloric acid</u> and <u>copper oxide</u>:

$$CuO_{(s)} + 2HCl_{(aq)} \rightarrow CuCl_{2\,(aq)} + H_2O_{(l)}$$

5) Here's the <u>method</u> for making a <u>soluble salt</u> using an acid and an insoluble base.

> 1) Gently <u>warm</u> the dilute acid using a <u>Bunsen burner</u>, then turn off the Bunsen burner.
>
> 2) Add the <u>insoluble base</u> to the <u>acid</u> until no more reacts (you'll see the solid at the bottom of the flask).
>
> 3) <u>Filter</u> out the solid that <u>hasn't reacted</u> to get the salt solution (see p.171).
>
> 4) To get <u>pure</u>, <u>solid</u> crystals of the <u>salt</u>, you need to <u>crystallise</u> it (see p.171).
>
> 5) To do this, gently heat the solution using a <u>water bath</u> or an <u>electric heater</u>. Some of the water will <u>evaporate</u>. Stop heating the solution and leave it to <u>cool</u>.
>
> 6) <u>Crystals</u> of the salt should form, which can be <u>filtered</u> out of the solution and then <u>dried</u>.

You might get to carry these experiments out in class

Remember, you could be asked to describe how you would make a pure, dry sample of a given <u>soluble salt</u>, so make sure you understand the <u>method</u> and that you could suggest a suitable <u>acid</u> and <u>base</u> to use.

Warm-Up & Exam Questions

So you think you know everything there is to know about acids? Time to put yourself to the test.

Warm-Up Questions

1) What range of values can pH take?
2) What term is used to describe a solution with a pH of 7?
3) True or false? Universal indicator will turn blue if it is added to a substance with a pH of 7.
4) Which of the following substances is a base?
   A. $CaCO_3$ B. HCl   C. HNO_3 D. CO_2
5) Name the two substances formed when sulfuric acid reacts with copper hydroxide.

Exam Questions

1 A student had a sample of acid in a test tube. He gradually added some base to the acid. *(Grade 3-4)*

1.1 Which negative ion is produced when a soluble base is added to an aqueous solution? Tick **one** box.

☐ H^- ☐ CO_3^{2-} ☐ O^{2-} ☐ OH^-

[1 mark]

1.2 What type of reaction took place in the student's experiment? Tick **one** box.

☐ thermal decomposition   ☐ redox   ☐ combustion   ☐ neutralisation

[1 mark]

2 All metal hydroxides are bases. They can react with acids to form a salt and water. *(Grade 3-4)*

2.1 Sodium hydroxide is a soluble base. What name is given to bases that dissolve in water? Tick **one** box.

☐ Alkalis   ☐ Acids   ☐ Indicators   ☐ Oxides

[1 mark]

2.2 Nitric acid reacts with magnesium hydroxide to produce magnesium nitrate and water.
Complete and balance the symbol equation for this reaction. The formula of a nitrate ion is NO_3^-.

$$2HNO_3 + Mg(OH)_2 \rightarrow \text{........................} + \text{........................}$$

[2 marks]

PRACTICAL

3 A student is making a sample of a salt by reacting calcium carbonate with hydrochloric acid. *(Grade 4-5)*

3.1 Name the salt formed in this reaction.

[1 mark]

The student adds solid calcium carbonate to the acid until the reaction is complete.
This is shown by a change in colour of an indicator in the solution.
The student then crystallises the solution to obtain the salt.

3.2 Suggest why the student's method will **not** produce a pure sample of the salt.

[1 mark]

3.3* Describe a method the student could use to make a sample of the soluble salt, that does
not involve measuring the pH of the solution. Include in your answer how the student
could use filtration and crystallisation to make pure and dry crystals of the soluble salt.

[6 marks]

Metals and Their Reactivity

*You can place **metals** in order of reactivity. This can be really useful for **predicting** their **reactions**.*

The **Reactivity Series** — How Easily a **Metal** Reacts

1) The reactivity series lists metals in order of how reactive they are (their reactivity).
2) Metals react to form positive ions.
3) So for metals, their reactivity depends on how easily they lose electrons and form positive ions.
4) The higher up the reactivity series a metal is, the more easily it forms positive ions.

The Reactivity Series

Potassium	K
Sodium	Na
Lithium	Li
Calcium	Ca
Magnesium	Mg
Carbon	C
Zinc	Zn
Iron	Fe
Hydrogen	H
Copper	Cu

Very Reactive
Fairly Reactive
Not very Reactive

Make sure you learn this list.

Carbon and hydrogen are non-metals but are often included in the reactivity series.

Metals React With Acids

1) Some metals react with acids to produce a salt and hydrogen gas.

HCl reacts to form chloride salts, H_2SO_4 reacts to form sulfate salts.

Acid + Metal → Salt + Hydrogen

hydrochloric acid + magnesium → magnesium chloride + hydrogen $2HCl + Mg → MgCl_2 + H_2$
sulfuric acid + zinc → zinc sulfate + hydrogen $H_2SO_4 + Zn → ZnSO_4 + H_2$
hydrochloric acid + iron → iron chloride + hydrogen $2HCl + Fe → FeCl_2 + H_2$

2) Very reactive metals like potassium, sodium, lithium and calcium react explosively with acids.
3) Less reactive metals such as magnesium, zinc and iron react less violently with acids.
4) In general, copper won't react with cold, dilute acids.

You need to make sure you know the reactivity series

The reactivity series is useful for predicting the reactions of metals, but you might not be given it in the exam. You need to learn it. If you're struggling, try making up a mnemonic to help you remember — or just use this one: People Say Long Calls Make Cartoon Zebras Into Happy Cows.

Topic C4 — Chemical Changes

Metals and Their Reactivity

*As well as reacting with acids, metals can also react with **water** and the **salts** of other metals.*

Some Metals React with **Water**

1) Many metals will react with water.

$$\text{Metal} + \text{Water} \rightarrow \text{Metal Hydroxide} + \text{Hydrogen}$$

For example, calcium: $\quad Ca_{(s)} + 2H_2O_{(l)} \rightarrow Ca(OH)_{2(aq)} + H_{2(g)}$

2) The metals potassium, sodium, lithium and calcium will all react with water.

3) Less reactive metals like zinc, iron and copper won't react with water.

You Can Work Out a **Reactivity Series** from the Reactions of Metals

1) If you put metals in order from most reactive to least reactive based on their reactions with either an acid or water, the order you get is the reactivity series (see the previous page).

2) To compare the reactivities of metals, you could watch how quickly bubbles of hydrogen are formed in their reactions with water or acid. The more reactive the metal, the faster the bubbles will form.

For these experiments to be fair, the mass and surface area of the metals should be the same each time.

3) You can also measure the temperature change of the reaction in a set time period. The more reactive the metal, the greater the temperature change should be.

More Reactive Metals can **Displace** Less Reactive Metals from Salts

Displacement reactions involve one metal kicking another one out of a compound. Here's the rule:

A more reactive metal will displace a less reactive metal from its compound.

- For example, iron is more reactive than copper. So if you add solid iron to copper sulfate solution, you get a displacement reaction.

- The iron kicks the copper out of copper sulfate. You end up with iron sulfate solution and copper solid.

$$\text{iron} + \text{copper sulfate} \rightarrow \text{iron sulfate} + \text{copper}$$
$$Fe_{(s)} + CuSO_{4(aq)} \rightarrow FeSO_{4(aq)} + Cu_{(s)}$$

Metals at the top of the reactivity series are highly reactive

There are plenty of chemical equations to get your head around here. If the question doesn't ask you for a name, you can save time in the exam if you just write a chemical symbol instead of a full name — but always check that you're using the right one, otherwise you could lose marks.

Q1 Video Solution

Q1   Give the balanced equation, including state symbols, for the reaction of sodium and water.

[3 marks]

Extracting Metals

*A **few metals** are found in the ground in their **pure forms**. No such luck with the rest though — they need to be **extracted** from other compounds before you can use them. Here's how it works...*

Metals Often Have to be Separated from their **Oxides**

1) Lots of common metals, like iron and aluminium, react with <u>oxygen</u> to form <u>oxides</u>.
2) This process is an example of <u>oxidation</u>.
3) These oxides are often the <u>ores</u> that the metals are removed (extracted) from.
4) A reaction that separates a metal from its oxide is called a <u>reduction reaction</u>.

An ore is a type of rock that contains metal compounds. Most metals are found in the earth as ores.

Oxidation = Gain of Oxygen	Reduction = Loss of Oxygen
For example, magnesium is <u>oxidised</u> to make magnesium oxide. $$2Mg + O_2 \rightarrow 2MgO$$	For example, copper oxide is <u>reduced</u> to copper. $$2CuO + C \rightarrow 2Cu + CO_2$$

Some Metals can be **Extracted** by **Reduction** with **Carbon**

1) Some metals can be <u>extracted</u> from their ores using a reaction with <u>carbon</u>.
2) In this reaction, the ore is <u>reduced</u> as oxygen is <u>removed</u> from it. Carbon <u>gains</u> oxygen, so it is <u>oxidised</u>.
3) For example:

$$\text{iron(III) oxide} + \text{carbon} \rightarrow \text{iron} + \text{carbon dioxide}$$
$$2Fe_2O_3 + 3C \rightarrow 4Fe + 3CO_2$$

Iron has lost oxygen.　　Carbon has gained oxygen.

4) The <u>reactivity series</u> can tell you if a metal can be extracted with carbon.

- Metals <u>above carbon</u> in the reactivity series are extracted using <u>electrolysis</u> (p.223-224). This is expensive as it takes lots of <u>energy</u> to <u>melt</u> the ore and to produce the <u>electricity</u>.
- Electrolysis is also used to extract metals that <u>react</u> with carbon.
- Metals <u>below carbon</u> in the reactivity series can be extracted by <u>reduction</u> using <u>carbon</u>. For example, <u>iron oxide</u> is reduced in a <u>blast furnace</u> to make <u>iron</u> (see above).
- This is because carbon <u>can only take the oxygen</u> away from metals which are <u>less reactive</u> than carbon <u>itself</u> is.

Make sure you can explain how and why different metals are extracted in different ways.

5) Some metals are <u>so unreactive</u> they are found in the earth as the metal <u>itself</u>. For example, gold.

Carbon can't reduce things above it in the reactivity series

Make sure you understand the difference between <u>reduction</u> and <u>oxidation</u> and make sure that you can spot which substance has been <u>reduced</u> and which substance has been <u>oxidised</u> in a reaction.

Q1 Video Solution

Q1　Write a balanced equation for the reduction of lead oxide, PbO, by carbon, C.　　[2 marks]

Q2　A mining company tried to extract calcium from its ore by reduction with carbon. The process did not work. Explain why.　　[1 mark]

Warm-Up & Exam Questions

Hoping to test your knowledge with some testing chemistry questions? You're in luck...

Warm-Up Questions

1) True or false? The reactivity of a metal is determined by how easily it forms a positive ion.
2) Magnesium is reacted with dilute hydrochloric acid. What is the name of the salt formed?
3) Which two substances are formed when a metal reacts with water?

Exam Questions

1 Which of the following metals would displace zinc from a solution of zinc chloride but **would not** displace calcium from a solution of calcium chloride?

Grade 3-4

☐ Magnesium   ☐ Sodium   ☐ Copper   ☐ Iron

[1 mark]

2 **Figure 1** shows part of the reactivity series of metals. Carbon and hydrogen have also been included in this reactivity series.

Grade 4-5

Figure 1

| Potassium K |
| Sodium Na |
| Calcium Ca |
| Magnesium Mg |
| CARBON C |
| Zinc Zn |
| Iron Fe |
| HYDROGEN H |
| Copper Cu |

2.1 Name **one** metal from **Figure 1** that is more reactive than magnesium.

[1 mark]

2.2 Name **one** metal from **Figure 1** which would **not** displace hydrogen from sulfuric acid.

[1 mark]

2.3 A student places a small piece of zinc into dilute acid. The mixture produces bubbles of hydrogen gas fairly slowly.

Predict whether the reaction would be more or less violent if iron was used instead of zinc. Explain your answer.

[2 marks]

2.4 Name **one** metal from **Figure 1** that could **not** be extracted from its ore by reduction with carbon.

[1 mark]

3 A student placed pieces of copper, zinc and an unknown metal, **X**, in zinc sulfate solution and copper sulfate solution and left them for an hour. The student's results are shown in **Table 1**.

Grade 4-5

3.1 Explain how you can tell that metal **X** is more reactive than copper.

[1 mark]

Table 1

	zinc	copper	metal X
reaction with zinc sulfate	no reaction	no reaction	no reaction
reaction with copper sulfate	reaction	no reaction	reaction

3.2 Explain why there was no reaction between copper and zinc sulfate.

[1 mark]

3.3 Suggest the name of the metal, **X**.

[1 mark]

Electrolysis

*Electrolysis uses **electricity** to cause a reaction. You need to know how it works, so here we go...*

Electrolysis Means 'Splitting Up with Electricity'

1) An <u>electrolyte</u> is just a <u>liquid or solution</u> that can <u>conduct electricity</u>.
For example, an ionic compound that's either <u>dissolved</u> in water, or <u>melted</u> so it's a liquid.

2) An <u>electrode</u> is a <u>solid</u> that is put in the electrolyte and <u>conducts electricity</u>.

3) In <u>electrolysis</u>, an electric current is passed through an electrolyte.
The ions move towards the electrodes, where they react.
The compound then <u>breaks down</u>.

4) <u>Positive ions</u> in the electrolyte move towards the <u>cathode</u> (negative electrode).
Here, they <u>gain</u> electrons.

5) <u>Negative ions</u> in the electrolyte move towards the <u>anode</u> (positive electrode).
Here, they <u>lose</u> electrons.

6) The ions form the <u>uncharged element</u>. The ions are said to be <u>discharged</u> from the electrolyte.

7) A <u>flow of charge</u> is created through the <u>electrolyte</u> as the ions travel to the electrodes.

Electrolysis of Molten Ionic Solids Forms Elements

1) <u>Molten ionic compounds can</u> be electrolysed because the ions can <u>move freely</u> and conduct electricity.

2) Molten ionic liquids are always broken up into their <u>elements</u>.

3) The <u>metal</u> forms at the <u>cathode</u>. The <u>non-metal</u> is formed at the <u>anode</u>.

> For example, when molten <u>lead bromide</u> is electrolysed, <u>lead</u> forms at the cathode and <u>bromine</u> forms at the anode.

See the next page for another example of how electrolysis of molten ionic compounds works.

4) The electrodes should be <u>inert</u> (unreactive) so they <u>don't react</u> with the electrolyte.

Positive ions move towards the negative electrode

It's easy to get in a muddle with electrolysis, but if you can remember that the <u>cathode</u> is the <u>negative</u> electrode and so it attracts the <u>positive metal ions</u> then you're halfway there.
And the anode is just the <u>opposite</u> — it's <u>positive</u>, so it attracts the <u>negative non-metal ions</u>.

Electrolysis

*You saw on page 221 how carbon can be used to **extract** some metals from their **ores**.*
*Now it's time to look at how **electrolysis** can also be used for extracting metals.*

Metals can be Extracted From Their Ores Using Electrolysis

1) Aluminium is extracted from an ore that contains <u>aluminium oxide</u>, Al_2O_3.
2) Aluminium oxide has a <u>very high</u> melting point so it's mixed with a substance called <u>cryolite</u>. This <u>lowers</u> the melting point.
3) The <u>positive Al^{3+} ions</u> are attracted to the <u>negative electrode</u> where they form <u>aluminium atoms</u>.
4) The <u>negative O^{2-} ions</u> are attracted to the <u>positive electrode</u> where they react to form <u>O_2</u> molecules.

At the **Negative** Electrode

1) <u>Metals</u> form <u>positive ions</u>.
2) They're attracted to the <u>negative</u> electrode.
3) <u>Aluminium</u> is produced.

At the **Positive** Electrode

1) <u>Non-metals</u> form <u>negative ions</u>.
2) They're attracted to the <u>positive</u> electrode.
3) <u>Oxygen</u> is produced.

Overall Equation:

aluminium oxide → aluminium + oxygen
$$2Al_2O_{3(l)} \rightarrow 4Al_{(l)} + 3O_{2(g)}$$

Electrolysis is used to extract reactive metals from their ores

Extracting aluminium by electrolysis is handy, but it does have <u>downsides</u>. In industry, the mixture of aluminium oxide and cryolite is heated to around 960 °C. These temperatures and the electrical current used in electrolysis require large amounts of <u>energy</u>. So the whole process is <u>expensive</u>.

Q1 A student carries out electrolysis on molten calcium chloride. What is produced at:
a) the anode? b) the cathode? [2 marks]

Q1 Video
Solution

Electrolysis of Aqueous Solutions

*When you electrolyse a salt that's dissolved in water, you also have to think about the ions from the **water**.*

You Can **Predict** what Forms when a **Salt Solution** is **Electrolysed**

1) <u>Water</u> can break down into H⁺ and OH⁻ ions.

$$H_2O_{(l)} \rightleftharpoons H^+_{(aq)} + OH^-_{(aq)}$$

The ⇌ symbol in this reaction shows that it's reversible. For more about reversible reactions see p.242-243.

2) So in <u>solutions</u> that contain <u>water</u>, there will be the <u>ions</u> from the ionic compound as well as <u>hydrogen ions</u> (H⁺) and <u>hydroxide ions</u> (OH⁻) from the <u>water</u>.

3) <u>H⁺ ions</u> and <u>metal ions</u> will move to the <u>cathode</u>.

4) If the metal's more reactive than hydrogen, <u>hydrogen gas</u> will form.

5) If the metal is <u>less reactive</u> than hydrogen, a solid layer of the <u>pure metal</u> will form.

6) If the salt contains <u>halide ions</u> (Cl⁻, Br⁻, I⁻), chlorine, bromine or iodine will form at the <u>anode</u>.

7) If <u>no halide ions</u> are present, then the OH⁻ ions lose electrons and <u>oxygen</u> will form at the anode.

Example 1: Electrolysis of **Copper Sulfate Solution**

A solution of <u>copper(II) sulfate</u> ($CuSO_4$) contains <u>four different ions</u>: Cu^{2+}, SO_4^{2-}, H^+ and OH^-.

At the cathode:
- <u>Copper</u> metal is less reactive than hydrogen.
- So <u>copper metal</u> is produced.

At the anode:
- There aren't any <u>halide ions</u> present.
- So <u>oxygen</u> and <u>water</u> are produced.

Electrolysis of Aqueous Solutions

Example 2: Electrolysis of **Sodium Chloride Solution**

A solution of sodium chloride (NaCl) contains four different ions: Na^+, Cl^-, OH^- and H^+.

At the cathode:
- Sodium metal is more reactive than hydrogen.
- So hydrogen gas is produced.

At the anode:
- Chloride ions are in the solution.
- So chlorine gas is produced.

You can do **Electrolysis** in the **Lab**

PRACTICAL

1) You can set up an electrolysis experiment in the lab like the set-up on page 396.

2) This will let you collect any gases that form in the reaction.

3) Once the experiment is finished you can test the gases to work out what they are.

- Chlorine bleaches damp litmus paper, turning it white.

- Hydrogen makes a "squeaky pop" with a lighted splint.

For more on tests for gases, turn to page 259

- Oxygen will relight a glowing splint.

Remember — all aqueous solutions contain OH^- and H^+ ions

There are two key things to remember: 1) At the cathode, hydrogen gas is made, unless the metal ions are less reactive than hydrogen — then you get a coating of the metal. 2) At the anode, oxygen and water are made, unless halide ions are present — then the halogen is made.

Q1 Video Solution

Q1   An aqueous solution of copper bromide, $CuBr_2$, is electrolysed using inert electrodes.
      State what is produced at: a) the anode,   b) the cathode.   [2 marks]

Warm-Up & Exam Questions

Time to test your knowledge. Try and get through the following questions. If there's anything you're not quite sure about, have a look at the pages again until you can answer all the questions.

Warm-Up Questions

1) Are metals deposited at the anode or the cathode during electrolysis?

2) True or False? The electrolysis of molten zinc chloride produces zinc and chlorine gas.

3) What is formed at the cathode during the electrolysis of an aqueous solution of potassium hydroxide?
   A. Potassium metal
   B. Hydrogen gas
   C. Oxygen and water
   D. Chlorine gas

Exam Questions

1   Sodium chloride, NaCl, is an ionic compound.
Use words from the box to complete the sentences below.

(Grade 1-3)

| negative | gaseous | sodium | aqueous | hydrogen | hydroxide |

When molten sodium chloride is electrolysed, the .... chloride ions move towards the

anode and form chlorine gas. At the cathode, the .... ions gain electrons.

[2 marks]

2   **Figure 1** shows the electrolysis of molten lead bromide, $PbBr_2$.   *(Grade 4-5)*

Figure 1

2.1   Which substance is represented in **Figure 1** by the letter **W**?

☐ Br_2 ☐ Br^-

☐ Molten lead   ☐ Pb^{2+}

[1 mark]

2.2   Which substance is represented in **Figure 1** by the letter **X**?

☐ Br_2 ☐ Br^-

☐ Molten lead   ☐ Pb^{2+}

[1 mark]

2.3   Which substance is represented in **Figure 1** by the letter **Y**?

☐ Br_2 ☐ Br^- ☐ Molten lead   ☐ Pb^{2+}

[1 mark]

2.4   Which substance is represented in **Figure 1** by the letter **Z**?

☐ Br_2 ☐ Br^- ☐ Molten lead   ☐ Pb^{2+}

[1 mark]

Topic C5 — Energy Changes

Exothermic and Endothermic Reactions

*Whenever chemical reactions occur, there are changes in **energy**. This means that when chemicals get together, things either **heat up** or **cool down**. I'll give you a heads up — this page is a good 'un.*

Energy is **Moved Around** in **Chemical Reactions**

1) Chemicals <u>store</u> a certain amount of energy — and <u>different chemicals</u> store <u>different amounts</u>.

2) Sometimes, the <u>products</u> of a reaction store <u>more</u> energy than the <u>reactants</u>. This means that the products have <u>taken in</u> energy from the <u>surroundings</u> during the reaction.

3) But if the products store <u>less</u> energy, then the <u>extra</u> energy was transferred (given out) <u>to the surroundings</u> during the reaction.

4) The amount of energy transferred is the <u>difference</u> between the energy of the products and the energy of the reactants.

5) The <u>overall</u> amount of energy doesn't change. This is because energy stays the <u>same</u> (is <u>conserved</u>) in reactions — it can't be made or destroyed, only <u>moved around</u>.

6) This means the amount of energy in the <u>universe</u> always stays the <u>same</u>.

In an **Exothermic** Reaction, Energy is **Given Out**

An <u>exothermic</u> reaction is one which <u>gives out</u> energy to the <u>surroundings</u>. This is shown by a <u>rise in temperature</u> of the surroundings.

1) <u>Examples</u> of exothermic reactions include:

- <u>Burning fuels</u> — also called <u>combustion</u>.
- <u>Neutralisation reactions</u> (acid + alkali).
- Many <u>oxidation reactions</u>.

Physical processes can also take in or release energy. E.g. freezing is an exothermic process, melting is endothermic.

2) Exothermic reactions have lots of everyday <u>uses</u>. For example:

Some <u>hand warmers</u> use an exothermic reaction to <u>release energy</u>. <u>Self-heating cans</u> of hot chocolate and coffee also use <u>exothermic reactions</u> between chemicals in their bases.

In an **Endothermic** Reaction, Energy is **Taken In**

An <u>endothermic</u> reaction is one which <u>takes in</u> energy <u>from</u> the surroundings. This is shown by a <u>fall in temperature</u> of the surroundings.

1) <u>Examples</u> of endothermic reactions include:

- The reaction between <u>citric acid</u> and <u>sodium hydrogencarbonate</u>.
- <u>Thermal decomposition</u> (when a substance breaks down when it's heated).

2) Exothermic reactions have lots of everyday <u>uses</u>. For example:

Endothermic reactions are used in some <u>sports injury packs</u>. The chemical reaction allows the pack to become <u>instantly cooler</u> without having to put it in the <u>freezer</u>.

Measuring Energy Changes

*Sometimes it's not enough to just know if a reaction is **endothermic** or **exothermic**.*
*You may also need to measure **how much** the **temperature** changes during a reaction.*

Energy Transfer can be Measured

You can use an experiment to investigate the <u>temperature change</u> of a chemical reaction.

1) You can do this by taking the <u>temperature of the reactants</u> and <u>mixing</u> them in a <u>polystyrene cup</u>.

2) If the temperature of the solution <u>rises</u> during the reaction, record the <u>highest temperature</u> that it reaches.
If the temperature of the solution <u>falls</u> during the reaction, record the <u>lowest temperature</u> that it reaches.

3) To find the temperature change, <u>take away</u> this temperature from the temperature of the <u>reactants</u>.

4) If the temperature goes <u>up</u>, the reaction's <u>exothermic</u>.
If the temperature goes <u>down</u>, the reaction's <u>endothermic</u>.

5) The biggest <u>problem</u> with temperature measurements is the amount of energy <u>lost to the surroundings</u>.

6) You can reduce this by putting a <u>lid</u> on the polystyrene cup and putting the cup into a <u>beaker of cotton wool</u>.

This method works for a number of <u>different</u> reactions. For example:

- <u>neutralisation</u> reactions.
- reactions between <u>metals</u> and <u>acids</u>.
- reactions between <u>acids</u> and <u>carbonates</u>.
- <u>displacement</u> reactions of metals.

The Temperature Change Depends on Different Variables

1) You can also use this method to investigate what effect different <u>variables</u> have on the temperature change — e.g. the <u>mass</u> or <u>concentration</u> of the reactants used.

2) Here's how you could test the effect of <u>acid concentration</u> on the temperature change of a <u>neutralisation</u> reaction between hydrochloric acid (HCl) and sodium hydroxide (NaOH):

1) Put 25 cm³ each of 10 g/dm³ hydrochloric acid and sodium hydroxide in <u>separate beakers</u>.
2) Place the beakers in a water bath set to 25 °C until they are both at the <u>same temperature</u> (25 °C).
3) Add the HCl followed by the NaOH to a polystyrene cup with a lid — as in the diagram above.
4) Take the temperature of the mixture <u>every 30 seconds</u>, and record the highest temperature.
5) Use your <u>results</u> to work out the <u>temperature change</u> of the reaction.
6) <u>Repeat</u> these steps using 20 g/dm³ and then 30 g/dm³ of hydrochloric acid. Then <u>compare</u> your results to see how acid concentration <u>affects</u> the temperature change of the reaction.

To get a reasonably accurate reading, insulate your reaction

It's really important the reaction mixture is well insulated in the method shown above. Without insulation, heat might escape and the temperature reading of the solution would be affected.

Reaction Profiles

Reaction profiles are handy little diagrams which show you the **changes in energy** during a reaction.

Activation Energy is Needed to Start a Reaction

1) The activation energy is the <u>minimum amount</u> of energy the reactants need to have to <u>react</u> when they <u>collide with each other</u>.

2) The <u>greater</u> the activation energy, the <u>more</u> energy needed to <u>start</u> the reaction. This energy has to be <u>given</u>, e.g. by <u>heating</u> the reaction mixture.

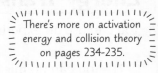
There's more on activation energy and collision theory on pages 234-235.

Reaction Profiles Show Energy Changes

<u>Reaction profiles</u> are diagrams that show the <u>difference between the energies</u> of the reactants and products in a reaction, and how the energy <u>changes</u> over the course of the reaction.

Exothermic Reactions

Reaction profiles are sometimes called energy level diagrams.

1) The reaction profile on the right shows an <u>exothermic reaction</u>.

2) You can tell because the products are at a <u>lower energy</u> than the reactants.

3) The difference in <u>height</u> between the reactants and the products shows the <u>overall energy change</u> in the reaction (the energy <u>given out</u>).

4) The <u>rise</u> in energy at the start shows the energy needed to <u>start the reaction</u>. This is the <u>activation energy</u>.

EXOTHERMIC

Energy

Activation Energy

reactants

Total energy given out

products

Progress of reaction

Endothermic Reactions

1) In this reaction profile, the products are at a <u>higher energy</u> than the reactants. So the reaction is <u>endothermic</u>.

2) The difference in <u>height</u> shows the <u>overall energy change</u> during the reaction (the energy <u>taken in</u>).

3) The rise in energy at the start is the <u>activation energy</u>.

ENDOTHERMIC

Energy

Activation energy

products

Total energy taken in

reactants

Progress of reaction

You can also write the formulas for the reactants and products on the reaction profile instead of 'reactants' and 'products'.

A reaction profile shows the energy levels during a reaction

The diagrams above might seem a bit confusing at first — remember, it's the energy in the <u>chemicals themselves</u>, not in their surroundings, which is being shown in the diagrams.
To help you remember them, why not <u>draw them out</u> and <u>label them</u> for yourself.

Q1 Video Solution

Q1 Here is the equation for the exothermic reaction between methane and oxygen:
$CH_{4(g)} + 2O_{2(g)} \rightarrow CO_{2(g)} + 2H_2O_{(g)}$. Draw a reaction profile for this reaction. [3 marks]

Warm-Up & Exam Questions

A whole bunch of reactions, an experiment, some funny diagrams — there's a lot to get your head around on the last few pages. Here are some questions so that you can check how you're getting on.

Warm-Up Questions

1) True or False? The amount of energy in the universe always stays the same.
2) Give one example of an everyday use of an exothermic reaction.
3) How will the temperature of the surroundings change during an endothermic reaction?
4) Is the reaction between citric acid and sodium hydrogencarbonate exothermic or endothermic?
5) What is shown by the difference in height between the reactants and products in the reaction profile for an exothermic reaction?

Exam Questions

1 Which of the following types of reaction is most likely to be endothermic? Tick **one** box.

☐ combustion ☐ neutralisation ☐ thermal decomposition ☐ oxidation

[1 mark]

2 A student measured the temperature change during a reaction between sodium hydroxide and hydrochloric acid using the apparatus shown in **Figure 1**.

PRACTICAL

Figure 1

2.1 Before mixing the reagents, the student measured the temperature of each of them. Suggest why.

[1 mark]

2.2 State the purpose of the cotton wool and the lid in the experimental set-up in **Figure 1**.

[1 mark]

2.3 How could the student test the repeatability of the temperature change that they recorded during the experiment?

[2 marks]

3 The diagrams in **Figure 2** represent the energy changes in four different chemical reactions.

Figure 2

Write the letter of **one** diagram, **A**, **B**, **C** or **D**, which correctly shows an endothermic reaction.

[1 mark]

Revision Summary for Topics C1-5

That's <u>Topics C1-5</u> done — time to check <u>how much you actually remember</u>.
- Try these questions and <u>tick off each one</u> when you <u>get it right</u>.
- When you're <u>completely happy</u> with a topic, tick it off.

For even more practice, try the Retrieval Quizzes for Topics C1-5 — just scan the QR codes!

Topic C1 — Atomic Structure and the Periodic Table (p.161-187) ☑

1) Draw an atom. Label the nucleus and the electrons.
2) What is the smallest part of an element that you can have?
3) Balance these equations: a) $Mg + O_2 \rightarrow MgO$ b) $H_2SO_4 + NaOH \rightarrow Na_2SO_4 + H_2O$
4) What method could you use to separate dyes in an ink?
5) Which method of separation is useful to separate an insoluble solid from a liquid?
6) What is the maximum number of electrons that can be in the third shell of an atom?
7) What is the electronic structure of sodium?
8) What does the group number of an element tell you about its electrons?
9) State two trends as you go down Group 1 of the periodic table.
10) How do the boiling points of halogens change as you go down the group?
11) Halogens form ions when they react with metals. What is the charge of the halogen ions?
12) Why are the Group 0 elements single atoms?

Topic C2 — Bonding, Structure and Properties of Matter (p.190-207) ☑

13) What type of bond is formed when a metal reacts with a non-metal?
14) Draw dot and cross diagrams to show the formation of:
   a) sodium chloride   b) magnesium oxide   c) magnesium chloride
15) List three properties of ionic compounds.
16) How do covalent bonds form?
17) What type of bonds form between the atoms in a polymer?
18) Explain why graphite can conduct electricity.
19) Give one reason why alloys are more useful than metals.
20) Name the three states of matter.

Topic C3 — Quantitative Chemistry (p.209-212) ☑

21) Write down the formula for the percentage mass of an element in a compound.
22) What do the following terms mean: a) solvent   b) solute?

Topic C4 — Chemical Changes (p.215-226) ☑

23) Name the products that will form when hydrochloric acid reacts with sodium carbonate.
24) What do you get if you react an acid with an insoluble base?
25) Complete the equation for the reaction of calcium with water: $Ca + ?H_2O \rightarrow ? + H_2$
26) During electrolysis, what are the names for the positive electrode and the negative electrode?
27) A salt solution contains halide ions. Will oxygen gas be released if this solution is electrolysed?

Topic C5 — Energy Changes (p.228-230) ☑

28) In an exothermic reaction, is energy transferred to or from the surroundings?
29) Define what is meant by an endothermic reaction.
30) Sketch a reaction profile for an exothermic reaction.

Rates of Reaction

*Rates of reaction are pretty **important**. In **industry**, the **faster** you make **chemicals**, the **faster** you make **money**.*

The **Speed** of a **Reaction** is Called its **Rate**

1) The <u>rate</u> of a chemical reaction is how <u>fast</u> the <u>reactants</u> are changed into <u>products</u>.

2) Some reactions are very <u>slow</u>, for example, rusting. Others, like burning, are <u>fast</u>.

3) <u>Graphs</u> can show you how the rate (speed) of a reaction changes.

4) The <u>steeper</u> the line on the graph, the <u>faster</u> the rate of reaction.

5) <u>Over time</u> the line becomes <u>less steep</u> as the reactants are <u>used up</u>.

Reaction Rates Can **Change** when the Reaction **Conditions** Change

1) Faster <u>reactions</u> have <u>steeper</u> lines to begin with and become <u>flat</u> more quickly.

2) The graph below shows how the <u>speed</u> of a particular reaction changes under <u>different conditions</u>.

- Line 1 shows the <u>original reaction</u>.

- Line 2 shows the same reaction taking place <u>faster</u>.
  It starts more <u>steeply</u> than line 1. It also goes <u>flat sooner</u>.

- Line 3 shows the same reaction taking place more <u>slowly</u>.
  It <u>isn't</u> as <u>steep</u> at the start as line 1 and goes <u>flat later</u>.

- Lines 1, 2 and 3 all meet at the <u>same level</u>.
  This shows that they all produce the <u>same amount</u> of product.
  They just take <u>different times</u> to produce it.

- Line 4 shows <u>more product</u> is formed.
  This can only happen if there were <u>more reactants</u> at the start.

Factors Affecting Rates of Reaction

*I'd ask you to **guess** what these two pages are about, but the **title** pretty much says it all really. Read on...*

Particles Must **Collide** with **Enough Energy** in Order to **React**

1) Reaction rates can be explained by an idea called <u>collision theory</u>.
2) Collision theory says that a <u>reaction</u> will <u>only</u> take place when particles <u>collide</u> (crash into each other).
3) The particles also have to have a certain amount of <u>energy</u> when they collide, otherwise they won't <u>react</u>.
4) The <u>minimum</u> (smallest) amount of energy they need is called the <u>activation energy</u>.
5) Collision theory can explain rates of reactions in a bit more detail too...

- The more <u>often</u> the particles collide, the <u>faster</u> the reaction will happen.
- For example, if the reactant particles in a certain reaction collide with enough energy <u>twice as often</u>, the reaction will happen <u>twice as fast</u>.
- The <u>more energy</u> the particles have, the <u>faster</u> the reaction will be.
- This is because there's more chance that they'll have <u>at least</u> the <u>activation energy</u>.

 How often the particles collide is sometimes called the 'collision frequency'.

The **Rate of Reaction** Depends on **Four Things**

1) <u>Temperature</u>.
2) <u>Concentration</u> of a solution (or <u>pressure</u> of a gas).
3) <u>Surface area</u> of a solid.
4) Whether a <u>catalyst</u> is used.

Increasing the **Temperature** Increases the Rate

1) When temperature <u>increases</u>, the particles move <u>faster</u>.
2) If they move faster, they collide more <u>frequently</u> (often).
3) They also have <u>more energy</u>, so <u>more collisions</u> have <u>enough energy</u> to make the reaction happen.

If particles collide twice as often with enough energy to react, the rate of reaction will be twice as fast. If they collide three times as often it'll be three times as fast.

Increasing the **Concentration** or **Pressure** Increases the Rate

1) If a solution is more <u>concentrated</u>, it has <u>more particles</u> in the <u>same volume</u>.
2) And when the <u>pressure</u> of a gas is increased, it means the <u>same number</u> of particles are now in a <u>smaller space</u>.
3) So <u>collisions</u> between the reactant particles are <u>more frequent</u>.

Low concentration/ pressure

High concentration/ pressure

Topic C6 — The Rate and Extent of Chemical Change

Factors Affecting Rates of Reaction

Increasing the **Surface Area** Increases the Rate

1) If one of the reactants is a <u>solid</u>, then breaking it up into <u>smaller pieces</u> will <u>increase</u> its <u>surface area to volume ratio</u>.

2) This means the same amount of solid has a <u>bigger surface area</u>.

3) So <u>more</u> of the solid's particles are available to particles of the other reactant. And collisions will be <u>more frequent</u>.

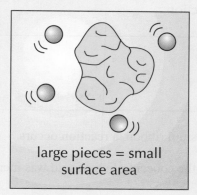

large pieces = small surface area

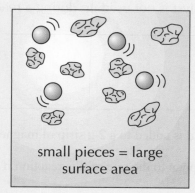

small pieces = large surface area

Using a **Catalyst** Increases the Rate

1) A catalyst is a substance that <u>speeds up</u> a reaction. <u>None</u> of it gets <u>used up</u> in the reaction.

2) This means it's <u>not</u> part of the reaction <u>equation</u>.

3) <u>Different</u> catalysts are needed for different reactions.

4) Catalysts work by providing a <u>different pathway</u> for a reaction. The new pathway has a lower <u>activation energy</u>, so less energy is needed for the reaction to happen.

5) <u>Enzymes</u> are <u>biological catalysts</u> — they catalyse reactions in <u>living things</u>.

This is a reaction profile. There's more on these on p.230.

It's easier to learn stuff when you know the reasons for it

Once you've learnt everything off these two pages, the rates of reaction stuff should start making a lot more sense to you. The idea's fairly simple — the <u>more often</u> particles bump into each other, and the <u>harder they hit</u> when they do, the <u>faster</u> the reaction happens.

Warm-Up & Exam Questions

It's easy to think that you've understood something when you've just read through it. These questions should test whether you really understand the previous chunk of pages, and get you set for the next bit.

Warm-Up Questions

1) Give an example of a reaction that happens very slowly, and a reaction that is very fast.
2) According to collision theory, what must happen in order for two particles to react?
3) Explain why breaking a solid reactant into smaller pieces can affect the rate of a reaction.
4) True or False? A catalyst is not used up during a reaction.

Exam Questions

1 When hydrochloric acid is added to a 2 g strip of magnesium ribbon, a reaction occurs. **Grade 1-3**

1.1 Predict what would happen to the rate of this reaction if the concentration of acid was increased.

[1 mark]

1.2 Predict what would happen to the rate of this reaction if 2 g of powdered magnesium was used instead of the strip of magnesium ribbon.

[1 mark]

2 **Figure 1** shows how the speed of a reaction changed under three different conditions. **Grade 4-5**

2.1 Which line shows the reaction that produced the most product? Tick **one** box.

☐ A   ☐ B   ☐ C

[1 mark]

2.2 Which line shows the slowest reaction? Tick **one** box.

☐ A   ☐ B   ☐ C

[1 mark]

Figure 1

Amount of product formed

A

B

C

Time

2.3 Explain why increasing the temperature of the reactants would increase the rate of the slowest reaction.

[4 marks]

3 **Figure 2** shows the reaction profile of a reaction without a catalyst. **Grade 4-5**

3.1 Draw an arrow on **Figure 2** to show the activation energy of the reaction **without** a catalyst.

[1 mark]

3.2 On **Figure 2**, draw a curve to show what the reaction profile would look like **with** a catalyst.

[1 mark]

Figure 2

Energy

Reactants

Products

Progress of Reaction

Topic C6 — The Rate and Extent of Chemical Change

Measuring Rates of Reaction

*All this **talk** about reaction rate is fine and dandy, but it's no good if you can't **measure** it. You can investigate how **concentration** affects the rate of a reaction by **measuring** the **volume of gas** given off.*

Marble Chips and Hydrochloric Acid React to Produce a Gas

1) Measure out a set volume of <u>dilute hydrochloric acid</u> using a measuring cylinder.
2) Carefully pour it into a <u>conical flask</u>.
3) Measure out a set mass of <u>marble chips</u>.
4) Add the <u>marble chips</u> to the flask and quickly attach a delivery tube and <u>gas syringe</u> to the flask. You need to do this <u>quickly</u> before any gas <u>escapes</u>.
5) Start the <u>stopwatch</u> straight away.
6) Carbon dioxide gas will start to <u>collect</u> in the gas syringe. Take readings of the <u>volume</u> of gas at <u>regular intervals</u> (e.g. every 10 seconds) and write them into a table.

Gas syringes usually give volumes to the nearest cm³, so they're quite <u>accurate</u>.
Be careful though — if the reaction is too <u>vigorous</u>, you could blow the plunger out of the syringe.

Repeat the Experiment Using Different Concentrations of Acid

1) To investigate the effect of <u>concentration</u> on the rate of reaction, you'll need to <u>repeat</u> the experiment using <u>different concentrations</u> of <u>acid</u>. For example, you might use three different concentrations.
2) To make your experiment a <u>fair test</u>, you should <u>only</u> change the <u>concentration of acid</u>.
3) All the other <u>variables</u> (that's everything else) need to be kept the <u>same</u>. For example, keep the <u>volume</u> of acid, the <u>mass</u> of marble chips and the <u>temperature</u> the same each time.

You Then Need to Interpret Your Results

1) The <u>more</u> gas given off in a set amount of time, the <u>faster</u> the reaction.
2) You can use the results in your table to draw a <u>graph</u>. This makes it easier to see how concentration has affected the <u>rate</u>. (See pages 240 and 241 for more on drawing graphs and calculating rates.)

Measuring the volume of gas means you can find the rate

As exciting as everything on this page is, don't get carried away and forget about safety precautions — working with acids and gases can be <u>dangerous</u>. Always wear safety goggles, and make sure you don't let harmful gases escape into the room.

Measuring Rates of Reaction

Measuring the volume of gas given off isn't the only way of investigating the rate of a reaction. There are two more methods you need to be familiar with.

You Can Use a **Mass Balance** to Measure **Amount** of **Gas Produced**

1) As the gas forms and escapes from the container, the <u>mass</u> of the reaction mixture <u>falls</u>.
2) The <u>quicker</u> the reading on the balance <u>drops</u>, the <u>faster</u> the reaction.
3) If you take measurements at <u>regular intervals</u>, you can plot a <u>graph</u>.
4) This is a <u>very accurate</u> method because the mass balance is very accurate.
5) But it does <u>release</u> the gas into the <u>room</u>. That's not good if the gas is <u>toxic</u> (poisonous).

Cotton wool lets the gas escape but stops the acid spitting out.

You Can **Time** How **Long** it Takes For a **Solid Product** to Form

1) Some reactions start with a <u>transparent</u> (see-through) <u>solution</u> and produce a <u>solid product</u>.
2) The solid product (called a <u>precipitate</u>) will make the solution go <u>cloudy</u>.
   Another way of saying this is to say that its <u>turbidity increases</u>.
3) You can look at a <u>mark</u> through the solution and measure how long it takes for it to <u>disappear</u>.
   The <u>faster</u> the mark disappears, the <u>quicker</u> the reaction.
4) The results are <u>subjective</u> (there isn't just one right answer).
   This is because <u>people</u> might not agree over the <u>exact</u> point when the mark 'disappears'.

 ## Each of these methods has pros and cons

For example, the mass balance method is only accurate if the flask isn't <u>too hot</u>. Otherwise, the loss in mass that you see might be partly due to <u>evaporation</u> of liquid as well as the loss of gas formed during the reaction. And of course, it only works if a gas is given off during the reaction.

Measuring Rates of Reaction

*Here's how to use the last method from the previous page. It's **less accurate** than using a mass balance, but you need to know how to do it in case you want to investigate a reaction that **doesn't produce a gas**.*

Sodium Thiosulfate and Hydrochloric Acid Produce a Precipitate

- Sodium thiosulfate and hydrochloric acid (HCl) are both <u>clear solutions</u>. They react together to form a <u>yellow precipitate</u> of <u>sulfur</u>.
- The yellow precipitate causes the solution to turn <u>cloudy</u>.
- The <u>time taken</u> for this to happen can be measured to calculate the <u>rate of reaction</u>.

1) Start by adding a set volume of <u>dilute sodium thiosulfate</u> to a conical flask.
2) Place the flask on a piece of paper with a <u>black cross</u> drawn on it.
3) Add some <u>dilute hydrochloric acid</u> to the flask and start the stopwatch.
4) Watch the black cross <u>disappear</u> through the <u>cloudy sulfur</u> and <u>time</u> how long it takes to go.

This reaction releases sulfur dioxide, so the experiment should be carried out in a well-ventilated place.

5) <u>Repeat</u> the reaction using <u>different concentrations</u> of <u>one</u> reactant, e.g. the hydrochloric acid. (Only change the concentration of <u>one reactant</u> at a time though.)
6) Make sure you <u>control</u> all the other <u>variables</u> (keep everything else the <u>same</u>). For example, the volumes of solutions, the temperature and the size of the flask all need to be kept the same.
7) You'll end up with a set of results that show <u>how long</u> it takes for the cross to disappear at <u>different concentrations</u> of acid. Like this:

Concentration of HCl (g/dm³)	20	35	50	65	80
Time taken for mark to disappear (s)	193	184	178	171	164

8) The <u>higher</u> the concentration, the <u>faster</u> the reaction, so the <u>less time</u> it takes for the mark to disappear.

Make sure you use the right method for your experiment

The method shown on this page only works if there's a <u>really obvious</u> change in the solution. If there's only a <u>small change</u> in colour, it <u>might not be possible</u> to observe and time the change.

Graphs of Reaction Rate Experiments

*You might remember a bit about **graphs on reaction rate** from page 233 — well this page shows you how to **draw** and **interpret** them for **real experiments**.*

You Can **Draw** a **Graph** of Your **Results**

The type of graph you can draw depends on what experiment you did.
Here's how to draw a graph to show the volume of gas given off during a reaction.

EXAMPLE

Draw a graph of the results in the table.

Time (s)	0	10	20	30	40	50	60
Volume of gas (cm³)	0	9.5	15	18.5	20	20	20

1) Put time on the x-axis and volume of gas on the y-axis.
(The x-axis goes along the page, the y-axis goes up it.)

2) Carefully draw a small cross to show how much gas had been produced at each time interval.

3) Draw a line of best fit through the points. You could do this by drawing a smooth curve of best fit.

4) Or, you could draw two straight lines of best fit, one for the sloped part of the graph and one for the flat part.

Tangents Help You **Compare Reaction Rates** at Different **Points**

If your graph is a curve, it's not always easy to see how the rate changes during a reaction. Tangents can help make this clearer. A tangent is a straight line that touches the curve at one point and doesn't cross it.

EXAMPLE

The graph below shows the volume of gas produced during a chemical reaction. Is the rate fastest at 20 seconds or 30 seconds?

1) Position a ruler on the graph at a point where you want to know the rate — here it's 30 seconds.

2) Adjust the ruler until the space between the ruler and the curve is equal on both sides of the point.

3) Draw a line along the ruler to make the tangent. Extend the line right across the graph.

4) Do the same thing at 20 seconds.

5) Compare how steep the tangents are.

6) The tangent at 20 seconds (the blue line) is steeper than the tangent at 30 seconds (the red line).

This means that the reaction is faster at 20 seconds.

You can use tangents to measure how the rate changes

When you draw a tangent, don't forget to make it just touch the curve without crossing it.

Q1 Draw a graph of the results in this table.
Include a curved line of best fit. [3 marks]

Time (s)	0	10	20	30	40	50
Volume of CO₂ (cm³)	0	18	29	33	34	35

Q1 Video Solution

Topic C6 — The Rate and Extent of Chemical Change

Working Out Reaction Rates

*You need to be able to do some **calculations** to work out **reaction rates**.*

Here's How to **Work Out** the **Rate** of a Reaction

$$\text{Mean Rate of Reaction} = \frac{\text{Amount of reactant used or amount of product formed}}{\text{Time}}$$

This equation is for <u>mean</u> rate of reaction. So it lets you work out the <u>average rate</u> over an <u>amount of time</u>.

EXAMPLE

A reaction takes 120 seconds. 3.0 g of product are made. Find the mean rate of reaction.

Mean Rate = amount of product formed ÷ time
= 3.0 g ÷ 120 s = 0.025 g/s

Gases can be measured in cm^3, so if the product you measured was a gas the rate could be measured in cm^3/s rather than in g/s.

You Can Calculate the **Mean Reaction Rate** from a **Graph**

1) To find the <u>mean rate</u> for the <u>whole reaction</u>, start by working out when the reaction <u>finished</u>. This is when the line goes <u>flat</u>.

2) Then work out how much <u>product</u> was <u>formed</u> (or how much <u>reactant</u> was <u>used up</u>).

3) Then <u>divide this</u> by the <u>total time taken</u> for the reaction to finish.

EXAMPLE

The graph shows the volume of gas released by a reaction, measured at regular intervals. Find the mean rate of the reaction.

1) Work out when the reaction <u>finished</u>.

The line goes flat at 50 s.

2) Work out how much <u>product</u> was <u>formed</u>.

20 cm^3 of gas was formed.

3) <u>Divide</u> this by the <u>time taken</u> for the reaction to finish.

mean rate = 20 cm^3 ÷ 50 s = 0.40 cm^3/s

4) You can also use the graph to find the <u>mean rate</u> of reaction between <u>two points</u> in time:

EXAMPLE

Find the mean rate of reaction between 20 s and 40 s.

1) Work out how much <u>gas</u> was produced <u>between</u> 20 s and 40 s.

At 20 s, 15 cm^3 had been produced.
At 40 s, 19 cm^3 had been produced.
Volume released between 20 and 40 s was:
19 cm^3 − 15 cm^3 = 4 cm^3

2) Work out the <u>time difference</u> between 20 s and 40 s.

40 s − 20 s = 20 s

3) <u>Divide</u> the amount of gas produced by the time taken.

mean rate = 4 cm^3 ÷ 20 s = 0.2 cm^3/s

The mean reaction rate is the average reaction rate over time

Q1 A reaction takes 200 s. 6.0 g of reactant are used up.
What is the mean rate of the reaction? [2 marks]

Q1 Video Solution

Reversible Reactions

*Reversible reactions are what they sound like — **reactions** that can be **reversed**. So they can go **backwards**.*

Reversible Reactions Go Both Ways

$$A + B \rightleftharpoons C + D$$

1) This equation shows a <u>reversible reaction</u>.

2) The <u>products</u> (C and D) react to form the <u>reactants</u> (A and B) again.

3) You can tell it's a reversible reaction because of the $\rightleftharpoons$ symbol.

4) The reaction of A and B is called the <u>forward reaction</u>.
The reaction of C and D is the <u>backward reaction</u>.

Reversible Reactions Will Reach **Equilibrium**

1) As the <u>reactants</u> react, their concentrations <u>fall</u>.
The <u>forward</u> reaction <u>slows down</u>.

2) As more and more <u>products</u> are made the
<u>backward reaction</u> will <u>speed up</u>.

3) After a while the forward reaction and backward reaction
will be going at <u>exactly the same rate</u>. The system is at <u>equilibrium</u>.

4) Equilibrium <u>doesn't</u> mean that there are the <u>same amounts</u>
of products and reactants. It just means that the amounts
of products and reactants <u>aren't changing</u> any more.

5) Equilibrium is only reached if the reaction takes place in a
'<u>closed system</u>'. A <u>closed system</u> just means that <u>none</u> of the
reactants or products can <u>escape</u> and nothing else can get <u>in</u>.

Equilibrium — lots of activity, but not to any great effect

The idea of <u>equilibrium</u> is something that you need to get to grips with, as things will get <u>more complicated</u> on the next page. Have <u>another read</u> and make sure you've got the basics sorted before moving on. Remember, equilibrium means that things are staying nice and <u>stable</u> — but that <u>doesn't</u> mean that the reactions aren't happening. It just means that the <u>amounts</u> of reactants and products <u>aren't changing</u>.

Reversible Reactions

*In a reversible reaction, both the forward and the backward reactions are happening **at the same time**.*
*Some conditions can be **more favourable** to one direction than the other, making that reaction happen faster.*

Reversible Reactions Have an **Overall Direction**

1) Once a reaction is at equilibrium, there could be <u>more</u> of the <u>products</u> than reactants.
   When this happens, we say the equilibrium <u>favours</u> the <u>forwards direction</u>.

2) If there are <u>more reactants</u> than products then the equilibrium <u>favours</u> the <u>backwards direction</u>.

3) You can <u>change</u> the <u>direction</u> by <u>changing</u> the <u>conditions</u> (the temperature, pressure or concentration).

- <u>Ammonium chloride</u> breaks down to form <u>ammonia</u> and <u>hydrogen chloride</u>.
- The hydrogen chloride can then react with the ammonia to make ammonium chloride again.
- The reaction equation is:

$$\text{ammonium chloride} \underset{cool}{\overset{heat}{\rightleftharpoons}} \text{ammonia} + \text{hydrogen chloride}$$

- If you <u>heat</u> this reaction, it will go in the <u>forwards</u> direction.
  You'll get more ammonia and hydrogen chloride.
- If you <u>cool</u> it, it will go in the <u>backwards</u> direction. You'll get more ammonium chloride.

Reversible Reactions Can Be **Endothermic** and **Exothermic**

1) If the reaction is <u>endothermic</u> (takes in heat) in one direction,
   it will be <u>exothermic</u> (give out heat) in the other.

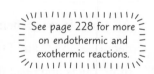
See page 228 for more on endothermic and exothermic reactions.

2) The amount of energy <u>taken in</u> by the endothermic reaction is the <u>same</u>
   as the amount <u>given out</u> during the exothermic reaction.

3) A good example is the <u>thermal decomposition</u> of hydrated copper sulfate:

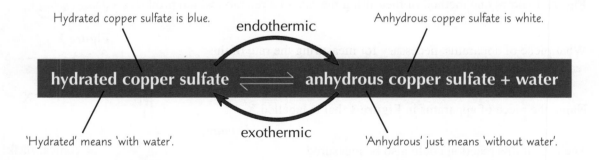

Hydrated copper sulfate is blue.   endothermic   Anhydrous copper sulfate is white.

hydrated copper sulfate ⇌ anhydrous copper sulfate + water

'Hydrated' means 'with water'.   exothermic   'Anhydrous' just means 'without water'.

More of the products = reaction favours the forwards direction

This whole exothermic/endothermic thing is a fairly simple idea — don't be put off by the long words.
Remember, "<u>exo</u>-" = <u>external</u>, "<u>-thermic</u>" = <u>heat</u>, so an exothermic reaction is one that <u>gives out</u> heat.
And "<u>endo</u>-" = erm... the other one. OK, there's no easy way to remember that one. Tough.

Warm-Up & Exam Questions

Not long now till this section's over, but first there are some questions for you to tackle.

1) Name one piece of apparatus that could be used to measure the rate of a reaction that gives off a gas.

2) Reaction A forms more product than Reaction B over 30 seconds.
   Which reaction, A or B, has a higher rate?

3) True or false? A steep tangent on a rate graph means that the rate is slow.

4) If there are more reactants than products in a reversible reaction at equilibrium, does the equilibrium favour the forwards or backwards direction?

Exam Questions

1   In the reaction below, substances A and B react to form substances C and D.

$$2A + B \rightleftharpoons 2C + D$$

1.1   What can you deduce about this reaction from the symbol $\rightleftharpoons$?

[1 mark]

1.2   When the reaction takes place in a closed system, equilibrium is reached.
Complete the sentences. Use words from the box.

equal	stay the same	forwards	rise	fall
reversible	changing	constant		backwards

As A and B react, their concentrations will .... and the rate of the forwards reaction will

decrease. As C and D are made, the .... reaction speeds up. After a while, the amounts

of products and reactants will be .... The system is at equilibrium.

[3 marks]

PRACTICAL

2   **Figure 1** shows one method of measuring the rate of a reaction which produces a gas.

2.1   What piece of apparatus, necessary for measuring the rate of this reaction, is missing from **Figure 1**?

[1 mark]

2.2   Name the piece of apparatus in **Figure 1** that is labelled **X**.

[1 mark]

The rate of this reaction could also be measured using a mass balance.

Figure 1

conical flask

2.3   Give **one** advantage of using a mass balance to measure the rate of a reaction.

[1 mark]

2.4   Give **one** possible safety concern when using a mass balance to measure the rate of this reaction.

[1 mark]

Exam Questions

3 Hydrogen peroxide is a liquid that decomposes into water and oxygen.

Samples of three catalysts with the same surface area were added to some hydrogen peroxide solution. The same volume and concentration of hydrogen peroxide was used each time.
The volume of oxygen produced over time was measured and recorded, and is shown in **Figure 2**.

3.1 How much oxygen was produced in the first 3 minutes with copper(II) oxide?

[1 mark]

3.2 Identify, with a reason, the most effective catalyst.

[2 marks]

3.3 Describe how you could use tangents to compare the rates of the reactions at 2 minutes.

[3 marks]

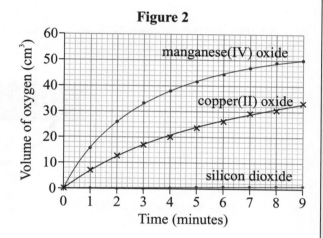

Figure 2

PRACTICAL

4* A reaction between two colourless solutions, **X** and **Y**, produces a yellow precipitate.

Describe how you could use the change in colour to investigate how the rate of this reaction changes with the concentration of Y.
Describe the method and equipment you would use, and the measurements you would make.

[4 marks]

5 **Figure 3** shows how the volume of hydrogen gas produced in a reaction varies with time.

The mean rate of a reaction is calculated using the equation:

$$\text{Mean rate of reaction} = \frac{\text{Amount of product formed}}{\text{Time}}$$

5.1 Use the equation to calculate the mean rate for the whole reaction. Include appropriate units in your answer.

[3 marks]

5.2 Use the equation to calculate the mean rate of reaction between 40 and 150 seconds.

[3 marks]

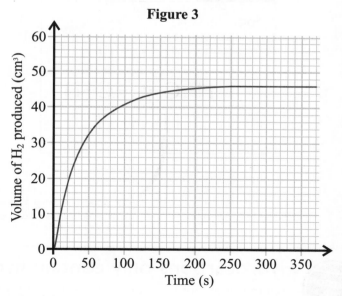

Figure 3

Topic C6 — The Rate and Extent of Chemical Change

Hydrocarbons

*Organic chemistry is about compounds that contain **carbon**. **Hydrocarbons** are the simplest organic compounds. As you're about to discover, their **properties** are affected by their **structure**.*

Alkanes Only Have C–C and C–H Single Bonds

1) <u>Hydrocarbons</u> are compounds formed from carbon and hydrogen atoms <u>only</u>.

2) <u>Alkanes</u> are the simplest type of hydrocarbon. They have the general formula:

$$C_nH_{2n+2}$$

'n' is the number of C atoms in the molecule.

3) In alkanes, each carbon atom forms four <u>single covalent bonds</u>.

4) The first four alkanes are <u>methane</u>, <u>ethane</u>, <u>propane</u> and <u>butane</u>.

Methane

Formula: CH_4

Ethane

Formula: C_2H_6

Propane

Formula: C_3H_8

Butane

Formula: C_4H_{10}

A drawing showing all the atoms and bonds in a molecule is called a displayed formula.

REVISION TIP

Hydrocarbons only contain hydrogen and carbon

To help remember the names of the <u>first four alkanes</u> just remember: <u>M</u>ice <u>E</u>at <u>P</u>eanut <u>B</u>utter. Practise drawing the structures and get to grips with their formulas using the general formula.

Hydrocarbons

Hydrocarbon **Properties Change** as the Chain Gets **Longer**

1) As the <u>length</u> of the carbon chain changes, the <u>properties</u> of the hydrocarbon change.

2) The <u>shorter</u> the hydrocarbon <u>chain</u>...

> ...the <u>more runny</u> a hydrocarbon is —
> that is, the <u>less viscous</u> (gloopy) it is.

> ...the <u>lower</u> its <u>boiling point</u> will be.

> ...the more <u>flammable</u> (easier to ignite) the hydrocarbon is.

Complete Combustion Occurs When There's Plenty of **Oxygen**

1) The <u>complete combustion</u> of a hydrocarbon in oxygen releases lots of energy.

2) This makes them useful as <u>fuels</u>.
The <u>properties</u> of the different hydrocarbons affect exactly how they're used for fuels.

3) The only waste products of complete combustion are <u>carbon dioxide</u> and <u>water</u> vapour.

> hydrocarbon + oxygen → carbon dioxide + water   (+ energy)

4) During combustion, both carbon and hydrogen from the hydrocarbon are <u>oxidised</u>.
<u>Oxidation</u> is the <u>gain of oxygen</u>.

5) You need to be able to give a <u>balanced symbol equation</u> for the <u>complete combustion</u>
of a simple hydrocarbon when you're given its <u>molecular formula</u>. Here's an example:

See p.166 for more on balancing equations.

EXAMPLE   **Write a balanced equation for the complete combustion of methane (CH_4).**

1) On the <u>left hand side</u>, there's <u>one</u> carbon atom, so
only <u>one</u> molecule of CO_2 is needed to balance this.

$$CH_4 + ?O_2 \rightarrow CO_2 + ?H_2O$$

2) On the <u>left hand side</u>, there are <u>four</u> hydrogen atoms,
so <u>two</u> water molecules are needed to balance them.

$$CH_4 + ?O_2 \rightarrow CO_2 + 2H_2O$$

3) There are <u>four</u> oxygen atoms on the <u>right hand side</u> of the equation.
<u>Two</u> oxygen molecules are needed on the left to balance them.

$$CH_4 + 2O_2 \rightarrow CO_2 + 2H_2O$$

Alkanes are useful fuels as they release energy when burnt

<u>Shorter</u> hydrocarbons are less viscous, more volatile and easier to ignite than <u>longer</u> hydrocarbons.

Q1   Write a balanced symbol equation for the complete combustion of ethane, C_2H_6.   [2 marks]

Q1 Video
Solution

Crude Oil

*Crude oil has fuelled **modern life** — it would be a very different world if we hadn't discovered oil.*

Crude Oil is Made Over a **Long Period of Time**

1) <u>Crude oil</u> is a <u>fossil fuel</u> found in <u>rocks</u>.
2) Fossil fuels are <u>natural</u> substances. They can be used as a source of <u>energy</u>.
3) Crude oil formed mainly from the remains of plankton, as well as other plants and animals. These died millions of years ago and were buried in mud.

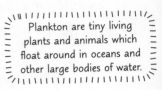

Plankton are tiny living plants and animals which float around in oceans and other large bodies of water.

- Fossil fuels like coal, oil and gas are called <u>non-renewable fuels</u>.
- This is because they take so long to make that they're being <u>used up</u> much faster than they're being formed.
- They're <u>finite</u> resources (see p.270) — one day they'll run out.

Crude Oil has Various Important Uses in Modern Life

1) <u>Oil</u> provides the <u>fuel</u> for most modern <u>transport</u> — cars, trains, planes, the lot.

2) Diesel oil, kerosene, heavy fuel oil and LPG (liquefied petroleum gas) all come from crude oil.

3) <u>Petrochemicals</u> are compounds that come from crude oil. The <u>petrochemical industry</u> uses some of the compounds from crude oil as a <u>feedstock</u> to make <u>new compounds</u> for use in things like...

- <u>polymers</u> (e.g. plastics)
- <u>solvents</u>
- <u>lubricants</u>
- <u>detergents</u>

A feedstock is a raw material used for a chemical process.

4) All the products you get from crude oil are examples of <u>organic compounds</u>. Organic compounds are compounds containing carbon atoms.

5) Most of the organic compounds in crude oil are <u>hydrocarbons</u> (see pages 246-247). These hydrocarbons are a range of <u>different sizes</u>.

6) You can get a large <u>variety</u> of products from crude oil. This is because carbon atoms can bond together to form different groups called <u>homologous series</u>.

7) These groups contain <u>similar compounds</u> which have many <u>properties</u> in common. <u>Alkanes</u> and <u>alkenes</u> are both examples of different homologous series.

Crude oil isn't only used for fuel

Crude oil is a <u>fossil fuel</u>, but the compounds found in it are useful for manufacturing all kinds of things. Make sure you can name some <u>examples</u> of the different <u>fuels</u> that come from crude oil, and of <u>product types</u> which are made from crude oil feedstocks (e.g. detergents).

Fractional Distillation

Crude oil can be used to make loads of useful things, such as fuels. But you can't just put crude oil in your car. First, the different hydrocarbons have to be separated. That's where **fractional distillation** comes in.

Fractional Distillation is Used to Separate Hydrocarbon Fractions

Crude oil is a <u>mixture</u> of <u>lots of different hydrocarbons</u>, most of which are <u>alkanes</u>.
The different compounds in crude oil are <u>separated</u> by <u>fractional distillation</u>.
Here's how it works:

Hydrocarbons are molecules containing only hydrogen and carbon.

1) The oil is <u>heated</u> until most of it has <u>evaporated</u> (turned into <u>gas</u>).
   The gases enter a <u>fractionating column</u> (and the liquid bit is drained off).

2) In the column it's <u>hot</u> at the <u>bottom</u> and gets <u>cooler</u> as you go up.

The <u>shorter</u> hydrocarbons have <u>low boiling points</u>. This means that they're still <u>gases</u> at low temperatures. So they <u>don't</u> condense and turn back into liquids until they move up near the <u>top</u> of the column, where they <u>cool down</u> a lot.

Approximate Number of Carbons in the Hydrocarbons in that Fraction

~3
~8
~15
~20
~40

COOL

LPG (Liquefied Petroleum Gas)

Petrol

Kerosene

Diesel oil

Heavy fuel oil

Crude Oil

Very Hot

Bitumen

The <u>longer hydrocarbons</u> have <u>high boiling points</u>. This means that they'll only stay a gas if it's <u>very hot</u>. As they move up the fractionating column, it gets cooler. So they condense back into <u>liquids</u> and <u>drain out</u> of the column <u>early on</u>, when they're near the <u>bottom</u>.

3) You end up with the crude oil mixture separated into <u>different fractions</u> (parts), e.g. petrol and diesel oil.

4) Each fraction contains a mixture of hydrocarbons. All of the hydrocarbons in one fraction contain a similar number of <u>carbon atoms</u>. This means they'll have similar <u>boiling points</u>.

Hydrocarbon fractions drain off according to their boiling points

Q1 Petrol drains further up a fractionating column than diesel.
Use the diagram of the fractionating column to explain
why the boiling point of petrol is lower than that of diesel.

[2 marks]

Q1 Video Solution

Cracking

*Crude oil fractions from fractional distillation can be split into **smaller molecules**. This is called **cracking**.
It's super important, otherwise we might not have enough fuel for cars and planes and things.*

Cracking Means Splitting Up Long–Chain Hydrocarbons

1) There is a <u>high demand</u> for fuels with small molecules.

2) This is because <u>short-chain hydrocarbons</u> tend to be more useful than <u>long-chain hydrocarbons</u>.

3) So, lots of longer alkane molecules are <u>turned</u> into <u>smaller</u>,
    <u>more useful</u> ones. This is done by a process called <u>cracking</u>.

4) Some of the products of cracking are useful as <u>fuels</u>, e.g. petrol for cars.

Cracking Makes Alkanes and Alkenes

1) <u>Alkenes</u> are another type of hydrocarbon.

2) Alkenes are a lot <u>more reactive</u> than alkanes.

3) They're used as a <u>starting material</u> when making lots of
    other compounds and can be used to make polymers.

See p.200 for more on polymers.

Bromine Water Can Be Used To Test for Alkenes

1) When orange <u>bromine water</u> is added to an <u>alkane</u>, no reaction will happen and it'll stay <u>bright orange</u>.

2) If it's added to an <u>alkene</u>, the <u>bromine</u> reacts with the alkene to make a <u>colourless</u> compound.
    So the bromine water turns colourless.

bromine water
+ an alkene

solution
goes colourless

Cracking produces more of the hydrocarbons we need

There's not much you can do with longer-chain hydrocarbons. But <u>shorter-chain</u> ones are useful as <u>fuels</u>
and to <u>make other compounds</u> like polymers. <u>Cracking</u> means we can <u>make use</u> of all those long chain
hydrocarbons that we otherwise wouldn't need, which is why it's so important to the petrochemical industry.

Cracking

There are Different Methods of Cracking

1) Cracking is a thermal decomposition reaction.
2) This means the molecules are broken down by heating them.
3) This can by done by catalytic cracking or by steam cracking.

Catalytic Cracking

1) Long-chain hydrocarbons are heated to turn them into a gas (vapour).
2) Then the vapour is passed over a hot powdered aluminium oxide catalyst.
3) The long-chain molecules split apart on the surface of the specks of catalyst.

Catalysts speed up reactions without getting used up (see p.235).

Steam Cracking

1) Long-chain hydrocarbons are heated to turn them into a gas.
2) The hydrocarbon vapour is mixed with steam.
3) They are then heated to a very high temperature which splits them into smaller molecules.

You Can Write Equations for Cracking Reactions

You might be asked to work out the formula of the products or reactants involved in a cracking reaction. You can do this by balancing the number of carbons and hydrogens on each side of the reaction.

EXAMPLE

Decane can be cracked to form octane and one other product. The equation for the cracking of decane, $C_{10}H_{22}$, is shown below. Complete the equation.

$$C_{10}H_{22} \rightarrow C_8H_{18} + \text{.....................}$$

1) There needs to be the same number of carbon and hydrogen atoms on each side of the equation.

2) The number of carbon atoms in the missing product equals the number of carbons in $C_{10}H_{22}$ minus the number of carbons in C_8H_{18}.

    number of C atoms = 10 − 8 = 2

3) The number of hydrogen atoms in the missing product equals the number of hydrogens in $C_{10}H_{22}$ minus the number of hydrogens in C_8H_{18}.

    number of H atoms = 22 − 18 = 4

4) Put these numbers into the formula of the missing product.

    $$C_{10}H_{22} \rightarrow C_8H_{18} + C_2H_4$$

Cracking always involves heating

In catalytic cracking the hydrocarbons are heated with a catalyst and in steam cracking they're heated with steam. Simple really. Which gives you more time to practise balancing your equations.

Q1 Pentane, C_5H_{12}, can be cracked into ethene and one other hydrocarbon. Give the balanced symbol equation for the cracking reaction. [1 mark]

Q1 Video Solution

Warm-Up & Exam Questions

Hydrocarbons contain only hydrogen and carbon atoms.
This page contains only Warm-Up and Exam Questions. Time to get thinking.

Warm-Up Questions

1) Name the first four alkanes.
2) What type of bonds hold the atoms in alkanes together?
3) Why are alkanes often used as fuels?
4) What size hydrocarbon molecules are cracked?

Exam Questions

1 Which alkane is shown in **Figure 1**? **Grade 3-4**
Tick **one** box.

Figure 1

H   H
| |
H–C–C–H
| |
H   H

☐ propane   ☐ ethane   ☐ methane

[1 mark]

2 Which statement correctly describes how the properties of hydrocarbons change **Grade 3-4**
as the length of the carbon chain increases?
Tick **one** box.

☐ Flammability increases and viscosity increases.

☐ Flammability increases and viscosity decreases.

☐ Flammability decreases and viscosity increases.

☐ Flammability decreases and viscosity decreases.

[1 mark]

3 Alkanes are a homologous series of hydrocarbons made up of chains **Grade 4-5**
of carbon atoms surrounded by hydrogen atoms.

Pentane is an alkane with the formula C_5H_{12}.

3.1 Name the alkane that has one fewer carbon atoms than pentane.

[1 mark]

3.2 Give the **formula** of the alkane that has one fewer carbon atoms than pentane.

[1 mark]

3.3 Alkanes are a product made from crude oil. They are often used as fuels.
Give **two** other uses of compounds made from crude oil.

[2 marks]

Exam Questions

4 Which of the following statements best describes what occurs during a combustion reaction? Tick **one** box.

☐ Oxygen reacts with a fuel and energy is released.

☐ A fuel takes in energy and decomposes.

☐ Carbon dioxide reacts with a fuel and energy is released.

☐ A fuel reacts with water vapour in clouds to produce acid rain.

[1 mark]

5 When nonane is cracked, heptane (an alkane) and ethene (an alkene) can be produced. **Figure 2** shows the displayed formulas of nonane, heptane and ethene.

Figure 2

5.1 Complete the chemical equation for the cracking of nonane to make heptane and ethene.

$C_9H_{20} \rightarrow$ .... + ...

[1 mark]

5.2 Samples of heptane and ethene were added to two separate test tubes of bromine water and shaken. Describe what you would expect to happen in each case.

[2 marks]

6 Crude oil can be separated into a number of different compounds in a fractional distillation column. **Figure 3** shows a fractional distillation column.

Figure 3

6.1 Which letter, **A-F**, represents the liquefied petroleum gas (LPG) fraction?

[1 mark]

6.2 The crude oil is heated until it becomes a gas and then enters the column at point **X** on **Figure 3**. The gas moves through the column and different fractions exit at different points. Explain why fractions with longer hydrocarbon chains exit near the bottom of the column.

[3 marks]

Purity and Formulations

*In a perfect world, every compound a chemist made would be **pure**. Unfortunately, in the real world it **doesn't** always work out like that. Luckily, there are ways to find out **how pure** a substance is.*

Purity Has a **Different** Meaning in **Chemistry** to **Everyday**

1) Usually when you say that a substance is pure you mean that nothing has been added to it. So it's in its natural state. For example: pure milk or beeswax.

2) In chemistry, a pure substance is something that only contains one compound or element all the way through. It's not mixed with anything else.

The **Boiling** or **Melting Point** Tells You How **Pure** a Substance Is

1) A chemically pure substance will melt or boil at a specific temperature.

2) You can test how pure a known substance is by measuring its melting or boiling point. You then compare this value with the melting or boiling point of the pure substance. You can find this in a data book.

3) The closer your measured value is to the actual melting or boiling point, the purer your sample is.

4) Impurities in your sample will lower the melting point. They may also cause the sample to melt across a wider range of temperatures.

5) Impurities in your sample will increase the boiling point. They may also cause the sample to boil across a range of temperatures.

A Formulation is a **Mixture** with **Exact Amounts** of its **Parts**

1) Formulations are useful mixtures that have been designed for a particular use.

2) They are made by following a 'formula' (a recipe).

Take a look at p.169 for more on mixtures.

3) Each part of a formulation is measured carefully so that it's there in the right amount. This makes sure the formulation has the right properties for it to work as it's supposed to.

> For example, paints are formulations.
> They are made up of:
> - Pigment — gives the paint colour.
> - Solvent — used to dissolve the other parts and change how runny the paint is.
> - Binder — holds the pigment in place after it's been painted on.
> - Additives — added to change the properties of the paint.
> The chemicals used and their amounts can be changed so the paint made is right for the job.

4) In everyday life, formulations can be found in cleaning products, fuels, medicines, cosmetics, fertilisers, metal alloys and even food and drink.

Make sure you can use data to identify pure and impure substances...

Knowing if a product is pure is really important for making things such as medicines or food. Extra stuff in it by mistake could change the properties of the product, and even make it dangerous.

Paper Chromatography

*You met chromatography on page 170. Now it's time to see **how it works**.*

Chromatography uses Two Phases

1) <u>Chromatography</u> is a method used to <u>separate</u> the substances in a mixture.

2) It can then be used to <u>identify</u> the substances.

3) The type of chromatography you need to know about is <u>paper chromatography</u>. Like all types of chromatography, it has two 'phases'.

   - A <u>mobile phase</u> — where the molecules <u>can</u> move.
     In paper chromatography, this is a <u>solvent</u> (e.g. water or ethanol).
   - A <u>stationary phase</u> — where the molecules <u>can't</u> move.
     In paper chromatography, this is the <u>paper</u>.

4) During paper chromatography the solvent <u>moves up</u> the paper. As the solvent moves, it <u>carries</u> the substances in the mixture with it.

The method for carrying out paper chromatography is on page 170.

5) In a chromatography experiment, the amount of <u>time</u> a chemical spends dissolved in the solvent or stuck on the paper is called its '<u>distribution</u>'.

6) The <u>more soluble</u> a chemical is, the <u>more</u> time it spends <u>dissolved</u> in the solvent. This means that the chemical will move <u>further</u> up the paper.

7) Different chemicals may be dissolved in the solvent for <u>different</u> amounts of time. So the <u>different chemicals</u> will move <u>different distances</u> up the paper.

8) This means they <u>separate</u> into <u>different spots</u>.

Chromatography revision — it's a phase you have to get through...

Chromatography works because each of the chemicals in a mixture spends different amounts of time dissolved in the <u>mobile phase</u> and stuck to the <u>stationary phase</u>. It's great — all you need is some <u>paper</u> and a bit of <u>solvent</u>. There's more about using it to <u>identify</u> chemicals coming up on the next few pages.

PRACTICAL Interpreting Chromatograms

*Now that you know a bit of the **theory** behind how paper chromatography works, here's how you can use a **chromatogram** to analyse a particular substance and find out **what's in it**.*

The **Result** of Chromatography is Shown on a **Chromatogram**

1) <u>Chromatograms</u> show the result of chromatography experiments.

2) The <u>solvent front</u> is the <u>furthest point</u> reached by the <u>solvent</u> during a chromatography experiment.

3) Chemicals move <u>different distances</u> up the paper. So <u>different spots</u> show <u>different chemicals</u>.

4) The <u>number of spots</u> on a chromatogram is the <u>smallest</u> possible number of chemicals in the mixture.

5) Sometimes more than one chemical may travel the <u>same distance</u> up the paper.
This means that these chemicals will only form <u>one spot</u> between them.

6) If you repeat the experiment with a <u>different solvent</u>, you'll get a <u>different chromatogram</u>.
The spots may have travelled different <u>distances</u> compared to the solvent front.
There might also be a different <u>number</u> of spots on the chromatogram.

7) If you only get <u>one spot</u> in <u>lots</u> of different solvents, there's only <u>one</u> chemical in the substance.
This means the substance is <u>pure</u>.

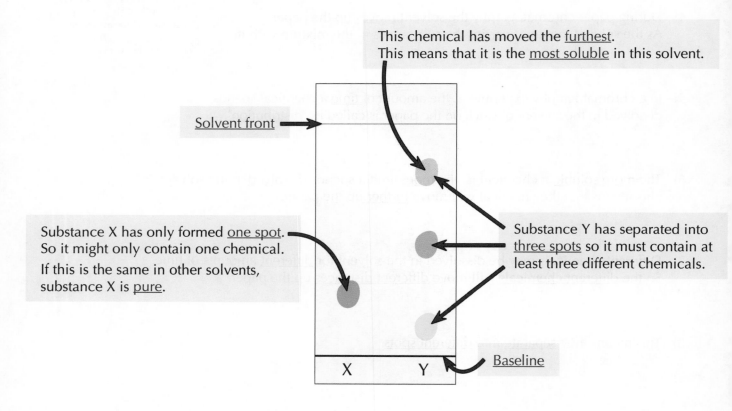

This chemical has moved the <u>furthest</u>.
This means that it is the <u>most soluble</u> in this solvent.

<u>Solvent front</u>

Substance X has only formed <u>one spot</u>.
So it might only contain one chemical.

If this is the same in other solvents, substance X is <u>pure</u>.

Substance Y has separated into <u>three spots</u> so it must contain at least three different chemicals.

<u>Baseline</u>

X   Y

A pure substance will only ever produce one spot

When you're doing paper chromatography, you might end up with a spot left sitting on the <u>baseline</u>, even after your solvent has run all the way up the paper. Any substance that stays on the baseline is <u>insoluble</u> in that solvent. If this happens, you could try the experiment using a <u>different solvent</u>, and see if the mystery substance dissolves in it.

Interpreting Chromatograms

*If you were sad the last page on **chromatography** was finished — fear not. There's more to come on this page.*

You can Calculate the R_f Value for Each Chemical

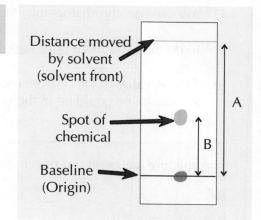

1) An R_f value is the ratio between the distance travelled by the dissolved substance and the distance travelled by the solvent.

2) The further a substance moves through the stationary phase, the larger the R_f value.

3) You can calculate R_f values using the formula:

$$R_f = \frac{\text{distance moved by substance (B)}}{\text{distance moved by solvent (A)}}$$

This is the distance from the baseline to the centre of the spot.

EXAMPLE

A chromatography experiment looking at the colours in a dye produces the chromatogram shown on the right. Calculate the R_f value for the red spot.

1) Measure the distance moved by the red spot (B). This is the distance from the baseline to the centre of the spot. 29 mm

2) Measure the distance moved by the solvent (A). 41 mm

3) Calculate the R_f value.

$$R_f = \frac{\text{distance moved by substance (B)}}{\text{distance moved by solvent (A)}} = \frac{29}{41} = 0.70731... = 0.71$$

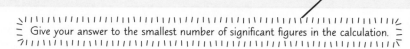

Give your answer to the smallest number of significant figures in the calculation.

4) The R_f value of a chemical will change if you change the solvent.

You need to learn the formula for R_f

R_f values always lie between 0 and 1, as the solvent always travels further than any of the substances in the mixture. If you work out an R_f value to be outside this range, you know you've gone wrong somewhere (e.g. you may have written the fraction in the formula upside-down).

Q1 Video Solution

Q1   A spot on a chromatogram moved 6.3 cm from the baseline. The solvent front moved 8.4 cm. Calculate the R_f value.   [1 mark]

PRACTICAL Interpreting Chromatograms

*Time for one last page on chromatography — this one's all about using **references** to identify substances.*

You Can **Identify Substances** in Mixtures Using Chromatography

1) You can use chromatography to see if a mixture <u>contains</u> a certain substance.

2) To do this, you run a <u>pure sample</u> of that substance (a <u>reference</u>) next to the mixture.

3) If the R_f value of the reference compound <u>matches</u> one of the spots in the mixture, the substance <u>could</u> be in the mixture. For example:

A <u>mixture</u> has been run next to <u>pure samples</u> of three different substances.

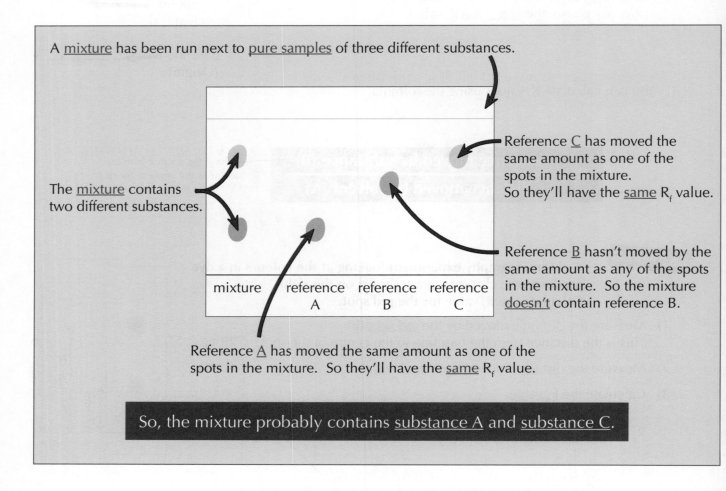

Reference <u>C</u> has moved the same amount as one of the spots in the mixture. So they'll have the <u>same</u> R_f value.

The <u>mixture</u> contains two different substances.

Reference <u>B</u> hasn't moved by the same amount as any of the spots in the mixture. So the mixture <u>doesn't</u> contain reference B.

mixture | reference A | reference B | reference C

Reference <u>A</u> has moved the same amount as one of the spots in the mixture. So they'll have the <u>same</u> R_f value.

So, the mixture probably contains <u>substance A</u> and <u>substance C</u>.

4) If the R_f values <u>match</u> in one solvent, you can <u>check</u> to see if the chemicals are the same by repeating with a <u>different solvent</u>. If they match again, it's <u>likely</u> that they're the <u>same</u>.

Reference spots are pure samples of known substances

Chromatography can be a bit tricky to get your head around sometimes, especially when you're given a chromatogram that contains quite a few different <u>spots</u>. Make sure you're really comfortable with how to use a chromatogram to <u>work out</u> what compounds are <u>present</u> in a <u>mixture</u>. It'll be worth it come the exam.

Tests for Gases

*Yep, that's right, you need to revise tests for your test. There are a few ways to **test for gases**, but you only need to know these **four**. And two of them use fire. Pretty cool.*

There are Tests for Four Common Gases

1) Chlorine

Chlorine <u>bleaches</u> damp <u>litmus paper</u>, turning it white.

Litmus paper

Chlorine

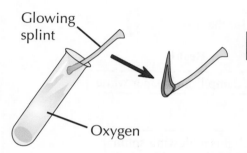

Glowing splint

Oxygen

2) Oxygen

If you put a glowing splint inside a test tube containing <u>oxygen</u>, the oxygen will <u>relight</u> the <u>glowing splint</u>.

3) Carbon Dioxide

You can test for carbon dioxide by bubbling it through a solution of <u>calcium hydroxide</u>.
If the gas is carbon dioxide, the solution will turn <u>cloudy</u>.
You can also do this test by <u>shaking</u> the gas with the solution.

CO$_2$ gas

Calcium hydroxide (limewater)

Calcium hydroxide solution is also called limewater.

POP!

Lighted splint

H$_2$ gas

4) Hydrogen

If you hold a <u>lit splint</u> at the open end of a test tube containing hydrogen, you'll get a "<u>squeaky pop</u>".

PRACTICAL TIP

These are all really useful tests to know...

The method you use to <u>collect a gas</u> will depend on whether it's <u>lighter</u> or <u>heavier</u> than <u>air</u>. If it's <u>heavier</u> (like chlorine), you have the test tube the <u>right way up</u> and the gas will <u>sink</u> to the bottom. If it's <u>lighter</u> (like hydrogen), you have the test tube <u>upside-down</u> and the gas will <u>rise</u> to fill it.

Warm-Up & Exam Questions

Look, a chromatography question — those things are fun. Get your detective hat on and get stuck in...

1) What effect will impurities in a substance have on its boiling point?
2) Give an example of a formulation used in everyday life.
3) What effect does chromatography have on a mixture?
4) True of False? In chromatography, an R_f value represents the ratio between the distance travelled by two dissolved substances.

Exam Questions

1 Draw **one** line from each gas to the correct result of the test for that gas.

Gas	Result

Gas

Hydrogen

Chlorine

Carbon dioxide

Result

Turns damp litmus paper white

Relights a glowing splint

Produces a "squeaky pop" with a lit splint

Turns a solution of calcium hydroxide cloudy

[3 marks]

2 A scientist is preparing a formulation that contains only pure substances.
She measures the melting point of three substances, **A – C**. Her results are shown in **Table 1**.

Table 1

Substance	Melting point (°C)	
	Experimental	Data book
A	14	17
B	49	49
C	21 – 24	24

Which of the substances could the scientist use in her formulation? Tick **one** box.

☐ Substance B only   ☐ Substance A and C

☐ Substance C only   ☐ Substance A, B and C

[1 mark]

Topic C8 — Chemical Analysis

Exam Questions

3 Different groups of seaweed contain different types of a pigment called chlorophyll.
Table 2 shows which types of chlorophyll each group of seaweed contains.
Figure 1 shows the results of a chromatography experiment to analyse an unknown seaweed.

Table 2

Group of seaweed	Type of chlorophyll		
	a	b	c
Red	✓		
Brown	✓		✓
Green	✓	✓	

Figure 1

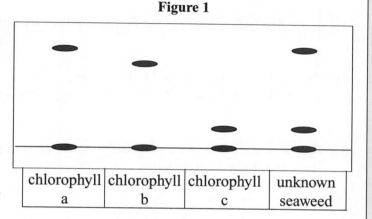

Use **Table 2** and **Figure 1** to identify which group the unknown seaweed belongs to.

[1 mark]

4 A scientist used chromatography to study the compounds present in five food colourings. Four of the colourings were unknown (**A – D**). The other colouring was sunrise yellow. The results are shown in **Figure 2**.

Figure 2

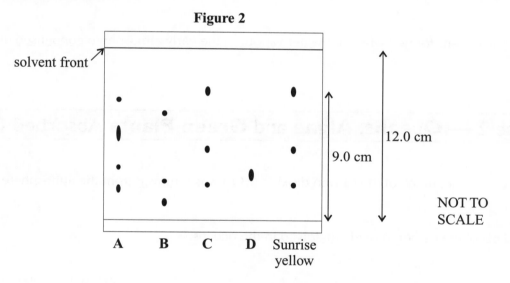

4.1 Which food colouring contained the compound that had the strongest attraction to the stationary phase?

[1 mark]

4.2 Which of the food colourings, **A-D**, could be the same as sunrise yellow?

[1 mark]

4.3 The R_f value of a spot can be calculated using the following formula:

$$R_f = \frac{\text{distance moved by substance}}{\text{distance moved by solvent}}$$

Calculate the R_f value for the spot of chemical in sunrise yellow which is furthest up the chromatogram.

[2 marks]

The Evolution of the Atmosphere

*Theories for how the Earth's atmosphere **evolved** have changed a lot over the years. It's hard to gather evidence from such a **long time period** and from **so long ago** (4.6 billion years). Here's one idea we've got:*

Phase 1 — **Volcanoes** Gave Out **Gases**

1) In the first <u>billion years</u> of the Earth's lifetime, its surface was covered in <u>volcanoes</u>.

2) These erupted and released lots of gases. Scientists think these gases formed the <u>early atmosphere</u>.

3) The early atmosphere was probably mostly <u>carbon dioxide</u> (CO_2). There was <u>little</u> or <u>no oxygen</u>.

4) This is quite like the atmospheres of <u>Mars</u> and <u>Venus</u> today.

5) Volcanoes also released <u>nitrogen</u> (this built up in the atmosphere over time), <u>water vapour</u> and small amounts of <u>methane</u> and <u>ammonia</u>.

6) The <u>oceans</u> formed when the <u>water vapour</u> in the early atmosphere <u>condensed</u> (turned to liquid).

Phase 2 — **Oceans, Algae** and **Green Plants** Absorbed CO_2

1) Over time, much of the carbon dioxide (CO_2) was <u>removed</u> from the atmosphere.

2) Lots of the carbon dioxide <u>dissolved</u> in the oceans.

3) The dissolved carbon dioxide formed <u>carbonates</u> that precipitated as small, solid particles (<u>sediments</u>).

> Precipitation is the formation of an insoluble solid from a solution.

4) When <u>green plants</u> and <u>algae</u> evolved, they took in some carbon dioxide during <u>photosynthesis</u> (see next page).

Before volcanic activity, the Earth didn't even have an atmosphere

One way scientists can get information about what Earth's <u>atmosphere</u> was like in the past is from <u>Antarctic ice cores</u>. Each year a layer of <u>ice</u> forms with tiny <u>bubbles of air</u> trapped in it. The <u>deeper</u> you go in the ice, the <u>older</u> the air. So analysing bubbles from different layers shows you how the atmosphere has <u>changed</u>.

The Evolution of the Atmosphere

Some **Carbon** Became **Trapped** in **Fossil Fuels** and **Rocks**

Some of the carbon that organisms took in from the atmosphere and oceans
became locked up in <u>rocks</u> and <u>fossil fuels</u> after the organisms died.

1) When sea organisms <u>die</u>, they fall to the seabed and get <u>buried</u>.
Over millions of years, they're <u>squashed</u> down.
This forms <u>sedimentary rocks</u> (e.g. coal and limestone), <u>oil</u> and <u>gas</u>.
The carbon gets trapped within them.

2) Things like coal, crude oil and natural gas that are made this way are called '<u>fossil fuels</u>'.

3) <u>Crude oil</u> and <u>natural gas</u> are formed from the remains of <u>plankton</u> that settled on the seabed.

4) <u>Coal</u> is made from thick layers of <u>plants</u> that died and then settled on the seabed.

5) <u>Limestone</u> is mostly made of <u>calcium carbonate</u> from the <u>shells</u> and <u>skeletons</u> of marine organisms.

Phase 3 — Green Plants and Algae **Produced Oxygen**

1) Algae evolved about <u>2.7 billion</u> years ago.
Then green plants evolved over the next <u>billion years</u> or so.

2) Green plants and algae produce <u>oxygen</u> in a reaction called <u>photosynthesis</u>:

$$carbon\ dioxide\ +\ water\ \xrightarrow{light}\ glucose\ +\ oxygen$$

$$6CO_2\ +\ 6H_2O\ \longrightarrow\ C_6H_{12}O_6\ +\ 6O_2$$

3) Over time, oxygen levels <u>built up</u> in the atmosphere. This meant that animals could <u>evolve</u>.

4) The <u>proportions</u> of gases in the atmosphere have been similar for about the last <u>200 million years</u>.
It is made up of about:

- 80% ($^4/_5$) <u>nitrogen</u>,
- 20% ($^1/_5$) <u>oxygen</u>,
- small amounts (<u>less than 1%</u>) of <u>other gases</u>
  (mainly carbon dioxide, noble gases and water vapour).

Not too much CO_2 and enough O_2 — perfect for life on Earth

You need to know the <u>rough proportions</u> of the gases in Earth's atmosphere, so don't just skip over
the numbers — you could get asked about them in the exam. Make sure you know that <u>nitrogen</u> is
<u>80%</u>, oxygen is <u>20%</u> and <u>everything else</u> makes up <u>less than 1%</u> of our atmosphere.

Climate Change and Greenhouse Gases

*Greenhouse gases are important but can also cause **problems** — it's all about keeping a delicate **balance**.*

Carbon Dioxide is a Greenhouse Gas

1) Greenhouse gases include <u>carbon dioxide</u>, <u>methane</u> and <u>water vapour</u>.

2) Greenhouse gases keep the Earth <u>warm</u> enough to support <u>life</u>. Here's how they work:

> 1) The <u>Sun</u> gives out <u>short wavelength</u> radiation.
>
> 2) This radiation is <u>reflected</u> back by the Earth as <u>long wavelength</u> radiation. This is <u>thermal</u> (heat) radiation. It's then <u>absorbed</u> by <u>greenhouse gases</u>.
>
> *Thermal radiation heats things up.*
>
> 3) Greenhouse gases then give out this radiation in <u>all directions</u>.
>
> 4) Some radiation heads back towards the <u>Earth</u> and <u>warms up</u> the surface. This is the <u>greenhouse effect</u>.

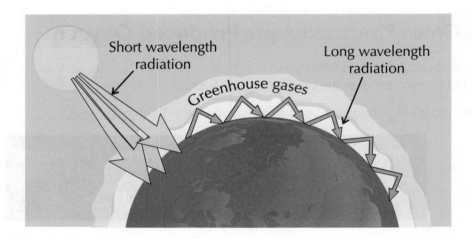

3) Some forms of <u>human activity</u> increase the amount of greenhouse gases in the atmosphere. For example:

> 1) <u>Deforestation</u>: fewer trees means that less carbon dioxide is taken in for <u>photosynthesis</u>.
>
> 2) Burning <u>fossil fuels</u>: <u>releases</u> carbon dioxide.
>
> 3) <u>Agriculture</u>: more <u>farm animals</u> produce more <u>methane</u> when they digest their food.
>
> 4) <u>Creating waste</u>: more <u>landfill sites</u> and more waste from <u>farming</u> means more carbon dioxide and methane is released when the waste breaks down.

Greenhouse gases aren't all bad — we need them to survive

Without greenhouse gases our planet would be incredibly <u>cold</u> — the greenhouse effect warms the Earth enough for it to support <u>living things</u>. Without it we wouldn't be here. But the overall <u>balance</u> of gases in the atmosphere matters, as you're about to find out...

Q1   Describe the greenhouse effect and how it affects global temperature.   [4 marks]

Q1 Video Solution

Topic C9 — Chemistry of the Atmosphere

Climate Change and Greenhouse Gases

Increasing Carbon Dioxide is Linked to Climate Change

1) Recently, the average temperature of the Earth's surface has been <u>going up</u>.

2) Most scientists think this has been caused by the extra carbon dioxide from <u>human activity</u>.

3) They believe this will lead to <u>climate change</u>.

4) Evidence for this has been <u>peer-reviewed</u> (see page 2).
   This means that the information is <u>reliable</u>.

5) However, the Earth's climate is very <u>complex</u>.
   So, it's very hard to make a <u>model</u> that isn't <u>oversimplified</u>.

   See page 3 for more on science in the media.

6) This has led to people forming their own <u>theories</u> and <u>opinions</u>, particularly in the <u>media</u>.
   These stories aren't based on good evidence —
   they may be <u>biased</u> or only give <u>some</u> of the information.

   If something's biased, it favours one point of view in a way that's not backed up by facts.

Climate Change Could Have Dangerous Consequences

1) Higher global temperature could cause <u>ice</u> in the Arctic and Antarctic to <u>melt</u> — causing <u>sea levels</u> to <u>rise</u>. This could lead to <u>more flooding</u>.

2) Changes in <u>rainfall</u> may cause some regions to get <u>too much</u> or <u>too little</u> water.

3) <u>Storms</u> may become more <u>frequent</u> and <u>severe</u>.

4) Changes in <u>temperature</u> and <u>rainfall</u> may affect the <u>production of food</u> in certain places.

People can get quite hot under the collar talking about all this...

That's because climate change could have a massive impact on many people's lives. So it's very important to recognise when results might be <u>biased</u> or changed in favour of <u>one particular view</u>. Data should always be <u>checked</u> and <u>peer-reviewed</u> before any final conclusions are made.

Carbon Footprints

*Many scientists believe that greenhouse gas emissions from **human activities** are causing **climate change**. Knowing what things release lots of carbon dioxide could help **stop** climate change from happening.*

Carbon Footprints are Tricky to Measure

1) Carbon footprints are a <u>measure</u> of the amount of <u>carbon dioxide</u> and other <u>greenhouse gases</u> released over the <u>full life cycle</u> of something. That can be almost <u>anything</u>:
   - a service (e.g. the school bus).
   - an event (e.g. the Olympics).
   - a product (e.g. a toastie maker).

2) <u>Measuring</u> the total carbon footprint of something can be <u>really hard</u> or even <u>impossible</u>.

3) But a <u>rough calculation</u> can give a good idea of what things release the <u>most</u> greenhouse gases. So, people can then <u>avoid using them</u> in the future.

There are Ways of Reducing Carbon Footprints

1) You can reduce a carbon footprint by <u>reducing</u> the amount of <u>greenhouse gases</u> given out by a process.

2) Here are some things that can be done:

   - Using <u>renewable energy sources</u> (sources that won't run out) or <u>nuclear energy</u> instead of <u>fossil fuels</u>.

   - Using <u>processes</u> that use <u>less energy</u> or produces less <u>waste</u> (decomposing waste releases methane).

   - Governments could <u>tax</u> companies or individuals based on the amount of greenhouse gases they <u>emit</u>. This could encourage people to use processes which use less fuel and are <u>less polluting</u>.

   - Governments can also put a <u>limit</u> on emissions of <u>all</u> greenhouse gases that companies make. They can then <u>sell licences</u> for emissions <u>up to</u> that cap.

   - There's also technology that <u>captures</u> carbon dioxide <u>before</u> it's released into the atmosphere. This carbon dioxide is then <u>stored deep underground</u>.

But Making Reductions is Still Difficult

1) Reducing greenhouse gas emissions <u>isn't</u> simple.

2) <u>Alternative technologies</u> that release <u>less</u> carbon dioxide still need a lot of work.

3) Many <u>governments</u> are worried that making these changes will affect the <u>economies</u> of communities. This could be <u>bad</u> for people's <u>well-being</u> — especially those in <u>developing</u> countries.

4) This makes it hard for countries to <u>agree</u> to reduce emissions.

5) <u>Individuals</u> in developed countries also need to make changes to their <u>lifestyles</u>. But this is tricky when some <u>don't want to</u> and others don't understand <u>why</u> the changes are important or <u>how</u> to make them.

Air Pollution

*Increasing carbon dioxide is causing climate change. But CO$_2$ isn't the only gas released when fossil fuels burn — you can also get other nasty gases like **oxides of nitrogen**, **sulfur dioxide** and **carbon monoxide**.*

Combustion of Fossil Fuels Releases Gases and Particles

1) <u>Fossil fuels</u>, such as crude oil and coal, contain <u>hydrocarbons</u> (see page 246).
2) Hydrocarbons can <u>combust</u> (burn in oxygen). There are two types of combustion:

There's more about complete combustion on p.247.

<u>Complete combustion</u> — when there's <u>plenty</u> of oxygen around <u>all</u> of the fuel burns.

<u>Incomplete combustion</u> — when there's <u>not</u> enough oxygen around some of the fuel <u>does not</u> burn.

3) Both types of combustion release carbon dioxide and water vapour into the <u>atmosphere</u>.
4) During incomplete combustion, <u>solid particles</u> (called <u>particulates</u>) of soot (carbon) and <u>unburnt fuel</u> are also released. <u>Carbon monoxide</u> gas is also produced.
5) Particulates in the air and carbon monoxide can cause all sorts of <u>problems</u>:

Particulates

1) If particulates are <u>breathed in</u>, they can get stuck in the <u>lungs</u> and cause <u>damage</u>. This can lead to <u>respiratory</u> (breathing) <u>problems</u>.
2) They're also bad for the <u>environment</u> — they <u>reflect</u> sunlight back into space. This means that <u>less light</u> reaches the Earth — causing <u>global dimming</u>.

Carbon Monoxide

1) Carbon monoxide (CO) is really <u>dangerous</u> because it can stop your <u>blood</u> from <u>carrying enough oxygen</u> around the body.
2) A <u>lack</u> of oxygen in the blood can lead to <u>fainting</u>, a <u>coma</u> or <u>even death</u>.
3) Carbon monoxide doesn't have any <u>colour</u> or <u>smell</u>, so it's <u>very hard to detect</u>. This makes it even more <u>dangerous</u>.

Sulfur Dioxide and Oxides of Nitrogen Can be Released

1) Other pollutants are also released from <u>burning fossil fuels</u>.
2) <u>Sulfur dioxide</u> (SO$_2$) is released during the <u>combustion</u> of fossil fuels that contain <u>sulfur impurities</u>.
3) <u>Nitrogen oxides</u> form in a reaction between <u>nitrogen</u> and <u>oxygen</u> in the <u>air</u>. This reaction is caused by the <u>heat</u> of the burning fossil fuels.
4) These gases mix with <u>clouds</u> and cause <u>acid rain</u>.
5) Acid rain kills <u>plants</u>. It also <u>damages</u> buildings, statues and metals.
6) Sulfur dioxide and nitrogen oxides also cause <u>respiratory problems</u> if they're breathed in.

You can test for sulfur impurities in a fuel by bubbling the gases from combustion through a solution containing Universal indicator. If the fuel contains sulfur, the Universal indicator will turn red.

Fossil fuels are bad news — but we need them for many things...

...so a big reduction in their use is probably <u>hard</u> to achieve. Make sure you know the different <u>pollutants</u> that are given out when fuels burn, and the differences between <u>complete</u> and <u>incomplete</u> combustion.

Warm-Up & Exam Questions

There's lots of important information in this section, from the Earth's atmosphere to climate change and pollution. Answer these questions to see what you can remember and what you need to go over again.

Warm-Up Questions

1) Where do scientists think the gases that made up Earth's early atmosphere came from?
   A. Space   B. The ocean   C. Volcanoes   D. Burning fossil fuels
2) Give an example of a sedimentary rock.
3) Give an example of a fossil fuel.
4) True or false? Nuclear energy has a lower carbon footprint than burning fossil fuels.
5) Give one problem caused by sulfur dioxide in the atmosphere.

Exam Questions

1   Green plants and algae had a significant effect on Earth's early atmosphere.

1.1   Use words from the box to complete the sentences below.

| oxygen   carbon   carbon dioxide   particulates   nitrogen |

When green plants first evolved, the Earth's atmosphere was mostly .... gas .

These plants produced .... by the process of photosynthesis.

Some of the .... from dead plants eventually became 'locked up' in fossil fuels.

[3 marks]

1.2   Complete the balanced symbol equation for photosynthesis.

$$6 \text{.....................} + \text{.........} H_2O \rightarrow C_6H_{12}O_6 + 6 \text{.....................}$$

[2 marks]

1.3   Which line in **Table 1** shows the correct percentages of each gas in the Earth's atmosphere today?

Table 1

	Percentage in atmosphere (%)			
	Carbon dioxide	**Oxygen**	**Nitrogen**	**Water vapour**
A	20	70	10	less than 1
B	10	20	70	less than 1
C	less than 1	20	80	less than 1
D	less than 1	10	80	10

☐ A   ☐ B   ☐ C   ☐ D

[1 mark]

Exam Questions

2 Fossil fuels contain hydrocarbons. *(Grade 3-4)*

2.1 Which of the following is a fossil fuel?
Tick **one** box.

☐ Limestone ☐ Natural gas ☐ Carbon dioxide ☐ Water

[1 mark]

When hydrocarbons burn without enough oxygen present,
solid particles and carbon monoxide can be produced.

2.2 Name the type of reaction that occurs when hydrocarbons burn in oxygen.

[1 mark]

2.3 What name is given to the solid particles that can be produced
when hydrocarbons burn without enough oxygen present?

[1 mark]

2.4 Describe **two** problems caused by these solid particles in the air.

[2 marks]

2.5 Give **two** reasons why carbon monoxide is difficult to detect.

[1 mark]

3 This question is about greenhouse gases and climate change. *(Grade 4-5)*

3.1 Which of the following is an example of a greenhouse gas?
Tick **one** box.

☐ Oxygen ☐ Nitrogen ☐ Methane ☐ Argon

[1 mark]

3.2 Greenhouse gases absorb thermal radiation that has been reflected by the Earth.
Explain how this leads to global warming.

[3 marks]

3.3 Give **two** human activities that have increased the amount of greenhouse gases in Earth's atmosphere.

[2 marks]

3.4 Give **one** possible consequence of climate change.

[1 mark]

3.5 Describe **one** action that governments could take to try to
reduce the amount of greenhouse gases in the atmosphere.

[1 mark]

4* Earth's early atmosphere contained large amounts of carbon dioxide. *(Grade 4-5)*

Describe how the oceans, plants and algae removed some of this carbon dioxide,
and how this eventually led to the formation of coal.

[4 marks]

Finite and Renewable Resources

*There are lots of different resources that humans use for things like **electricity**, **heating**, **travelling**, **building materials** and **food**. Some of these resources can be replaced, some can't.*

Natural Resources Come From the Earth, Sea and Air

1) Natural resources form by themselves — they're not made by humans.
    They include anything that comes from the earth, sea or air, e.g. cotton and oil.

2) Some natural products can be replaced or improved by man-made products or processes.
    For example:

> • Rubber is a natural product that comes from the sap of a tree.
>   But we can now make polymers (see p.200) to replace some natural rubber to make things like tyres.
> • Wool is a natural product that comes from animals such as sheep. But scientists have developed
>   synthetic (man-made) fibres that we can use instead of wool to make things like jumpers and blankets.

3) Agriculture (farming) helps to increase our supply of natural resources to provide food, timber,
    clothing and fuel. It also provides conditions which can make natural resources better for our needs.

> E.g. the development of fertilisers means we can increase the amount of crops grown in a given area.

Some Natural Resources will Run Out

1) Renewable resources can be remade at least as fast as we use them.

2) This means that they can be replaced fairly quickly.

> • For example, timber is a renewable resource.
>   Trees can be planted following a harvest and only take a few years to regrow.
> • Other examples of renewable resources include fresh water and food.

3) Finite (non-renewable) resources are remade very slowly (or not at all).
    So we use them up quicker than we can replace them. This means that they'll eventually run out.

4) Finite resources include fossil fuels and nuclear fuels, as well as minerals and metals found in the ground.

5) We can process many finite resources to provide fuels and materials necessary for modern life.
    For example:

> • Fractional distillation (see p.249) is used to produce usable products such as petrol from crude oil.
> • Metal ores are reduced to produce pure metals (see p.221).

Natural resources can be renewable or finite

It's important that we're always able to get the resources we need to survive. Make sure you know the difference between a finite and a renewable resource and a few examples of each.

Resources and Sustainability

Tables, Charts and Graphs can Tell You About Different Resources

You can interpret information about resources from information that's given to you.

EXAMPLE

The table below shows how long it takes for three resources to form. The resources are coal, wood and cotton. Work out which resource is coal.

	Time it takes to form
Resource 1	10 years
Resource 2	120-180 days
Resource 3	10^6 years

Wood and cotton are both renewable resources.

Coal is a finite resource.

Finite resources take a very long time to form.

Resource 3 takes a much longer amount of time to form compared to Resources 1 and 2.

Coal is Resource 3.

10^6 is a quick way of showing 1 000 000. This is because $10^6 = 10 \times 10 \times 10 \times 10 \times 10 \times 10 = 1 000 000$.

We Need to Consider the Future When Choosing Resources

1) Sustainable development means thinking about the needs of people today without damaging the lives of people in the future.

2) Using, extracting and processing resources can be unsustainable. This could be because:

- Some resources are non-renewable — they'll run out one day. For example, the raw materials used to make metals, building materials, many plastics and things made from clay and glass are limited.

- Extraction processes can use lots of energy and produce lots of waste.

  Extraction processes separate the materials you want from the other things that they're mixed with.

- Turning resources into useful materials, like glass or bricks, often uses energy made from finite resources.

3) One way to be more sustainable is to use fewer finite resources. This reduces both the use of finite resources and anything needed to produce them.

4) We can do this by reusing and recycling materials when we're finished with them. During recycling, waste is processed so that it can be used to make new products.

   There's more on reusing and recycling on the next page.

5) We can't stop using finite resources completely. But scientists can develop processes that use less and reduce damage to the environment.

We need to be responsible with resources that won't last forever

Sustainable development is talked about a lot these days, however it's often quite hard to achieve in practice. It can be a difficult topic, too — making the changes we need to isn't always easy and can have a big impact on many people's lives. Plus people can't always agree on the best thing to do.

Reuse and Recycling

*Supplies of many materials used in the modern world are **limited**. Once they're finished with, it's usually far better to **recycle** them than to use new finite resources, which will run out.*

Recycling Metals is Important

1) <u>Mining</u> and <u>extracting</u> metals takes lots of <u>energy</u>.
   Most of this energy comes from burning <u>fossil fuels</u>.

2) It's usually <u>better</u> to <u>recycle</u> metals instead of making new metals.

   <u>Benefits of recycling</u>:
   - It often uses much <u>less energy</u> than the amount needed to make a new metal.
   - It helps <u>save</u> some of the finite amount of each metal in the earth.
   - It cuts down on the amount of <u>waste</u> getting sent to <u>landfill</u>.

3) Metals can be recycled by <u>melting</u> them and then moulding (<u>recasting</u>) them into the shape of a new product.

4) Sometimes, different metals won't need to be completely <u>separated</u> before recycling. The amount of <u>separation</u> depends on what the final product will be.

   For example, waste steel and iron can be kept together. This is because they can both be added to iron in a <u>blast furnace</u>. This means that <u>less iron ore</u> will be needed.

   A blast furnace is used to extract iron from its ore at a high temperature using carbon.

Glass can be Reused or Recycled

1) <u>Reusing</u> or <u>recycling</u> glass can help <u>sustainability</u>.

2) This <u>reduces</u> the amount of <u>energy</u> used for making new glass.

3) It also means that <u>less</u> glass is thrown away, so less <u>waste</u> is produced.

   - <u>Glass bottles</u> can often be <u>reused</u> without reshaping.
   - Some glass products can't be reused so they're <u>recycled</u> for a different use instead.
   - The glass is <u>crushed</u> and <u>melted</u>. It's then reshaped to make other glass products like jars.

Recycling is key to sustainability — it's useful in lots of ways...

Remember that recycling doesn't just reduce the use of raw materials, it also reduces the amount of <u>energy</u> used, the amount of <u>damage</u> to the environment and the amount of <u>waste</u> that is produced.

Life Cycle Assessments

*If a company wants to manufacture a new product, they carry out a **life cycle assessment (LCA)**.*

Life Cycle Assessments Show Total Environmental Costs

1) A life cycle assessment (LCA) looks at every stage of a product's life to assess the impact (effect) it would have on the environment.

2) Here are the four different stages:

1) Getting the Raw Materials

1) Lots of raw materials need to be extracted (separated from other materials) before we can use them for a product.

2) Extracting raw materials can damage the local environment, e.g. mining metals.

3) Extraction uses lots of energy. This can result in pollution.

4) Raw materials often need to be processed (e.g. by changing their shape and properties) to turn them into useful materials.

5) This often needs large amounts of energy. E.g. extracting metals from ores (see p.221 and 224) or fractional distillation of crude oil (see p.249).

2) Manufacture and Packaging

1) Making products and their packaging can use a lot of energy and other resources.

2) It can cause lots of pollution too.

3) Chemical reactions are sometimes used to make products. These reactions also produce waste products which need to be got rid of.

4) Some of this waste can be turned into other useful chemicals. This reduces the amount that ends up polluting the environment.

3) Using the Product

See page 264 for more on greenhouse gases.

1) The use of a product can also damage the environment.

2) For example, burning fuels releases greenhouse gases and other harmful substances. Fertilisers can drain into streams and rivers, causing harm to plants and animals.

3) It's also important to think about how long a product is used for or how many uses it gets. Products that need lots of energy to produce but are used for ages mean less waste in the long run.

4) Product Disposal

1) Products are often thrown away in landfill sites.

2) This takes up space and pollutes land and water. For example, paint can wash off a product and get into rivers.

3) Energy is used to transport waste to landfill. This can release pollutants into the atmosphere, such as carbon monoxide (see p.267) and carbon dioxide.

4) Products might be incinerated (burnt), which causes air pollution.

LCAs look at the effect a product has on the environment

LCAs can show us how to improve products, so we can make them less damaging to the environment. However, LCAs can also be very time consuming and expensive, because there is so much to think about.

Life Cycle Assessments

*You can compare the life cycle assessments of **similar products** to see which has the **smallest effect** on the environment. You might want to do this to see which material will affect the environment the **least**.*

You Can **Compare** Life Cycle Assessments for **Plastic** and **Paper Bags**

1) You may be asked to compare life cycle assessment (LCA) information about paper and plastic bags.

2) You can then decide which type of bag is the least harmful to the environment.

Life Cycle Assessment Stage	Plastic Bag	Paper Bag
Raw Materials	Crude oil	Wood
Manufacturing and Packaging	Plastics are made from compounds extracted from crude oil by fractional distillation and processed by cracking and polymerisation. Waste is reduced as the other fractions of crude oil have other uses.	Pulped wood is processed using lots of energy. Lots of waste is made.
Using the Product	Can be reused several times. Can be used for other things as well as shopping. For example, as bin liners.	Usually only used once.
Product Disposal	Recyclable but many types aren't biodegradable. Take up space in landfill and pollute land.	Can be recycled. Biodegradable and non-toxic.

3) LCAs have shown that even though plastic bags aren't usually biodegradable, they may be less harmful to the environment.

4) This is because they take less energy to make and have a longer lifespan than paper bags.

> If something's biodegradable, it can be broken down naturally by microorganisms (tiny living things like bacteria).

There are **Problems** with **Life Cycle Assessments**

1) It's quite easy to measure things like the use of energy or resources, and the production of some types of waste. So we can give all of these measurements a number in an LCA.

2) But measuring some effects is much harder.

> - For example, plastic bags that litter the environment don't look very nice.
> - But measuring how unattractive something looks isn't easy. The person measuring it has to use their own judgement.

3) So, producing an LCA can involve the feelings of the person carrying out the assessment as well as facts. So the results could change depending on who does the assessment. This means LCAs can be biased.

4) Selective LCAs only show some of the impacts that a product has on the environment. So these can also be biased because they can be written to purposely support the claims of a company. This would give the company positive advertising.

> If something is biased, that means it favours one point of view in a way that isn't backed up by facts.

LCAs aren't all they are cracked up to be...

In the exam, you may have to compare LCAs for plastic and paper bags and decide which one is the most environmentally friendly. Each bag has good and bad points, but don't forget that not all environmental impacts can be measured in an LCA. Also, the results of an LCA can be biased.

Warm-Up & Exam Questions

That's some more revision done and dusted — now it's time to test yourself on how much you've taken in. Have a go at the questions on this page to see if you need to look back at some topics.

Warm-Up Questions

1) Give one example of a natural resource which has been replaced by a man-made alternative.
2) True or false? One way to be more sustainable is to use fewer finite resources.
3) Give two positive effects of recycling metals.
4) What is the purpose of a life cycle assessment?

Exam Questions

1 Natural resources are formed without human input and are used for construction, fuel and food.

1.1 What is a renewable natural resource?
Tick **one** box.

☐ A natural resource that can't be remade by humans.

☐ A natural resource that can be remade at least as fast as we use it.

☐ A natural resource that is only remade very slowly.

[1 mark]

1.2 Aluminium is used to make soft drink cans.
Extracting aluminium uses a large amount of energy.
Suggest **one** way that the use of soft drink cans can be made more sustainable.

[1 mark]

2 **Table 1** shows part of a life cycle assessment for two types of bag.

Table 1

	Raw materials	Manufacturing	Reusability	Disposal
Plastic bag	Crude oil	Waste from manufacturing process can be used to make other products.	Can be reused many times, in different ways.	Recyclable, but often not biodegradable. Many end up in landfill sites or the oceans.
Paper bag	Wood	High energy process that generates lots of waste.	Usually not reusable.	Can be recycled. Biodegradable and non-toxic.

2.1* Use the information in **Table 1** and your own knowledge to evaluate which type of bag is better for the environment.

[6 marks]

2.2 Give **two** reasons why a life cycle assessment may be biased.

[2 marks]

Potable Water and Water Treatment

*We all need safe drinking water. The **way** that water's made safe depends on **local conditions**.*

Potable Water is Water You Can Drink

1) Potable water is water that's safe for humans to drink. We need it to live.

2) Some water is naturally potable, but most water needs to be treated before it's safe to drink.

3) Potable water isn't pure. Pure water only contains H_2O molecules but potable water can contain lots of other dissolved substances.

See p.254 for more on purity.

4) For water to be safe to drink, it must:
   - not have high levels of dissolved salts,
   - have a pH between 6.5 and 8.5,
   - not have any bad things in it (like bacteria or other microbes).

How Potable Water is Produced Depends on Where You Are

1) Fresh water is water that doesn't have much dissolved in it. Rainwater is a type of fresh water.

2) When it rains, water can either collect as surface water or as ground water.

   Surface water: collects in lakes, rivers and reservoirs (places for storing liquids).
   Ground water: collects in rocks that trap water underground.

3) When producing potable water, companies need to choose a suitable source of freshwater. In the UK, the source of fresh water used depends on location.

4) Surface water tends to dry up first. So in warm areas, such as the south-east, most of the water supply comes from ground water. This is because it is underground so doesn't dry up.

Most Fresh Water Needs to be Treated to Make it Safe

1) Fresh water contains low levels of dissolved substances.

2) It still needs to be treated to make it safe before we use it.

3) This process includes:

Filtration — the water is passed through a wire mesh. This stops large things like twigs from passing through. Next, filter beds are used to filter out any other solid bits.

Filter beds are made from grains of sand and gravel. Tiny bits of solid in the water are captured by the grains.

mesh filtration

filtration through filter beds

Sterilisation — the water is sterilised. This means that any harmful bacteria or microbes in the water are killed. This can be done by bubbling chlorine gas through it or by using ozone or ultraviolet light.

Ozone is a gas.

sterilisation

Waste water must be treated before it's safe to drink

A lot of the water that we drink comes from rain. Thankfully in the UK, we have an endless supply...

Q1 Describe the steps used to treat fresh water to make it potable. [2 marks]

Q1 Video Solution

Potable Water and Water Treatment

*Some countries have **limited supplies** of fresh water. They need to use **other** water sources, like the sea.*

Potable Water Can Be Made From Seawater

1) In some very <u>dry</u> countries there's <u>not enough</u> surface or ground water.
So instead they use <u>seawater</u> to provide potable water.

2) Seawater contains <u>salts</u> which need to be <u>removed</u> before we can drink it.

3) These salts are removed by a process called <u>desalination</u>.

Distillation Can Be Used to Purify Seawater

1) <u>Distillation</u> can be used to remove the salt from seawater (<u>desalination</u>).

2) You can <u>test</u> and <u>purify</u> a <u>sample</u> of water in the lab using distillation:

> Seawater can also be purified by a process called reverse osmosis (see next page).

   1) Use a <u>pH meter</u> to test the pH of a sample of water (see p.217).
If the pH is too high or too low, you'll need to <u>neutralise</u> it (make it neutral).
You do this by adding some acid (if the sample's alkaline) or some alkali
(if the sample's acidic) until the pH is <u>7</u>.

   2) Set up the <u>equipment</u> as shown in the diagram below.

> Neutral solutions are neither acidic nor alkaline. They have a pH of 7.
> E.g. pure water is neutral.
> There's more on this on page 215.

   3) <u>Heat</u> the water in the flask using a Bunsen burner.

   4) As the water heats up, it becomes a gas (it <u>evaporates</u>).
The gas then enters the condenser as <u>steam</u>.
<u>Cold water</u> is pumped around the condenser to <u>cool</u> the steam inside of it.
This <u>drop in temperature</u> makes the steam <u>condense back</u> into <u>liquid water</u>.

   5) <u>Collect</u> the water running out of the condenser in a <u>beaker</u>.

   6) Retest the <u>pH</u> of the water with a pH meter to check it's neutral.

   7) After the water has been <u>distilled</u> (all of the water has evaporated from the flask),
see whether there are any <u>crystals</u> in the round bottomed flask.
If there are crystals it means that there were <u>salts</u> in the water before you distilled it.

Potable Water and Water Treatment

*You saw on the previous page how **distillation** can be used to purify seawater.*
*There's another method you need to know about — **reverse osmosis**.*

Seawater can be Purified Using Reverse Osmosis

1) Seawater can be purified by processes that use thin layers of material called <u>membranes</u>.
   Membranes have really <u>tiny holes</u> that only let certain things <u>pass</u> through them.

2) One of these processes is called <u>reverse osmosis</u>.
   The salty water is passed through a <u>membrane</u>.
   The membrane lets water molecules pass through but <u>traps</u> the salts.
   This <u>separates</u> them from the water.

There's more on purifying seawater using distillation on the previous page.

3) Both distillation and reverse osmosis need <u>loads of energy</u> to work which makes them <u>expensive</u>.
   This is why they're <u>not</u> used when there are other sources of fresh water available.

Waste Water Comes from Lots of Different Sources

1) We use water for lots of things at home — like <u>having a bath</u>,
   going to the <u>toilet</u> and doing the <u>washing-up</u>.
   When you flush this water and other waste matter down the drain,
   it goes into the <u>sewers</u> forming <u>sewage</u>.
   The sewage is then carried by the sewers to <u>sewage treatment plants</u>.

2) <u>Agricultural</u> (farming) <u>systems</u> also produce a lot of waste water.

3) Waste water has to be <u>treated</u> before it can be put <u>back</u> into fresh water sources like <u>rivers</u> or <u>lakes</u>.
   This is to remove any pollutants such as <u>organic matter</u> and <u>harmful microbes</u>
   (e.g. bacteria and viruses) so that the water doesn't cause <u>health problems</u>.

4) Waste water from <u>industrial processes</u> also has to be <u>collected</u> and <u>treated</u>.

Organic matter contains carbon compounds that come from the remains and waste of organisms.

5) Industrial waste water can contain organic matter and <u>harmful chemicals</u>.
   So it needs further treatment before it's safe to put back into the environment.

The water that comes out of our taps has been treated

<u>Location</u> is a really important factor in determining <u>how</u> water is treated. For example, in the UK, there is a lot of <u>fresh water</u> available so this is filtered and then sterilised. However, in very <u>dry</u> countries a more <u>expensive</u> process may have to be used, such as the <u>distillation</u> or <u>reverse osmosis</u> of sea water.

Potable Water and Water Treatment

*Dealing with waste water is really important to make sure we don't **pollute** our environment.*

Sewage **Treatment** Happens in **Several Stages**

1) Some of the <u>processes</u> involved in treating waste water at sewage treatment plants are shown below.

1) Screening

The sewage is <u>screened</u> to remove any <u>large bits</u> of material (like twigs or plastic bags) and any <u>grit</u> (small bits of stone and sand).

2) Sedimentation

Then it goes through <u>sedimentation</u>. The <u>heavier</u> solids sink to the bottom to produce <u>sludge</u>. The lighter <u>effluent</u> (liquid waste) floats on the top.

① screening

② sedimentation

③ aerobic digestion

effluent

4) Anaerobic Digestion

The <u>sludge</u> is also <u>broken down</u> by bacteria in a process called <u>anaerobic digestion</u>. This produces <u>methane gas</u> which can be used as an <u>energy source</u>. The remaining waste can be used as <u>fertiliser</u>.

sludge

④ anaerobic digestion

3) Aerobic Digestion

The <u>effluent</u> is <u>removed</u> and treated by <u>biological aerobic digestion</u>. This is where <u>bacteria</u> break down any <u>organic matter</u> — including <u>other microbes</u> in the water.

<u>Aerobic</u> just means with oxygen, whereas <u>anaerobic</u> means without oxygen.

2) Waste water containing <u>toxic substances</u> needs extra stages of treatment. This may include adding <u>chemicals</u>, <u>UV radiation</u> or using <u>membranes</u>.

3) Sewage treatment has <u>more stages</u> than treating <u>fresh water</u> but uses <u>less energy</u> than the <u>desalination</u> of <u>salt water</u>. So it could be used as an option in areas where there's not much fresh water. However, people don't like the idea of drinking water that used to be sewage.

Waste water can be recycled to produce potable water

To learn the stages of water treatment, <u>cover</u> the diagram, <u>write out</u> each step and then <u>check</u> it.

Q1   Name and describe the first two stages of waste water treatment at a sewage treatment plant.

[2 marks]

Q1 Video Solution

Warm-Up & Exam Questions

Now you know all there is to possibly know about water it's time to test yourself with some questions.

Warm-Up Questions

1) Describe one feature of potable water that makes it safe for drinking.
2) True or False? The first step in treating fresh water involves mesh filtration.
3) What two things are produced following the sedimentation stage of water treatment?
4) True or False? Sewage treatment has more stages than the treatment of fresh water.

Exam Questions

1 Waste water needs to be treated before it can be returned to the environment. *(Grade 1-3)*

1.1 What is the first step in the process of sewage treatment? Tick **one** box.

☐ Sedimentation

☐ Anaerobic digestion

☐ Aerobic digestion

☐ Screening

[1 mark]

1.2 What is used to break down sewage during anaerobic digestion? Tick **one** box.

☐ Acid

☐ UV radiation

☐ Bacteria

☐ Oxygen

[1 mark]

2 Fresh water can be treated to produce potable water. *(Grade 3-4)*

2.1 What is potable water?
Tick **one** box.

☐ Water that only contains H_2O molecules.

☐ Water with a pH above 9.

☐ Water that comes from the surface.

☐ Water that is safe to drink.

[1 mark]

2.2 Why is fresh water filtered during the production of potable water?

[1 mark]

2.3 Suggest **one** thing that could be used to sterilise the water during the sterilisation stage of the process.

[1 mark]

Exam Questions

3   A student wants to carry out distillation of a sample of seawater.
     Figure 2 shows the apparatus that the student is going to use.

Figure 2

3.1   Use an **X** to label the point on **Figure 2** where the pure water is collected.

[1 mark]

3.2   Describe how the processes of evaporation and condensation are used to obtain a sample of
      pure water from seawater.

[2 marks]

3.3   The sample of seawater has a high pH.
      Suggest **one** thing that the student could do to change the pH of the water so that it is safe to drink.

[1 mark]

3.4   How will the student know when all the water has been distilled?

[1 mark]

      When the distillation was complete, the student noticed crystals in the round bottomed flask.

3.5   Explain why crystals formed in the flask at the end of the distillation.

[1 mark]

4   This question is about waste water.

4.1   Explain why waste water has to be treated before it can be returned to the environment.

[2 marks]

4.2   During the sedimentation step of sewage treatment, effluent and sludge are separated from each other.
      Describe how effluent and sludge are then treated before being returned to the environment.

[3 marks]

     A factory makes cleaning products.

4.3   The factory's waste water needs more treatment than household waste water before it can
      be returned to the environment. Explain why.

[1 mark]

5   Membranes are thin layers of material that contain very small holes.

5.1   Explain how reverse osmosis uses membranes to purify seawater.

[2 marks]

5.2   Why is reverse osmosis an expensive process?

[1 mark]

Revision Summary for Topics C6-10

That wraps up <u>Topics C6-10</u> — time to see if you've got this topic in the bag.
- Try these questions and <u>tick off each one</u> when you <u>get it right</u>.
- When you're <u>completely happy</u> with a topic, tick it off.

For even more practice, try the Retrieval Quizzes for Topics C6-10 — just scan the QR codes!

Topic C6 — The Rate and Extent of Chemical Change (p.233-243) ☑

1) What are the four factors that affect the rate of a chemical reaction?
2) Why does increasing the temperature of a reaction mixture increase the reaction rate?
3) What is a catalyst?
4) Explain why measuring a mass change during a reaction is an accurate method of measuring rate.
5) Give two possible units for the rate of a chemical reaction.
6) What symbol shows that a reaction is reversible?
7) What is a closed system?
8) How can you change the direction of a reversible reaction?

Topic C6 Quiz

Topic C7 — Organic Chemistry (p.246-251) ☑

9) What two elements do hydrocarbons contain?
10) Draw the displayed formula of butane.
11) What did crude oil form from?
12) Where do the shortest carbon chains condense in a fractional distillation column?
13) How is catalytic cracking carried out?

Topic C7 Quiz

Topic C8 — Chemical Analysis (p.254-259) ☑

14) In chemistry, what does it mean if a substance is pure?
15) Describe how you could use the boiling point of a substance to test whether it is pure.
16) What is the solvent front on a chromatogram?
17) Give the formula for working out the R_f value of a substance.
18) How can you test if a gas in a test tube is oxygen?

Topic C8 Quiz

Topic C9 — Chemistry of the Atmosphere (p.262-267) ☑

19) Name three of the gases that scientists think were present in the early atmosphere.
20) Give one way that the levels of carbon dioxide in the early atmosphere were reduced.
21) How do greenhouse gases help to support life on Earth?
22) Give two things that can be done to reduce carbon footprints.
23) Describe how acid rain forms.

Topic C9 Quiz

Topic C10 — Using Resources (p.270-279) ☑

24) What is sustainable development?
25) What happens to glass when it is sent to be recycled into a new product?
26) What are the four stages of a life cycle assessment (LCA)?
27) Why might companies want to use selective life cycle assessments?
28) Name two processes you could use to purify sea water.
29) Name two different sources of waste water.
30) What happens during the screening step of sewage treatment?

Topic C10 Quiz

Energy Stores

*Energy is **never used up**. It's just the way that it's **stored** that **changes**.*
*There are eight **energy stores** you need to know about, so let's get cracking...*

Energy is **Transferred** Between **Energy Stores**

Energy is <u>stored</u> in the different <u>energy stores</u> of an object.
You need to know the following energy stores:

1) <u>KINETIC</u> — anything <u>moving</u> has energy in its <u>kinetic energy store</u>.

2) <u>THERMAL</u> — <u>all objects</u> have energy in this store. The <u>hotter</u> the object, the <u>more</u> energy in the store.

You may also see thermal energy stores called internal energy stores.

3) <u>CHEMICAL</u> — anything that can release energy by a <u>chemical reaction</u> has energy in this store, e.g. <u>food</u>.

4) <u>GRAVITATIONAL POTENTIAL</u> — any object <u>raised above ground level</u> has energy in this store.

5) <u>ELASTIC POTENTIAL</u> — anything stretched has energy in this store, like <u>springs</u> and <u>rubber bands</u>.

6) <u>ELECTROSTATIC</u> — e.g. two <u>charges</u> that attract or repel each other have energy in this store.

7) <u>MAGNETIC</u> — e.g. two <u>magnets</u> that attract or repel each other have energy in this store.

8) <u>NUCLEAR</u> — the <u>nucleus of an atom</u> releases energy from this store in <u>nuclear reactions</u>.

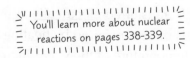
You'll learn more about nuclear reactions on pages 338-339.

EXAM TIP

No matter what store it's in, it's all energy...

In the exam, make sure you refer to <u>energy</u> in terms of the <u>store</u> it's in. For example, if you're describing energy in a <u>hot object</u>, say it '<u>has energy in its thermal energy store</u>'.

Energy Transfer

*Now you know about the different energy stores, it's time to find out how energy is **transferred** between them.*

Energy can be **Transferred** in **Four** Ways

MECHANICALLY

1) This happens when a <u>force does work</u> (p.349) on an object.
2) For example, a force <u>pushing</u> an object along the floor.

ELECTRICALLY

1) This happens when a <u>moving charge does work</u> (p.321).
2) For example, when a <u>current flows</u> through a <u>light bulb</u>.

BY HEATING

1) When energy is transferred from a <u>hotter</u> object to a <u>colder</u> object.
2) For example, when a pan of water is <u>heated</u> on a hob.

BY RADIATION

1) This happens when energy is transferred by e.g. <u>sound</u> or <u>light</u>.
2) For example, when energy from the <u>Sun</u> travels to <u>Earth</u> by <u>light</u>.

When a **System Changes**, **Energy** is **Transferred**

1) A <u>system</u> is just the <u>single</u> object or a <u>group</u> of <u>objects</u> that you're interested in.
2) When a system <u>changes</u>, the way energy is <u>stored</u> changes in one of the ways above.
3) <u>Closed systems</u> are systems where <u>no matter</u> (stuff) or <u>energy</u> can <u>enter or leave</u>.
4) When a closed system changes, there is no <u>net (overall) change</u> in the <u>total energy</u> of the system.
5) For example...

> A <u>cold spoon</u> sealed in a flask of <u>hot soup</u> is a closed system.
> Energy is <u>transferred</u> from the thermal energy store of the <u>soup</u> to the thermal energy store of the <u>spoon</u> by heating.
> But <u>no energy</u> leaves the system. The total energy <u>stays the same</u>.

Heating a Material Transfers Energy to its **Thermal Energy Store**

1) As a material is <u>heated</u>, energy is <u>transferred</u> to its <u>thermal</u> energy store.
2) This causes its <u>temperature to increase</u>.
3) You need to be able to <u>describe</u> the changes in how energy is stored when an object is <u>heated</u>.
4) For example, if you <u>boil water in an electric kettle</u>:

> Energy is transferred <u>electrically</u> to the <u>thermal</u> energy store of the kettle's heating element.
> Energy is then transferred <u>by heating</u> to the water's <u>thermal</u> energy store.
> So the <u>temperature</u> of the water <u>increases</u>.

Don't talk about 'electrical energy stores'...

It's easy to accidentally refer to <u>electrical energy stores</u>, rather than talk about how <u>energy</u> is <u>transferred electrically</u>. Make sure you don't get it mixed up the exam.

Mechanical Energy Transfer

*It's time to look at **mechanical energy transfers** a bit more. They happen when a **force does work**.*

Forces Cause Mechanical Energy Transfers

1) If a <u>force</u> moves an object, then <u>work is done</u>.
2) Work done is <u>the same</u> as energy transferred.
3) So energy is transferred <u>mechanically</u> when a force moves an object.
4) For any given situation, you'll have to <u>describe</u> the changes in how energy is <u>stored</u>.
5) Here are a few <u>examples</u>:

There's more on work done on p.349.

Example 1 — A ball <u>thrown into the air</u>
A boy throws a ball <u>upwards</u>. The boy <u>exerts a force</u> on the ball.
Energy is transferred <u>mechanically</u> from the <u>chemical</u> energy store of the boy's <u>arm</u> to the <u>kinetic</u> energy stores of the <u>ball and arm</u>.

Example 2 — A ball <u>dropped from a height</u>
The ball is <u>accelerated</u> by the <u>constant force</u> of <u>gravity</u>.
Energy is <u>transferred mechanically</u> from the ball's <u>gravitational potential energy</u> store to its <u>kinetic</u> energy store.

frictional forces cause
a transfer of energy

Example 3 — A car <u>slowing down</u>
<u>Friction</u> acts between the car's <u>brakes</u> and its <u>wheels</u>.
Energy is transferred <u>mechanically</u> from the <u>wheels' kinetic energy</u> stores to the <u>thermal</u> energy store of the <u>surroundings</u>.

Example 4 — A car <u>hitting a wall</u>
When the <u>car</u> and the <u>wall touch</u>, there is a <u>normal contact force</u> (p.347) on both of them.
Energy is transferred <u>mechanically</u> from the car's <u>kinetic</u> energy store to <u>lots</u> of other energy stores.
Some energy is transferred to the <u>elastic potential</u> and <u>thermal</u> energy stores of the <u>wall</u> and the <u>car</u>.
Some energy might also be <u>transferred away</u> by <u>sound</u> waves.

Energy is transferred between the different stores of objects...

Energy stores pop up <u>everywhere</u> in physics. You need to be able to describe <u>how energy is transferred</u>, and <u>which stores</u> it gets transferred between, for <u>any scenario</u>.

Q1   Describe the energy transfers that occur when the wind causes a windmill to spin.   [3 marks]

Q1 Video
Solution

Kinetic and Potential Energy Stores

Kinetic, gravitational potential and *elastic potential* are three important energy stores.
Here's how to **calculate** the amount of energy in each of them.

Movement Means Energy in an Object's Kinetic Energy Store

1) Energy is transferred <u>to</u> the kinetic energy store when an object <u>speeds up</u>.
2) Energy is transferred <u>away</u> from this store when an object <u>slows down</u>.
3) There's a <u>slightly tricky</u> formula for finding the energy in an object's kinetic energy store:

Kinetic energy (J) — $E_k = \frac{1}{2}mv^2$ — (Speed)² (m/s)²

Mass (kg)

½mv² means ½ × m × v².

EXAMPLE

A car of mass 2500 kg is travelling at 20 m/s. Calculate the energy in its kinetic energy store.

$E_k = \frac{1}{2} \times 2500 \times 20^2 = 500\ 000$ J

Raised Objects Store Energy in Gravitational Potential Energy Stores

1) All objects raised <u>above the ground</u> gain energy in their <u>gravitational potential energy</u> (g.p.e.) store.
2) You can find the <u>energy</u> in an object's g.p.e. store using:

g.p.e. (J) — $E_p = mgh$ — Height (m)

Mass (kg)   Gravitational field
strength (N/kg)

Gravitational field strength on
Earth is equal to 9.8 N/kg.

Stretching can Transfer Energy to Elastic Potential Energy Stores

1) <u>Stretching</u> or <u>squashing</u> an object can transfer energy to its <u>elastic potential energy store</u>.
2) The energy in the <u>elastic potential energy store</u> of a stretched spring can be found using:

Elastic potential
energy (J) $E_e = \frac{1}{2}ke^2$ — (Extension)²
(m)²

Spring constant (N/m)

3) This equation only works if the <u>limit of proportionality</u> has not been <u>passed</u> (p.352).

Greater height = more energy in gravitational potential stores...

Make sure you know what all the <u>variables</u> are in the equations above, and the <u>units</u> they're in.

Q1   A 2.0 kg object is dropped from a height of 10 m.
Calculate the speed of the object after it has fallen 5.0 m, assuming there is no air resistance.
Give your answer to 2 significant figures. g = 9.8 N/kg.   [5 marks]

Q1 Video
Solution

Conservation of Energy

*Repeat after me: **energy** is **NEVER** destroyed. Make sure you learn that fact, it's really important.*

Energy is Always Wasted in any Energy Transfer

1) When energy is <u>transferred</u> between stores, some energy is transferred to the store you <u>want</u> it in.
2) This energy is <u>usefully</u> transferred.
3) But in <u>any</u> energy transfer, some energy is <u>always dissipated</u>.
4) This means the energy is transferred to <u>useless stores</u>.
5) These useless energy stores are usually <u>thermal energy stores</u>.
6) This energy is often described as '<u>wasted</u>' energy.

> When you use a mobile phone, energy is transferred from the <u>chemical</u> energy store of the <u>battery</u>.
> Some energy is <u>usefully</u> transferred.
> But some is <u>dissipated</u> to the <u>thermal</u> energy store of the <u>phone</u>.

You Need to Know the Conservation of Energy Principle

> Energy can be <u>transferred</u> usefully, stored or dissipated, but can <u>never</u> be <u>created</u> or <u>destroyed</u>.

1) This means that whenever a system <u>changes</u>, all the energy is simply <u>moved between stores</u>.
2) It <u>never</u> disappears.
3) This is true for <u>every</u> energy transfer.
4) Even when energy is <u>dissipated</u> (or wasted), it <u>isn't</u> gone.
5) It's just been transferred to an energy store that <u>we didn't want</u>.
6) Ways of reducing <u>unwanted energy transfers</u> are given on p.294.

You Can Calculate Energy Transfers Using Conservation of Energy

You can make <u>calculations</u> when energy is <u>transferred</u> between <u>two stores</u>. For example:

1) You saw on p.285 that a falling object transfers energy from its <u>g.p.e. store</u> to its <u>kinetic energy store</u>.
2) The <u>conservation of energy principle</u> (above) says that energy <u>can't</u> be destroyed.
3) So for a falling object when there's <u>no air resistance</u>:

> Energy lost from the g.p.e. store = Energy gained in the kinetic energy store

Energy is always conserved, but it can be wasted...

The energy transferred <u>away</u> from a falling object's <u>gravitational potential energy store</u> is only equal to the energy <u>gained</u> in its <u>kinetic energy store</u> if there's <u>no air resistance</u>. In reality, some energy would be wasted. For example, some energy would be transferred <u>mechanically</u> to the <u>thermal energy stores</u> of the <u>air</u>.

Specific Heat Capacity

*Specific heat capacity is really just a sciencey way of saying **how hard** it is to **heat** something up...*

Different Materials Have Different Specific Heat Capacities

1) Some materials need <u>more energy</u> to <u>increase their temperature</u> than others.
2) These materials also <u>transfer</u> more energy when they <u>cool down</u> again.
3) They can '<u>store</u>' a lot of energy.
4) The <u>amount of energy</u> stored or released as a material <u>changes temperature</u> depends on the <u>specific heat capacity</u> of the material:

> <u>Specific heat capacity</u> is the amount of <u>energy</u> needed to raise the temperature of <u>1 kg</u> of a material by <u>1 °C</u>.

There's a Helpful Formula Involving Specific Heat Capacity

Below is the equation that links <u>energy transferred</u> to <u>specific heat capacity</u> (the Δ's just mean "change in").

Change in thermal energy (J)   Temperature change (°C)

$$\Delta E = mc\Delta\theta$$

Mass (kg)   Specific heat capacity (J/kg°C)

EXAMPLE

A hot block of metal cools from 55 °C to 25 °C. The block has a mass of 0.50 kg and is made from a material that has a specific heat capacity of 320 J/kg°C. Calculate the energy transferred from the block as it cooled.

1) First, <u>calculate</u> the <u>change</u> in the block's <u>temperature</u>.   55 °C − 25 °C = 30 °C
2) The numbers are in the <u>correct units</u>. $\Delta E = mc\Delta\theta$
   So put them into the <u>equation</u>.   = 0.50 × 320 × 30
3) The <u>unit</u> for energy is <u>joules</u> (J).   = 4800 J

If you're <u>not</u> working out the energy, you'll have to rearrange the equation, so a <u>formula triangle</u> will come in dead handy. To use them, <u>cover up</u> the thing you want to find and write down what's left <u>showing</u>.

You write the bits of the formula in the triangle like this:

The line through the centre of the triangle means divide.

$$\frac{\Delta E}{m \times c \times \Delta\theta}$$

Some substances can store more energy than others...

Learn the <u>definition</u> of specific heat capacity and make sure you know how to use the <u>formula</u> above.

Q1   Find the final temperature of 5 kg of water, at an initial temperature of 5 °C, after 50 kJ of energy has been transferred to it.
The specific heat capacity of water is 4200 J/kg°C.   [3 marks]

Q1 Video Solution

Investigating Specific Heat Capacity

*Time for a **practical**. Woohoo I hear you shout! Maybe not, but you do have to know it I'm afraid.*

Investigate the Specific Heat Capacity of a **Solid Block**

1) Measure the <u>mass</u> of the <u>block</u>.

2) Wrap it in an insulating layer (e.g. thick newspaper) to reduce <u>energy losses</u>.

3) Set up the <u>apparatus</u> as shown.

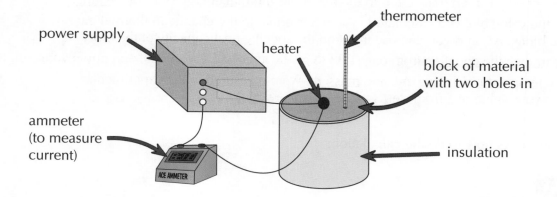

4) Measure the <u>starting temperature</u> of the block.

5) <u>Turn on</u> the power supply and <u>start</u> a <u>stopwatch</u>.

6) Record the <u>potential difference</u>, *V*, of the power supply and the <u>current</u>, *I*. They shouldn't change at all.

7) After <u>10 minutes</u>, take a reading of the block's <u>temperature</u>.

8) Turn off the heater and work out the <u>temperature change</u>.

9) Calculate the power of the heater using <u>$P = VI$</u> (p.322).

10) You can use this to calculate the <u>specific heat capacity</u> of the <u>material</u> the block is made from (see the next page).

Think about how you could improve your experiments...

If the hole in your material is <u>bigger</u> than your <u>thermometer</u>, you could put a small amount of water in the hole with the thermometer. This helps the thermometer to measure the temperature of the block more accurately, as water is a better thermal conductor than <u>air</u>.

PRACTICAL Investigating Specific Heat Capacity

*You're not quite done yet — now that the fiddly bit is over, it's time to whip your calculator out to find the **specific heat capacity** of the **material** from your results.*

Calculating the **Specific Heat Capacity**

To calculate the specific heat capacity from your results from the previous page, you need ideas about work done and energy transferred:

1) When you turn on the power, the current in the circuit does work on the heater.
2) Energy is transferred electrically from the power supply to the heater's thermal energy store.
3) The energy transferred to the heater is given by $E = Pt$ (p.293). (P is the power of the heater and t is how long the heater is on for.)
4) This energy is then transferred to the material's thermal energy store by heating.
5) So the value of E you calculated in step 3 is equal to the change in thermal energy of the block, ΔE, and you can use it to find the specific heat capacity of the block, c.
6) Rearrange the equation from page 288 to give you $c = \Delta E \div (m \times \Delta\theta)$, and put in your results.
7) The temperature change, $\Delta\theta$, and mass, m, were measured in the experiment. Use your value of E from step 3 as ΔE.

This example shows how to do the calculation:

EXAMPLE

A 1.0 kg block of material is heated using a 10 V power supply.
The starting temperature of the block is 20 °C.
The current through the heater is recorded as 10 A.
After 60 seconds, the final temperature of the block is 26 °C.
Calculate the specific heat capacity of the material of the block.

1) Calculate the power of the heater. $P = V \times I = 10 \times 10 = 100$ W
2) Calculate the energy transferred. $E = P \times t = 100 \times 60 = 6000$ J
3) Find the change in temperature. $\Delta\theta = 26 - 20 = 6$ °C
4) Calculate the specific heat capacity. $c = \Delta E \div (m \times \Delta\theta) = 6000 \div (1.0 \times 6) = 1000$ J/kg °C

You Can Find the **Specific Heat Capacities** of **Liquids** Too

1) You can repeat the experiment shown on the previous page with different materials to see how their specific heat capacities compare.
2) For a liquid, place the heater and thermometer into an insulated beaker with a known mass of the liquid.
3) Then carry out the rest of the experiment in exactly the same way as above.

Insulation reduces the energy transferred to the surroundings...

If you repeat the experiment with a liquid, don't let it start boiling as this will affect your results.

Q1   A student uses an 80 W heater to heat a 2 kg block of metal for 200 s. The temperature of the block increases by 20 °C. Calculate the specific heat capacity of the metal. Assume that all the energy from the heater is transferred to the metal block.   [5 marks]

Q1 Video
Solution

Warm-Up & Exam Questions

These questions give you chance to use your knowledge about energy transfers and specific heat capacity.

Warm-Up Questions

1) Give two ways in which energy can be transferred.

2) Describe how energy is transferred between stores as someone throws a ball upwards.

3) True or false? The energy in an object's gravitational potential energy store is proportional to its mass.

4) Which has more energy in its kinetic energy store: a person walking at 3 miles per hour, or a lorry travelling at 60 miles per hour?

5) State the principle of the conservation of energy.

Exam Questions

1   An electric heater is placed in a hole in a metal block and switched on. Energy is transferred from the thermal energy store of the heater. Where is the energy transferred to? Tick **one** box.

(Grade 1-3)

☐   The thermal energy store of the metal block

☐   The chemical energy store of the heater

☐   The kinetic energy store of the metal block

☐   The kinetic energy store of the heater

[1 mark]

2   This question is about energy transfers.   (Grade 3-4)

Draw one line from each scenario to the energy store that energy is transferred away from.

	elastic potential
A skydiver falling from an aeroplane.	
	gravitational potential
A substance undergoing a nuclear reaction.	
	chemical
A piece of burning coal.	
	nuclear

[3 marks]

Exam Questions

3 **Figure 1** shows a toy car that is launched by pulling it backwards onto a spring. The spring compresses, and then the car is released.

Figure 1

3.1 Name the store that energy is transferred from as the car is released.

[1 mark]

Immediately after the launch, the car moves away at a speed of 0.9 m/s.
The car has a mass of 0.20 kg.

3.2 Write down the equation that links the energy in an object's kinetic energy store, mass and speed.

[1 mark]

3.3 Calculate the energy in the kinetic energy store of the car immediately after it is released.

[2 marks]

4 A motor lifts a load of mass 20 kg.
The load gains 137.2 J of energy in its gravitational potential energy store.

4.1 Write down the equation that links the energy in an object's gravitational potential energy store, mass, gravitational field strength and height.

[1 mark]

4.2 Calculate the height through which the motor lifts the load.
Assume the gravitational field strength = 9.8 N/kg

[3 marks]

4.3 The motor releases the load and the load falls.
Ignoring air resistance, describe the changes in the way energy is stored that take place as the load falls.

[2 marks]

4.4 Describe how your answer to **4.3** would differ if air resistance was not ignored.

[1 mark]

5 36 000 J of energy is transferred to change the temperature of a 0.5 kg concrete block by 80 °C.

Calculate the specific heat capacity of the concrete block in J/kg °C.
Use the correct equation from the Physics Equation Sheet on page 538.

[3 marks]

Power

*The **more powerful** a device is, the **more energy** it will transfer in a certain amount of **time**.*

Power is the 'Rate of Doing Work'

1) Power is the <u>rate of energy transfer</u>.
2) You can also say it's the <u>rate of doing work</u>.
3) This just means that power is <u>how fast energy is transferred</u> or <u>how fast work is done</u>.
4) <u>Power</u> is measured in <u>watts</u>.
5) <u>One watt = 1 joule of energy transferred per second</u>.
6) You can calculate power using these equations:

Take two cars that are <u>the same</u> in every way apart from the <u>power</u> of their <u>engines</u>. Both cars race the <u>same distance</u> along a straight race track to a finish line. The car with the <u>more powerful</u> engine will reach the finish line <u>faster</u> than the other car. This is because it will transfer the <u>same amount of energy</u> but over <u>a shorter time</u>.

EXAMPLE

a) It takes 8000 J of work to lift a stuntman to the top of a building.
A motor takes 50 s to make the lift.
Calculate the power of the motor.

1) The numbers are in the <u>correct units</u>. $P = W \div t$
2) Put the numbers into the equation $= 8000 \div 50$
   for <u>power</u> in terms of <u>work</u>. $= 160$ W

b) A second motor has a power of 200 W.
It lifts the stuntman for 30 s.
Calculate the energy transferred by the motor.

1) <u>Rearrange</u> the power equation $P = E \div t$ so $E = P \times t$
   for <u>energy transferred</u>. $= 200 \times 30$
2) Put the <u>numbers in</u>. $= 6000$ J
3) Remember <u>energy</u> is in <u>joules</u>.

A large power doesn't always mean a large force...

A <u>powerful</u> device is not necessarily one which can exert a strong <u>force</u> (although it usually ends up that way). A <u>powerful</u> device is one which transfers <u>a lot of energy</u> in <u>a short space of time</u>.

Q1   A motor transfers 4.8 kJ of energy in 2 minutes. Calculate its power output.   [3 marks]

Q1 Video Solution

Reducing Unwanted Energy Transfers

*There are a few ways you can **reduce** the amount of energy running off to a **completely useless** store.*

Lubrication Reduces **Frictional Forces**

1) <u>Friction</u> acts between all objects that <u>rub together</u>.
2) This causes some energy in the system to be <u>dissipated</u>.
3) <u>Lubricants</u> can be used to <u>reduce the friction</u> between the objects.
4) For example, <u>oil</u> in <u>car engines</u> reduces friction between all of the moving parts.
5) This <u>reduces</u> the amount of <u>dissipated energy</u>.

Insulation Has a **Low Thermal Conductivity**

1) When part of a material is <u>heated</u>, that part of the material gains <u>energy</u>.
2) This energy is <u>transferred</u> across the material so that the rest of the material gets <u>warmer</u>.
3) For example, if you heated <u>one end</u> of a <u>metal rod</u>, the <u>other end</u> would <u>eventually</u> get warmer. This is known as <u>conduction</u>.
4) <u>Thermal conductivity</u> is a measure of how <u>quickly</u> energy is transferred by conduction through a material.
5) Materials with a <u>high thermal conductivity</u> transfer <u>lots</u> of energy in a <u>short time</u>.
6) Materials with a <u>low thermal conductivity</u> are called <u>thermal insulators</u>.
7) Thermal insulators can reduce unwanted transfers <u>by heating</u>, e.g. in the <u>home</u>.

Insulation is Important for Keeping **Buildings Warm**

You can keep your home cosy and <u>warm</u> by <u>reducing</u> the <u>rate of cooling</u>.
How <u>quickly</u> a building cools depends on:

1) How <u>thick</u> its <u>walls</u> are. The <u>thicker</u> the walls are, the <u>slower</u> a building will <u>cool</u>.
2) The <u>thermal conductivity</u> of its walls. Building walls from a material with a <u>low thermal conductivity</u> reduces the rate of cooling.
3) How much <u>thermal insulation</u> there is, e.g. <u>loft insulation</u> reduces energy losses through the roof.

Energy Transfers Involve Some **Wasted Energy**

1) You saw on page 287 that some energy is always wasted when energy is transferred.
2) The <u>less energy</u> that is <u>wasted</u>, the <u>more efficient</u> the energy transfer is.
3) The <u>efficiency</u> of an energy transfer is a measure of the amount of energy that ends up in <u>useful</u> energy stores.
4) But as <u>some</u> energy is <u>always</u> wasted, <u>nothing is 100% efficient</u>.

How to calculate the efficiency of a transfer is on the next page.

Having a well-insulated home can reduce your heating bills...

When people talk of <u>energy loss</u>, it's <u>not</u> that the energy has disappeared. It still exists (see page 287), just not in the <u>store</u> we'd like it to be. For example, in a car, you want the energy to transfer to the <u>kinetic energy store</u> of the wheels, and not to the <u>thermal energy stores</u> of the moving components.

Efficiency

*Devices have **energy transferred** to them, but only transfer **some** of that energy to **useful energy stores**. Wouldn't it be great if we could tell **how much** it **usefully transfers**? That's where **efficiency** comes in.*

There Are **Two Efficiency Equations**

1) The efficiency for any energy transfer can be <u>worked out</u> using this equation:

$$\text{Efficiency} = \frac{\text{Useful output energy transfer}}{\text{Total input energy transfer}}$$

This gives efficiency as a decimal, but you can turn it into a percentage — see below.

EXAMPLE

36 000 J of energy is transferred to a television. It transfers 28 800 J of this energy usefully. Calculate the efficiency of the television. Give your answer as a percentage.

1) Put the numbers you're given <u>into the equation</u>.

2) To change a <u>decimal</u> to a <u>percentage</u>, <u>multiply</u> your answer <u>by 100</u>.

efficiency = useful output energy transfer
    ÷ total input energy transfer
    = 28 800 ÷ 36 000
    = 0.8
0.8 × 100 = 80, so efficiency = 80%

2) You might not know the <u>energy</u> input and output of a device.

3) But you can use its <u>power input</u> and <u>output</u> to calculate its <u>efficiency</u>:

$$\text{Efficiency} = \frac{\text{Useful power output}}{\text{Total power input}}$$

EXAMPLE

A blender is 70% efficient. It has a total input power of 600 W. Calculate the useful power output.

1) Change the <u>efficiency</u> from a <u>percentage</u> to a <u>decimal</u>. To do this, <u>divide</u> the percentage <u>by 100</u>.

2) <u>Rearrange</u> the equation for <u>useful power output</u>.

3) <u>Stick in</u> the numbers and find the useful power output.

efficiency = 70% ÷ 100 = 0.7

useful power output = efficiency × total power input
useful power output = 0.7 × 600 = 420 W

The less energy a device wastes, the higher its efficiency...

Make sure you can <u>use</u> and <u>rearrange</u> the equations for efficiency, then have a go at these questions.

Q1   A motor in a remote-controlled car transfers 300 J of energy into the car's energy stores. 225 J are transferred to the car's kinetic energy stores. Calculate the efficiency of the motor. [2 marks]

Q2   A machine has a useful power output of 900 W and a total power input of 1200 W. In a given time, 72 kJ of energy is transferred to the machine. Calculate the amount of energy usefully transferred by the machine in this time. [4 marks]

Q2 Video Solution

Warm-Up & Exam Questions

Don't let your energy dissipate. These questions will let you see how efficient your revision has been.

Warm-Up Questions

1) What is power?
2) What is 1 watt equivalent to: 1 J, 1 Js or 1 J/s?
3) What should you consider when choosing a material to build house walls from to minimise the rate of cooling?
4) Which has a greater rate of energy transfer: a material with a high thermal conductivity or a material with a low thermal conductivity?
5) Why is the efficiency of an appliance always less than 100%?

Exam Questions

1 The motor of an electric scooter moves the scooter along a flat, horizontal course in 20 seconds. During this time the motor does 1 kJ of work. *(Grade 3-4)*

1.1 Write down the equation that links power, work done and time.

[1 mark]

1.2 Calculate the power of the motor.

[2 marks]

1.3 Suggest **one** way in which unwanted energy transfers in the scooter could be reduced.

[1 mark]

1.4 The scooter's motor is replaced with a more powerful, but otherwise identical, motor. It moves along the same course. How will the performance of the scooter differ from before? Tick **one** box.

☐ It will be faster.   ☐ It will be slower.   ☐ It will use less energy.   ☐ It will use more energy.

[1 mark]

2 An electric fan transfers 7250 J of energy. 2 kJ of this is wasted energy. *(Grade 4-5)*

2.1 Suggest **one** way in which energy is wasted by the fan.

[1 mark]

The useful output energy of the fan is given by the equation below:

useful output energy transfer = total input energy transfer − wasted output energy transfer

2.2 Calculate the energy that is usefully transferred by the fan.

[2 marks]

2.3 The efficiency of a device is given by the equation below:

$$\text{efficiency} = \frac{\text{useful output energy transfer}}{\text{total input energy transfer}}$$

Calculate the efficiency of the fan. Give your answer to **two** significant figures.

[2 marks]

Energy Resources and their Uses

*There are lots of **energy resources** available on Earth. They are either **renewable** or **non-renewable** resources.*

Non-Renewable Energy Resources Will Run Out One Day

1) Non-renewable energy resources are fossil fuels and nuclear fuel.
2) The three main fossil fuels are coal, oil and (natural) gas.
3) We can't replace non-renewable energy resources as quickly as we're using them.

Renewable Energy Resources Will Never Run Out

1) Renewable energy resources can be replenished (replaced) as quickly as they are being used.
2) The renewable energy resources you need to know are:

1)	The Sun (Solar)	3)	Water waves	5)	Biofuels	7)	Geothermal
2)	Wind	4)	Hydro-electricity	6)	Tides		

Energy Resources can be Used for Transport...

1) Transport uses both renewable and non-renewable energy resources. For example:

NON-RENEWABLE ENERGY RESOURCES	RENEWABLE ENERGY RESOURCES
Petrol or diesel is used in most vehicles. They're both created from oil. Coal is used in steam trains to boil water to produce steam.	Vehicles can run on pure biofuels (p.298) or a mix of a biofuel and petrol or diesel.

2) Electricity can also be used for transport — e.g. electric cars and some trains.
3) The electricity can be generated using renewable or non-renewable energy resources (p.298-302).

...And for Heating

Energy resources are also needed for heating things, like your home.

NON-RENEWABLE ENERGY RESOURCES	RENEWABLE ENERGY RESOURCES
Natural gas is burnt to heat water in a boiler. This hot water is then pumped into radiators. Gas fires burn natural gas to heat rooms. Coal is burnt in open fireplaces. Electric heaters use electricity which can be generated from non-renewable energy resources.	Biofuel boilers work in the same way as gas boilers. A geothermal heat pump uses geothermal energy resources (p.300) to heat buildings. Solar water heaters use the Sun to heat water which is then pumped into radiators in the building. Electric heaters can use electricity generated from renewable resources.

Fossil fuels are produced over millions of years — quite a wait...

Make sure you know the difference between renewable and non-renewable energy resources.

Biofuels

*Biofuels are a promising renewable energy resource, as they can be **used** and **stored** in much the same way as **fossil fuels**. However, they need a lot of **space** to grow...*

You Need to Be Able to **Compare Resources**

1) You're about to learn all about the <u>main energy resources</u>.

2) You need to be able to:

- describe their effects on the <u>environment</u> (e.g. pollution).
- compare their <u>reliability</u> (whether they can be <u>trusted</u> to provide energy when we need it).

3) So make sure you're <u>paying attention</u>.

No energy resource is 100% reliable as power plants may unexpectedly break or need to be shut down.

Biofuels are Made from **Plants** and **Waste**

1) <u>Biofuels</u> are fuels created from <u>plant</u> products or <u>animal dung</u>.

2) They can be burnt to produce <u>electricity</u> or used to run <u>cars</u> in the same way as <u>fossil fuels</u>.

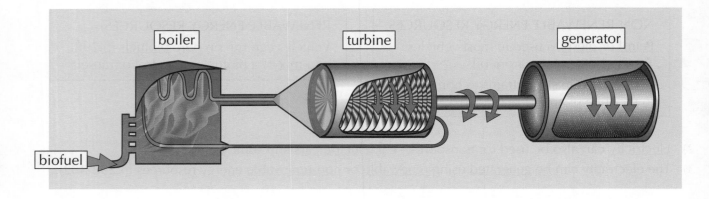

3) They produce <u>carbon dioxide</u> when they're <u>burnt</u>.

4) But the plants used to make biofuels will have <u>absorbed</u> a lot of carbon dioxide while they were <u>growing</u>.

5) In some places, large areas of <u>forest</u> have been <u>cleared</u> to make room to grow <u>biofuels</u>.

6) This leads to lots of animals losing their <u>natural habitats</u>.

7) Crops can be grown <u>throughout the year</u>.

8) Extra biofuels can be constantly produced and <u>stored</u> for when they are needed.

9) So biofuels are fairly <u>reliable</u>.

In theory, biofuels are carbon neutral...

You've probably heard that releasing carbon dioxide (CO_2) into the atmosphere is bad as it leads to <u>global warming</u>. When you <u>burn biofuels</u>, you do <u>release</u> CO_2 into the atmosphere. But, when the plants grew, they <u>absorbed</u> this CO_2 from the atmosphere for <u>photosynthesis</u>. This is why biofuels are often said to be '<u>carbon neutral</u>'.

Wind Power and Solar Power

*Coming up are two of the most visible renewable energy resources — **wind** and **solar power**.*

Wind Power — Lots of Wind Turbines

1) <u>Wind turbines</u> are usually put up in <u>open spaces</u>.
2) When the wind <u>turns the blades</u>, electricity is produced.
3) They produce <u>no pollution</u> once they're built.
4) And they do <u>no permanent</u> (lasting) <u>damage</u> to the landscape. If you <u>remove</u> the turbines, the area goes <u>back to normal</u>.
5) However, they're <u>not as reliable</u> as other energy resources.
6) They don't produce electricity <u>when the wind stops</u>.
7) Turbines are also stopped if the wind is <u>too strong</u>. This stops them getting <u>damaged</u>.
8) It's also <u>impossible</u> to <u>increase supply</u> when there's <u>extra demand</u> (p.323) for electricity.

Solar Cells — Expensive but No Environmental Damage

<u>Solar cells</u> generate electricity directly from sunlight.

1) They create <u>no pollution</u> once they're built.
2) But quite a lot of energy is used to <u>build them</u>.
3) Solar power <u>only</u> generates electricity <u>during the day</u>.
4) In <u>sunny</u> countries solar power is a <u>very reliable source</u> of energy.
5) It's still <u>fairly reliable</u> in <u>cloudy countries</u> like Britain.
6) Like wind, you <u>can't increase the power output</u> when there is <u>extra demand</u>.

People love the idea of wind power — just not in their back yard...

It's easy to think that renewables are the answer to the world's energy problems. However, they have their <u>downsides</u>, and we definitely <u>couldn't</u> rely on them totally at present. Make sure you know the <u>pros</u> and <u>cons</u> for <u>wind</u> and <u>solar</u> power because there are more renewables coming up on the next page.

Geothermal and Hydro-electric Power

*Here are some more examples of **renewable energy resources** — **geothermal** and **hydro-electric**.*
*These ones are a bit more **reliable** than wind and solar — read on to find out why.*

Geothermal Power uses Underground Thermal Energy Stores

1) Geothermal power uses energy from the thermal energy stores of hot rocks below the Earth's surface.

2) It can be used to generate electricity or to heat buildings.

3) Geothermal power is very reliable because the hot rocks are always hot.

4) Most geothermal power stations only have a small impact on the environment.

Hydro-electric Power Uses Falling Water

1) Hydro-electric power usually involves building a big dam across a valley.

2) The valley is usually flooded.

3) Water is allowed to flow out through turbines, which generates electricity.

4) There is no pollution when it's running.

5) But there is a big impact on the environment due to the flooding of the valley.

6) Plants rot and release greenhouse gases which lead to global warming (see p.302).

7) Animals and plants also lose their habitats (where they live).

8) There's no problem with reliability in countries that get rain regularly.

9) And it can respond straight away when there's extra demand (p.323) for electricity.

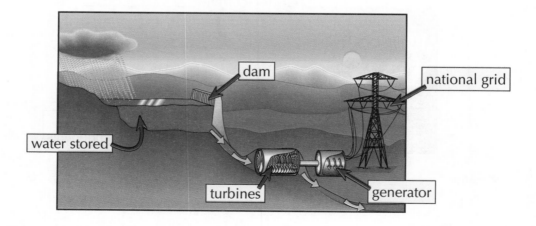

Falling water loses energy from its gravitational potential energy store...

You don't need to be able to describe how these power sources work in detail, but you should be able to comment on their reliability and describe the impact that they have on the environment.

Wave Power and Tidal Barrages

*Good ol' **water**. Not only can we drink it, we can also use it to **generate electricity**. It's easy to get confused between **wave** and **tidal** power as they both involve the seaside — but don't. They are completely different.*

Wave Power — Lots of Little Wave-Powered Turbines

1) Turbines around the coast are turned by water waves and electricity is generated.
2) There is no pollution.
3) But they disturb the seabed and the habitats of animals.
4) They are fairly unreliable, as waves tend to die down when the wind drops.

Tidal Barrages Use the Tides of the Sea

1) Tidal barrages are big dams (with turbines in them) built across rivers.
2) Water passing through the turbines generates electricity.
3) The amount of energy generated changes with the tides.
4) But tidal barrages are very reliable, as we can predict the tides (we know what they're going to do).
5) There is no pollution.
6) But they do change the habitat of the wildlife, e.g. birds and sea creatures.
7) And often fish are killed as they swim through the turbines.

Wave and tidal — power from the motion of the ocean...

The first large-scale tidal barrages started being built in the 1960s, so tidal power isn't a new thing.
Wave power is still pretty experimental though. Make sure you can tell the two of them apart.

Non-Renewables

*Renewable resources may sound like **great news** for the **environment**. But when it comes down to it, they **don't** currently meet all our needs — so we still need those nasty, polluting **non-renewables**.*

Non-Renewables are **Reliable**...

1) <u>Fossil fuels</u> and <u>nuclear energy</u> are <u>reliable</u>.
2) There's enough <u>fossil</u> and <u>nuclear fuels</u> to meet <u>current demand</u>.
3) We always have some in <u>stock</u> so power plants can respond <u>quickly</u> to <u>changes in demand</u>.
4) However, these fuels are <u>slowly running out</u>.
   Some <u>fossil fuels</u> may run out within a hundred years.

...But Create **Environmental Problems**

1) <u>Coal, oil and gas</u> release CO_2 into the atmosphere when they're burned. All this CO_2 leads to <u>global warming</u>.

Global warming is where greenhouse gases cause the Earth to warm up.

2) Burning coal and oil also releases <u>sulfur dioxide</u>, which causes <u>acid rain</u>.
3) <u>Acid rain</u> makes <u>lakes</u> and <u>rivers</u> acidic, which can kill animals and plants. It can also <u>damage trees</u> and <u>soils</u>.
4) <u>Coal mining</u> makes a <u>mess</u> of the landscape.
5) And it <u>destroys the habitats</u> of local animals and plants.
6) <u>Oil spills</u> cause <u>big environmental problems</u> and harm sea creatures.
7) <u>Nuclear power</u> is <u>clean</u> but the <u>nuclear waste</u> is very <u>dangerous</u> and difficult to <u>get rid of</u>.
8) <u>Nuclear power</u> also carries the risk of a big <u>accident</u> that could release a lot of <u>radiation</u>, like the <u>Fukushima disaster</u> in Japan.

Radiation can be very dangerous to humans — see p.342-343 for more.

Currently we Still Need **Non-Renewables**

1) Our <u>use</u> of electricity <u>increased</u> a lot in the <u>1900s</u>.
2) This was because the <u>population</u> and the <u>number</u> of things that <u>used electricity</u> increased.
3) But electricity use in the UK has been <u>falling slowly</u> since around the year <u>2000</u>.
4) This is because we're trying harder to be <u>energy efficient</u> and <u>save energy</u>.
5) At the moment, we use <u>non-renewables</u> for most of our <u>electricity</u>, <u>transport</u> and <u>heating</u>.

We're just going to have to deal with non-renewables for now...

Non-renewables cause a lot of <u>long-term problems</u>, but they also have a few <u>short-term advantages</u>. Make sure you can balance up the <u>advantages</u> and <u>disadvantages</u> of fossil and nuclear fuels.

Limitations on the Use of Renewables

*Although we still rely on **non-renewables** for **a lot** of our energy needs at the moment, the balance is **shifting**.*

People Want to use **More Renewable** Energy Resources

1) We now know that non-renewables are <u>very bad</u> for the <u>environment</u> and will <u>run out</u> one day (p.302).

2) This makes many people want to use <u>renewable energy resources</u> as they are <u>better</u> for the <u>environment</u>.

3) Many people also think it's better to move to renewables <u>before</u> non-renewables run out.

4) <u>Pressure from other countries</u> and the <u>public</u> has meant that governments have begun to introduce <u>targets</u> for using renewable energy resources.

5) This puts pressure on <u>energy providers</u> to build new renewable power plants. If they don't, they may lose <u>business</u> and <u>money</u> in the future.

6) <u>Car companies</u> have also had to change to become more environmentally-friendly.

7) Cars that can run on <u>electricity</u> are already on the <u>market</u>. The electricity can be generated using <u>renewable energy resources</u>.

The Use of **Renewables** is **Limited** by Lots of **Factors**

1) There's a lot of <u>scientific evidence</u> supporting renewables.

2) But scientists can only give <u>advice</u>. They don't have the <u>power</u> to make people, companies or governments <u>change their ways</u> (see p.4).

3) Moving to renewables can be limited by <u>money</u>.

- Building new renewable power plants costs <u>money</u>.
- Some renewable resources are <u>less reliable</u> than other resources, so a <u>mixture</u> of different resources would need to be used.
- This costs <u>even more</u> money.
- Cars that run on <u>electricity</u> are <u>more expensive</u> than <u>petrol cars</u>.

4) Moving to renewables can also be affected by <u>politics</u>, <u>people</u> and <u>ethics</u> (if something is <u>right</u> or <u>wrong</u>).

- The <u>cost</u> of switching to renewable power will have to be paid through energy <u>bills</u> or <u>taxes</u>.
- Governments often don't want to suggest <u>raising taxes</u> as this may make them <u>unpopular</u>.
- Some people <u>don't want</u> to or <u>can't afford</u> to <u>pay</u>. There are arguments about whether it's <u>ethical</u> (right or wrong) to <u>make them</u> pay.
- Many people also don't want to <u>live near</u> to a power plant (like a wind farm or hydro-electric dam).
- And some think it's not <u>ethical</u> to <u>make people</u> put up with new power plants built near to them.

Going green is on-trend this season...

So with some people wanting to <u>help the environment</u>, others not wanting to be <u>inconvenienced</u>, and greener alternatives being <u>expensive to set up</u>, the energy resources we use are <u>changing</u>. Just <u>not</u> particularly <u>quickly</u>.

Warm-Up & Exam Questions

This is the last set of warm-up and exam questions on Topic 1. They're not *too* horrendous, I promise.

Warm-Up Questions

1) Name two fossil fuels.
2) Explain why solar power is usually less reliable than fossil fuels.
3) Describe one way that renewable energy resources can be used to power vehicles.
4) Give two ways in which using coal as an energy resource causes environmental problems.
5) True or false? Geothermal power is a reliable energy resource.

Exam Questions

1 Which of the following energy resources is a renewable energy resource? Tick **one** box. *(Grade 1-3)*

☐ coal   ☐ nuclear   ☐ wind   ☐ oil

[1 mark]

2 Which of the following is a possible disadvantage of using fossil fuels to generate electricity? Tick **one** box. *(Grade 3-4)*

☐ They cannot generate electricity at night.

☐ They don't release very much energy.

☐ The waste produced is dangerous to dispose of.

☐ They can produce sulfur dioxide and cause acid rain.

[1 mark]

3 Natural gas is a non-renewable energy resource that can be used to generate electricity. *(Grade 4-5)*

3.1 Name **one** other use of natural gas.

[1 mark]

3.2 Give **two** reasons why we still use non-renewable energy resources.

[2 marks]

4 The government of a country needs to generate more electricity to support a growing population. The government has considered using wind, hydro-electric power and tides to generate electricity. *(Grade 4-5)*

4.1* Compare the environmental impact and reliability of wind power and hydro-electric power.

[6 marks]

4.2 The government choose to generate electricity using tidal barrages.
Give **one** environmental advantage of generating electricity using tidal barrages.

[1 mark]

Current and Circuit Symbols

Circuit diagrams are a useful way of showing how the **components** of a circuit are **arranged**. You need to be able to **recognise** the **symbols** used to represent different components. Read on for the complete run down...

Learn these Circuit Diagram Symbols

1) You need to be able to <u>understand circuit diagrams</u> and <u>draw them</u> using the <u>correct symbols</u>.

The parts in a circuit e.g. bulbs, resistors, etc. are called 'components'.

2) These are the <u>symbols</u> you need to know:

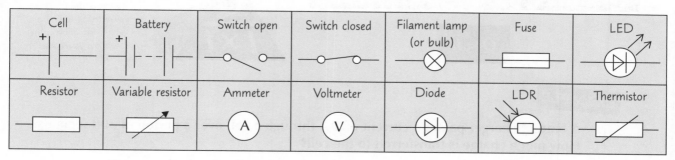

| Cell | Battery | Switch open | Switch closed | Filament lamp (or bulb) | Fuse | LED |
| Resistor | Variable resistor | Ammeter | Voltmeter | Diode | LDR | Thermistor |

3) Follow these <u>rules</u> to draw a circuit diagram:

- Make sure all the <u>wires</u> in your circuit are <u>straight lines</u>.
- Make sure that the circuit is <u>closed</u>. This means you can follow a wire from one end of the <u>cell</u> or <u>battery</u>, through any <u>components</u>, to the other end of the cell or battery.

Potential Difference Causes Charge to Flow Round a Circuit

1) <u>Electric current</u> is a flow of <u>electrical charge</u>.

- Current is measured in <u>amperes</u>, A.
- Charge is measured in <u>coulombs</u>, C.
- In a <u>single</u>, closed <u>loop</u> the current is the same <u>everywhere</u> in the circuit (see p.315).
- The <u>size</u> of the <u>current</u> tells you <u>how fast</u> the charge is <u>flowing</u>. This is known as the <u>rate of flow of charge</u>.

2) The <u>potential difference</u> is the '<u>driving force</u>' that pushes charge around the circuit.

- Electrical charge will <u>only flow</u> round a complete (closed) circuit if something is providing a <u>potential difference</u>, e.g. a battery.
- Potential difference is measured in <u>volts</u> (<u>V</u>).

'Potential difference' is sometimes called 'voltage'. Exam questions will use 'potential difference', but you can use either.

3) <u>Resistance</u> is anything that <u>slows down</u> the flow of charge.

- Resistance is measured in <u>ohms</u> (<u>Ω</u>).

Charge won't flow without a push...

Left to its own devices, charge won't move anywhere. To get a current flowing, charge needs a 'push'. This push comes in the form of a potential difference, supplied by a source like a cell.

Charge and Resistance Calculations

*Prepare yourself to meet two of the most **important equations** in electricity. They're all about **charge**, **current** and **potential difference**... Now if that doesn't tempt you to read this page, I don't know what will.*

Total Charge Through a Circuit Depends on Current and Time

Charge flow, current and time are related by this handy equation:

Charge flow (C) = Current (A) × Time (s)

$$Q = It$$

Use this formula triangle to rearrange the equation. Just cover up the thing you're trying to find, and what's left visible is the formula you're after.

EXAMPLE

A battery charger passes a current of 2 A through a cell over a period of 300 seconds. How much charge is transferred to the cell?

Just substitute the values into the equation above and calculate the charge.

$Q = It = 2 × 300$
$= 600\ C$

Remember charge is measured in coulombs.

There's a Formula Linking Potential Difference and Current

1) The current flowing through a component depends on the potential difference across it and the resistance of the component.

Resistance measures how much the current is slowed down.

The greater the resistance across a component, the smaller the current that flows (for a given potential difference across the component).

2) The formula linking potential difference (pd) and current is:

Potential Difference (V) = Current (A) × Resistance (Ω)

$$V = IR$$

EXAMPLE

A 4.0 Ω resistor in a circuit has a potential difference of 6.0 V across it. What is the current through the resistor?

1) Cover the *I* in the formula triangle to find that $I = V ÷ R$. $I = V ÷ R$

2) Substitute in the values you have, and work out the current. $I = 6.0 ÷ 4.0 = 1.5\ A$

Increasing resistance reduces current...

There's more coming up on resistance, so make sure you're happy with this page before moving on.

Q1   An appliance is connected to a 230 V source.
      Calculate the resistance of the appliance if a current of 5.0 A is flowing through it.   [3 marks]

Q1 Video Solution

Ohmic Conductors

*A circuit **component** can be either **ohmic** or **non-ohmic**. It all depends on whether or not its **resistance** stays the same when the **current** is increased. Read on to find out all the details.*

Ohmic Conductors Have a **Constant Resistance**

1) The resistance of an ohmic conductor doesn't change with current.

2) Ohmic conductors only have a fixed resistance if their temperature doesn't change.

3) Wires and resistors are examples of ohmic conductors.

4) $V = IR$ (see p.306), so if resistance is constant, increasing potential difference will lead to an increase in current.

5) So,

> For an ohmic conductor at a fixed temperature, the current flowing through it is directly proportional to the potential difference across it.

6) This means that if you multiply the potential difference by a certain amount, the current will be multiplied by the same amount. For example, if the potential difference doubles, the current doubles too.

Some Components Have a **Changing Resistance**

The resistance of some components does change with current.
For example, a filament lamp or a diode.

Filament Lamps

1) Filament lamps contain a wire (the filament), which is designed to heat up and 'glow' as the current increases.

2) So as the current increases, the temperature of the filament increases.

3) Resistance increases with temperature, so the resistance increases with current.

A higher current makes a filament glow brighter. So a higher pd means a brighter lamp.

Diodes

1) For diodes, the resistance depends on the direction of the current.

2) A diode will let current flow in one direction. It has a very high resistance in the opposite direction, which makes it hard for a current to flow that way.

Resistance changes when temperature changes...

Remember that ohmic conductors will only have a constant resistance at a constant temperature. In general, resistance increases with temperature (though there are some exceptions, like thermistors — see p.312). So if the temperature is changing, the resistance of your component will be changing too.

Investigating Resistance

*Resistance depends on various things. Here's an **experiment** you can do to investigate one of them — how the resistance **varies** with the **length of the conductor**.*

You Can **Investigate** the Factors Affecting **Resistance**

The resistance of a circuit can depend on a number of factors, like whether components are in series or parallel, p.314 and p.316, or the length of wire used in the circuit. You can investigate the effect of wire length using the circuit below.

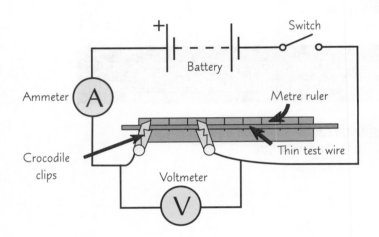

The **Ammeter**

1) Measures the current (in amps) flowing through the test wire.

2) The ammeter must always be placed in series with whatever you're investigating.

The **Voltmeter**

1) Measures the potential difference (or pd) across the test wire (in volts).

2) The voltmeter must always be placed in parallel around whatever you're investigating (p.316) — NOT around any other bit of the circuit, e.g. the battery.

Measure **Potential Difference** and **Current** for **Different Lengths**

1) Attach a crocodile clip to the wire level with 0 cm on the ruler.

2) Attach the second crocodile clip to the wire a short distance from the first clip.

3) Write down the length of the wire between the clips.

4) Close the switch, then record the current through the wire and the pd across it.

5) Use $R = V \div I$ (from the equation $V = IR$ on p.306) to calculate the resistance of the wire.

6) Open the switch and move the second crocodile clip along the wire.

7) Repeat steps 3 to 6 for a range of wire lengths.

Plot a **Graph** of your **Results**

1) Plot a graph of resistance against wire length.

2) Draw a line of best fit through your points.

3) Your graph should be a straight line through the origin (where length and resistance are both zero).

4) This means resistance is directly proportional to length — the longer the wire, the greater the resistance.

Be careful with the temperature of the wire...

If a large current flows through a wire, it can cause it to heat up (which will increase the resistance). So use a low pd to stop it getting too hot and turn off the circuit between readings to let it cool.

I-V Characteristics

I-V characteristics tell you how the **current** through a component changes as the **potential difference** across it is increased. You need to know the I-V characteristics of **ohmic conductors**, **filament lamps** and **diodes**.

I-V Characteristics Show How **Current** Changes With **Pd**

1) An '*I-V characteristic*' graph shows how the <u>current</u> (*I*) flowing through a component changes as the <u>potential difference</u> (*V*) across it changes.

2) Components with <u>straight line</u> *I-V* characteristics are called <u>linear components</u> (e.g. a fixed resistor).

3) Components with <u>curved</u> *I-V* characteristics are <u>non-linear components</u> (e.g. a filament lamp or a diode).

4) To find the <u>resistance</u> at any <u>point</u> on the *I-V* characteristic, first <u>read off</u> the values of *I* and *V* at that point. Then use <u>$R = V \div I$</u> (from $V = IR$ on page 306).

Three Very Important *I-V* **Characteristics**

Make sure you know these <u>graphs</u> really well — you might be asked to <u>sketch</u> one in the exam.

<u>Ohmic Conductor</u> (e.g. <u>resistor</u> at a <u>constant temperature</u>)

1) Current is <u>directly proportional</u> to <u>potential difference</u>.

2) So the <u>graph</u> of current against potential difference is a <u>straight line</u>.

<u>Filament Lamp</u>

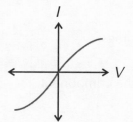

1) <u>Temperature</u> increases as current increases.

2) So <u>resistance increases</u>.

3) This makes it <u>harder</u> for current to flow.

4) So the graph gets <u>less steep</u>.

<u>Diode</u>

1) Current only flows in <u>one direction</u>.

2) The diode has very <u>high resistance</u> in the reverse direction.

You may be asked to interpret an *I-V* characteristic...

Make sure you take care when reading values off the graph. Pay close attention to the <u>axes</u>, and make sure you've converted all values to the <u>correct units</u> before you do any calculations.

Q1   Explain the shape of the filament lamp *I-V* characteristic above, for the quadrant where *I* and *V* are positive.

[3 marks]

Q1 Video Solution

Investigating *I-V* Characteristics

*On the previous page you met **I-V characteristics**. Now, here's all you need to know to set up a **practical** in order to collect data to draw some I-V characteristics of your very own.*

You Can **Investigate** *I-V* Characteristics

You should do this experiment for <u>different components</u>, including a <u>filament lamp</u>, a <u>diode</u> and a <u>resistor at a fixed temperature</u>.

1) Set up the <u>test circuit</u> shown below.

This type of circuit uses direct current (dc) (p.320) and is a series circuit (p.314).

2) The <u>variable resistor</u> is used to <u>change</u> the <u>current</u> in the circuit. This changes the <u>potential difference</u> across the <u>component</u>.

3) Now you need to get <u>sets</u> of <u>current</u> and <u>potential difference</u> readings:
   • Set the <u>resistance</u> of the variable resistor.
   • Measure the <u>current through</u> and <u>potential difference across</u> the component.
   • Take measurements at a number of <u>different</u> resistances.

4) <u>Swap</u> over the wires connected to the battery to reverse the <u>direction of the current</u>. The ammeter should now display <u>negative readings</u>.

5) <u>Repeat</u> step 3 to get results for negative values of current.

6) Plot a <u>graph</u> with <u>current</u> on the *y*-axis and <u>potential difference</u> on the *x*-axis.

PRACTICAL TIP

Ammeters must be connected in series, voltmeters in parallel...

With any circuit, ammeters and voltmeters need to be connected correctly. <u>Ammeters</u> must be in <u>series</u> and <u>voltmeters</u> must be <u>parallel</u> to the component you're investigating (see p.308).

Warm-Up & Exam Questions

Phew — circuits aren't the easiest thing in the world, are they? Make sure you've understood the last few pages by trying these questions. If you get stuck, just go back and re-read the relevant page.

Warm-Up Questions

1) Draw the symbol for a light-emitting diode (LED).
2) What is an electric current?
3) What are the units of resistance?
4) Give an example of an ohmic conductor.
5) How should a voltmeter be connected in a circuit to measure the pd across a component?
6) What is an *I-V* characteristic?

Exam Questions

1   **Figure 1** shows a circuit diagram. The circuit's switch is closed for 2 minutes. While the switch is closed the ammeter reads 0.30 A.

Grade 3-4

Figure 1

1.1   Write down the equation that links current, charge and time.

[1 mark]

1.2   Calculate the total charge that flows through the filament lamp.

[2 marks]

1.3   Use words from the box to complete the sentence.

ohmic	current	potential difference
non-linear	resistance	linear

A filament lamp is a _____ component. As the temperature of the filament increases, the _____ of the lamp increases.

[2 marks]

2   A student wants to produce a graph of current against potential difference for component X. **Figure 2** shows an incomplete diagram of the circuit he is going to use.

Grade 4-5

Figure 2

component X

2.1   Complete the circuit by adding an ammeter and a voltmeter.

[2 marks]

2.2   Predict the shape of the graph that the student will produce. Explain your answer.

[2 marks]

Circuit Devices

*You might consider yourself a bit of an expert in **circuit components** — you're enlightened about bulbs, you're switched on to switches... Just make sure you know these ones as well — they're a bit trickier.*

A **Light-Dependent Resistor** or "LDR"

This is the circuit symbol for a light-dependent resistor.

1) The <u>resistance</u> of an LDR changes as the <u>intensity</u> of <u>light</u> changes.
2) In <u>bright light</u>, the resistance is <u>low</u>.
3) In <u>darkness</u>, the resistance is <u>high</u>.
4) LDRs have lots of <u>uses</u> including turning on lights when it gets <u>dark</u>.
5) This can be used in <u>automatic night lights</u>, or outdoor lighting.
6) They're also used in <u>burglar detectors</u>.

Thermistor Resistance Decreases as Temperature Increases

1) A <u>thermistor</u> is a <u>temperature dependent</u> resistor.
2) In <u>hot</u> conditions, the resistance <u>drops</u>.
3) In <u>cool</u> conditions, the resistance goes <u>up</u>.
4) Thermistors are used in <u>car engines</u> and central heating <u>thermostats</u>.
5) <u>Thermostats</u> turn the heating <u>on</u> when it's <u>cool</u> and <u>off</u> when it's <u>warm</u>.

This is the circuit symbol for a thermistor.

Thermistors and LDRs have many applications...

And they're not just limited to the examples on this page. Oh no. For example, LDRs are used in <u>digital cameras</u> to control how long the <u>shutter</u> should stay open for. If the <u>light level</u> is <u>low</u>, changes in the <u>resistance</u> cause the shutter to <u>stay open for longer</u> than if the light level was higher. How interesting.

Sensing Circuits

*Now you've learnt about what **LDRs** and **thermistors** do, it's time to take a look at how they're put to use.*

You Can Use Thermistors in **Sensing Circuits**

<u>Sensing circuits</u> can be used to automatically <u>change the pd</u> across components depending on changes in the <u>environment</u>.

1) The circuit on the right is a <u>sensing circuit</u> used to <u>control</u> a fan in a room.

2) The <u>potential difference</u> of the power supply is <u>shared out</u> between the thermistor and the fixed resistor (see p.314).

3) How much pd each one gets depends on their <u>resistances</u>.

4) The <u>larger</u> a component's resistance, the <u>more</u> of the pd it takes.

5) This circuit means that the pd across the fan <u>goes up</u> as the room <u>gets hotter</u>. Here's why:

- As the room gets hotter, the resistance of the thermistor <u>decreases</u>.
- The thermistor takes a <u>smaller share</u> of the pd from the power supply.
- So the pd across the fixed resistor <u>rises</u>.
- The pd across the fixed resistor is <u>equal to</u> the pd across the <u>fan</u> (you'll see why on p.316).
- So the pd across the <u>fan</u> rises too, making the fan go <u>faster</u>.

6) If you connected the fan across the thermistor <u>instead</u>, the circuit would do the <u>opposite</u>.

7) The fan would <u>slow down</u> as the room got <u>hotter</u>.

You Can Also Use **LDRs** in **Sensing Circuits**

1) If you used an <u>LDR</u> instead of a thermistor in the circuit above it would be a <u>light sensing circuit</u>.

2) For example, the <u>bulb</u> in the sensing circuit on the right is connected <u>across the LDR</u>. This means it gets <u>brighter</u> as the room gets <u>darker</u>.

Sensing circuits react to changes in the surroundings...

<u>Sensing circuits</u> are a useful <u>application</u> of <u>thermistors</u> and <u>LDRs</u>, but can be tricky to make sense of. They rely on the properties of <u>series</u> and <u>parallel</u> circuits, which are coming up on the next few pages.

Q1 An engineer wants to make a circuit containing a bulb that will get brighter when the surroundings get darker. Draw a diagram of a circuit the engineer could make. You can assume the light from the bulb does not affect any of the circuit components. [3 marks]

Series Circuits

*You need to be able to tell if components are connected in series or parallel **just by looking at circuit diagrams**. You also need to know the **rules** about what happens with both types. Read on to find out more.*

Series Circuits — All or Nothing

1) In <u>series circuits</u>, the components are all connected <u>in a line</u> between the ends of the power supply.

2) Only <u>voltmeters</u> break this rule.
They're <u>always</u> in <u>parallel</u> (see p.316).

3) If you remove <u>one</u> component, the circuit is <u>broken</u>.
So <u>all</u> the components <u>stop working</u>.

4) You can use the rules on this page and the next to <u>design</u> series circuits to <u>measure</u> and <u>test</u> all sorts of things.

5) For example the <u>test circuit</u> on p.310 and the <u>sensing circuits</u> on p.313.

Cell Potential Differences Add Up

1) There is a bigger potential difference when more cells are in series, provided the cells are all <u>connected</u> the <u>same way</u>.

2) For example when two batteries of voltage 1.5 V are <u>connected in series</u> they supply a <u>total</u> of 3 V.

Potential Difference is Shared

1) In series circuits the <u>total pd</u> of the <u>supply</u> is <u>shared</u> between all of the <u>components</u>.

2) If you <u>add up</u> the pd across <u>each component</u>, you get the <u>pd of the power supply</u>.

$$V_{total} = V_1 + V_2 + ...$$

EXAMPLE

In the circuit diagram on the right $V_1 = 3.5$ V.
Calculate the potential difference across the filament lamp, V_2.

<u>Substitute</u> into the equation above, then <u>rearrange</u> for the unknown voltage.

$8 = 3.5 + V_2$
$V_2 = 8 - 3.5 = 4.5$ V

3) The <u>bigger</u> a component's <u>resistance</u>, the bigger its <u>share</u> of the <u>total pd</u>.

There are two main types of circuit — series and parallel...

Ammeters and voltmeters don't affect how you describe a circuit — you can have a <u>parallel circuit</u> (p.316) with <u>ammeters</u> connected in <u>series</u>, or a <u>series circuit</u> with <u>voltmeters</u> connected in <u>parallel</u> with components.

Series Circuits

*We're not done with **series circuits** yet. Here's the low-down on **current** and **resistance**...*

Current is the **Same Everywhere**

In series circuits the <u>same current</u> flows through <u>all components</u>.

$$I_1 = I_2 = ...$$

Resistance **Adds Up**

1) In series circuits, the <u>total resistance</u> of two components is found by <u>adding up</u> their resistances.

2) R_{total} is the <u>total resistance</u> of the circuit. R_1 and R_2 are resistances of the <u>components</u>:

$$R_{total} = R_1 + R_2$$

Total resistance = 6 + 3 = 9 Ω

EXAMPLE

For the circuit diagram on the right, calculate the current passing through the circuit.

20 V

1) First find the <u>total resistance</u> by <u>adding together</u> the resistance of the two resistors.

$R_{total} = 2 + 3 = 5\ \Omega$

2) Then <u>rearrange</u> $V = IR$ for I.

3) <u>Substitute</u> in the values you have and calculate the current.

$I = V \div R$
$= 20 \div 5$
$= 4\ A$

3) You need to be able to <u>explain</u> why adding resistors <u>in series</u> increases the total resistance of the circuit:

- Adding a resistor in <u>series</u> means the resistors have to <u>share</u> the total pd.
- This means the pd across each resistor is <u>lower</u>, so the <u>current</u> through each resistor is lower ($V = IR$).
- The current is the <u>same everywhere</u>.
- So the <u>total current</u> in the circuit is <u>reduced</u> when a resistor is added.
- This means the total <u>resistance</u> of the circuit has <u>gone up</u>.

Series circuits aren't used very much in the real world...

Since series circuits put all components on the same loop of wire, if <u>one</u> component breaks, it'll <u>break the circuit</u>, and all other components will <u>stop working</u> too.

Q1 Video Solution

Q1   A battery is connected in series with a 4 Ω resistor, a 5 Ω resistor and a 6 Ω resistor. A current of 0.6 A flows through the circuit. Calculate the potential difference of the battery.

[3 marks]

Parallel Circuits

*Parallel circuits can be a little bit trickier to wrap your head around, but they're much more **useful** than series circuits. Most electronics use a combination of series and parallel circuitry.*

Parallel Circuits — Every Component Connected Separately

1) In <u>parallel circuits</u>, each component is <u>separately</u> connected to the ends of the power supply.

2) Only <u>ammeters</u> break this rule, they're <u>always in series</u> (see p.314).

3) If you take out <u>one</u> of the loops in a parallel circuit, the things in the <u>other</u> loops <u>won't</u> be affected.

4) This means things <u>in parallel</u> can be switched on and off without affecting each other.

5) Everyday circuits often include a <u>mixture</u> of series and parallel parts.

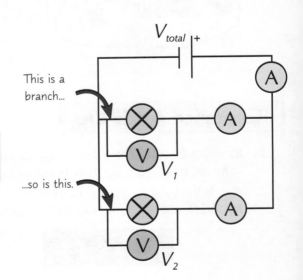

This is a branch...

...so is this.

V_1

V_2

V_{total}

Potential Difference is the Same Across All Components

1) In parallel circuits <u>all</u> components get the <u>full source pd</u>.

2) So the potential difference is the <u>same</u> across all components.

$$V_1 = V_2 = V_3 = ...$$

3) This means that <u>identical bulbs</u> connected in parallel will all be at the <u>same brightness</u>.

Parallel circuits have a big advantage over series circuits...

If a <u>component</u> in a parallel circuit <u>breaks</u>, only that component's <u>branch</u> will be <u>affected</u>. Current will continue to flow through all of the circuit's other branches. A classic example of this is <u>fairy lights</u>. If a bulb breaks, only the broken bulb will go out, since they're <u>wired in parallel</u>.

Parallel Circuits

*In some ways current in a circuit is a little like water flowing in a river. And, just as like flowing water splits when it reaches a fork in the river, **current** will split **when** it reaches a **branch** in the circuit.*

Current is **Shared** Between Branches

1) In parallel circuits the total current in a circuit is equal to the sum of all the currents through the separate components.

2) At junctions, the current either splits or rejoins.

3) The total current going into a junction must equal the total current leaving it.

$$I_{total} = I_1 + I_2 + ...$$

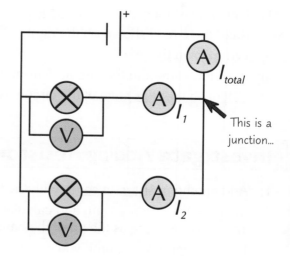

EXAMPLE

For the circuit diagram on the right, find the pd measured by V_1 and the current measured by A_3.

1) The resistors are in parallel, so the pd across each resistor is the same as the cell pd.

2) The current into the first junction is the same as the current out of it.

Cell pd = 6 V
V_1 = 6 V

In: 2 A   Out: 1 A + A_3
So A_3 = 2 − 1 = 1 A

Adding a Resistor in Parallel **Reduces** the **Total Resistance**

The total resistance of two resistors connected in parallel is less than the resistance of the smallest of the two resistors. Here's why:

1) If you add a resistor in parallel, both resistors still have the same potential difference across them as the power supply.

2) This means the 'pushing force' making the current flow is still the same.

3) But by adding another loop, the current has more than one direction to go in.

4) More current can flow around the circuit, so the total current increases.

5) This means the total resistance of the circuit is lower (as $R = V \div I$).

The current flowing into a junction equals the current out

Q1 A circuit contains three resistors, each connected in parallel with a cell. Explain what happens to the total current and resistance in the circuit when one resistor is removed. [4 marks]

Q1 Video Solution

Investigating Circuits

You saw on page 308 how the length of the wire used in a circuit affects its resistance. Now it's time to do an **experiment** *to see how placing* **resistors** *in series or in parallel can affect the resistance of the* **whole circuit**.

First Set Up the **Basic Circuit**

1) Find at least four <u>identical resistors</u>.
2) Build the circuit shown on the right.
3) Write down the <u>pd of the battery</u>. This is the pd of the circuit (*V*).
4) Read the <u>current</u> in the circuit (*I*) from the <u>ammeter</u>.
5) <u>Calculate the resistance</u> of the circuit using $R = V \div I$.

Investigate Adding **Resistors in Series**...

1) Add another <u>resistor</u>, in <u>series</u> with the first.
2) Measure the <u>current</u> again and calculate resistance again. The pd is the <u>same</u> as the pd of the battery.
3) Repeat <u>steps 1 and 2</u> until you've added all of your resistors.

... and in **Parallel**

1) Build the <u>basic circuit</u> again. You already know its <u>resistance</u>.
2) Use the same equipment so it's a <u>fair test</u>.
3) Add another <u>resistor</u>, in <u>parallel</u> with the first.
4) Measure the <u>total current</u> through the circuit and calculate the overall <u>resistance of the circuit</u>. The pd is still the same as before.
5) Repeat <u>steps 3 and 4</u> until you've added all of your resistors.

Draw **Graphs** so you can **Compare** your Results

1) Plot a <u>graph</u> of the <u>number of resistors</u> in the circuit against the <u>total resistance</u>.
2) You should get graphs that look like this:

Adding resistors in <u>series increases</u> the total <u>resistance</u> of the circuit.

The <u>more</u> resistors you add, the <u>smaller</u> the overall resistance becomes.

Warm-Up & Exam Questions

Time to check and see what you can remember about those circuit devices, plus parallel and series circuits.

Warm-Up Questions

1) Give one use of a light-dependent resistor (LDR).
2) What happens to the resistance of a thermistor as its temperature increases?
3) Describe what a series circuit is.
4) True or false? In a series circuit, if you add up the pd across each component, you get the pd of the power supply.
5) How do you work out the total resistance in a series circuit?
6) Which has the higher total resistance: two resistors in series, or the same two resistors in parallel?

Exam Questions

1 Which of the following statements does **not** apply to parallel circuits? Tick **one** box. (Grade 3-4)

If one branch is disconnected, the other branches will not be affected. ☐

Total resistance is equal to the sum of the individual resistances. ☐

Current splits when it reaches a junction. ☐

Each branch experiences the whole supply pd. ☐

[1 mark]

2 **Figure 1** shows a series circuit. (Grade 3-4)

2.1 Calculate the total resistance in the circuit.
[2 marks]

2.2 The current through A_1 is 0.4 A.
What is the current through A_2? Explain your answer.
[2 marks]

2.3 V_1 reads 1.6 V.
Calculate the reading on V_2.
[2 marks]

Figure 1

4.0V

A_2 A_1

3Ω 2Ω

V_2 V_1

3 **Figure 2** shows a circuit that contains an LED, a light-dependent resistor and a cell. (Grade 4-5)

3.1 Describe how you could tell that a current is flowing in the circuit.
[1 mark]

3.2 The circuit is placed in a well lit room. At the end of the day, the lights in the room are turned off. Describe and explain how the resistance of the circuit changes when the room lights are switched off.
[2 marks]

Figure 2

Electricity in the Home

*Now you've learnt the basics of **electrical circuits**, it's time to see how **electricity** is used in **everyday life**.*

Mains Supply is **ac**, Battery Supply is **dc**

1) An <u>alternating potential difference</u> is a potential difference that is <u>constantly changing direction</u>. It produces an <u>alternating current</u> (<u>ac</u>).

2) In an <u>alternating current</u>, the <u>current</u> (flow of charge) is also <u>constantly changing direction</u>.

3) The <u>UK mains supply</u> (the electricity in your home) is an ac supply at around <u>230 V</u>.

4) The <u>frequency</u> (p.371) of the ac mains supply is <u>50 Hz</u> (hertz).

5) <u>Direct current</u> (<u>dc</u>) is a current that is always flowing in the <u>same direction</u>.

6) It's created by a <u>direct potential difference</u>. The <u>direction</u> of a direct potential difference is always the <u>same</u>.

Cells and batteries supply dc.

Most Cables Have **Three** Separate **Wires**

1) Most electrical appliances are connected to the mains supply by <u>three-core</u> cables.

2) They have <u>three wires</u> covered with <u>plastic insulation</u> inside them.

3) They are <u>coloured</u> so that it is easy to tell the different wires <u>apart</u>.

<u>LIVE WIRE</u> — <u>brown</u>.
1) The live wire provides the <u>alternating potential difference</u> from the mains supply.
2) It is at about <u>230 V</u>.

<u>NEUTRAL WIRE</u> — <u>blue</u>.
1) The neutral wire <u>completes</u> the circuit.
2) When the appliance is operating normally, <u>current</u> flows through the <u>live</u> and <u>neutral</u> wires.
3) It is around <u>0 V</u>.

<u>EARTH WIRE</u> — <u>green</u> and <u>yellow</u>.
1) The earth wire is a <u>safety wire</u>.
2) It <u>stops</u> the appliance <u>becoming live</u>:

- It is connected to the <u>metal casing</u> of an appliance.
- If a <u>fault</u> causes the <u>live wire</u> to touch the casing, the <u>current</u> flows <u>away</u> through the <u>earth wire</u>.

3) It's <u>also</u> at 0 V.

The **Live Wire** Can Give You an **Electric Shock**

1) There is a <u>pd</u> between the <u>live wire</u> and your <u>body</u> (which is at 0 V).

2) Touching the live wire can cause a <u>current</u> to flow through your body.

3) This can give you a dangerous <u>electric shock</u>.

4) Even if a switch is turned <u>off</u> (the switch is <u>open</u>), touching the live wire is still <u>dangerous</u>. This is because it still has a pd of <u>230 V</u>.

5) <u>Any</u> connection between <u>live</u> and <u>earth</u> can be <u>dangerous</u>.

6) The pd could cause a <u>huge current</u> to flow, which could result in a <u>fire</u>.

Power of Electrical Appliances

Energy is transferred between stores **electrically** *(like you saw on page 284)* by **electrical appliances**.

Energy is **Transferred** from Cells and Other **Sources**

1) When a <u>charge moves</u> around a circuit, <u>work is done</u> against the <u>resistance</u> of the circuit.
2) Whenever work is done, <u>energy is transferred</u>.
3) When the work is done by a <u>charge</u>, the energy is <u>transferred electrically</u>.
4) Electrical appliances <u>transfer energy</u> to components in the circuit when a <u>current</u> flows.

Kettles transfer energy <u>electrically</u> from the mains supply to the <u>thermal</u> energy store of the heating element inside the kettle.

Energy is transferred <u>electrically</u> from the <u>battery</u> of a handheld fan to the <u>kinetic</u> energy store of the fan's motor.

Energy Transferred Depends on the **Power**

1) The <u>total</u> energy transferred by an appliance depends on <u>how long</u> the appliance is on for and its <u>power</u>.
2) The <u>power</u> of an appliance is the energy that it <u>transfers per second</u>.
3) So the <u>more</u> energy it transfers in a <u>given time</u>, the <u>higher</u> its power.
4) The amount of <u>energy transferred by electrical work</u> is given by:

This equation should be familiar from page 293.

$$\text{Energy transferred (J)} = \text{Power (W)} \times \text{Time (s)}$$

$$E = Pt$$

EXAMPLE

A 600 W microwave is used for 5 minutes. How much energy does it transfer?

1) <u>Convert</u> the time into <u>seconds</u>. $t = 5 \times 60 = 300$ s
2) <u>Substitute</u> the numbers into $E = Pt$ to find the <u>energy transferred</u>. $E = Pt = 600 \times 300$ $= 180\ 000$ J

5) Appliances are often given a <u>power rating</u>. This is the power that they <u>work at</u>.
6) The power rating tells you <u>how much</u> energy is transferred <u>between stores</u> when the appliance is used.
7) An appliance with a <u>higher power</u> will <u>cost more</u> to run for a given time, as it uses <u>more energy</u>.

A <u>850 W</u> microwave will transfer <u>more energy</u> between stores during 5 minutes than the <u>600 W</u> microwave in the example above. This means it will <u>cost more</u> to use it for 5 minutes.

Power is the rate of energy transfer...

Remember, the <u>power rating</u> of an <u>electrical appliance</u> is the amount of <u>energy transferred</u> to the appliance <u>per second</u>, not the amount that it transfers to <u>useful energy stores</u>.

Q1 An appliance transfers 6000 J of energy in 30 seconds. Calculate its power. [3 marks]

Q2 Calculate the difference in the amount of energy transferred by a 250 W TV and a 375 W TV when they are both used for two hours. [4 marks]

More on Power

*And we're not done yet. There are even more **power equations** for you to get your head around. How fun.*

Potential Difference is **Energy Transferred** per **Charge Passed**

1) As a charge moves around a circuit, <u>energy</u> is transferred <u>to</u> or <u>from</u> it.

2) The <u>energy transferred</u> by a component depends on the <u>potential difference</u> across it and the <u>charge flowing</u> through it.

3) The <u>formula</u> is really simple:

Energy transferred (J) = Charge Flow (C) × Potential Difference (V) $E = QV$

> **EXAMPLE**
>
> **An electric toothbrush contains a 3.0 V battery. 140 C of charge passes through the toothbrush as it is used. Calculate the energy transferred.**
>
> <u>Substitute</u> the numbers into $E = QV$ $E = QV = 140 × 3.0 = 420$ J
> to find the <u>energy transferred</u>.

Power Also Depends on **Current** and **Potential Difference**

1) You saw on the previous page that power is <u>energy transferred</u> in a given <u>time</u>.

2) The <u>power</u> of an appliance can also be found using:

Power (W) = Potential difference (V) × Current (A) $P = VI$

Resistance (Ω)

3) You can also find the power if you <u>don't know</u> the <u>potential difference</u>, using: $P = I^2R$

> **EXAMPLE**   **A motor with a power of 1250 W has a resistance of 50 Ω. Calculate the current flowing through the motor.**
>
> *Your calculator should have a '√' (square root) button to help with these calculations.*
>
> 1) First <u>rearrange</u> the formula $P = I^2R$ to make I the subject.
>   - <u>Divide</u> both sides by R.
>   - Find the <u>square root</u> of both sides.
>
> $P ÷ R = I^2$ so $I^2 = P ÷ R$
> $I = \sqrt{P ÷ R}$
>
> 2) Now just <u>plug in</u> the numbers.
>
> $I = \sqrt{1250 ÷ 50} = \sqrt{25}$
> $= 5$ A

Power is measured in watts, W — one W is equal to one J/s...

The best way to learn all of this is to just <u>practise</u> using these equations <u>again and again</u>.

Q1   Calculate the energy transferred in a circuit with a pd of 200 V
when 10 000 C of charge flows.   [2 marks]

Q2   An appliance is connected to a 12 V source. A current of 4.0 A flows through it.
Calculate the power of the appliance.   [2 marks]

Q3   An appliance has a power of 2300 W and has a current of 10.0 A flowing through it.
Calculate the resistance of the appliance.   [3 marks]

Q3 Video Solution

The National Grid

*The **national grid** is a giant web of wires that covers **the whole of Britain**, getting electricity from power stations to homes everywhere. Whoever you pay for your electricity, it's the national grid that gets it to you.*

Electricity is Distributed via the National Grid

1) The <u>national grid</u> is a giant system of <u>cables</u> and <u>transformers</u> that covers the UK.

2) It transfers <u>electrical power</u> from <u>power stations</u> to <u>consumers</u> (anyone who is using electricity) across the UK.

Electricity Production has to Meet Demand

1) <u>Throughout the day</u>, the amount of electricity used (the <u>demand</u>) changes.

2) Power stations have to produce <u>enough</u> electricity for everyone to have it when they need it.

3) More electricity is used when people <u>get up</u> in the morning, <u>come home</u> from <u>school</u> or <u>work</u> and when it starts to get <u>dark</u> or <u>cold</u> outside.

4) Power stations often run at well below their <u>maximum power output</u>, so that they can <u>increase</u> their power if needed.

5) This means that the national grid can cope with a <u>high demand</u>, even if another station shuts down <u>without warning</u>.

Energy demands are ever increasing...

The <u>national grid</u> has been working since the 1930s and has gone through <u>many changes</u> and <u>updates</u> since then to meet <u>increasing energy demands</u>. Using <u>energy-efficient appliances</u> and switching unneeded lights off are some ways we might ensure that <u>supply and demand</u> stay in balance. It'll do wonders for the electricity bill too, so it's worth bearing in mind.

The National Grid

*To transfer electricity **efficiently**, the national grid makes use of some clever tech called **transformers**.*

The National Grid Uses a **High Pd** and a **Low Current**

1) The national grid transfers <u>loads</u> of energy, so the <u>power</u> has to be <u>very high</u>.

2) To transmit this <u>huge</u> amount of <u>power</u> you need either a <u>high potential difference</u> or a <u>high current</u>.

3) This is because *P = VI* (from page 322).

4) A <u>high current</u> means <u>loads of energy</u> is lost to thermal energy stores as the wires <u>heat up</u>.

5) So the national grid transmits electricity at a very <u>high pd</u>.
   For a <u>given power</u>, the higher the pd the <u>lower the current</u>.

6) This <u>reduces the energy lost</u>, making the national grid an <u>efficient</u> way of transferring energy.

Potential Difference is Changed by **Transformers**

1) <u>Step-up transformers</u> are used to <u>increase the pd</u> from <u>power stations</u> to electric <u>cables</u>.
2) <u>Step-down transformers</u> bring the pd <u>back down</u> to <u>safe levels</u> before the electricity gets to <u>homes</u>.

3) Transformers all have two coils, a <u>primary coil</u> and a <u>secondary coil</u>, joined with an <u>iron core</u>.
4) The <u>power</u> of a primary coil is given by <u>power = pd × current</u>.
5) The <u>power in primary coil = power in secondary coil</u>.

The national grid — it's a powerful thing...

The key to the <u>efficiency</u> of the <u>national grid</u> is the power equation, *P = VI* (see page 322). If you have a <u>constant</u> power, but <u>increase</u> the potential difference using a transformer, the current must <u>decrease</u>. Having as <u>low</u> a <u>current</u> as possible makes sure that power is transferred as <u>efficiently</u> as possible.

Warm-Up & Exam Questions

Who knew there was so much to learn about electricity in the home and across the country?
See if it's switched on a light bulb in your brain by trying out these questions.

Warm-Up Questions

1) Name the three wires in a three-core cable that connect electrical appliances to the mains supply.
2) What is the main energy transfer when electric current flows through an electric kettle?
3) What is the equation linking power, current and resistance?
4) What is the national grid?

Exam Questions

1   This question is about the national grid. *(Grade 1-3)*

1.1   Use words from the box to complete the sentence.

current	potential difference	step-up	step-down

_____ transformers are used between the power station and the transmission cables.

This increases the _____ , so that power may be transferred more efficiently.

[2 marks]

1.2   Which describes the UK mains electricity supply? Tick **one** box.

☐ 230 V ac   ☐ 170 V ac   ☐ 230 V dc   ☐ 170 V dc

[1 mark]

2   **Table 1** shows the power and potential difference ratings for two kettles. *(Grade 4-5)*

Table 1

	Power (W)	Potential Difference (V)
Kettle A	2760	230
Kettle B	3000	230

2.1   Write down the equation linking power, potential difference and current.

[1 mark]

2.2   Calculate the current, in amps, drawn from the mains supply by kettle A.

[2 marks]

2.3   A student wants to test which kettle heats water most quickly. He measures the increase in water temperature in each kettle after 1 minute. Identify one variable the student must control.

[1 mark]

2.4   The kettles are equally efficient.
A second student states: 'Kettle B has the greatest power so it will heat water most quickly.'
Justify the student's statement.

[2 marks]

Particle Model

*Everything is made up of **small particles**. The particle model **describes** how these particles behave.*

There are **Three States of Matter**

1) The <u>three states of matter</u> are <u>solid</u> (e.g. ice), <u>liquid</u> (e.g. water) and <u>gas</u> (e.g. water vapour).

2) The <u>particle model</u> explains the <u>differences</u> between the <u>states of matter</u>:
   - The <u>particles</u> of a <u>certain material</u> are <u>always</u> the <u>same</u>, no matter what <u>state</u> it is in.
   - But the particles have different <u>amounts of energy</u> in different states.
   - And the <u>forces</u> between particles are <u>different</u> in each state.
   - This means that the particles are <u>arranged</u> (laid out) <u>differently</u> in different states.

Solids

1) Particles are held <u>close together</u> by <u>strong forces</u> in a <u>regular, fixed pattern</u>.
2) The particles don't have <u>much energy</u>.
3) So they can only <u>vibrate</u> (jiggle about) around a <u>fixed position</u>.

Liquids

1) The particles are held <u>close together</u> in an <u>irregular pattern</u>.
2) The particles have <u>more energy</u> than the particles in a solid.
3) They can <u>move past</u> each other in <u>random directions</u> at <u>low speeds</u>.

Gases

1) The particles <u>aren't</u> held close together. There are <u>no forces</u> between them.
2) The particles have <u>more energy</u> than in liquids and solids.
3) The particles <u>constantly move</u> around in <u>random directions</u> at a <u>range of speeds</u>.

The more energy in their kinetic stores, the faster the particles move...

Learn those diagrams above and make sure that you can describe the <u>arrangement</u> and <u>movement</u> of particles in solids, liquids and gases. You should also be able to talk about how much <u>energy</u> they have.

Particle Motion in Gases

*The **particle model** explains how **temperature**, **pressure** and **energy in kinetic stores** are all related.
And this page is here to explain it all to you. I bet you're just itching to find out more...*

Gas Particles **Bump into Things** and Create **Pressure**

1) Particles in a gas are <u>free to move</u> around.

2) They <u>collide with</u> (bump into) each other and the sides of the <u>container</u> they're in.

3) When they hit something, they <u>apply a force</u> to it. <u>Pressure</u> is the <u>force</u> applied over a <u>given area</u>.

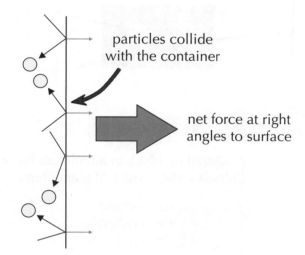

particles collide with the container

net force at right angles to surface

Increasing the **Temperature** of a Gas Increases its **Pressure**

1) The <u>temperature</u> of a gas depends on the <u>average energy</u> in the <u>kinetic energy stores</u> of the gas particles.

- The <u>hotter</u> the gas, the <u>higher</u> the average energy.

- If particles have <u>more energy</u> in their kinetic stores, they <u>move faster</u>.

- So the <u>hotter</u> the gas, the <u>faster</u> the particles move on average.

- <u>Faster particles</u> hit the sides of the container <u>more often</u>. This <u>increases</u> the <u>force</u> on the container.

- So increasing the <u>temperature</u> of a gas increases its <u>pressure</u>.

2) This <u>only</u> works if the <u>space</u> the gas takes up (the <u>volume</u>) <u>doesn't change</u>.

Higher temperatures mean higher average energies in kinetic stores...

The <u>particle model</u> can be used to explain what happens when you <u>change</u> the <u>temperature</u> of a <u>gas</u> which is kept at a <u>constant volume</u>. Have a look back on page 326 for more about the particle model.

Density of Materials

*The **density** of an object tells you how many of its **particles** are squished into a **given space**.*

The **Particle Model** can also Explain **Density**

1) Density is a measure of how much mass there is in a certain space.
2) You can work out density using:

$$\rho = \frac{m}{V}$$

density (kg/m³), mass (kg), volume (m³)

> **EXAMPLE**
>
> A 0.0020 m³ block of aluminium has a mass of 5.4 kg.
> Calculate the density of aluminium.
>
> density = mass ÷ volume
> = 5.4 ÷ 0.0020
> = 2700 kg/m³

3) The density of an object depends on what it's made of and how its particles are arranged.
4) A dense material has its particles packed tightly together.
5) So, solids are generally denser than liquids.
6) And liquids are generally denser than gases.

You Can Find the **Density** of a **Regularly Shaped Object**

1) Use a balance to measure its mass (see p.392).
2) Measure its length, width and height with a ruler.
3) Then calculate its volume using the formula for that shape.
4) Use density = mass ÷ volume to find the density.

The volume of a cuboid is equal to length × width × height.

height, width, length

The denser the substance, the closer together its particles are...

When you're measuring the dimensions of an object, think about which apparatus is best to use. If what you're measuring is pretty small, a ruler won't give you very accurate measurements. For small measurements, a micrometer or Vernier callipers would be more appropriate.

Measuring Density

*You need to be able to carry out practicals to work out the **densities** of different **solids** and **liquids**.*

Find the Density of an **Irregularly Shaped Object** Using a **Eureka Can**

1) Use a <u>balance</u> to measure the object's <u>mass</u>.

2) <u>Fill</u> a <u>eureka can</u> (a can with a spout in its side) with water.

3) The <u>water level</u> should end up <u>just below</u> the start of the spout.

4) Place a <u>measuring cylinder</u> (p.392) under the end of the spout.

5) Place your object <u>into the water</u>.
This will <u>push</u> some of the water <u>out</u> through the spout.

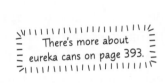

There's more about eureka cans on page 393.

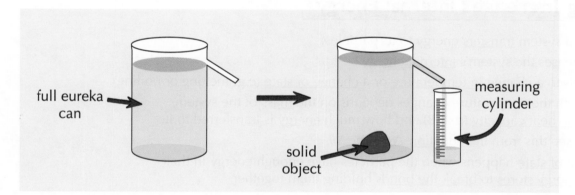

full eureka can

solid object

measuring cylinder

6) <u>Measure the volume</u> of water that has collected in the measuring cylinder.

7) This is <u>equal to</u> the <u>volume</u> of the <u>object</u>.

8) Use the <u>formula</u> on the previous page to find the object's <u>density</u>.

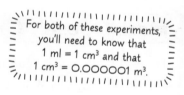

For both of these experiments, you'll need to know that 1 ml = 1 cm³ and that 1 cm³ = 0.000001 m³.

Find the Density of a **Liquid** Using a **Measuring Cylinder**

1) Place a <u>measuring cylinder</u> on a balance and <u>zero</u> the balance (p.392).

2) Pour <u>50 ml</u> of the liquid into the measuring cylinder.

3) Record the liquid's <u>mass</u> shown on the mass balance.

4) Use the <u>formula</u> on the previous page to find the <u>density</u>.
The <u>volume</u> is <u>50 cm³</u>, or <u>0.00005 m³</u>.

46.568

A eureka can makes it pretty easy to find an object's volume...

Try not to put your fingers in the water as you're dropping your object into the eureka can.
This will displace <u>more water</u>, and make your volume measurement <u>too big</u>.

Q1   A 0.019 kg gemstone is placed into a full eureka can, causing
7.0 cm³ of water to be pushed out the spout into a measuring cylinder.
Calculate the density of the gemstone in g/cm³.   [3 marks]

Q1 Video Solution

Internal Energy and Changes of State

*This page is all about heating things. Take a look at your **specific heat capacity** notes (p.288) before you start. You need to understand it and be able to use $\Delta E = mc\Delta\theta$ for this topic too I'm afraid.*

Internal Energy is the Total Energy Stored by Particles in a System

1) The energy stored in a system (p.284) is stored by its particles (atoms and molecules).
2) The particles have energy in their kinetic energy stores.
3) They also have energy in their potential energy stores because of their positions.
4) The internal energy of a system is the total energy that all its particles have in their kinetic and potential energy stores.

Heating Increases Internal Energy

1) Heating a system transfers energy to its particles.
2) This increases the system's internal energy.
3) This leads to a change in temperature or a change of state (e.g. melting or boiling).
4) How much the temperature changes depends on the mass of the system, its specific heat capacity (p.288) and how much energy is transferred to it.
5) You can see this from the equation $\Delta E = mc\Delta\theta$.
6) A change of state happens when the particles have enough energy in their kinetic energy stores to break the bonds holding them together.

Mass Doesn't Change in a Change of State

1) A change of state can happen because of cooling, as well as heating.
2) The changes of state are:

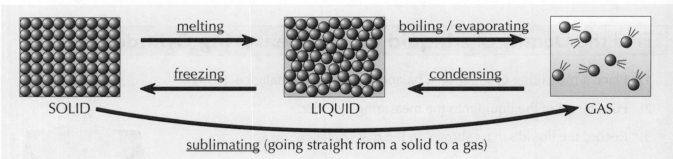

3) A change of state is a physical change (not a chemical change).
4) This means you don't end up with a new material.
5) The particles are just arranged in a different way (p.326).
6) The number of particles stays the same when the state changes.
7) This means the mass is conserved (it doesn't change).
8) If you reverse a change of state, the material will get back all the properties it had before the change.

Physical changes are different from chemical changes...

You should make sure you know all the changes of state, and why they are physical changes.

Specific Latent Heat

*The **energy needed** to change the state of a substance is called **latent heat**. This is exciting stuff I tell you...*

Temperature Doesn't Change During a Change of State

1) <u>Heating</u> a material <u>transfers energy</u> to the material.

2) This either increases the <u>temperature</u> of the material or changes its <u>state</u> (p.330).

3) During a <u>change of state</u>, the temperature <u>doesn't change</u>. But the <u>internal energy</u> does.

4) The energy transferred is used to <u>break bonds</u> between particles. It is <u>not</u> used to raise the temperature.

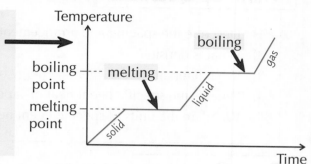

5) When a material <u>cools</u>, energy is <u>transferred away</u> from it.

6) As a material <u>condenses</u> or <u>freezes</u>, <u>bonds form</u> between particles. This causes <u>energy</u> to be <u>released</u>.

7) So its <u>internal energy decreases</u>, but its temperature <u>stays the same</u> during the change of state.

8) The <u>flat spots</u> on these graphs show that the <u>temperature doesn't change</u> during a change of state.

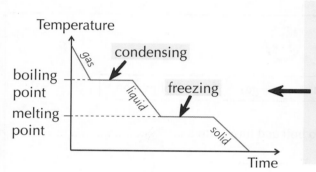

Specific Latent Heat is the Energy Needed to Change State

1) The <u>energy transferred</u> during a change of state is called <u>latent heat</u>.

2) For <u>heating</u>, latent heat is the <u>energy gained</u> to cause a change of state.

3) For <u>cooling</u>, it is the energy <u>released</u> by a change in state.

4) The <u>specific latent heat</u> of a material is the <u>amount of energy</u> needed to <u>change the state</u> of <u>1 kg</u> of the material <u>without changing its temperature</u>.

5) You can work out the <u>energy needed</u> (or <u>released</u>) during a change of state using this <u>formula</u>:

> **Energy (J) = Mass (kg) × Specific Latent Heat (J/kg)**   or: $E = mL$

6) Specific latent heat has <u>different names</u> for different changes of state:

7) For changing between a <u>solid</u> and a <u>liquid</u> it is called the <u>specific latent heat of fusion</u>.

8) For changing between a <u>liquid</u> and a <u>gas</u> it is called the <u>specific latent heat of vaporisation</u>.

EXAMPLE   **The specific latent heat of vaporisation for water is 2 260 000 J/kg. How much energy is needed to completely boil 1.50 kg of water once it has reached its boiling point?**

1) The mass and specific latent heat are in the <u>right units</u>, so just put them into the <u>formula</u>.

2) The units for the answer are <u>joules</u> because it's <u>energy</u>.

$E = mL$
$= 1.50 × 2\ 260\ 000$
$= 3\ 390\ 000\ J$

Temperature doesn't change during a change of state

Q1   The SLH of fusion for a particular substance is 120 000 J/kg. How much energy is needed to melt 250 g of the substance when it is already at its melting temperature?   [2 marks]

Q1 Video Solution

Warm-Up & Exam Questions

So that's it, you've covered everything from the particle model to changes of state. Once you think you've got to grips with the stuff in this topic, it's time to test yourself with these questions.

Warm-Up Questions

1) Describe the spacing and arrangement of particles in a solid.
2) What is density?
3) What happens to the internal energy of a system when it is heated?
4) What is the specific latent heat of vaporisation?
5) What are the units of specific latent heat?

Exam Questions

1 Use words in the box to complete the sentence below. *Grade 1-3*

| solid | condensation | evaporation | gas | sublimation |

If a liquid is heated to a certain temperature it starts to boil and turns into a ....

Another process that causes this change of state is ....

[2 marks]

2 A student has a collection of metal toy soldiers of different sizes made from the same metal. *Grade 3-4*

2.1 Which of the following statements is true? Tick **one** box.

☐ The masses and densities of each of the toy soldiers are the same.

☐ The masses of each of the toy soldiers are the same, but their densities may vary.

☐ The densities of each of the toy soldiers are the same, but their masses may vary.

[1 mark]

2.2 One of the soldiers has a mass of 200 g and a volume of 2.5×10^{-5} m^3.

The equation below can be used to calculate density.

density = mass ÷ volume

Calculate the density of the soldier.

[2 marks]

3 0.40 kg of liquid methanol is at its boiling point. *Grade 3-4*
The specific latent heat of vaporisation of methanol is 1200 J/kg.

Calculate the amount of energy needed to convert the liquid methanol to gaseous methanol.
Use the correct equation from the Physics Equation Sheet on page 538.

[2 marks]

Exam Questions

4 A student wants to measure the density of a pendant. He can use the equipment shown in **Figure 1**. **PRACTICAL**

Figure 1

eureka can →

measuring cylinder →

← mass balance

4.1 Name the **two** quantities the student should measure.

[2 marks]

4.2 Describe the steps the student could take to find the density of the pendant with the equipment shown.

[5 marks]

5 The graph in **Figure 2** shows the temperature of a substance against time as it is heated.

5.1 Describe what is happening during the period between 3 and 8 minutes from the beginning of heating.

[1 mark]

5.2 Give the melting and boiling points of the substance.

[2 marks]

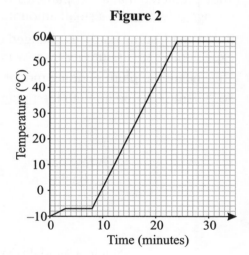

Figure 2

6* A gas is sealed in a rigid container. A scientist heats the container.

Figure 3 shows gas particles as represented in the particle model. Use the particle model to explain why the pressure of the gas increases as the container is heated. In your answer, you should include a description of how gas particles create pressure in the container.

[6 marks]

Figure 3

Developing the Model of the Atom

*You might have thought **atomic structure** was all Chemistry. But you need to know it for Physics too.*

Models of the Atom Have Changed Over Time

1) <u>Scientific models</u> (p.3) change over <u>time</u>. This happens when <u>new evidence</u> is found that <u>can't</u> be explained by the <u>current model</u>.

2) This is what happened with the <u>model of the atom</u>.

3) Scientists used to think that atoms were <u>solid spheres</u>.

4) They then found atoms contain even smaller, negatively charged particles — <u>electrons</u>.

5) This led to a model called the '<u>plum pudding model</u>' being created.

6) The plum pudding model showed the atom as a <u>ball</u> of <u>positive charge</u> with <u>electrons scattered</u> in this ball.

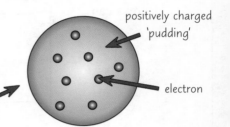

Experiments Showed that the Plum Pudding Model Was Wrong

1) Later, scientists carried out <u>alpha particle scattering experiments</u>. They fired positively charged <u>alpha particles</u> at a very thin sheet of gold.

2) From the plum pudding model, they <u>expected</u> most of the particles to <u>go straight through</u> the sheet. They predicted that a few particles would <u>change direction</u> by a <u>small</u> amount.

3) But instead, some particles changed direction <u>more than expected</u>. A small number even went <u>backwards</u>.

4) This meant the plum pudding model <u>couldn't</u> be right.

5) So, scientists came up with the <u>nuclear model</u> of the atom:

A few particles go backwards.

Most of the particles pass through empty space, but a few change direction.

<u>Nuclear Model of Atom</u>
- There's a tiny, positively charged <u>nucleus</u> at the centre of the atom.
- Most of the <u>mass</u> is in the nucleus.
- The nucleus is surrounded by a 'cloud' of negative <u>electrons</u>.
- Most of the atom is <u>empty space</u>.

Bohr Improved the Nuclear Model

1) <u>Niels Bohr</u> changed the nuclear model of the atom.

2) He suggested that the electrons <u>orbit</u> (go around) the nucleus in <u>energy levels</u>:

3) Each energy level (or shell) is a <u>fixed distance</u> from the nucleus.

4) Bohr's theory was supported by many <u>experiments</u>. Experiments later showed that Bohr's theory was correct.

Developing the Model of the Atom

*Bohr's model was pretty good. But the discovery of **protons** and **neutrons** made it even better.*

The **Nucleus** was Found to Contain **Protons** and **Neutrons**

1) Eventually experiments by scientists showed that the nucleus can be <u>divided</u> into smaller particles. Each particle has the <u>same positive charge</u>. These particles were named <u>protons</u>.

2) Experiments by <u>James Chadwick</u> showed that the nucleus also contained <u>neutral particles</u> — neutrons. This happened about 20 years after scientists agreed that atoms have nuclei.

3) This led to a model of the atom which was <u>pretty close</u> to the one we have today.

You Need to Know the **Current Model** of the Atom

The current model of the atom is a <u>nuclear model</u>.
This means there is a <u>nucleus</u> in the <u>centre</u> surrounded by electrons.

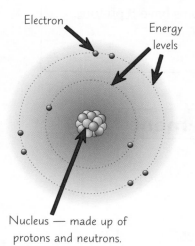

Electron

Energy levels

Nucleus — made up of protons and neutrons.

1) Atoms are <u>very small</u>. The <u>radius</u> of an atom is about 1×10^{-10} m (see p.19 for more on standard form).

2) The <u>nucleus</u> is <u>tiny</u>, but it makes up most of the <u>mass</u> of the atom.

3) The radius of the nucleus is about <u>10 000</u> times smaller than the <u>radius</u> of the <u>atom</u>.

4) The <u>nucleus</u> is made up of <u>protons</u> and <u>neutrons</u>.

5) <u>Protons</u> are <u>positively charged</u> and <u>neutrons</u> have <u>no charge</u>. So the <u>nucleus</u> is <u>positively charged</u>.

6) Electrons have a <u>negative charge</u>. They move <u>around</u> (orbit) the nucleus at different distances.

7) These distances are known as <u>energy levels</u>.

8) <u>Atoms</u> have <u>no overall charge</u>. The <u>number of protons = the number of electrons</u>.

Electrons can **Move** Between **Energy Levels**

1) The <u>further</u> an <u>energy level</u> is from the <u>nucleus</u>, the <u>more energy</u> an electron in that energy level has.

2) <u>Electrons</u> can <u>move between energy levels</u> by <u>absorbing</u> (taking in) or <u>releasing electromagnetic radiation</u> (p.378).

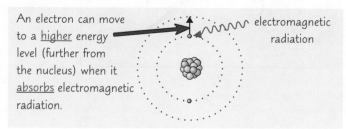

An electron can move to a <u>higher</u> energy level (further from the nucleus) when it <u>absorbs</u> electromagnetic radiation.

electromagnetic radiation

An electron can move to a <u>lower</u> energy level (closer to the nucleus) by <u>releasing</u> electromagnetic radiation.

electromagnetic radiation

3) If an electron in an <u>outer</u> energy level <u>absorbs</u> electromagnetic radiation, it can <u>leave the atom</u>.

4) If an atom <u>loses one or more electrons</u> it turns into a <u>positively charged ion</u>.

WORKING SCIENTIFICALLY

The model of the atom has developed over time...

Due to lots of scientists doing lots of <u>experiments</u>, we now have a better idea of what the atom's really like. We now know about the particles in atoms — <u>protons</u>, <u>neutrons</u> and <u>electrons</u>.

Isotopes

Isotopes of an element look pretty similar, but watch out — they have **different numbers of neutrons**.

Atoms of the Same Element have the Same Number of Protons

1) The number of protons in an atom is called its atomic number.

2) The protons in a nucleus give the nucleus its positive charge.
So the atomic number of an atom tells you the charge on the nucleus.

3) The mass number of an atom is the sum of the number of protons and the number of neutrons.

4) An element is a substance only containing atoms with the same number of protons.

5) You can show information about an atom of an element like this:

Mass number →→ $^{16}_{8}O$ ←← Element symbol (oxygen)
Atomic number →→

- Oxygen has an atomic number of 8, this means all oxygen atoms have 8 protons.
- This atom of oxygen has a mass number of 16.
Since it has 8 protons, it must have $16 - 8 = $ 8 neutrons.

Isotopes are Different Forms of the Same Element

1) Atoms of an element with the same number of protons but a different number of neutrons are called isotopes.

2) Isotopes of an element have the same atomic number, but a different mass number.

Example: Carbon-12 and carbon-13 are isotopes.

$^{12}_{6}C$ $^{13}_{6}C$

one extra neutron

Some Isotopes Emit Radiation

1) Some isotopes are unstable.

2) They emit (give out) radiation from their nuclei to try and become more stable.

3) This process is called radioactive decay.

4) The radiation emitted is called nuclear radiation.

5) There are four different types of nuclear radiation — see the next page.

6) Isotopes that give out nuclear radiation are called radioactive isotopes.

Types of Nuclear Radiation

*The four types of **nuclear radiation** all come from the nucleus, but they have some **key differences**...*

There are **Four Types** of **Nuclear Radiation**

Alpha Particles, (α)

An alpha particle is two neutrons and two protons (like a helium nucleus).

Beta Particles, (β)

A beta particle is a fast-moving electron.

Gamma Rays, (γ)

Gamma rays are waves of electromagnetic radiation (p.378).

Neutrons, (n)

Isotopes can also give out neutrons when they decay.

You Need to Know the **Properties** of **Ionising Nuclear Radiation**

1) Ionising radiation is radiation that can knock electrons off atoms and turn them into ions.

2) The ionising power of radiation is how easily it can do this.

3) Alpha particles, beta particles and gamma rays are all types of ionising radiation.

> Example: an alpha particle colliding with an atom and ionising it.
>
> emitted electron
>
> atom

4) They all have different properties:

Type of radiation	Ionising power	Range in air	Stopped by
alpha particles	strong	a few centimetres	a sheet of paper
beta particles	moderate	a few metres	a sheet of aluminium
gamma rays	weak	a long distance	thick sheets of lead or metres of concrete

'Range in air' is the distance the radiation can travel through air.

5) Their different ionising powers, ranges and abilities to penetrate (get through) materials make them suitable for different uses.

> E.g. A medical tracer is a radioactive isotope that is injected into a patient. The radiation it emits needs to be detected outside the patient's body.
>
> You couldn't use a source of alpha radiation as a medical tracer. Alpha particles wouldn't be able to pass through the body and be detected outside the body. They are also very ionising and so could do a lot of damage (see p.342).
>
> Medical tracers usually emit gamma rays. Gamma rays are only weakly ionising and easily pass through the body. This means they can be easily detected and do less harm than alpha particles.

Alpha particles are more ionising than beta particles...

...and beta particles are more ionising than gamma rays. Make sure you've got that memorised, as well as what makes up each type of radiation, as this isn't the last you'll see of this stuff. No siree.

Q1 Video Solution

Q1   In order to sterilise medical equipment, radiation is directed at the equipment while it is sealed in packaging. Explain whether alpha radiation would be suitable for this use.

[2 marks]

Nuclear Equations

Nuclear equations show *radioactive decay*. The next few pages will help you get the hang of them.

Mass and Atomic Numbers Have to Balance

1) Nuclear equations are a way of showing radioactive decay (p.336).

2) They're normally written like this:

nucleus before decay → nucleus after decay + radiation emitted

3) There is one golden rule to remember:

The total mass and atomic numbers must be equal on both sides of the arrow.

Alpha Decay Decreases the Charge and Mass of the Nucleus

1) Alpha decay is when an alpha particle is emitted from a radioactive nucleus.

2) An alpha particle is made up of two protons and two neutrons. It is the same as a helium nucleus.

3) When a nucleus emits an alpha particle, its atomic number goes down by 2 and its mass number goes down by 4.

Gamma rays are sometimes also released when a nucleus decays by alpha or beta decay.

4) The charge of the nucleus decreases when it gives out an alpha particle.

5) An alpha particle is usually written as a helium nucleus in a nuclear equation: $^4_2$He.

The nuclear equation for the decay of uranium (U) to thorium (Th) is:

Mass number →
Atomic number →

$$^{238}_{92}U \rightarrow {}^{234}_{90}Th + {}^{4}_{2}He$$

$$238 \rightarrow 234 + 4$$
$$92 \rightarrow 90 + 2$$

The mass numbers on each side are equal... ... and so are the atomic numbers.

Mass and atomic numbers must balance in nuclear equations

Q1 After undergoing alpha decay, a nucleus has a mass number of 14.
What was the mass number of the nucleus before the decay? [1 mark]

Q2 Write the nuclear equation for $^{219}_{86}$Rn decaying to polonium (Po)
by emitting an alpha particle. [3 marks]

Q2 Video Solution

Nuclear Equations

*On the last page you saw how to write **nuclear equations** for **alpha decay**. Well, now it's time for **beta**.*

Beta Decay Increases the Charge of the Nucleus

1) Beta decay is when a beta particle is emitted from a radioactive nucleus.

2) During beta decay, a neutron in the nucleus turns into a proton.

3) This means the nucleus has one more proton, so its atomic number goes up by 1.

4) It also means the positive charge of the nucleus increases.

5) A beta particle has an atomic number of –1 so the atomic numbers balance on each side of the equation.

6) Protons and neutrons have the same mass, so the mass of the nucleus doesn't change.

7) A beta particle is an electron. It is written as $_{-1}^{0}e$ in nuclear equations.

Carbon-14 → beta decay → Nitrogen-14 + beta particle

The nuclear equation for the decay of carbon (C) to nitrogen (N) is:

Mass number ⟶
Atomic number ⟶
$$_{6}^{14}C \rightarrow \,_{7}^{14}N + \,_{-1}^{0}e$$

$14 \rightarrow 14 + 0$
$6 \rightarrow 7 + (-1)$

The mass numbers on each side are equal...
...and so are the atomic numbers.

Gamma Rays Don't Change the Charge or Mass of the Nucleus

1) Gamma rays are a way of getting rid of extra energy from a nucleus.

2) When they are emitted, they don't change the mass or charge of the atom and nucleus.

REVISION TIP

Beta particles are electrons but they come from the nucleus...

It seems a bit odd that beta decay causes the atomic number to increase. It makes sense if you understand what's happening to the particles — beta decay happens when a neutron turns into a proton and an electron. So there's one more proton, and the atomic number = number of protons.

Half-Life

*How quickly **unstable nuclei** decay is measured using **activity** and **half-life** — two very important terms.*

The **Activity** of a Source is the **Number of Decays per Second**

1) The radiation given out by a radioactive decay can be measured with a Geiger-Muller tube and counter detector.

2) The number of decays the counter measures every second is called the count-rate.

3) The activity of a radioactive source is the rate at which it decays. This means how many unstable nuclei decay every second.

4) Activity is measured in becquerels, Bq. 1 Bq is 1 decay per second.

Radioactivity is a Totally **Random Process**

1) Radioactive decay is entirely random. So you can't predict exactly which nucleus in a sample will decay next, or when any one of them will decay.

2) But you can predict how long it will take for half of the nuclei to decay. This is known as a half-life.

> The half-life is the time taken for the number of nuclei of a radioactive isotope in a sample to halve.

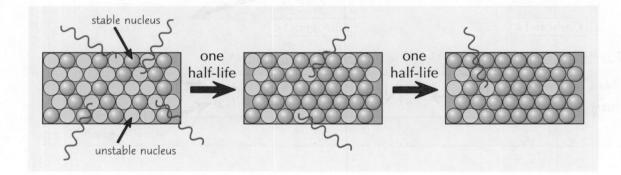

3) Half-life is also the time taken for the count-rate or activity of a sample to fall to half of its initial (starting) value.

4) The half-life of a radioactive sample will always be the same. This means it doesn't matter what activity you start with when doing half-life calculations (see the next page).

Different substances have different half-lives...

Some substances take a long time to decay, giving them a long half-life, while others decay in the blink of an eye. For example, neodymium-144 has a half-life of 2 million billion years, while helium-5 has a half-life of 7.6×10^{-22} seconds. That's 0.00000000000000000000076 seconds. Pretty speedy eh?

Half-Life

*You learnt all about what **half-life** is on the last page, but now it's time to find out how to **calculate** it.*

You Need to be able to Calculate a Half-Life

1) You may be asked to calculate the half-life of a source.

2) You just need to find out how long it takes for the activity or count-rate of the source to halve.

> **EXAMPLE**
>
> **The activity of a radioactive isotope was measured. Initially it was 64 Bq. 12 seconds later it had fallen to 16 Bq. Calculate the half-life of the sample.**
>
> 1) First, find how many half-lives it takes for the activity to fall to from 64 Bq to 16 Bq.
>
> 2) So you know 12 s is equal to two half-lives. Divide 12 by 2 to find one half-life.
>
> After one half life, the activity will be 64 ÷ 2 = 32 Bq
> After two half lives, the activity will be 32 ÷ 2 = 16 Bq
>
> Time for one half life = 12 ÷ 2 = 6 s

You Can Find the Half-Life of a Sample from a Graph of its Activity

1) A graph of activity against time is always shaped like the one below.

2) The half-life is found from the graph by finding the time interval on the bottom axis corresponding to a halving of the activity on the vertical axis. Easy.

> **EXAMPLE**
>
> **The activity of a sample of a radioactive material, X, is shown on the graph below. Calculate the half-life of material X.**
>
> 1) Read the initial activity off the graph. This is the activity when time = 0.
>
> 2) Divide the initial activity by 2 to find the value of half the initial activity.
>   80 ÷ 2 = 40
>
> 3) Find this value on the y-axis and read along horizontally to the curve.
>
> 4) Then read down from the curve at this point to find the half-life.

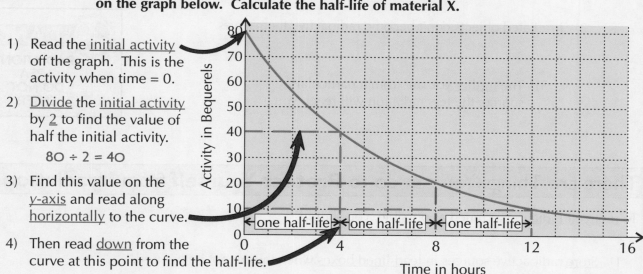

So the half-life of the sample is 4 hours.

You can get useful information from activity-time graphs...

Make sure you can use graphs like the one above to work out half-lives. All you've got to do is read off the initial activity from the y-axis, then work out what half this activity would be by dividing by two. Then, just read off the time from the x-axis for this value, which is one half-life.

Q1 The activity of a radioactive isotope fell from 82 Bq to 41 Bq in 16 seconds. What is the half-life of the sample? [1 mark]

Q2 The initial count-rate of a sample is 168 counts per second (cps). After 60 minutes, the count-rate of the sample is 21 cps. Calculate the half-life of the sample. [3 marks]

Q2 Video Solution

Irradiation and Contamination

*You need to be **very careful** when working with radiation. You don't even need to touch a source to be **irradiated** by it — just being near it is enough. Make sure you know how to **protect yourself**.*

Ionising Radiation can Damage Cells

1) There are <u>hazards</u> (dangers) you need to <u>protect yourself</u> from when working with <u>radioactive sources</u>.

2) <u>Ionising radiation</u> can enter <u>living cells</u> and <u>ionise</u> (p.337) atoms in them.

3) This can <u>damage</u> the cells. This may cause <u>cancer</u> or <u>kill</u> cells off completely.

> We need to know how radiation affects the human body, so we can <u>protect</u> ourselves from harm.
> So it's really important for <u>research</u> into the effects of radiation to be <u>published</u> and checked by <u>peer review</u> — see page 2.

Exposure to Radiation is called Irradiation

1) Objects <u>near</u> a radioactive source can be <u>irradiated</u> by it. This means <u>radiation</u> from the radioactive <u>source</u> will reach the object.

2) Irradiated objects <u>don't become radioactive</u> themselves.

3) The <u>further</u> you are from a particular source, the <u>less radiation</u> will <u>reach</u> you.

There are Things You can do to Protect Yourself from Irradiation

To <u>reduce irradiation</u> as much as possible, you should:

1) <u>Store</u> radioactive sources in <u>lead-lined boxes</u> when they're not being used.

2) Stand behind <u>barriers</u> that will absorb radiation when using sources.

3) Keep the source as <u>far away</u> from you as possible, e.g. hold it at arm's length.

Safety precautions can help protect against hazards from radiation...

Radiation can be pretty <u>dangerous</u> stuff, so it's important to <u>protect yourself</u> when you're working with <u>radioactive substances</u>. <u>Lead</u> is often used to line <u>storage boxes</u> and in <u>protective screens</u> because it is very good at <u>absorbing</u> radiation, so it stops a lot of the radiation from reaching what's on the other side.

Irradiation and Contamination

*On the previous page you saw how **irradiation** can result from even just being near a source. Now for **radioactive contamination**. This only happens if you **touch** or **breathe in** a radioactive substance.*

Contamination is Radioactive Particles **Getting Onto Objects**

1) If <u>unwanted radioactive atoms</u> get onto or into an object, the object is <u>contaminated</u>.

2) These <u>contaminating atoms</u> might then decay and release <u>radiation</u> which could <u>harm</u> you.

3) Being contaminated by a source may cause <u>more damage</u> than if you are irradiated by the same source, as you may <u>carry</u> it for a <u>long time</u>.

4) To help <u>stop contamination</u>, you should wear <u>gloves</u> and use <u>tongs</u> when handling radioactive sources.

People whose jobs involve radioactive materials often wear protective suits and face masks to help stop them being contaminated.

Irradiation and **Contamination Dangers** Depend on the **Source**

The amount of harm <u>contamination</u> or <u>irradiation</u> by a source can cause depends on the <u>radiation type</u>.

Irradiation

1) <u>Beta</u> and <u>gamma</u> sources are the <u>most dangerous</u> to be <u>irradiated</u> by. These types of radiation have <u>long ranges</u> (p.337). That means <u>more radiation</u> will <u>reach you</u> from a beta or gamma source than from an alpha source at the same distance.

2) They can also <u>penetrate</u> (travel through) your body and may damage your <u>organs</u>. Alpha is <u>less</u> dangerous because it <u>can't get through the skin</u> and is easily blocked, e.g. by a <u>small air gap</u> (p.337).

Contamination

1) <u>INSIDE the body</u>, <u>alpha</u> sources are the <u>most dangerous</u> to be <u>contaminated</u> by. This is because <u>alpha particles</u> are the <u>most ionising</u> type of radiation.

2) <u>Beta</u> particles and <u>gamma rays</u> are <u>less damaging</u> because they are <u>less ionising</u>.

3) <u>Gamma</u> sources are the <u>least dangerous</u> inside the body. This is because <u>gamma rays</u> are the <u>least ionising</u> type of radiation and they mostly <u>pass straight</u> out without doing any damage.

4) <u>OUTSIDE</u> of the body, an <u>alpha</u> source is the <u>least dangerous</u> to be <u>contaminated</u> by. This is because alpha particles <u>can't</u> get through the <u>skin</u> and <u>damage your organs</u>.

Warm-Up & Exam Questions

Atoms may be tiny, but you could bag some big marks in your exams if you know them inside-out.
Here are some questions to check just how great your understanding of atoms and radiation really is...

Warm-Up Questions

1) Why was the plum pudding model of an atom replaced with a nuclear model?
2) Describe our current nuclear model of the atom.
3) What is emitted when an electron moves to a lower energy level?
4) What does an atom become if it loses an electron?
5) What does the mass number tell you about an atom?
6) Describe what happens to the mass number and atomic number of an atom if it undergoes alpha decay. What happens to them if the atom undergoes gamma decay?
7) What is the difference between contamination and irradiation by a radioactive source?
8) Why are gamma sources the least dangerous type of radioactive source to have inside you?

Exam Questions

1   Two different atoms can be isotopes of one another.   Grade 1-3

1.1   Name the particles found in the nucleus of an atom.

[2 marks]

1.2   What is meant by the term **isotopes**?

☐   Atoms with the same atomic number but a different mass number

☐   Atoms with the same mass number but a different atomic number

☐   Atoms with the same number of protons but a different atomic number

☐   Atoms with the same number of neutrons but a different number of electrons

[1 mark]

2   **Table 1** shows some information about iodine-131 ($^{131}_{53}$I), an isotope of iodine.   Grade 3-4

Table 1

Particle	Type of Charge	Number present in an atom of iodine-131
Proton	positive	
Neutron	zero	
Electron		53

Complete **Table 1**.

[3 marks]

Exam Questions

3   This question is about the effects on the nucleus of different types of radioactive decay. **Grade 4-5**
    Draw **one** line from each description to the correct type of decay.

Both the mass and charge of the nucleus change.

Neither the mass or charge of the nucleus changes.

The charge of the nucleus changes but the mass stays the same.

alpha
beta
gamma
neutron

[3 marks]

4   Sources A, B and C each emit a single type of radiation. Radiation from each source **Grade 4-5**
    was directed at thin sheets of paper and aluminium. A detector was used to measure
    where radiation had passed through the sheets. The results are shown in **Figure 1**.

Figure 1

radioactive sources   paper   aluminium

A --→ radiation detected

B ----------------------------→ no radiation detected

C ··→ no radiation detected

4.1   Name the type of radiation that source C emits. Explain your answer.

[2 marks]

4.2   Give **one** example of a detector that could have been used to detect the radiation.

[1 mark]

5   A student measured the activity of a radioactive source every 10 minutes. **Grade 4-5**
    Her results are shown in **Table 2**.

Table 2

Time (mins)	0	10	20	30	40	50
Activity (Bq)	740	575	450	350	270	210

5.1   Which value below is the half-life of the source?

☐ 20 minutes   ☐ 28 minutes   ☐ 34 minutes   ☐ 40 minutes

[1 mark]

5.2   The source emits only alpha radiation. It must be removed from a lead-lined box before the
      activity can be measured. The student believes that they should be more concerned about
      avoiding contamination by the source rather than irradiation by it. Suggest why.

[2 marks]

Revision Summary for Topics P1-4

Well, that's <u>Topics P1-4</u> — hopefully they weren't too painful.
Time to see how much you've absorbed.

- Try these questions and <u>tick off each one</u> when you <u>get it right</u>.
- When you're <u>completely happy</u> with a topic, tick it off.

Topic P1 — Energy (p.283-303) ☑

1) Write down four energy stores.
2) What kind of energy store is energy transferred to when you heat an object?
3) Give the equation for finding the energy in an object's gravitational potential energy store.
4) What units must extension, e, be in before it can be used in the equation $E_e = \frac{1}{2}ke^2$?
5) Describe an experiment to find the specific heat capacity of a material.
6) Give two equations you could use to calculate power.
7) How can you reduce unwanted energy transfers in a machine with moving parts?
8) Name four renewable energy resources and four non-renewable energy resources.
9) Give one environmental issue associated with using biofuels to generate electricity.
10) Explain why the UK is trying to use more renewable energy resources in the future.

Topic P2 — Electricity (p.305-324) ☑

11) Draw the circuit diagram symbols for a resistor, a voltmeter, an LED and a diode.
12) What is the equation that links potential difference, current and resistance?
13) Describe how you would investigate how the length of a wire affects its resistance.
14) Sketch the *I-V* characteristic of a diode.
15) How does the resistance of an LDR change as light intensity increases?
16) A circuit consists of a battery and a resistor. How does the overall resistance of the circuit change when a second resistor is added in parallel?
17) What is the potential difference and the frequency of the UK mains supply?
18) Give the potential differences for the three wires in a three-core mains cable.
19) Describe the useful energy transfer that occurs for a battery-powered fan.
20) Explain why electricity is transferred by the national grid at a high pd but low current.

Topic P3 — Particle Model of Matter (p.326-331) ☑

21) Describe how particles are arranged in a liquid.
22) Briefly describe an experiment to find the density of a liquid.
23) What happens to the particles in a substance when that substance is heated?
24) Is a change of state a physical change or a chemical change?

Topic P4 — Atomic Structure (p.334-343) ☑

25) What happens when an electron in an atom absorbs electromagnetic radiation?
26) How do atoms of two isotopes of an element differ from each other?
27) How does the emission of a beta particle change the atomic number of an atom?
28) Describe how to find a radioactive source's half-life, given a graph of its activity over time.
29) Give two examples of how to stop: a) irradiation,   b) contamination.
30) Compare the hazards of being irradiated and contaminated by a gamma source.

Contact and Non-Contact Forces

*When you're talking about the **forces** acting on an object, it's not enough to just talk about the **size** of each force. You need to know their **direction** too — force is a **vector**, with a size and a direction.*

Force is a **Vector** Quantity

1) Vector quantities have a <u>magnitude (size)</u> and a <u>direction</u>. For example:

> <u>Vector quantities</u>: force, velocity, displacement, acceleration

2) Some quantities have a magnitude but <u>no direction</u>. These are called <u>scalar quantities</u>. Here are some examples of scalar quantities:

> <u>Scalar quantities</u>: speed, distance, mass, temperature, time

3) Vectors are usually represented by an <u>arrow</u>.
4) The <u>length</u> of the arrow shows the <u>magnitude</u>.
5) The <u>direction</u> of the arrow shows the <u>direction of the quantity</u>.

Forces Can be **Contact** or **Non-Contact**

1) A <u>force</u> is a <u>push</u> or a <u>pull</u> that acts on an object.
2) Forces are caused by objects <u>interacting</u> with each other.
3) All forces are either <u>contact</u> or <u>non-contact</u> forces.
4) When <u>two objects</u> have to be <u>touching</u> for a force to act, the force is a <u>contact force</u>.

> <u>Contact force examples</u>: friction, air resistance, tension, normal contact force

> *When an object exerts a force on a second object, the second object pushes back. This is the normal contact force.*

5) If the objects <u>do not need to be touching</u> for the force to act, the force is a <u>non-contact force</u>.

> <u>Non-contact force examples</u>: magnetic force, gravitational force, electrostatic force

6) When two objects <u>interact</u>, a <u>force</u> is produced on <u>both</u> objects. The forces on the two objects are <u>equal in size</u> but act in <u>opposite directions</u>.
7) These two forces are called an <u>interaction pair</u>.

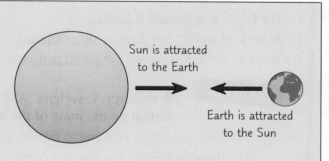

The <u>gravitational attraction</u> between the Earth and the Sun is an example of an <u>interaction pair</u>.

A gravitational force acts on the Earth <u>attracting</u> it to the Sun.

At the same time a force acts on the Sun <u>attracting</u> it towards the Earth.

These forces are the <u>same size</u> but act in <u>opposite directions</u>.

Sun is attracted to the Earth

Earth is attracted to the Sun

An interaction between two objects produces a force on each object...

Whether it's a <u>contact</u> or <u>non-contact</u> force, it's always acting as part of a <u>pair</u>. Remember it's the two <u>forces</u>, not the objects, which are called the <u>interaction pair</u> — and they are <u>always equal and opposite</u>.

Weight, Mass and Gravity

*Mass and weight are **NOT** the same... Read on to find out **why**. You know you want to.*

Mass is Measured in kg

1) <u>Mass</u> is just the amount of <u>matter (stuff)</u> in an object.

2) It's measured in <u>kilograms</u>, kg.

3) Scientists sometimes think of all the mass in an object as being at <u>one single point</u> in the object.

4) This point is called the <u>centre of mass</u>.

centre of mass

weight

Weight is Measured in **Newtons**

1) <u>Weight</u> is the <u>force</u> acting on an object due to <u>gravity</u>.

2) You can think of this force as acting from an object's <u>centre of mass</u>.

3) Close to Earth, this force is caused by the <u>gravitational field</u> around the Earth.

4) The <u>weight</u> of an object depends on its <u>mass</u> and the <u>strength of the gravitational field</u> it's in.

5) The <u>gravitational field strength of Earth</u> changes slightly depending on <u>where you are</u>.

6) So the weight of an object depends on its <u>location</u>.

7) Unlike the <u>mass</u> of an object which is <u>always the same</u>.

8) Weight is measured in <u>newtons</u>, <u>N</u>.

9) It can be measured with a calibrated <u>spring</u> balance (or <u>newtonmeter</u>).

Mass and Weight are Directly Proportional

1) You can calculate the <u>weight</u> of an object if you know its <u>mass</u> (*m*) and the <u>strength</u> of the <u>gravitational field</u> that it is in (*g*):

Weight (N) = Mass (kg) × Gravitational Field Strength (N/kg)

2) For Earth, <u>*g* is around 9.8 N/kg</u>.

3) Mass and weight are <u>directly proportional</u>.

4) You can write this, using the <u>direct proportionality symbol</u>, as $W \propto m$.

$$\frac{W}{m \times g}$$

> **EXAMPLE**
>
> **A motorcycle weighs 2450 N on Earth.**
> **Calculate the mass of the motorcycle. (*g* = 9.8 N/kg)**
>
> 1) First, <u>rearrange</u> *W = mg* to find <u>mass</u>.　　mass = weight ÷ gravitational field strength
> 2) Then, put in the numbers to <u>calculate</u> the mass.　　mass = 2450 ÷ 9.8 = 250 kg

An object's weight depends on the gravitational field it is in

Q1　Calculate the weight in newtons of a 5 kg mass:
　　a) on Earth (*g* ≈ 9.8 N/kg)　　　　b) on the Moon (*g* ≈ 1.6 N/kg)　　　　[4 marks]

Q1 Video Solution

Resultant Forces and Work Done

*I'm sure you're no stranger to **doing work**, but in physics it's all to do with **transferring energy**.*

A **Resultant Force** is the **Overall Force** on a Point or Object

1) If a <u>number of forces</u> act at a single point, you can replace them with a <u>single force</u>.

2) This single force is called the <u>resultant force</u>.

3) It has the <u>same effect</u> as all the original forces added together.

4) You can find the resultant force when forces are acting in a <u>straight line</u>.
   <u>Add together</u> forces acting in the <u>same</u> direction and <u>take away</u> any going in the <u>opposite</u> direction.

A <u>trolley</u> is pulled by two children. One child pulls the trolley with a force of 5 N to the <u>left</u>. The other pulls the trolley with a force of 10 N to the <u>right</u>.

So the resultant force, *F*, is:
$$F = 10\,\text{N} - 5\,\text{N}$$
$$= \underline{5\,\text{N to the right}}.$$

If a Force **Moves** an Object, **Work is Done**

When a <u>force</u> moves an object through a <u>distance</u>, <u>energy is transferred</u> and <u>work is done</u> on the object.

1) To make an object move, a force <u>must</u> act on it.

2) The force does '<u>work</u>' to move the object.

3) This causes <u>energy</u> to be <u>transferred to</u> the object.

4) The force usually <u>does work</u> against frictional forces too.

5) Doing work against frictional forces causes energy to be transferred to the <u>thermal energy store</u> of the object.

6) This causes the <u>temperature</u> of the object to <u>increase</u>.

> 'Work done' and 'energy transferred' are the same thing. You need to be able to describe how energy is transferred when work is done. Look back at p.285 for more on this.

- When you <u>push</u> something along a <u>rough surface</u> (like a <u>carpet</u>) you are doing work <u>against frictional forces</u>.
- Some energy is <u>transferred</u> to the <u>kinetic energy store</u> of the <u>object</u> because it starts <u>moving</u>.
- Some is also transferred to <u>thermal energy stores</u> due to the work done against friction.
- This causes the overall <u>temperature</u> of the object to <u>increase</u>.

7) You can find out <u>how much work</u> has been done using:

Work done (J) — $W = Fs$ — Force (N) / Distance (moved along the line of action of the force) (m)

> The line of action of the force is the direction of the force.

8) <u>One joule of work</u> is done when a <u>force of one newton</u> causes an object to move a <u>distance of one metre</u> in the direction of the force.

9) You need to be able to <u>convert</u> joules to newton metres: <u>1 J = 1 Nm</u>.

Work done is measured in joules, J — one J equals one Nm...

Although "<u>work done</u>" may sound like an odd phrase, all it means is "<u>energy transferred</u>".

Q1   A force of 20 N pushes an object 20 cm. Calculate the work done on the object.   [3 marks]

Q1 Video Solution

Warm-Up & Exam Questions

Now you've learnt the basics of forces, it's time to act on your new knowledge.
Give these questions a go and test how well you've forced those facts into your brain.

Warm-Up Questions

1) Which of the following is a contact force: magnetic force, gravitational force or friction?
2) Vectors can be drawn as arrows. What is represented by the length of the arrow?
3) State the units of: a) mass,   b) weight.
4) If two forces are acting in the same direction, how can you find the resultant force?

Exam Questions

1   Most quantities can be divided into two groups: scalars and vectors.   *Grade 1-3*

1.1   Which of the following is a vector? Tick **one** box.

☐ speed   ☐ time   ☐ mass   ☐ force

[1 mark]

1.2   Which of the following is a scalar? Tick **one** box.

☐ 14 kg   ☐ 300 kN down   ☐ 24 m/s west   ☐ 1 m/s² up

[1 mark]

2   **Figure 1** shows two hot air balloons, labelled with the forces acting on them.   *Grade 3-4*

Figure 1

Balloon A

200 N ⇧   ⇧ 300 N

800 N ⬇

Balloon B

⇧ x

400 N ⬇

2.1   Calculate the size of the resultant force acting on Balloon A and give its direction.

[2 marks]

2.2   The resultant force acting on Balloon B is zero. Calculate the size of force *x*.

[1 mark]

3   A train moves 750 m in a straight line along a flat track.
The resultant force acting on the train is 44 000 N forwards along the track.   *Grade 4-5*

3.1   Write down the equation that links work done, force and distance.

[1 mark]

3.2   Calculate the work done by the resultant force as the train moves. Give your answer in kilojoules.

[3 marks]

Forces and Elasticity

*Forces don't just make objects **move**, they can also make them **deform** (change shape).*

Stretching, Compressing or Bending Transfers Energy

1) When you apply a force to an object you may cause it to <u>deform</u> (<u>stretch</u>, <u>compress</u> or <u>bend</u>).

2) To do this, you need <u>more than one</u> force acting on the object. <u>One</u> force would just make the object <u>move</u>, not change its shape.

3) An object has been <u>elastically deformed</u> if it can <u>go back</u> to its <u>original shape</u> and <u>length</u> after the force has been removed.

4) If the object <u>doesn't</u> go back to how it was, it has been <u>inelastically deformed</u>.

5) Objects that can be elastically deformed are called <u>elastic objects</u> (e.g. a spring).

6) <u>Work is done</u> when a force stretches or compresses an object. This causes energy to be transferred to the <u>elastic potential energy</u> store of the object.

Elastic objects are only elastic up to a certain point...

Remember the difference between <u>elastic deformation</u> and <u>inelastic deformation</u>. If an <u>object</u> has been <u>elastically deformed</u>, it will <u>return</u> to its <u>original shape</u> when you <u>remove the force</u>. If it's been <u>inelastically deformed</u>, its shape will have been <u>changed permanently</u> — for example, an over-stretched spring will stay stretched even after you remove the force.

Forces and Elasticity

*Springs obey a really handy little **equation** that relates the **force** on them to their **extension** — for a while at least. Thankfully, you can **plot a graph** to see where this equation is **true**.*

Extension is **Directly Proportional** to **Force**...

Force, *F*

Natural length, *l*

Extension, *e*

Force, *F*

The length of the unstretched spring is sometimes called the spring's natural length.

1) When a force <u>stretches</u> a spring, it causes it to <u>extend</u>.

2) This <u>extension</u> is the <u>difference in length</u> between the stretched and unstretched spring.

3) Up to a <u>given force</u>, the extension is <u>directly proportional</u> to force.

4) So long as a spring hasn't been stretched <u>past</u> its <u>limit of proportionality</u> (see below), you can use:

Spring constant (N/m)

Force (N) —— $F = ke$

Extension (m)

5) The <u>spring constant</u> depends on the <u>object</u> that you are stretching.

6) The equation also works for <u>compression</u> (where *e* is the <u>difference</u> between the <u>natural</u> and <u>compressed</u> lengths).

...but this **Stops Working** when the **Force** is **Great Enough**

1) You can plot a <u>graph</u> of the force applied to a spring and the extension caused.

2) When the graph is a <u>straight line</u>, there is a <u>linear relationship</u> between force and extension.

3) This shows force and extension are <u>directly proportional</u>.

4) The <u>gradient</u> of the <u>straight line</u> is equal to *k*, the <u>spring constant</u>.

5) When the line begins to <u>bend</u>, the relationship is now <u>non-linear</u>. Force and extension are <u>no longer</u> directly proportional.

6) Point P on the graph (when the line starts to bend) is the <u>limit of proportionality</u>. <u>Past</u> this point, the equation *F = ke* is <u>no longer</u> true.

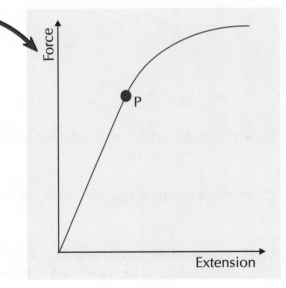

Force

P

Extension

The spring constant is measured in N/m...

Be careful with <u>units</u> when doing calculations with springs. Your values for <u>extension</u> will usually be in <u>centimetres</u> or <u>millimetres</u>, but the <u>spring constant</u> is measured in <u>newtons per metre</u>. So <u>convert</u> the extension into metres <u>before</u> you do any calculations, or you'll get the wrong answer.

Q1 Video Solution

Q1   A spring is fixed at one end and a force of 1 N is applied to the other end, causing it to stretch. The spring extends by 2 cm. Calculate the spring constant of the spring.   [4 marks]

Investigating Springs

*Oh look, here's one of those **Required Practicals**... There might be a few ways this experiment can **stretch** you. **Read on** and take your time with **each step**, so you won't be past your limits in the exam.*

You Can **Investigate** the Link Between **Force** and **Extension**

1) Set up the <u>apparatus</u> as shown in the diagram.

2) Measure the <u>mass</u> of each mass.

3) Calculate its <u>weight</u> (the <u>force</u> applied) using $W = mg$ (p.348).

4) Measure the original (natural) <u>length</u> of the spring.

5) Add a mass to the spring and allow it to come to <u>rest</u>.

6) Record the force and measure the new <u>length</u> of the spring.

7) Find the <u>extension</u>.

extension = new length – original length

8) <u>Repeat</u> steps 5 to 7 until you've added all the masses.

9) <u>Plot</u> a <u>force-extension graph</u> of your results.

10) You should make sure you have <u>at least</u> 5 measurements before the <u>limit of proportionality</u> (where the line starts to curve).

Investigating Springs

*Believe it or not there's another **equation** involving the **extension** of a spring — lucky you.*

You Can **Work Out Energy Stored** for **Linear** Relationships

1) If a spring is not stretched <u>past</u> its <u>limit of proportionality</u>, the <u>work done</u> in stretching the spring can be found using:

Spring constant (N/m)

$$E_e = \tfrac{1}{2} ke^2$$

Elastic potential energy (J)

(Extension)²
(m)²

Remember the limit of proportionality (shown by point P) is the point at which the force on a spring and the spring's extension stop being proportional to each other (see p.352).

Force

P

Extension

2) For an <u>elastic deformation</u>, this formula can be used to calculate the energy stored in a spring's <u>elastic potential energy store</u>.

3) It's also the energy <u>transferred to</u> the spring as it's <u>deformed</u>, or <u>transferred by</u> the spring as it returns to its <u>original shape</u>.

EXAMPLE

A spring with a spring constant of 50 N/m extends elastically by 10 cm. It doesn't pass its limit of proportionality. Calculate the amount of energy stored in its elastic potential energy store.

You can also use this equation to calculate the energy stored when a spring is compressed.

1) First, you need to <u>convert</u> the extension of the spring into <u>metres</u>.

10 cm ÷ 100 = 0.1 m

2) Then put in the <u>numbers</u> you've been given.

$E_e = \tfrac{1}{2}ke^2 = 0.5 \times 50 \times 0.1^2$
$= 0.25$ J

Elastic potential energy equals the work done to stretch a spring...

As a spring is stretched <u>work is done</u> and the <u>energy is transferred</u> to the spring's <u>elastic potential energy store</u>, so the two are <u>equal</u>. This means the equation for elastic potential energy can be used to calculate work done — but <u>remember</u> it only works before the <u>limit of proportionality</u> is passed.

Q1 Video Solution

Q1   A spring with a spring constant of 40 N/m extends elastically by 2.5 cm.
     Calculate the amount of energy stored in its elastic potential energy store.   [3 marks]

Warm-Up & Exam Questions

It's time to stretch those thinking muscles with another round of questions. Give these a go to test the limits of your newly extended knowledge of springs and elasticity.

Warm-Up Questions

1) True or false? An object which is inelastically deformed will not return to its original shape when the force is removed.
2) True or false? The formula $F = ke$ cannot be used if a spring is compressed.
3) What units must extension be in before you use the formula for work done on a spring?

Exam Questions

1 A force of 4 N is applied to a spring which causes the spring to extend elastically by 0.05 m.

1.1 Write down the equation which links force, extension and the spring constant.

[1 mark]

1.2 Calculate the spring constant of the spring.

[3 marks]

PRACTICAL

2 A teacher does an experiment to show how a spring extends when masses are hung from it, using the setup shown in **Figure 1**.

He hangs a number of 90 g masses from a 50 g hook attached to the base of the spring. He records the extension of the spring and the total weight of the masses and hook each time he adds a mass to the bottom of the spring.

2.1 State **one** control variable in this experiment.

[1 mark]

2.2 State the independent variable in this experiment.

[1 mark]

Figure 2 shows the force-extension graph of the results of the experiment.

2.3 Calculate the work done when the spring is stretched with a force of 7.0 N. The spring constant is 175 N/m. Use the correct equation from the Physics Equation Sheet on page 538.

Choose the correct unit from the box.

| N/m | J | cm |

[3 marks]

Figure 1

Figure 2

Distance, Displacement, Speed, Velocity

*This page is about a bunch of **scalars** and **vectors**. Still a little unsure on the difference between **scalar** and **vector quantities**? Take a look back at p.347 before starting this page.*

Distance is a **Scalar**, Displacement is a **Vector**

1) <u>Distance</u> is just <u>how far</u> an object has moved.
2) Distance is a <u>scalar</u> quantity (p.347), so it doesn't involve <u>direction</u>.
3) <u>Displacement</u> is a <u>vector</u> quantity.
4) It measures the distance and direction in a <u>straight line</u> from an object's <u>starting point</u> to its <u>finishing point</u>.
5) The direction could be <u>in relation to a point</u>, e.g. <u>towards the school</u>.
6) If you walk 5 m <u>north</u>, then 5 m <u>south</u>, your <u>displacement</u> is <u>0 m</u> but the <u>distance</u> travelled is <u>10 m</u>.

Speed and **Velocity** are Both **How Fast You're Going**

1) <u>Speed</u> is a <u>scalar</u> and <u>velocity</u> is a <u>vector</u>:

> <u>Speed</u> is just <u>how fast</u> you're going (e.g. 30 mph or 20 m/s) with no regard to the direction.
> <u>Velocity</u> is speed in a given <u>direction</u>, e.g. 30 mph north or 20 m/s to the right.

2) To <u>measure</u> the <u>speed</u> of an object that's moving with a <u>constant speed</u>, <u>time</u> how long it takes the object to travel a certain <u>distance</u>. Make sure you use the correct equipment (see p.399).
3) You can then <u>calculate</u> the object's <u>speed</u> using this <u>formula</u>:

$$s = vt$$

distance travelled (m) = speed (m/s) × time (s)

4) Objects <u>rarely</u> travel at a <u>constant speed</u>.
5) When you <u>walk</u>, <u>run</u> or travel in a <u>car</u>, your speed is <u>always changing</u>.
6) In these cases, the formula above gives the <u>average</u> (<u>mean</u>) speed during that time.

You Need to Know Some **Typical** Everyday **Speeds**

1) You need to know the <u>typical</u> (usual) <u>speeds</u> of objects:

> A person <u>walking</u> — <u>1.5 m/s</u>   A person <u>cycling</u> — <u>6 m/s</u>   A <u>train</u> — <u>30 m/s</u>
> A person <u>running</u> — <u>3 m/s</u>   A <u>car</u> — <u>25 m/s</u>   A <u>passenger plane</u> — <u>250 m/s</u>

2) Lots of different things can <u>affect</u> the speed something travels at.
3) The speed at which a person can <u>walk</u>, <u>run</u> or <u>cycle</u> depends on, among other things:

> • their <u>fitness</u>   • the <u>distance they've travelled</u>
> • their <u>age</u>   • the <u>terrain</u> (what type of ground they are on)

4) The speeds of <u>sound</u> and <u>wind</u> also vary. A typical speed for sound in air is <u>330 m/s</u>.

You can also think of that equation as speed = distance ÷ time...

Remember those typical speeds of objects — you might need to use them to make <u>estimates</u>.

Q1   A sprinter runs 200 m in 25 s. Calculate his speed.   [3 marks]

Q1 Video Solution

Acceleration

*Acceleration is the **rate of change** of velocity — if it stays **constant**, there's a handy **equation** you can use.*

Acceleration is How **Quickly** You're **Speeding Up**

1) Acceleration is the <u>change in velocity</u> in a certain amount of <u>time</u>.

2) You can find the <u>average acceleration</u> of an object using:

Acceleration (m/s²)⟶ $a = \dfrac{\Delta v}{t}$ ⟵Change in velocity (m/s)

⟵Time taken (s)

3) <u>Deceleration</u> (when something <u>slows down</u>) is just <u>negative</u> acceleration.

You Need to be Able to **Estimate Accelerations**

You might have to <u>estimate</u> the <u>acceleration</u> of an object.
To do this, you need the <u>typical speeds</u> from the previous page:

An estimate is just a guess using rough numbers for things.

EXAMPLE   **A woman gets onto a bike and accelerates to a typical speed from stationary in 10 seconds. Estimate the acceleration of the bicycle.**

1) First, give a <u>sensible speed</u> for the bicycle to be travelling at.

2) Put these numbers into the <u>acceleration equation</u>.

3) The <u>~ symbol</u> just means it's an approximate answer.

The typical speed of a bike is about 6 m/s.

The bicycle accelerates in 10 s.

$a = \Delta v \div t$
$= 6 \div 10 = 0.6 \text{ m/s}^2$

So the acceleration is ~0.6 m/s²

Uniform Acceleration Means a **Constant Acceleration**

1) <u>Constant acceleration</u> is sometimes called <u>uniform acceleration</u>.

2) Acceleration <u>due to gravity</u> (*g*) is <u>uniform</u> for objects falling freely.

3) It's roughly equal to <u>9.8 m/s²</u> near the Earth's surface.

4) You can use this <u>equation</u> for <u>uniform</u> acceleration:

Acceleration (m/s²)

(Final velocity)² (m/s)² ⟶ $v^2 - u^2 = 2as$ ⟵Distance (m)

(Initial velocity)² (m/s)²

Initial velocity is just the starting velocity of the object.

EXAMPLE   **A van travelling at 23 m/s starts decelerating uniformly at 2.0 m/s² as it heads towards a built-up area 112 m away. What will its speed be when it reaches the built-up area?**

1) First, <u>rearrange</u> the equation so v^2 is on one side.

2) Now put the <u>numbers</u> in — remember *a* is <u>negative</u> because it's a deceleration.

3) Finally, <u>square root</u> the whole thing.

$v^2 = u^2 + 2as$

$v^2 = 23^2 + (2 \times -2.0 \times 112)$
$= 81$

$v = \sqrt{81} = 9 \text{ m/s}$

An object is accelerating if its velocity is changing...

Don't forget — you can only use that second equation when the acceleration is <u>uniform</u>.

Q1   A ball is dropped from a height, *h*, above the ground. The speed of the ball just before it hits the ground is 7 m/s. Calculate the height the ball is dropped from. (acceleration due to gravity ≈ 9.8 m/s²)

Q1 Video Solution

[3 marks]

Distance-Time Graphs

*You need to be able to **draw** and **understand** distance-time graphs.*

You Can **Show Journeys** on **Distance-Time Graphs**

1) If an object moves in a <u>straight line</u>, the <u>distance</u> it travels can be plotted on a <u>distance-time</u> graph.

2) You may be asked to <u>draw</u> a distance-time graph for a journey.

3) Or you might have to <u>describe</u> a journey if you're shown a distance-time graph.

- <u>Gradient = speed</u>. The <u>steeper</u> the graph, the <u>faster</u> it's going.
- <u>Flat</u> sections are where it's <u>stationary</u> — it's <u>stopped</u>.
- <u>Straight</u> uphill (/) sections mean it is travelling at a <u>steady speed</u>.
- <u>Curves</u> represent <u>acceleration</u> or <u>deceleration</u> (p.357).
- A curve that is <u>getting steeper</u> means it's <u>speeding up</u> (accelerating).
- A <u>levelling off</u> curve means it's <u>slowing down</u> (decelerating).

4) You might also have to <u>calculate</u> an object's <u>speed</u> from the graph:

EXAMPLE

Using the distance-time graph on the right, calculate the speed of the car.

1) The <u>gradient</u> of the graph is the <u>speed</u> of the car.

2) Gradient = $\dfrac{\text{change in vertical axis}}{\text{change in horizontal axis}}$.

3) Draw a <u>large triangle</u>, that takes up most of the straight line.

4) Use the <u>horizontal</u> side of the triangle to find the change in time.

5) Use the <u>vertical side</u> of the triangle to find the change in distance.

6) Put the values for vertical and horizontal into the <u>equation</u>.

Change in time = 4.4 − 0.8 = 3.6 s

Change in distance = 11 − 2 = 9 m

Gradient = 9 ÷ 3.6 = 2.5

So speed = 2.5 m/s

A steeper gradient means a faster speed...

Make sure you know how to use a <u>distance-time graph</u> to find an object's <u>speed</u>.

Q1 Sketch the distance-time graph for an object that accelerates, then travels at a steady speed, and then comes to a stop.

[3 marks]

Q1 Video Solution

Velocity-Time Graphs

*You also need to know about **velocity-time graphs** — they can be used to calculate **acceleration**.*

Journeys Can be Shown on a Velocity-Time Graph

1) How an object's <u>velocity</u> changes as it travels can be plotted on a <u>velocity-time</u> graph.
2) You might have to <u>draw</u> a velocity-time graph for a journey.
3) Or you might have to <u>describe</u> a journey from a velocity-time graph.

1) <u>Gradient = acceleration</u>. You can calculate this with a similar method to the example on the last page.

2) <u>Flat sections</u> represent travelling at a <u>steady speed</u>.

3) The <u>steeper</u> the graph, the <u>greater</u> the <u>acceleration</u> or <u>deceleration</u>.

4) <u>Uphill</u> sections (/) are <u>acceleration</u>.

5) <u>Downhill</u> sections (\) are <u>deceleration</u>.

6) A <u>curve</u> means <u>changing acceleration</u>.

Read the axes of any graph you get given carefully...

Don't get <u>confused</u> between <u>distance-time graphs</u> and <u>velocity-time graphs</u>. They can <u>look similar</u>, but <u>different parts</u> of the graphs tell you very different things about the motion of an object.

Q1 Sketch a velocity-time graph for an object that travels at a constant speed, then accelerates at a constant rate, then moves at a constant speed (that is different to the initial speed). [3 marks]

Q2 A stationary car starts accelerating increasingly for 10 s until it reaches a speed of 20 m/s. It travels at this speed for 20 s until the driver sees a hazard and brakes. He decelerates uniformly, coming to a stop 4 s after braking. Draw the velocity-time graph for this journey. [3 marks]

Q2 Video Solution

Drag and Terminal Velocity

*If an object **falls** for long enough, it will reach its **terminal velocity**. It's all about **balance** between **weight** and **air resistance**. **Parachutes** work by **decreasing** your terminal velocity.*

Drag Always **Slows Things Down**

1) Gases and liquids are both <u>fluids</u>.

2) Objects moving through fluids experience <u>drag</u>.

3) Drag is the <u>resistance</u> you get in a fluid. <u>Air resistance</u> is a type of <u>drag</u>.

4) <u>Drag</u> acts in the <u>opposite direction</u> to the movement of the object.

5) Drag <u>increases</u> as the speed of the object increases.

Falling Objects Reach a **Terminal Velocity**

1) When an object first <u>starts falling</u>, the force of gravity is <u>much larger</u> than the drag slowing it down.

2) This means the object <u>accelerates</u> (the object <u>speeds up</u>).

3) As the <u>speed increases</u>, so does the drag.

4) This <u>reduces</u> the <u>acceleration</u> until the drag is <u>equal</u> to the gravitational force. The <u>resultant force</u> (p.349) on the object is then <u>zero</u>.

5) The object will fall at a <u>constant speed</u>. This speed is called its <u>terminal velocity</u>.

All objects falling in air have a terminal velocity...

...but some hit the ground before they reach it. When a falling object is at its <u>terminal velocity</u> the resultant force acting on the object is <u>zero</u>. This doesn't mean the object stops moving, it just means that it <u>stops accelerating</u> — so it continues to fall at a <u>constant speed</u> (its terminal velocity).

Warm-Up & Exam Questions

Slow down, it's not quite time to move on to Newton's Laws just yet. First it's time to check that all the stuff you've just read is still running around your brain. Dive into these questions.

Warm-Up Questions

1) What is the difference between speed and velocity?
2) Suggest the typical speeds of:　　a) a person running,　　　b) a train,　　　c) a plane.
3) True or false? Acceleration is shown as a curve on a distance-time graph.
4) An object travelling at a steady speed will be represented by which of the following on a velocity-time graph?　a) an uphill section,　　b) a downhill section,　　c) a flat section.
5) What is the resultant force acting on object falling at its terminal velocity?

Exam Questions

1　A cyclist travels from his house to his local shops.

It takes the cyclist 20 seconds to accelerate from 2.0 m/s to 10 m/s with a steady acceleration. Using the following formula, calculate the cyclist's acceleration:
acceleration = change in velocity ÷ time

[2 marks]

2　**Figure 1** shows the velocity-time graph of a cyclist.

2.1　Describe the motion of the cyclist between 5 and 10 seconds.

[2 marks]

2.2　Calculate the acceleration of the cyclist between 2 and 5 seconds.

[2 marks]

Figure 1

3　A coin is rolled in a straight line along a balcony edge at a steady speed of 0.46 m/s.

3.1　Write the equation which links speed, distance and time.

[1 mark]

3.2　Calculate how far the coin rolls in 2.4 s. Give your answer to two significant figures.

[3 marks]

3.3　Another coin is dropped from a height of 8 m.
It accelerates from rest at a constant rate and hits the ground at a speed of 12 m/s.
Calculate the acceleration of the coin during its fall.
Use the correct equation from the Physics Equation Sheet on page 538.

[3 marks]

Newton's First and Second Law

*In the 1660s, **Isaac Newton** worked out some really useful **Laws of Motion**. Here are the first **two**.*

A **Force** is Needed to **Change Motion**

1) <u>Newton's First Law</u> says that a resultant force (p.349) is needed to make something <u>start moving</u>, <u>speed up</u> or <u>slow down</u>:

> If the resultant force on a <u>stationary</u> object is <u>zero</u>, the object will <u>remain stationary</u>. If the resultant force on a <u>moving object</u> is <u>zero</u>, it'll just carry on moving at the <u>same velocity</u> (the same speed <u>and</u> direction).

2) So, when a train or car or bus or anything else is <u>moving</u> at a <u>constant velocity</u>, the <u>driving</u> and <u>resistive</u> forces on it must be <u>balanced</u>.

3) Its velocity will <u>only</u> change if there's a <u>non-zero</u> resultant force acting on it.

4) A non-zero <u>resultant</u> force will always produce <u>acceleration</u> (or deceleration) in the <u>direction of the force</u>.

Acceleration is **Proportional** to the **Resultant Force**

1) The <u>larger</u> the <u>resultant force</u> acting on an object, the <u>more</u> the object accelerates.

2) <u>Newton's Second Law</u> says that the force acting on an object and the acceleration of the object are <u>directly proportional</u>. This can be shown as $F \propto a$.

3) Newton's Second Law also says that acceleration is <u>inversely proportional</u> to the mass of the object.

4) So an object with a <u>larger</u> mass will accelerate <u>less</u> than one with a smaller mass, for a <u>given force</u>.

5) There's a <u>formula</u> that describes <u>Newton's Second Law</u>:

Resultant force (N) — $F = ma$ — Acceleration (m/s²)

Mass (kg)

6) You can use <u>Newton's Second Law</u> to get an idea of the forces involved in <u>large accelerations</u> of everyday transport.

7) You may need some typical vehicle masses first though:
<u>Car</u> — 1000 kg, <u>Bus</u> — 10 000 kg, <u>Loaded Lorry</u> — 30 000 kg

EXAMPLE   **Estimate the resultant force on a car as it accelerates from rest to a typical speed.**

1) <u>Estimate</u> the <u>speed</u> of the car and the <u>time</u> taken to reach that speed.

A typical speed of a car is ~25 m/s. It takes ~10 s to reach this.

Remember, the ~ sign means approximately.

2) Use the <u>speed</u> and <u>time</u> taken to estimate the <u>acceleration</u> of the car.

So $a = \Delta v \div t = 25 \div 10 = 2.5$ m/s²

3) Put the acceleration and the mass of the car into $F = ma$.

Mass of a car is ~1000 kg.
$F = ma = 1000 \times 2.5 = 2500$ N
So the resultant force is ~2500 N.

Newton's second law says $F = ma$...

Make sure you've got your head around <u>both</u> of these laws, before moving on to <u>Newton's third law</u>.

Q1   Find the force needed for an 80 kg man on a 10 kg bike to accelerate at 0.25 m/s². [2 marks]

Q1 Video Solution

Newton's Third Law

*This page is on **Newton's Third Law**. Make sure you really understand what's going on with it.*

Newton's Third Law — Interaction Pairs are Equal and Opposite

Newton's Third Law says:

> When two objects interact, the forces they exert on each other are equal and opposite.

1) This means if you push something, it will push back against you, just as hard.
2) And as soon as you stop pushing, so does the object.
3) You may be thinking "if the forces are always equal, how does anything ever go anywhere?".
4) The important thing to remember is that the two forces are acting on different objects.

Push → | Normal contact force

Skater A   Skater B

mass = 55 kg   mass = 65 kg

- Skater A pushes on skater B.
- When she does, she feels an equal and opposite force from skater B's hand.
- Both skaters feel the same sized force, in opposite directions.
- This causes them to accelerate away from each other.
- Skater A will be accelerated more than skater B, because she has a smaller mass.
- Remember $a = F \div m$.

It's More Complicated for an Object in Equilibrium

Imagine a book sat on a table in equilibrium (the resultant force on the book is zero):

1) The weight of the book pulls it down, and the normal contact force from the table pushes it up.
2) This is NOT Newton's Third Law.
3) These forces are different types and they're both acting on the book.

The pairs of forces due to Newton's Third Law in this case are:

- The book being pulled down by gravity towards the Earth (W_B) and the Earth being pulled up by the book (W_E).
- The normal contact force from the table pushing up on the book (R_B) and the normal contact force from the book pushing down on the table (R_T).

Newton's Third Law is only true for interaction pairs...

Make sure you get your head around Newton's laws of motion. His third law can be tricky — take your time, look at each object one by one, and work out all the forces acting on it.

Q1   A car moves at a constant velocity along a road, so that it is in equilibrium. Give an example of a pair of forces that demonstrate Newton's Third Law in this situation.   [1 mark]

Q1 Video Solution

Investigating Motion

*Here comes another **Required Practical**. This one's all about testing **Newton's Second Law**. It uses some nifty bits of kit that you may not have seen before, so make sure you follow the instructions closely.*

You can **Investigate** how **Mass** and **Force** Affect Acceleration

This page shows you how to set up the experiment that tests <u>Newton's Second Law</u>, $F = ma$ (p.362). On the next page you can find out how to <u>investigate</u> the variables that affect Newton's Second Law.

1) Set up the <u>apparatus</u> as shown on the right.

2) The <u>mass</u>, *m*, that you'll be accelerating is the <u>total mass</u> of the <u>trolley</u>, <u>hook</u> and the <u>added masses</u>.

3) You can measure *m* using a <u>mass balance</u>.

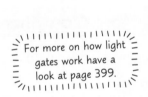

trolley of known mass

piece of card

light gate connected to data logger (or computer)

pulley

starting line

hook of known mass

masses

4) The <u>force</u>, *F*, causing the acceleration is the <u>weight</u> of the <u>hook and the masses on the hook</u>.

5) To find *F*, first measure the <u>mass</u> of the <u>hook</u> and any masses <u>on the hook</u>. Then <u>multiply this by g</u> (as $W = mg$, see page 348).

For more on how light gates work have a look at page 399.

6) The <u>acceleration</u>, *a*, is found by following this method:

- Mark a <u>starting line</u> on the table the trolley is on. This is so that the trolley always travels the <u>same distance</u> to the light gate.
- Place the trolley on the <u>starting line</u>.
- Hold the trolley so the string is <u>tight</u> and not touching the table. Then <u>release</u> it.
- Record the <u>acceleration</u> measured by the light gate as the trolley passes through it.

This experiment has a lot of steps, so don't speed through it...

Make sure the <u>string</u> is the <u>right length</u> and there's <u>enough space</u> for the hanging masses to <u>fall</u>. There needs to be enough space so that the masses <u>don't</u> hit the floor <u>before</u> the trolley has <u>passed through the light gate fully</u> — if they hit the floor, the force won't be applied the whole way through the trolley's journey, so you won't get an accurate measurement for the <u>acceleration</u>.

Investigating Motion

*Now you know how to set up the **equipment** (p.364) it's time to start looking at **adjusting** your **variables**. Take care with the **method** here — there are some important points you don't want to miss.*

Investigating How **Mass** Affects **Acceleration**

To investigate the effect of mass, you need to <u>change the mass</u> but keep the force <u>the same</u>. Remember, the <u>mass</u> (m) is the mass of the trolley, the hook and any extra masses <u>added together</u>.

1) The force is the <u>weight</u> of the <u>hook and any masses on the hook</u>.

2) So, keep the mass <u>on the hook</u> the <u>same</u>.

3) <u>Add masses</u> to the <u>trolley</u> one at a time to increase the <u>total mass</u> being accelerated.

4) Record the <u>acceleration</u>, *a*, for <u>each total mass</u>, *m*.

5) You should find that as the mass <u>goes up</u>, the acceleration <u>goes down</u>.

6) This <u>agrees</u> with Newton's Second Law — mass and acceleration are <u>inversely proportional</u>.

Investigating How **Force** Affects **Acceleration**

This time, you need to <u>change</u> the force <u>without changing</u> the <u>total mass</u> of the trolley, hook and masses.

1) Start with <u>all</u> the extra masses loaded onto the <u>trolley</u>.

2) Moving the masses <u>from</u> the trolley to the hook will keep the <u>total mass</u>, *m*, the same.

3) But it will <u>increase</u> the force, *F* (the <u>weight</u> of the <u>hook and the masses on the hook</u>).

4) <u>Each time</u> you <u>move</u> a mass, record the <u>new force</u>, and measure the <u>acceleration</u>.

5) You should find that as the force <u>goes up</u>, the acceleration <u>goes up</u>.

6) This <u>agrees</u> with Newton's Second Law — force and acceleration are <u>directly proportional</u>.

Warm-Up & Exam Questions

Now you've gotten yourself on the right side of the law(s of motion), it's time to put your knowledge on trial. Have a go at the warm-up questions first and then knuckle down to those exam questions.

Warm-Up Questions

1) True or false? The resultant force acting on an accelerating object must have a magnitude greater than zero.
2) Boulders A and B are accelerated at 2 m/s². Boulder A required a force of 70 N, and Boulder B required a force of 95 N. Which boulder has a greater mass?
3) True or false? Two interacting objects exert equal and opposite forces on each other.

Exam Questions

1 A ball hits a stationary cricket bat. The bat exerts a force of 520 N on the ball when they are in contact. The cricket bat has a mass of 1.6 kg and the ball has a mass of 160 g.

Grade 3-4

1.1 State the force that the ball exerts on the bat.

[1 mark]

1.2 Complete the sentence below using words from the box.

less than	the same as	greater than

The acceleration of the ball will be .... that of the bat because it has a smaller mass.

[1 mark]

1.3 Use the following formula to calculate the size of the acceleration of the bat when the ball hits it.
Force = mass × acceleration

[3 marks]

2 The camper van shown in **Figure 1** has a mass of 2500 kg. It is driven along a straight, level road at a constant speed of 90.0 kilometres per hour.

Grade 4-5

Figure 1

90.0 km/h

2500 kg

2.1 State the resultant force acting on the camper van.

[1 mark]

2.2 The camper van slows down. What changes from those below could have caused the van to slow down? Tick **two** boxes.

☐ The driving force decreases

☐ The wind blowing in the opposite direction to the van's movement increases

☐ The drag acting on the van decreases

☐ The van becomes lighter

[2 marks]

2.3 The camper van slows down with a deceleration of 1.4 m/s². What is the resultant force acting on the van during its deceleration? Give the direction of the resultant force.

[3 marks]

Stopping Distance and Thinking Distance

*This page is all about cars, but unfortunately it's not as fun as it sounds... It's even better — it's about **safety**...*

Stopping Distance = Thinking Distance + Braking Distance

1) In an emergency, a driver may perform an emergency stop.
2) During an emergency stop, the maximum force is applied by the brakes.
   This is so the vehicle stops in the shortest possible distance.
3) The distance it takes to stop a vehicle in an emergency is its stopping distance. It is found by:

> Stopping Distance = Thinking Distance + Braking Distance

4) Thinking distance is how far the vehicle travels during the driver's reaction time.
5) The reaction time is the time between the driver seeing a hazard and applying the brakes.
6) Braking distance is the distance taken to stop under the braking force (once the brakes are applied).

Stopping Distances for Different Speeds can be Estimated

1) You need to be able to estimate the stopping distance of vehicles.
2) The heavier a vehicle is, or the faster it's travelling, the longer its stopping distance will be.
3) As a guide, typical car stopping distances are: 23 m at 30 mph, 73 m at 60 mph, 96 m at 70 mph.

Stopping Distances Affect Safety

1) The longer it takes to perform an emergency stop, the higher the risk of crashing into whatever's in front.
2) So the shorter a vehicle's stopping distance, the safer it is.
3) You need to be able to describe how different factors can affect the safety of a journey.
4) For example, how driving if you're tired is unsafe. There's more on this below.

Thinking Distance is Determined by the Driver's Reactions

1) Thinking distance is affected by:

   - Your speed — the faster you're going, the further you'll travel during the time you take to react.
   - Your reaction time — the longer your reaction time (p.369), the longer your thinking distance.

2) A driver's reaction times can be affected by tiredness, drugs or alcohol.
3) Distractions can also affect your ability to react.

   - Driving while tired is unsafe as it makes you slower to react.
   - This increases your reaction time, which increases your thinking distance.
   - This means your stopping distance is longer, so you're more likely to crash.

   - Driving above the speed limit is unsafe.
   - You travel further in your reaction time than you would at a lower speed.
   - This increases your thinking (and so stopping) distance.

Braking Distance

*So you know the basics of **stopping distances** now, but how do the brakes actually work to **slow down a car**? Well, it's all down to **friction** and **transferring energy** away from the wheels to the brakes.*

Braking Distance Depends on a Few Different Factors

Braking distance is affected by:

1) Your speed: for a given braking force, the faster a vehicle travels, the longer it takes to stop.
2) Weather or road surface:
   - If there is less grip between a vehicle's tyres and the road, it can cause the vehicle to skid.
   - Skidding increases the braking distance of a car.
   - Water, ice, oil or leaves on the road all reduce grip.

   > Icy conditions increase the chance of skidding. This increases the braking distance, which increases the stopping distance. So more room should be left between cars to be safe.

3) The condition of your tyres:
   - Bald tyres (ones that don't have any tread left) cannot get rid of water in wet conditions.
   - This leads to them skidding on top of the water.
4) How good your brakes are:
   - If brakes are worn, they won't be able to apply as much force.
   - So it takes longer to stop a vehicle travelling at a given speed (see below).

Braking Relies on Friction Between the Brakes and Wheels

1) When the brake pedal is pushed, brake pads are pressed onto the wheels.
2) The brake pads cause friction, which causes work to be done (p.349).
3) Remember, when work is done, energy is transferred (p.285).
4) Energy is transferred from the kinetic energy store of the vehicle to the thermal energy stores of the brakes
5) The brakes increase in temperature.
6) To stop a vehicle, the brakes must transfer all of the energy from the kinetic store, so:

Energy in the vehicle's kinetic energy store = Work done by the brakes
$$\tfrac{1}{2} \times m \times v^2 \qquad = \qquad F \times d$$

mass of the car · speed of car · braking force · braking distance

7) The faster a vehicle is going, the more energy it has in its kinetic energy store.
8) So more work needs to be done to stop it.
9) This means that as the speed of a vehicle increases, the force needed to make it stop within a certain distance also increases.
10) A larger braking force means a larger deceleration.
11) Very large decelerations can be dangerous because they may cause brakes to overheat. This means the brakes won't work as well.
12) Very large decelerations may also cause the vehicle to skid.

The faster a car is travelling, the more work is needed to stop it

Q1 A car with a mass of 1000 kg is travelling in a straight line at a speed of 10 m/s. The driver spots a hazard and applies the brakes. The car is 50 m from the hazard when the brakes are applied. Calculate the minimum braking force required for the car to stop before the hazard.

[5 marks]

Q1 Video Solution

Reaction Times

*Reaction times are an **important factor** in **thinking distances**. They're also super easy to **test** for yourself.*

A Typical **Reaction Time** is **0.2 s – 0.9 s**

1) Everyone's reaction time is different.
2) A typical reaction time is between 0.2 and 0.9 s.
3) You can do simple experiments to investigate your reaction time — more on these below.

You can **Measure** Reaction Times with the **Ruler Drop Test**

1) As reaction times are so short, you haven't got a chance of measuring one with a stopwatch.
2) One way of measuring reaction times is to use a computer-based test. For example, clicking a mouse when the screen changes colour.

Another method to measure reaction times is the ruler drop test:

1) Sit with your arm resting on the edge of a table.
2) Get someone else to hold a ruler so it hangs between your thumb and forefinger, lined up with zero.
3) You may need a third person to be at eye level with the ruler to check it's lined up.
4) Without giving any warning, the person holding the ruler should drop it.
5) Close your thumb and finger to try to catch the ruler as quickly as possible.
6) The measurement on the ruler at the point where it is caught is how far the ruler dropped in the time it took you to react.
7) The longer the distance, the longer the reaction time.
8) You can calculate how long the ruler falls for (the reaction time) because acceleration due to gravity is constant.
9) To find the reaction time, you can use the equation:

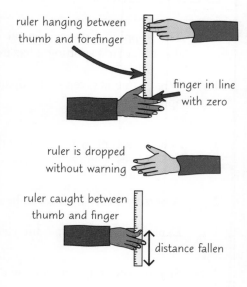

ruler hanging between thumb and forefinger

finger in line with zero

ruler is dropped without warning

ruler caught between thumb and finger

distance fallen

$$t = \frac{\sqrt{2as}}{a}$$

t is the reaction time in seconds, s.
a is the acceleration due to gravity. *a* = 9.8 m/s².
s is how far the ruler fell before it was caught, in metres, m.

You **don't** need to learn this equation. It comes from squishing $v^2 - u^2 = 2as$ and $a = \Delta v \div t$ from p.357 together.

It's hard to do this experiment accurately, but you can do a few things to improve your results.

- Do a lot of repeats and calculate an average reaction time.
- Add a blob of modelling clay to the bottom to help the ruler to fall straight down.
- Make it a fair test — use the same ruler for each repeat, and have the same person dropping it.

The further the ruler falls, the longer the reaction time

Q1 Mark's reaction time is tested using the ruler drop test. He is tested in the early afternoon and at night. In the afternoon, he catches the ruler after it has fallen a distance of 16.2 cm. At night, he catches the ruler after it has fallen 18.5 cm.

Q1 Video Solution

    a) Calculate Mark's reaction time in the afternoon.
       Give your answer to 2 significant figures.   **[5 marks]**

    b) Explain why Mark's thinking distance might be longer
       when driving in the evening.   **[2 marks]**

Warm-Up & Exam Questions

Time to apply the brakes for a second and put your brain through its paces. Try out these questions.
If you can handle these, your exam should be clear of hazards.

Warm-Up Questions

1) Give one factor that can affect thinking distance.
2) What must be added to the thinking distance to find the total stopping distance of a car?
3) Give one reason that the large deceleration of a car can be dangerous.
4) True or false? The larger the braking force, the greater the deceleration of a car.

Exam Questions

1 The stopping distance of a car is the distance covered in the time between the driver first spotting a hazard and the car coming to a complete stop. *(Grade 1-3)*

1.1 What name is given to the distance travelled between the driver first spotting a hazard and then applying the brakes?

[1 mark]

1.2 What is meant by the braking distance of a car?

[1 mark]

2 A person is driving a car in heavy rain. *(Grade 3-4)*

2.1 Explain why heavy rain increases a car's stopping distance.

[1 mark]

2.2 Suggest **one** way a driver can decrease their stopping distance when driving in heavy rain.

[1 mark]

2.3 When a car brakes, work is done. What energy transfer occurs?
Tick **one** box in each row.

	The car's kinetic energy stores	The car's chemical energy stores	The brakes' thermal energy stores	The brakes' elastic energy stores
Energy transferred from	☐	☐	☐	☐
Energy transferred to	☐	☐	☐	☐

[2 marks]

3 A student tries to catch a falling ruler as quickly as possible.
The distance the ruler falls can be used to calculate the student's reaction time.
The student repeats the test three times. Their results are shown below. *(Grade 4-5)*

0.24 s   0.19 s   0.23 s

3.1 Calculate the student's mean reaction time.

[2 marks]

3.2 State **one** way the student could improve their results.

[1 mark]

Wave Basics

*Waves **transfer energy** from one place to another **without** transferring any **matter** (stuff).*

Waves Transfer Energy but not Matter

1) When a wave <u>travels through</u> a medium, the particles of the <u>medium</u> vibrate.

2) A <u>medium</u> is just a fancy word for whatever the wave is <u>travelling through</u> (e.g. water, air).

3) The particles <u>transfer energy</u> between each other as they vibrate (see p.284).

4) <u>BUT</u> overall, the particles stay in the <u>same place</u> — <u>only energy</u> is transferred.

> - For example, if you drop a twig into calm water, <u>ripples</u> spread out. The ripples <u>don't</u> carry the <u>water</u> (or the twig) away with them though.
> - And if you strum a <u>guitar string</u>, the sound waves don't carry the <u>air</u> away from the guitar. If they did, you'd feel a <u>wind</u> whenever there was a sound.

Waves have an Amplitude, Wavelength and Frequency

1) The <u>amplitude</u> of a wave is the <u>maximum displacement</u> of a point on the wave from its <u>undisturbed (rest) position</u>.

2) The <u>wavelength</u> is the distance between <u>one point</u> on a wave and the <u>same point</u> on the <u>next wave</u>. For example, the distance between the <u>trough</u> of one wave and the <u>trough</u> of the wave <u>next to it</u>.

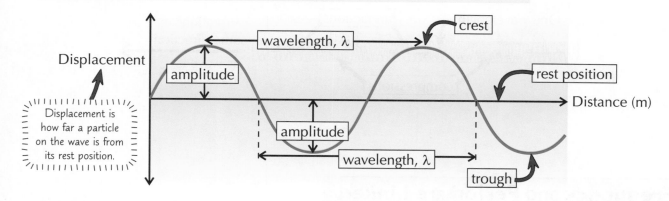

3) <u>Frequency</u> is the <u>number of complete waves</u> passing a certain point <u>each second</u>. Frequency is measured in <u>hertz</u> (Hz). 1 Hz is <u>1 wave per second</u>.

4) <u>Period</u> is the amount of <u>time</u> it takes for <u>one</u> complete wave to <u>pass</u> a certain point.

The only thing a wave transfers is energy...

It's <u>really</u> important that you understand this stuff <u>really</u> well, or the rest of this topic will be a blur. Make sure you can sketch the <u>wave diagram</u> above and can <u>label</u> all the features from memory.

Transverse and Longitudinal Waves

*All waves are either **transverse** or **longitudinal**. Read on to find out more...*

Transverse Waves Have **Perpendicular** Vibrations

1) In transverse waves, the vibrations are perpendicular (at right angles) to the direction of energy transfer.
2) Examples of transverse waves are light (p.378), ripples on water (see p.374) and waves on a string (p.375).
3) A spring wiggled up and down gives a transverse wave:

Longitudinal Waves Have **Parallel** Vibrations

1) In longitudinal waves, the vibrations are in the same direction as the energy transfer.
2) They have compressions (where the particles squish together), and rarefactions (where they spread out).
3) A sound wave is an example of a longitudinal wave.
4) If you push the end of a spring, you get a longitudinal wave:

Frequency and Period are **Linked**

You can find the period of a wave from its frequency:

Period (s) — $T = \dfrac{1}{f}$ — Frequency (Hz)

EXAMPLE

Calculate the period of a wave with a frequency of 2 Hz.

$T = 1 \div f = 1 \div 2 = 0.5$ s

Light waves are transverse and sound waves are longitudinal...

The equation that links period and frequency together is pretty useful — it means that you can always work one out from the other. Make sure you practise using the equation until you're comfortable with it.

Wave Speed

*Measuring the **speed of waves** isn't that simple. It calls for crafty methods...*

Wave Speed = Frequency × Wavelength

1) The <u>wave speed</u> is how fast the <u>wave</u> is moving.
2) It is the speed at which <u>energy is being transferred</u> through the <u>medium</u>.
3) The <u>wave equation</u> applies to <u>all waves</u>:

Wave speed (m/s) ——— $v = f\lambda$ ——— Wavelength (m)

Frequency (Hz)

EXAMPLE   **A radio wave has a frequency of 12 000 000 Hz.**
Find its wavelength. (The speed of radio waves in air is 3×10^8 m/s.)

1) <u>Rearrange</u> the wave speed equation for <u>wavelength</u>. $\lambda = v \div f$
2) Put in the <u>values</u> you've been <u>given</u>. $= (3 \times 10^8) \div (12\ 000\ 000)$
   Watch out — the speed is in <u>standard form</u> (p.19). $= 25$ m

Use an **Oscilloscope** to Measure the **Speed** of **Sound**

1) Connect <u>two microphones</u> to an <u>oscilloscope</u> (a device which shows waves on a screen).
2) Connect a <u>signal generator</u> to a speaker. This will let you generate <u>sound waves</u> at a <u>set frequency</u>.

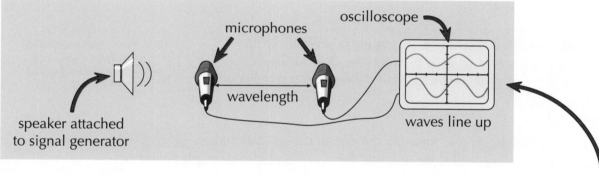

3) Set up the oscilloscope so the <u>waves</u> reaching each microphone are shown <u>separately</u>.
4) Start with <u>both microphones</u> next to the speaker. The waves on the oscilloscope <u>should line up</u>.
5) Slowly <u>move one microphone</u> away. Stop when the two waves <u>line up</u> again on the display.
6) This means the microphones are now <u>exactly one wavelength apart</u>.
7) Measure the <u>distance between the microphones</u> to find the <u>wavelength</u> (λ).
8) Use the formula <u>$v = f\lambda$</u> to find the <u>speed</u> (v) of the <u>sound waves</u> passing through the <u>air</u>.
9) The <u>frequency</u> (f) is whatever you set the <u>signal generator</u> to.
10) The speed of sound in air is around <u>330 m/s</u>, so check your results <u>roughly agree</u> with this.

That was the first of three wave speed practicals to learn...

Make sure you <u>understand</u> each step of that method above — you could be <u>tested</u> on it in the exams.

Q1   A wave has a speed of 0.15 m/s and a wavelength of 7.5 cm.
     Calculate its frequency.   [4 marks]

Q1 Video Solution

Investigating Waves

*Choosing **suitable equipment** means making sure it's **right** for the job. It's important here.*

Measure the **Speed** of **Water Ripples** Using a **Ripple Tank**

1) Attach a <u>signal generator</u> to the <u>ripple tank dipper</u>. Turn on the signal generator to create <u>waves</u>.

Make sure you do this experiment in a darkened room.

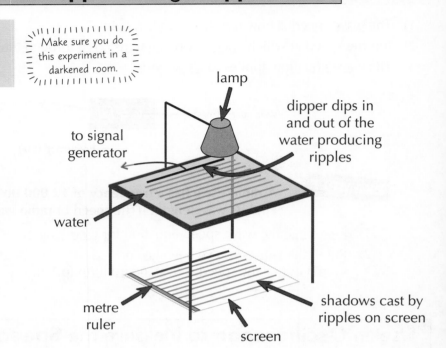

lamp

dipper dips in and out of the water producing ripples

to signal generator

water

metre ruler

shadows cast by ripples on screen

screen

2) Find the <u>frequency</u> of the waves by <u>counting</u> the number of <u>ripples</u> that pass a point in 10 seconds and <u>dividing by 10</u>.

3) Use a <u>lamp</u> to create <u>shadows</u> of the ripples on a screen below the tank. Place a <u>metre ruler</u> beside the shadows.

4) The distance between each shadow line is equal to <u>one wavelength</u>.

5) Measure the wavelength <u>accurately</u> by measuring the <u>distance</u> across <u>10 gaps</u> between the shadow lines. <u>Divide</u> this distance <u>by 10</u> to find the <u>average wavelength</u>.

This is a good method for measuring the wavelength of moving waves or small wavelengths.

6) If you're struggling to measure the distance, you could take a <u>photo</u> of the <u>shadows and ruler</u>, and find the wavelength from the photo instead.

7) Use $v = f\lambda$ to calculate the wave <u>speed</u> of the waves.

8) This set-up is <u>suitable</u> for investigating waves, because it allows you to <u>measure</u> the wavelength without <u>disturbing</u> the waves.

Make sure your measurements are accurate...

You should be careful that the <u>screen</u> beneath the tank is <u>flat</u>, or the shadows will become distorted and difficult to measure properly. You should also make sure that the metre <u>ruler</u> is at a <u>right angle</u> to the shadow wavefronts — if the ruler is skewed then your measured wavelength will be too long.

Investigating Waves

*One more **wave experiment** coming up. This time, it's to do with **waves on strings**.*

You can Use the **Wave Equation** for Waves on **Strings**

In this practical, you create a wave on a string. Again, you use a signal generator, but this time you attach it to a vibration generator which converts the signals to vibrations.

1) Set up the equipment shown below.

2) The vibration generator vibrates at a fixed frequency, set by the signal generator.

3) Turn on the signal generator and the string will start to vibrate.

4) Adjust the frequency of the signal generator until there's a clear wave on the string.

5) To measure the wavelength of these waves accurately:
   - Count how many wavelengths are on the string. Each vibrating loop is half a wavelength.
   - Measure the length of the whole vibrating string.
   - Divide by the number of wavelengths to give the length of one wavelength.

measure this distance

there are 2 wavelengths on the string, so divide the distance by 2

6) The frequency of the wave is whatever the signal generator is set to.

It's ok if you don't have a whole number of wavelengths on the string. If there are 3 loops, there are one-and-a-half wavelengths on the string. Divide the length of the string by 1.5.

7) You can find the speed of the wave using $v = f\lambda$.

8) This set-up is suitable for investigating waves on a string because it's easy to see and measure the wavelength (and frequency).

Learn the methods for all the wave speed practicals...

The experiments on pages 373-375 seem complicated, but they all have a few things in common. First, you set the frequency on the signal generator, then find the length of the resulting wave (this tends to be the fiddly bit). You can then use the equation $v = f\lambda$ to find the wave speed.

Refraction

*Grab a glass of water and put a straw in it. The straw looks like it's **bending**. But it's not magic, it's refraction.*

Refraction — Waves **Changing Direction**

1) When a wave crosses a <u>boundary</u> between two materials it can change direction.
2) This is known as <u>refraction</u>.
3) Waves are <u>only refracted</u> if they meet the boundary <u>at an angle</u>.
4) <u>How much</u> a wave is refracted by depends on the two materials it's passing between.

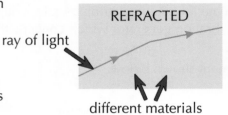

ray of light

REFRACTED

different materials

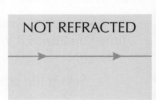

NOT REFRACTED

Ray Diagrams Show the **Path** of a **Wave**

- Rays are <u>straight lines</u> that show the <u>direction</u> a wave is <u>travelling</u> in.
- You can construct a <u>ray diagram</u> for a <u>refracted light ray</u>.

1) Start by drawing the <u>boundary</u> between your two materials.
2) Then draw a dotted line <u>at right angles</u> to the boundary.
3) This line is known as the 'normal' to the boundary. Normal just means 'at right angles'.
4) Next draw the <u>incident ray</u>. This is the ray that <u>meets</u> the <u>boundary</u> at the <u>normal</u>.
5) The angle <u>between</u> the incident <u>ray</u> and the <u>normal</u> is called the <u>angle of incidence</u>.
6) You need to use a <u>protractor</u> to draw or measure it.
7) So to draw an incident ray with an <u>angle of incidence</u> of <u>50°</u>:

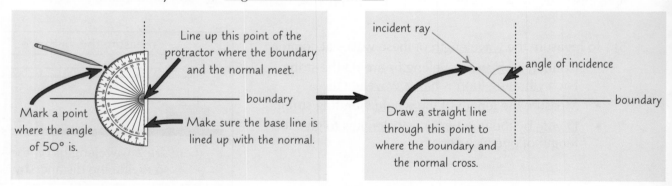

Line up this point of the protractor where the boundary and the normal meet.

Mark a point where the angle of 50° is.

Make sure the base line is lined up with the normal.

boundary

incident ray

angle of incidence

boundary

Draw a straight line through this point to where the boundary and the normal cross.

8) Now draw the <u>refracted</u> ray on the <u>other side</u> of the boundary.
9) <u>The angle of refraction</u> is the angle between the <u>refracted ray</u> and the normal.

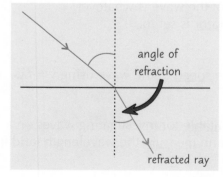

angle of refraction

refracted ray

Hitting a boundary at an angle leads to refraction...

Refraction is a common behaviour of waves, so make sure you really <u>understand</u> it before moving on.

Q1   Draw a ray diagram for a ray of light meeting a boundary at an angle of incidence of 55°, and crossing into a second material with an angle of refraction of 35°.   [3 marks]

Q1 Video Solution

Warm-Up & Exam Questions

Now to check what's actually stuck in your mind over the last few pages...

Warm-Up Questions

1) Waves travel through a medium. Describe one piece of evidence that shows the medium's particles do not travel with the wave.
2) Describe the direction of vibrations in a longitudinal wave.
3) What is the name for the stretched out areas of a longitudinal wave?
4) True or false? A wave entering a new medium along the path of the normal won't be refracted.

Exam Questions

1 **Figure 1** shows a graph of a water wave.

1.1 Give **one** reason why water waves are classified as transverse waves rather than longitudinal waves.

[1 mark]

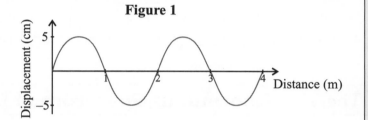

Figure 1

1.2 Give the amplitude of this wave.

[1 mark]

1.3 Give the wavelength of this wave.

[1 mark]

2 **Figure 2** shows how an oscilloscope can be used to display sound waves by connecting microphones to it. Trace 1 shows the sound waves detected by microphone 1 and trace 2 shows the sound waves detected by microphone 2.

Figure 2

A student begins with both microphones at equal distances from the speaker and the signal generator set at a fixed frequency. He gradually moves microphone 2 away from the speaker, which causes trace 2 to move. He stops moving microphone 2 when both traces line up again as shown in **Figure 2**. He then measures the distance between the microphones.

2.1 What does this measurement tell the student about the sound waves detected?

[1 mark]

2.2 Give the equation that links wavelength, frequency and wave speed.

[1 mark]

2.3 With the signal generator set to 50.0 Hz, the distance between the microphones was measured as 6.8 m. Calculate the speed of sound in air. Give the correct unit.

[3 marks]

Electromagnetic Waves

*The **light waves** that we see are just one small part of a big group of **electromagnetic waves**...*

Electromagnetic Waves Transfer Energy

1) Electromagnetic (EM) waves are transverse waves (p.372).

2) They transfer energy from a source to an absorber.

> - A camp fire is a source.
> - It transfers energy to its surroundings by giving out infrared radiation.
> - Infrared radiation is a type of EM wave.
> - These infrared waves are absorbed by objects.
> - Energy is transferred to the objects' thermal energy stores.
> - This causes the objects to warm up.

3) All EM waves travel at the same speed through air or a vacuum (space).

4) This speed is much faster than the speed of sound in air.

Sound waves have a much bigger wavelength and a much lower frequency than light.

There's a Continuous Spectrum of EM Waves

1) EM waves vary in wavelength and frequency.

2) There are EM waves of every wavelength within a certain range.

3) This is known as a continuous spectrum.

4) The spectrum is split up into seven groups based on wavelength and frequency.

RADIO WAVES	MICRO WAVES	INFRA RED	VISIBLE LIGHT	ULTRA VIOLET	X-RAYS	GAMMA RAYS

Long wavelength
Low frequency
→
Short wavelength
High frequency

5) Our eyes can only detect a small part of this spectrum — visible light.

Changes In Atoms Produce the Spectrum of EM Waves

1) EM radiation can be absorbed or produced by changes in atoms and their nuclei.

2) There are lots of different changes that can happen in atoms. For example:
   - Electrons can move between energy levels in atoms (see p.335).
   - Changes in the nucleus of an atom can create gamma rays (see p.339).

3) Each different change produces or absorbs a different frequency of EM wave.

4) This is why atoms can generate (create) EM waves over a large range of frequencies.

5) It is also why atoms can absorb a range of frequencies.

Study the EM spectrum and wave goodbye to exam stress...

There are a lot of facts to remember here, and you need to know them all. Here's a handy way to remember the order of EM waves: 'Rock Music Is Very Useful for eXperience with Guitars'.

Uses of EM Waves

*EM waves are used for all sorts of stuff — and **radio waves** are definitely the most fun.*
*They make your car **radio** and your **TV** work. Life would be pretty quiet without them.*

Radio Waves are Used Mainly for Communication

1) <u>Radio</u> and <u>TV</u> signals can be sent by radio waves.
2) <u>Very short wavelength</u> signals are used for FM radio and TV.
3) They have to be <u>in direct sight</u> of the receiver when they're sent, with nothing in the way, so they <u>can't</u> travel <u>very far</u>.
4) <u>Longer wavelength</u> radio waves can travel further.
5) They can be used to send radio signals <u>around the world</u>.

Microwaves are Used for Satellites and Cooking

1) Communication with <u>satellites</u> uses microwaves, e.g. for <u>satellite TV</u> and <u>satellite phones</u>.
   - A signal is sent into space to a satellite dish <u>high</u> above the Earth.
   - The satellite <u>sends</u> the signal back to Earth in a different direction.
   - A <u>satellite dish</u> on the ground receives the signal.

2) <u>Microwave ovens</u> use microwaves to <u>cook food</u>.
   - The oven gives out microwaves, which are <u>absorbed</u> by <u>water</u> in the food.
   - <u>Energy carried</u> by the microwaves is <u>transferred to</u> the water molecules, causing them to heat up.
   - This causes the rest of the <u>food</u> to heat up and quickly <u>cooks</u> it.

Infrared Radiation Can be Used to Cook and Heat Things

1) <u>Infrared</u> (IR) radiation is <u>given out</u> by all <u>objects</u>.
2) The <u>hotter</u> the object, the <u>more</u> infrared radiation it gives out.
3) When an object <u>absorbs</u> infrared radiation, <u>energy is transferred</u> to the object's <u>thermal energy store</u>. This makes it <u>warm up</u>.
4) Infrared radiation can be <u>used</u> in many ways:

   - <u>Infrared cameras</u> detect IR radiation and create a <u>picture</u>.
   - This is useful for seeing where a house is <u>losing energy</u>.
   - It can also allow you to see <u>hot objects</u> in the <u>dark</u>.

   - Infrared radiation can also be used to <u>warm things</u>.
   - <u>Electric heaters</u> release lots of IR radiation to warm a room.
   - And <u>food</u> can be <u>cooked</u> using infrared radiation.

The different colours mean different amounts of IR radiation are being detected from those areas. Here, the redder the colour, the more infrared radiation is being detected.

The uses of EM waves depend on their properties...

Differences in wavelength, frequency and energy between types of EM wave give them <u>different properties</u>. For example, some types of EM wave are <u>very harmful</u> (see page 383). Luckily, radio waves are considered <u>safe</u> to beam round the world. IR radiation is generally fairly safe, although too much of it will burn you.

More Uses of EM Waves

*And we're still not finished with **uses** of **EM waves** — there's just no end to their talents...*

Fibre Optic Cables Use **Visible Light** to **Send Data**

1) <u>Optical fibres</u> are thin <u>glass or plastic tubes</u> that can <u>carry data</u> over long distances.
2) They're often used to send information to <u>telephones</u> or <u>computers</u>.
3) Information is sent <u>as light rays</u> that bounce <u>back and forth</u> along the fibre.

Glass fibre

Light ray

Ultraviolet Radiation Gives You a **Suntan**

1) When some materials <u>absorb UV light</u>, they <u>give off visible light</u>.
2) This can be pretty useful:

- <u>Energy-efficient lights</u> use <u>UV radiation</u> to produce <u>visible light</u>.
- <u>Security pens</u> can be used to <u>mark</u> property with your name (e.g. laptops).
- Under <u>UV light</u> the ink will <u>glow</u>, but it's <u>invisible</u> otherwise.
- This can help the police find out who <u>stolen property</u> belongs to.

3) <u>Ultraviolet radiation (UV)</u> is also produced by the Sun. It's what gives you a <u>suntan</u>.
4) <u>UV lamps</u> can be used to give people a <u>suntan</u> without the Sun (but this can be <u>dangerous</u>).

X-rays and **Gamma Rays** are Used in **Medicine**

1) X-rays pass <u>easily through flesh</u> but not through <u>bones</u> or <u>metal</u>.
2) This can be used to create an <u>X-ray image</u> to check for <u>broken bones</u>.
3) <u>X-rays</u> can also treat people with <u>cancer</u>.
4) This is because they can <u>kill cells</u>.
   They are aimed at the <u>cancer cells</u> to kill them.

1) <u>Gamma rays</u> (p.339) can also <u>kill cells</u>.
2) They can be used to <u>treat cancer</u> in the same way as X-rays.
3) They can also be used to <u>sterilise</u> (remove germs from) medical equipment.
   The equipment is <u>blasted</u> with <u>gamma rays</u> which <u>kills</u> any <u>living</u> things on it.
4) Gamma rays are also really good at <u>passing through</u> your body.
5) This is why <u>small</u> amounts of them are used in '<u>medical tracers</u>'.
   How they <u>move around</u> the body can be tracked.
   This can tell doctors if <u>organs</u> are working as they should.

Communications, security and imaging — pretty important stuff...

I hate to say it, but go back to page 379 and read all of the <u>uses</u> for EM waves again to really <u>learn</u> them.

Investigating IR Radiation

*Time for another **Required Practical**. In this one, you'll meet a fun, new piece of kit called a **Leslie cube**. Read on to find out more about how you can use this equipment to investigate **infrared radiation emissions**.*

Different Surfaces Emit Different Amounts of IR Radiation

1) The amount of <u>infrared radiation</u> an object gives out depends on its <u>temperature</u> — see p.379.

2) It also depends on its <u>surface</u>.

3) This includes how <u>rough</u> or <u>shiny</u> it is, and its <u>colour</u>.

4) You can investigate <u>how much</u> IR radiation different surfaces emit using a <u>Leslie cube</u>.

5) A <u>Leslie cube</u> is a <u>hollow</u>, metal cube.

6) The <u>four side faces</u> have <u>different surfaces</u>.

7) For example, <u>matt</u> (dull) <u>black paint</u>, matt <u>white paint</u>, <u>shiny</u> metal and <u>dull</u> metal.

You Can Investigate Emission With a Leslie Cube

1) Place an <u>empty Leslie cube</u> on a <u>heat-proof</u> mat. <u>Draw</u> a square around the cube that is 10 cm from <u>all faces</u> of the cube.

2) <u>Fill</u> the <u>Leslie cube</u> with boiling water and wait for the cube to <u>warm up</u>.

3) Use the square you've drawn to hold an <u>infrared detector</u> 10 cm away from one of the cube's vertical faces. Record the <u>amount of IR radiation</u> it detects.

4) <u>Repeat</u> step 3) for <u>each</u> of the <u>four faces</u>.

5) The face that had the <u>highest reading</u> is giving off the most IR radiation.

6) You should find that the <u>black</u> surface is radiating more IR radiation than the <u>white</u> one. <u>Matt</u> surfaces should give off more than <u>shiny</u> ones.

7) As always, you should <u>repeat</u> the experiment to check your <u>results</u>.

You can feel which face is giving off the most heat...

When doing this experiment, you could also place your hand <u>near</u> each surface of the cube (but not touching, it'll be super hot). You'll be able to feel which surface is giving off <u>more infrared radiation</u>.

Investigating IR Absorption

*Have you ever noticed that wearing **black clothes** on a **hot day** makes you feel really warm?*
*Turns out there's some **science** behind it...*

You Can Investigate **Absorption** with the **Melting Wax Trick**

The amount of infrared radiation <u>absorbed</u> by different materials also depends on the <u>surface</u>.
You can do an experiment to show this.

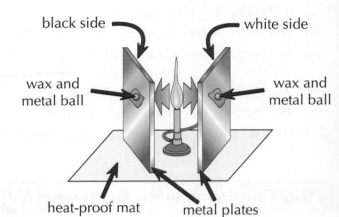

black side → ← white side

wax and metal ball →

← wax and metal ball

heat-proof mat

metal plates

1) You'll need a <u>Bunsen burner</u>, <u>candle wax</u>, <u>metal plates</u> and <u>metal balls</u>.

2) The metal plates should be identical except their <u>back surface</u>, e.g. one plate will have a <u>black back</u>, and the other will have a <u>white back</u>.

3) Place the Bunsen burner on a <u>heat-proof mat</u>.

4) Stick a <u>metal ball</u> to each <u>identical side</u> of the metal plates with hot <u>candle wax</u>.

5) Leave the candle wax to <u>cool</u>. The wax will harden and hold the ball in place.

6) Then face the <u>back</u> of these plates towards the <u>flame</u>. They should both be the <u>same distance</u> away from the flame.

7) Record which ball <u>falls first</u>.

Explaining the **Results**

1) The plates absorb <u>infrared radiation</u> given out by the <u>Bunsen burner</u>.
2) <u>Energy is transferred</u> to the <u>thermal energy stores</u> of the candle wax.
3) The candle wax starts to <u>melt</u>, causing the <u>balls to fall</u>.
4) The <u>ball</u> will fall <u>quicker</u> from the plate that is <u>better</u> at absorbing <u>infrared radiation</u>.
5) You should find that the ball on the plate with the <u>black back</u> falls first.
6) This means the black surface was <u>better</u> at <u>absorbing infrared radiation</u> than the white surface.

 PRACTICAL TIP

Make sure you work safely during this practical...

You need to be <u>really careful</u> when handling the <u>hot objects</u> in this practical — make sure you use <u>protective gloves</u>. You should also <u>turn off</u> the Bunsen burner when it's not in use.

Dangers of Electromagnetic Waves

*Okay, so you know how **useful** electromagnetic radiation can be — well, it can also be pretty **dangerous**.*

Some **EM Radiation** Can be **Harmful** to **People**

1) When EM radiation enters <u>living tissue</u> — like <u>you</u> — it can be <u>dangerous</u>.
2) <u>High frequency</u> waves like <u>UV</u>, <u>X-rays</u> and <u>gamma rays</u> can all cause <u>lots of damage</u>.
3) <u>UV radiation</u> damages surface cells.
4) This can lead to <u>sunburn</u> and can cause <u>skin</u> to <u>age faster</u> than it should.
5) Some more serious effects are <u>blindness</u> and a <u>higher risk of skin cancer</u>.
6) <u>X-rays</u> and <u>gamma rays</u> are types of <u>ionising radiation</u>. This means they can <u>knock electrons off atoms</u>, p.337.
7) This can <u>destroy</u> cells or <u>mutate</u> (change) genes. This can cause <u>cancer</u>.

You Can **Measure Risk** Using the **Radiation Dose** in **Sieverts**

1) UV radiation, X-rays and gamma rays can all be <u>useful</u> as well as <u>harmful</u> (see page 380).
2) <u>Radiation dose</u> (measured in <u>sieverts</u>) is a measure of the <u>risk</u> of harm from the body being exposed to radiation.
3) The risk depends on the <u>total amount of radiation</u> absorbed <u>and</u> how <u>harmful</u> the <u>type</u> of radiation is.
4) A sievert is pretty big, so <u>millisieverts</u> (mSv) are often used. <u>1000 mSv = 1 Sv</u>.

Risk can be **Different** for **Different Parts** of the **Body**

1) A CT scan uses <u>X-rays</u> to create a detailed picture of inside a patient's body.
2) The table shows the <u>radiation dose</u> received by two <u>different parts</u> of a patient's body when having CT scans.

	Radiation dose (mSv)
Head	2.0
Chest	8.0

3) You can see that the radiation dose from a <u>chest scan</u> is <u>4 times larger</u> than from a <u>head scan</u> — <u>(2.0 mSv × 4 = 8.0 mSv)</u>.
4) Remember, radiation dose measures the <u>risk</u> of harm.
5) This means that if a patient has a CT scan on their <u>chest</u>, they are <u>four times more likely</u> to be harmed than if they have a <u>head</u> scan.

The risks and benefits must be weighed up...

<u>Ionising radiation</u> can be <u>dangerous</u>, but the risk can be worth taking. <u>X-ray machines</u> used to be installed in shoe shops for use in <u>shoe fittings</u>. They were removed when people realised X-rays were harmful and the <u>risks far outweighed</u> the <u>benefits</u> of using X-rays rather than tape measures...

Warm-Up & Exam Questions

There are lots of electromagnetic waves — you never know which ones might come up in the exams so make sure you know about all of them. See how much you can remember by trying these questions.

Warm-Up Questions

1) Which type of EM wave has the highest frequency?
2) How many types of EM wave are there?
3) How are gamma rays created?
4) Give one use of infrared radiation.
5) Describe two effects that ultraviolet exposure has on the skin.

Exam Questions

1 Optical fibres have many practical uses. (Grade 1-3)

Which type of electromagnetic wave is typically transmitted in optical fibres?

☐ radio waves   ☐ microwaves

☐ visible light   ☐ X-rays

[1 mark]

2 **Figure 1** shows an image of the bones in a patient's foot. (Grade 1-3)

Figure 1

2.1 Which type of EM radiation could have been used to produce this image?

☐ radio waves   ☐ visible light

☐ microwaves   ☐ X-rays

[1 mark]

2.2 Give **one** risk to the patient from being exposed to this type of radiation.

[1 mark]

3 Some satellite signals are microwaves. (Grade 4-5)

3.1 Which of the following is high-frequency microwave radiation closest in frequency to?

☐ high-frequency ultraviolet   ☐ low-frequency visible light

☐ high-frequency radio waves   ☐ low-frequency infrared

[1 mark]

3.2 Do microwave signals travel faster in a vacuum than radio signals?
Explain your answer.

[1 mark]

Exam Questions

PRACTICAL

4   A student uses four identical beakers to investigate the infrared radiation emitted by different surfaces.

He wraps a piece of card around each beaker. Each piece of card has a different surface.

The student fills the beakers with boiling water and places a thermometer next to each one, as shown in **Figure 2**. He then records the temperature increase measured by each thermometer after two minutes.

Figure 2

4.1   Name **one** control variable for this experiment.

[1 mark]

4.2   Name **one** safety precaution that needs to be taken in this experiment.

[1 mark]

Figure 3 shows the reading on a thermometer after it has been placed next to one of the beakers. The scale on the thermometer is in °C.

4.3   Write down the temperature shown on the thermometer. Give your answer to the nearest °C.

[1 mark]

Figure 3

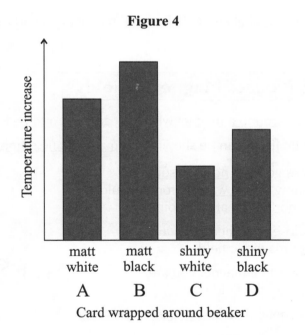

Figure 4

The student's results are displayed in **Figure 4**.

4.4   Some of the surfaces used in the experiment were shiny and others were matt (not shiny). Draw a conclusion from the data in **Figure 4** about how this characteristic affects infrared radiation emission.

[1 mark]

4.5   Suggest **one** way that the experiment could be made more accurate.

[1 mark]

Magnetism

*I think magnetism is an **attractive** subject, but don't get **repelled** by the exam — **revise**.*

Magnets Exert **Forces** on Each Other

1) All magnets have a <u>north</u> (or <u>north seeking</u>) <u>pole</u> and a <u>south</u> (or <u>south seeking</u>) <u>pole</u>.

2) When two magnets are close, they exert a <u>non-contact force</u> on each other.

3) Two poles that are the <u>same</u> (<u>like poles</u>) <u>repel</u> each other.

> Objects don't need to be touching for a non-contact force to act between them — see p.347.

4) Two <u>different</u> (<u>unlike</u>) poles <u>attract</u> each other.

5) There are also forces between magnets and <u>magnetic materials</u>. These forces are <u>always attractive</u>.

6) <u>Iron</u>, <u>steel</u>, <u>nickel</u> and <u>cobalt</u> are all magnetic materials.

Magnets Produce **Magnetic Fields**

1) The area <u>around a magnet</u> where it can exert a <u>force</u> is its <u>magnetic field</u>.

2) Magnetic fields can be shown with <u>magnetic field lines</u>.

3) The lines go from <u>north to south</u>. They show <u>which way</u> the force would push a <u>north pole</u> at that point.

4) Lines <u>closer together</u> mean a <u>stronger</u> magnetic field.

5) The <u>closer</u> to a magnet you are, the <u>stronger</u> the field is.

6) The magnetic field is <u>strongest</u> at the <u>poles</u>.

7) This means the magnetic <u>force</u> is strongest here too.

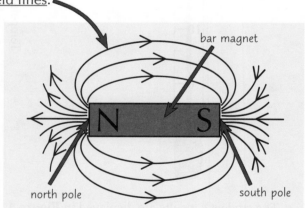

bar magnet

north pole   south pole

Remember magnetic field lines go from north to south...

You can see the shape of a <u>magnetic field</u> using <u>iron filings</u>. They give you a pretty pattern but they don't show you the <u>direction</u> of the <u>magnetic field</u>. That's where compasses really shine — there's more on using compasses to investigate magnetic fields on the next page.

Magnetism

*Compasses aren't just useful when you're lost up a hill. They're also great tools to use to **plot** a **magnetic field**.*

A **Compass** Shows the **Direction** of a Magnetic Field

1) The <u>needle</u> of a <u>compass</u> is a tiny <u>bar magnet</u>. It <u>points</u> in the <u>direction</u> of any <u>magnetic field</u> that it's in.

2) So you can use a <u>compass</u> to plot magnetic field patterns:

- <u>Draw around</u> a magnet on a <u>piece of paper</u>.
- Put a <u>compass</u> by the magnet.
- <u>Mark</u> the <u>direction</u> the compass needle points in by drawing <u>a dot at each end</u> of the needle.
- <u>Move</u> the compass so that the <u>tail end</u> of the needle is where the <u>tip</u> of the needle was before.
- Repeat this lots of times. <u>Join up</u> all the marks. You will end up with a <u>drawing</u> of one <u>field line</u>.

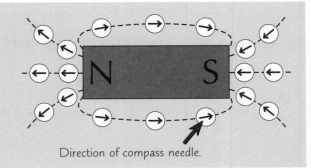

Direction of compass needle.

3) When they're not <u>near</u> a magnet, compasses <u>always point north</u>.

4) This is because they point in the direction of the <u>Earth's magnetic field</u>.

5) So the <u>inside</u> (<u>core</u>) of the Earth must be <u>magnetic</u>.

Magnets Can be **Permanent** or **Induced**

1) <u>Permanent</u> magnets create their <u>own</u> magnetic field.

2) An <u>induced</u> magnet <u>turns into</u> a magnet when it's put into another magnetic field.

3) When you <u>take away</u> the magnetic field, induced magnets quickly <u>stop being magnets</u>. A fancy way to say this is to say that they <u>lose their magnetism</u> (or most of it).

4) Permanent magnets and induced magnets <u>always attract</u> each other.

Electromagnetism

*A **magnetic field** is also found around a **wire** that has a **current** passing through it.*

A **Current** Creates a Magnetic Field

1) A <u>current</u> flowing through a <u>wire</u> creates a <u>magnetic field</u>.

2) You can see this by placing a <u>compass</u> near to the wire.
The compass will <u>move</u> to point in the <u>direction of the field</u>.

3) You can use this to <u>draw the field</u>, just like on the previous page.

4) The field is made up of <u>circles</u> around the wire (see below).

5) You can also use the <u>right-hand thumb rule</u> to quickly work out which way the field goes:

<u>The Right-Hand Thumb Rule</u>
- Point your <u>right thumb</u> in the direction of <u>current</u>.
- <u>Curl</u> your fingers.
- The direction of your <u>fingers</u> is the direction of the <u>field</u>.

6) Reversing (swapping) the <u>direction</u> of the <u>current</u> reverses the direction of the <u>magnetic field</u>.

7) The <u>closer</u> to the wire you are, the <u>stronger</u> the magnetic field gets.

8) And the <u>larger</u> the <u>current</u> through the wire is, the <u>stronger</u> the field is.

Just point your thumb in the direction of the current...

...and your fingers show the direction of the field. Remember, it's always your <u>right thumb</u>.

Q1   Draw the magnetic field for a current-carrying wire.   [2 marks]

Q1 Video Solution

Topic P7 — Magnetism and Electromagnetism

Solenoids

Electric currents can create **magnetic fields** *(see previous page). We can use this effect to make magnets that can be switched on and off — these are* **electromagnets** *(which are made using* **solenoids**).

A **Solenoid** is a Coil of Wire

1) If you <u>wrap</u> a wire into a <u>coil</u> it's called a <u>solenoid</u>.

2) The magnetic field <u>inside</u> a solenoid is <u>strong</u> and <u>uniform</u>.

3) <u>Uniform</u> means the field has the <u>same strength</u> and <u>direction</u> everywhere.

4) The magnetic field <u>outside</u> a coil is just like the one around a <u>bar magnet</u>.

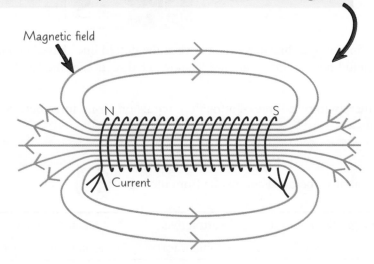

Magnetic field

Current

5) Wrapping a wire into a solenoid <u>increases the strength</u> of the magnetic field produced by the current in the wire.

   • This is because the <u>field lines</u> around <u>each loop</u> of wire <u>line up</u> with each other.
   • So <u>lots</u> of <u>field lines</u> end up <u>close</u> to each other and pointing in the <u>same direction</u>.
   • The <u>closer together</u> field lines are, the <u>stronger the field</u> is.

6) You can <u>increase</u> the field strength <u>even more</u> by putting a block of <u>iron</u> in the coil.

7) A <u>solenoid with an iron core</u> is called an <u>electromagnet</u>.

Fields around solenoids and bar magnets are the same shape...

Electromagnets pop up in lots of different places — they're used in <u>electric bells</u>, <u>car ignition circuits</u> and some <u>security doors</u>. Electromagnets aren't all the same strength though — how <u>strong</u> they are depends on stuff like the number of <u>turns</u> of wire there are and the <u>size</u> of the <u>current</u> going through the wire.

Warm-Up & Exam Questions

Time to test your knowledge — as usual, make sure you're switched on by doing the warm-up questions, then dive into the exam questions. Don't forget to go back and check up on any bits you can't do.

Warm-Up Questions

1) Draw a diagram to show the magnetic field around a single bar magnet. Indicate its direction with arrows.
2) When using the right-hand thumb rule, what does the direction of your fingers represent?
3) How can you form a solenoid from a current-carrying wire?

Exam Questions

1 A student arranges two magnets as shown in **Figure 1**.

Figure 1

1.1 Magnetic field lines in the shaded region between the dotted lines have been drawn on **Figure 1**. Complete the field lines by adding arrows to show the direction of the field.

[1 mark]

1.2 State whether there will be a force of attraction, repulsion, or no force between the two magnets. Explain your answer.

[2 marks]

2 Complete the sentences below using words from the box.

| magnetic material | attractive | electromagnet |
| repulsive | a contact force | permanent magnet |

Cobalt is an example of a .... The force between

a piece of cobalt and a bar magnet is always ....

[2 marks]

3 A student is investigating magnetic fields. She passes a wire through a horizontal piece of card and connects it in an electrical circuit, as shown in **Figure 2**.

Figure 2

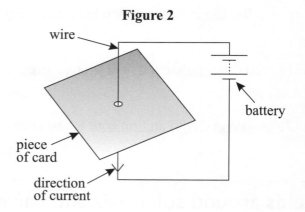

3.1 The student uses a compass to plot the magnetic field lines on the piece of card. Describe the shape and direction of the magnetic field the student will plot.

[2 marks]

3.2 The student forms the wire into a coil. Explain why this leads to an increase in the magnetic field strength.

[2 marks]

Revision Summary for Topics P5-7

That wraps up <u>Topics P5-7</u> — time to put yourself to the test and find out <u>how much you really know</u>.

- Try these questions and <u>tick off each one</u> when you <u>get it right</u>.
- When you're <u>completely happy</u> with a topic, tick it off.

For even more practice, try the Retrieval Quizzes for Topics P5-7 — just scan the QR codes!

Topic P5 — Forces (p.347-369) ☐

1) Explain the difference between scalar and vector quantities.
2) What is the difference between contact and non-contact forces?
3) What is the formula for calculating the weight of an object?
4) What is a resultant force?
5) Why does the temperature of an object increase when it is pushed along a rough surface?
6) Sketch a typical force-extension graph for a spring where its limit of proportionality is exceeded.
7) Describe an experiment you could do to investigate the relationship between force and extension.
8) Estimate the speed of a person walking.
9) Write down the equation that links acceleration, velocity and time.
10) What does the gradient represent for: a) a distance-time graph? b) a velocity-time graph?
11) State Newton's three laws of motion.
12) Describe an experiment that you could do to investigate Newton's Second Law.
13) What is a typical stopping distance of a car travelling at 60 mph?
14) Give two things that affect a person's reaction time.
15) Briefly describe an experiment you could do to compare people's reaction times.

Topic P6 — Waves (p.371-383) ☐

16) What is: a) the amplitude of a wave? b) the wavelength of a wave?
17) What is the difference between transverse and longitudinal waves?
18) Give the units that each quantity in the following equations should be given in:

   a) $\text{period} = \dfrac{1}{\text{frequency}}$ b) $v = f\lambda$

19) Describe an experiment you could do to measure the speed of waves on a string.
20) Sketch a ray diagram showing the refraction of a light ray between two materials.
21) True or false? All electromagnetic waves are transverse.
22) Give a common use of radio waves.
23) Which type of electromagnetic wave is used in suntanning?
24) How could you use a Leslie cube to investigate infrared emission by different surfaces?
25) Name two types of ionising electromagnetic radiation.

Topic P7 — Magnetism and Electromagnetism (p.386-389) ☐

26) Give three magnetic materials.
27) In what direction do magnetic field lines point?
28) Where on a bar magnet is the magnetic force strongest?
29) What is meant by an 'induced magnet'?
30) How can the direction of the magnetic field around a current-carrying wire be reversed?
31) Sketch the shape of the magnetic field around a solenoid.

Measuring Techniques

*Get your lab coat on, it's time to find out about the skills you'll need in **experiments**...*

Mass Should Be Measured Using a Balance

1) To measure mass, put the <u>container</u> you're measuring the substance <u>into</u> on the <u>balance</u>.
2) Set the balance to exactly <u>zero</u>. Then <u>add</u> your substance and <u>read off</u> the <u>mass</u>.
3) If you want to transfer the substance to a new container, you need to make sure that the mass you <u>transfer</u> is the <u>same</u> as the mass you <u>measured</u>. There are different ways you can do this. For example:

> - If you're <u>dissolving</u> a mass of a solid in a solvent to make a <u>solution</u>, you could <u>wash</u> any remaining solid into the new container using the <u>solvent</u>.
> - You could set the balance <u>to zero</u> before you put your <u>weighing container</u> on the balance. Then <u>reweigh</u> the weighing container <u>after</u> you've transferred the substance. Use the <u>difference</u> in mass to work out <u>exactly</u> how much substance you've transferred.

Different Ways to Measure Liquids

1) There are a few methods you might use to transfer a volume of liquid:

> <u>Dropping pipette</u> — Use this if you only want a <u>couple of drops</u> of liquid. It's also used if you <u>don't</u> need an <u>accurate volume</u> of liquid.

> <u>Pipette</u> — Use this if you want an <u>accurate</u> volume of liquid. The <u>pipette filler</u> lets you <u>safely control</u> the amount of liquid you're drawing up.

> <u>Measuring cylinders</u> — These come in many different <u>sizes</u>. You need to use one that's the <u>right size</u> for the measurement you want to make (you don't want one that's <u>too big</u>).

pipette filler

10 cm³

bottom of the meniscus

2) To measure the volume of a liquid, read the volume from the <u>bottom</u> of the <u>meniscus</u> (the curved upper surface of the liquid) when it's at <u>eye level</u>.

You Can Measure Gas Volumes

There are a few ways you can measure the volume of a gas:

1) <u>Gas syringe</u> — this is the <u>most accurate</u> way to measure gas volume.

gas syringe

collected gas

delivery tube

reaction mixture

> - Make sure the gas syringe is the <u>right size</u> for your measurements.
> - Make sure the plunger moves <u>smoothly</u>.
> - Read the volume from the <u>scale</u> on the syringe.

2) <u>Upturned measuring cylinder</u> filled with <u>water</u> — read more about this on page 237.
3) <u>Counting the bubbles</u> produced or measuring the <u>length</u> of a <u>gas bubble</u> drawn along a tube (see p.88).

> - These methods are <u>less accurate</u>.
> - But they will give you <u>results</u> that you can <u>compare</u>.

Always make sure your equipment is <u>sealed</u> so no gas can escape.
This will make your results more <u>accurate</u>.

Measuring Techniques

Eureka Cans Measure the Volumes of Solids

1) A <u>eureka can</u> is a <u>beaker with a spout</u>.

2) It's used with a <u>measuring cylinder</u> to find the <u>volume</u> of an <u>irregularly shaped solid object</u> (p.329).

3) Here are a few things you need to do when you <u>use</u> one:

eureka can

starting water level is just below spout

measuring cylinder

object

- Fill it with water so the water level is <u>above the spout</u>.
- Let the water <u>drain</u> from the spout, leaving the water level <u>just below</u> the start of the spout. (This means <u>all</u> the water moved by an object goes into the measuring cylinder.)
- After adding the object, wait until the spout has <u>stopped dripping</u> before measuring the volume. This will give you a more <u>accurate</u> result.

Measure Most Lengths with a Ruler

1) Make sure you <u>choose</u> the <u>right ruler</u> to measure length:
   - In most cases a <u>centimetre ruler</u> can be used.
   - <u>Metre rulers</u> are handy for <u>large</u> distances.
   - <u>Micrometers</u> are used for measuring <u>tiny</u> things (e.g. the <u>diameter of a wire</u>).

2) The ruler should always be <u>alongside</u> what you want to measure.

3) It may be <u>tricky</u> to measure just <u>one</u> of something (e.g. water ripples, p.374). Instead, you can measure the length of <u>ten</u> of them together. Then <u>divide by ten</u> to find the <u>length of one</u>.

4) You might need to take <u>lots of measurements</u> of the <u>same</u> object (e.g. a spring). If so, make sure you always measure from the <u>same point</u> on the object. Draw or stick small <u>markers</u> onto the object to line your ruler up against.

ruler   spring

marker

5) Make sure the ruler and the object are always at <u>eye level</u> when you take a reading.

Use a Protractor to Find Angles

1) Place the <u>middle</u> of the protractor on the <u>pointy bit</u> of the angle.

2) <u>Line up</u> the <u>base line</u> of the protractor with one line of the angle.

3) Use the <u>scale</u> on the protractor to measure the angle of the other line.

4) Use a <u>sharp pencil</u> to draw lines at an angle (e.g. in ray diagrams). This helps to <u>reduce errors</u> when measuring the angles.

base line

Measure Temperature Using a Thermometer

bulb   thermometer

1) Make sure the <u>bulb</u> of your thermometer is <u>completely under the surface</u> of the substance.

2) If you're taking a <u>starting temperature</u>, you should wait for the temperature to <u>stop changing</u>.

3) Read your measurement off the <u>scale</u> at <u>eye level</u>.

You May Have to Measure the Time Taken for a Change

stopwatch

1) You should use a <u>stopwatch</u> to <u>time</u> experiments. These measure to the nearest <u>0.1 s</u>.

2) Always make sure you <u>start</u> and <u>stop</u> the stopwatch at exactly the right time.

3) You can set an <u>alarm</u> on the stopwatch so you know exactly when to stop an experiment or take a reading.

Practical Skills

Measuring Techniques

There are **Different Methods** for **Measuring pH**

1) <u>Indicator solutions</u> can be used to estimate pH. Add a <u>couple of drops</u> of the indicator to the solution you want to test. It will <u>change colour</u> depending on if it's in an <u>acid</u> or an <u>alkali</u> (see p.215).

2) There are also <u>paper indicators</u>. These are <u>strips of paper</u> that contain indicator.
If you <u>spot</u> some solution onto indicator paper, the paper will <u>change colour</u> to show the pH.

litmus paper

- <u>Litmus paper</u> turns <u>red</u> in acidic conditions and <u>blue</u> in alkaline conditions.
- <u>Universal indicator paper</u> can be used to <u>estimate</u> the pH based on its colour.

3) Indicator paper is <u>useful</u> when:

- You <u>don't</u> want to change the colour of <u>all</u> of the substance.
- The substance is <u>already</u> coloured (so it might <u>hide</u> the colour of the indicator).
- You want to find the pH of a <u>gas</u> — hold a piece of <u>damp indicator paper</u> in a <u>gas sample</u>.

4) <u>pH probes</u> measure pH <u>electronically</u> (see page 217). They are more <u>accurate</u> than indicators.

You Can **Measure** the **Size** of a **Single Cell**

When viewing <u>cells</u> under a <u>microscope</u>, you might need to work out their <u>size</u>. To work out the size of a <u>single cell</u>:

1) Place a <u>clear, plastic ruler</u> on <u>top</u> of your microscope <u>slide</u>.
2) <u>Clip</u> the <u>ruler</u> and <u>slide</u> onto the <u>stage</u>.
3) Select the <u>objective lens</u> that gives an overall magnification of <u>x 100</u>.
4) Use the <u>coarse adjustment knob</u> and the <u>fine adjustment knob</u> to see a <u>clear image</u> of the cells.
5) <u>Move</u> the ruler so that the cells are <u>lined up</u> along <u>1 mm</u>.
6) <u>Count</u> the <u>number of cells</u> along this <u>1 mm sample</u>.
7) 1 mm = 1000 µm. So you can <u>calculate</u> the <u>size</u> of a <u>single cell</u> using this <u>formula</u>:

You can read all about using a microscope on pages 20-21.

1 mm

cells   ruler marking

$$\text{length of cell (µm)} = \frac{1000 \text{ µm}}{\text{number of cells counted in sample}}$$

EXAMPLE

Under a microscope, 4 cells were counted in 1 mm.
Calculate the size of one cell. Give your answer in µm.

1 mm is the <u>same</u> as 1000 µm, so you just need to put the <u>number of cells</u> into the formula. $\text{length of cell (µm)} = \dfrac{1000 \text{ µm}}{4} = 250 \text{ µm}$

PRACTICAL TIP

You might have to bend down a little...

Whether you're reading off a ruler, a pipette or a measuring cylinder, make sure you take all readings at <u>eye level</u>. And, if you're taking a reading for a volume, make sure you measure from the bottom of the <u>meniscus</u> (that's from the dip in the curved surface at the top of the liquid).

Safety and Ethics

Before you start any experiment, you need to know what **safety measures** you should be taking. They depend on your **method**, your **equipment** and the **chemicals** you're using.

To Make Sure You're **Working Safely** in the **Lab** You Need to...

1) Wear <u>sensible clothing</u> (e.g. shoes that will protect your feet from spillages). Also:

- Wear a <u>lab coat</u> to protect your <u>skin</u> and <u>clothing</u>.
- Wear <u>safety goggles</u> to protect your <u>eyes</u>, and <u>gloves</u> to protect your <u>hands</u>.

2) Be aware of <u>general safety</u> in the lab. E.g. don't touch any <u>hot equipment</u>.

3) Follow any <u>instructions</u> that your teacher gives you <u>carefully</u>.

4) <u>Chemicals</u> and <u>equipment</u> can be <u>hazardous</u> (dangerous). E.g. some chemicals are <u>flammable</u> (they <u>catch fire easily</u>) — this means you must be careful <u>not</u> to use a <u>Bunsen burner</u> near them.

5) Here are some <u>tips</u> for working with <u>chemicals</u> and <u>equipment</u> safely...

Working with chemicals

1) Make sure you're working in an area that's <u>well ventilated</u> (has a good flow of air).
2) If you're doing an experiment that produces nasty <u>gases</u> (such as chlorine), carry out the experiment in a <u>fume hood</u>. This means the gas <u>can't escape</u> out into the room you're working in.
3) Never <u>touch</u> any chemicals (even if you're wearing gloves):
- Use a <u>spatula</u> to transfer <u>solids</u> between containers.
- Carefully <u>pour</u> liquids between containers using a <u>funnel</u>. This will help <u>prevent spillages</u>.
4) Be careful when you're <u>mixing</u> chemicals, as a reaction might occur. E.g. if you're <u>diluting</u> a liquid, always add the <u>concentrated substance</u> to the <u>water</u>. This stops it getting <u>hot</u>.

Working with equipment

1) Use <u>clamp stands</u> to stop masses and equipment falling.
2) Make sure <u>masses</u> are <u>not too heavy</u> (so they <u>don't break</u> the equipment they're used with).
3) Use <u>pulleys</u> that are <u>not too long</u> (so hanging masses <u>don't hit the floor</u> during the experiment).
4) Let hot materials <u>cool</u> before moving them. Or wear <u>insulated gloves</u> while handling them.
5) If you're using an <u>immersion heater</u>, you should always let it <u>dry out</u> in air. This is just in case any liquid has <u>leaked</u> inside the heater.
6) When working with electronics, make sure you use a <u>low voltage</u> and <u>current</u>. This prevents the wires <u>overheating</u>. It also stops <u>damage to components</u>.

You Need to Think About **Ethical Issues**

Any <u>organisms</u> that you use in your experiments need to be treated <u>safely</u> and <u>ethically</u>. This means:
1) Animals should be <u>handled carefully</u>.
2) Any captured <u>wild animals</u> should be <u>returned to their habitat</u> after the experiment.
3) Any animals <u>kept</u> in the <u>lab</u> should be <u>well cared for</u>. E.g. they should have <u>plenty of space</u>.
4) Other <u>students</u> that <u>take part</u> in any experiment should be <u>happy</u> to do so.

BEWARE — hazardous experiments about...

<u>Before</u> you carry out an experiment, it's important to consider all of the <u>hazards</u>. They can be anything from <u>chemicals</u> to <u>sharp objects</u> to <u>heating equipment</u>. Whatever the hazard, make sure you know all the <u>safety precautions</u> you should follow to keep yourself, and others, safe.

Setting Up Experiments

Setting up the equipment for an experiment in the right way is **important**. *Learn these set-ups...*

You Can **Identify** the **Products** of Electrolysis

There's more about electrolysis on p.223-226.

1) When you electrolyse a salt solution:

   - At the cathode, you'll get a pure metal coating the electrode OR bubbles of hydrogen gas.
   - At the anode, you'll get bubbles of oxygen gas OR a halogen.

2) You may have to do some tests to find out what's been made.

3) To do this, you need to set up the equipment correctly to collect any gas that's produced. The easiest way to collect the gas is in a test tube.

4) Here's how to set up the equipment...

upside down test tube filled with solution

gas produced at electrodes collecting inside test tubes

electrodes (where gas is made)

power supply

The tests for gases are described on page 259.

electrolyte solution

Set Up a **Potometer** to **Measure Transpiration Rate**

1) A potometer is a special piece of equipment.

2) You set it up as shown in the diagram. ➡

3) You can use a potometer to estimate transpiration rate (see page 69). Here's what you do:

   1) Record the starting position of the air bubble.
   2) Start a stopwatch.
   3) As the plant takes up water, the air bubble gets sucked along the tube.
   4) Record how far the air bubble moves in a set time.
   5) Then you can estimate the transpiration rate.

Water

Tap is shut off during experiment.

Water moves this way.

Air bubble

Bubble moves this way.

Beaker of water.

Capillary tube with a scale

 EXAMPLE

A potometer was used to estimate the transpiration rate of a plant cutting. The bubble moved 25 mm in 10 minutes. Estimate the transpiration rate.

To estimate the transpiration rate, divide the distance the bubble moved by the time taken.

$$\text{Transpiration rate} = \frac{\text{distance bubble moved}}{\text{time taken}} = \frac{25 \text{ mm}}{10 \text{ min}}$$

$$= 2.5 \text{ mm/min}$$

Setting Up Experiments

You Can **Collect** a **Gas** in a **Measuring Cylinder**

1) You can use a <u>measuring cylinder</u> turned <u>upside down</u> and filled with <u>water</u> to <u>collect gas</u>.

2) Then you can <u>measure</u> the <u>gas volume</u>. Here's how you do it:

1) <u>Set up</u> the <u>equipment</u> like in the <u>diagram</u>.
2) Record the <u>starting level</u> of the water in the measuring cylinder.
3) Any gas from the reaction will pass <u>through</u> the delivery tube and <u>into</u> the <u>measuring cylinder</u>.
4) The gas will <u>push the water out</u> of the measuring cylinder.
5) Record the <u>end level</u> of water in the measuring cylinder.
6) Calculate the <u>volume</u> of gas produced — <u>subtract</u> the <u>end level</u> of water from the <u>starting level</u> of water.

Make sure the delivery tube is inside the measuring cylinder. This stops the gas escaping out into the air.

3) You can use the method above to collect a <u>gas sample</u> to <u>test</u>.
   - Use a <u>test tube</u> instead of a measuring cylinder.
   - When the test tube is full of gas, you can <u>put a bung in it</u>. This lets you <u>store</u> the gas for later.

Make Sure You Can **Draw Diagrams** of Your Equipment

1) Your <u>method</u> should include a <u>labelled diagram</u> of how your equipment will be <u>set up</u>.
2) Use <u>scientific drawings</u> — each piece of equipment is drawn as if you're looking at it <u>from the side</u>.
3) For example:

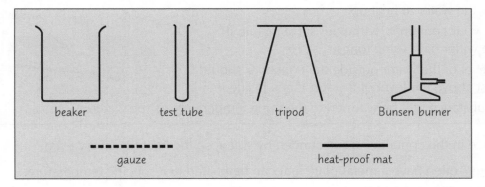

4) The <u>beaker</u> and <u>test tube</u> above <u>aren't sealed</u>. To show them <u>sealed</u>, draw a <u>bung</u> in the top.

These simple diagrams are clear and easy to draw...

Have a go at <u>drawing diagrams</u> of the experimental set-ups on these last few pages. It'll give you some practice at doing them and you can revise how to set up the experiments as well.

Practical Skills

Heating Substances

*You need to be able to decide on the **best** and **safest** method for heating a substance...*

Bunsen Burners Heat Things Quickly

Here's how to <u>use</u> a Bunsen burner...

splint

Heat-proof mat

Hole is closed

to gas

Hottest part of the flame

Hole is open

to gas

1) Connect the Bunsen burner to a <u>gas tap</u>.
   Check that the <u>hole</u> is <u>closed</u>.

2) Place the Bunsen burner on a <u>heat-proof mat</u>.

3) Light a <u>splint</u> and hold it over the Bunsen burner.

4) Now, <u>turn on</u> the gas.
   The Bunsen burner should light with a <u>yellow flame</u>.

5) <u>Open</u> the <u>hole</u> to turn the flame <u>blue</u>.
   The <u>more open</u> the hole, the <u>hotter</u> the flame.

6) Heat things <u>just above</u> the <u>blue cone</u> — this is the <u>hottest</u> part of the flame.

7) When the Bunsen burner <u>isn't heating</u> anything, <u>close</u> the hole.
   This makes the flame <u>yellow</u> and <u>easy to see</u>.

8) If you're heating a container (with your substance in it) <u>in</u> the flame,
   hold it at the <u>top</u> with a pair of <u>tongs</u>.

9) If you're heating a container <u>over</u> the flame, put a <u>tripod and gauze</u> over the Bunsen burner
   before you light it. Then place the container on the gauze.

Water Baths & Electric Heaters Have Set Temperatures

1) A <u>water bath</u> is a <u>container</u> filled with <u>water</u>. It can be heated to a <u>specific temperature</u>.

2) A <u>simple</u> water bath can be made by heating a <u>beaker of water</u> over a <u>Bunsen burner</u>.
   • The temperature is checked with a <u>thermometer</u>.
   • However, it's <u>hard</u> to keep the temperature of the water <u>constant</u>.

3) An <u>electric water bath</u> will <u>check</u> and <u>change</u> the temperature for you. Here's how you use one:

> • <u>Set</u> the <u>temperature</u> on the water bath.
> • Allow the water to <u>heat up</u>.
> • Place your container (with your substance in it)
>   in the water bath using <u>tongs</u>.
> • The level of the water <u>outside</u> the container should
>   be <u>just above</u> the level of the substance <u>inside</u> it.
> • The substance will be warmed to the <u>same temperature</u> as the water.
>
> A water bath
>
> reaction container
>
> temperature control

The substance in the container is surrounded by water, so the heating is very <u>even</u>.

4) <u>Electric heaters</u> often have a metal <u>plate</u> that can be heated to a <u>specific temperature</u>.
   • Place your container on <u>top</u> of the <u>hot plate</u>.
   • You can heat substances to <u>higher temperatures</u> than you can in a water bath.
     (You <u>can't</u> use a water bath to heat something higher than <u>100 °C</u>.)
   • You have to <u>stir</u> the substance to make sure it's <u>heated evenly</u>.

Bunsen burners are useful, but need to be used in the right way...

When the Bunsen burner <u>isn't heating</u> anything, it's important to <u>close the hole</u>. This turns the flame <u>yellow</u> — that flame isn't as hot and is much <u>easier to spot</u>, so it helps to prevent any burns...

Working with Electronics

Electrical devices are used in loads of experiments. Make sure you know how to use them.

There Are a Few Ways to Measure **Potential Difference** and **Current**

Voltmeters Measure Potential Difference

1) Connect the voltmeter in <u>parallel</u> (p.316) across the component you want to test.
2) The wires that come with a voltmeter are usually <u>red</u> (positive) and <u>black</u> (negative). These go into the red and black coloured <u>ports</u> on the voltmeter.
3) Then read the potential difference from the <u>scale</u> (or from the <u>screen</u> if the voltmeter is digital).

Ammeters Measure Current

1) Connect the ammeter in <u>series</u> (p.314) with the component you want to test.
2) Ammeters usually have <u>red</u> and <u>black</u> ports to show you where to connect your wires.
3) Read off the current shown on the <u>scale</u> (or <u>screen</u>).

Turn your circuit off between readings. This stops wires overheating and affecting your results (page 308).

Multimeters Measure Both

1) <u>Multimeters</u> measure a range of things — usually potential difference, current and resistance.
2) To find <u>potential difference</u>, plug the <u>red</u> wire into the port that has a '<u>V</u>' (for volts).
3) To find the <u>current</u>, use the port labelled '<u>A</u>' (for amps).
4) The <u>dial</u> on the multimeter should then be turned to the <u>relevant section</u> — for example, to measure the <u>current</u> in <u>amps</u>, turn the dial to '<u>A</u>'.
5) The <u>screen</u> will display the value you're measuring.

Light Gates Measure **Time**, **Speed** and **Acceleration**

1) A <u>light gate</u> sends a <u>beam</u> of light from <u>one side</u> of the gate to a <u>detector</u> on the <u>other side</u>.
2) When something passes through the gate, the light beam is <u>interrupted</u>.
3) The gate measures <u>when</u> the beam was interrupted and <u>how long</u> it was interrupted for.
4) Light gates can be connected to a <u>computer</u>.
5) To find the <u>speed</u> of an object, type the <u>length</u> of the object into the computer. The computer will <u>calculate</u> the speed of the object as it passes through the beam.
6) To measure <u>acceleration</u>, use an object that interrupts the signal <u>twice</u>, e.g. a piece of card with a gap cut into the middle.
7) The light gate measures the speed for <u>each section</u> of the object. It uses this to calculate the object's <u>acceleration</u>. This can then be read from the <u>computer screen</u>.
8) Light gates can be used instead of a <u>stop watch</u>. This will <u>reduce the errors</u> in your experiment.

Light gate

Beam of light

Piece of card

Have a look at page 364 for an example of a light gate being used.

PRACTICAL TIP

Don't get your wires in a tangle when you're using circuits...

When you're dealing with <u>voltmeters</u>, <u>ammeters</u> and <u>multimeters</u>, you need to make sure that you <u>wire</u> them into your circuit correctly, otherwise you could mess up your readings. Just remember, the <u>red wires</u> should go into the <u>red ports</u> and the <u>black wires</u> should go into the <u>black ports</u>.

Sampling

*You need to be able to carry out **sampling** that'll give you **non-biased** results. First up why, then how...*

Sampling Should be **Random**

1) When you're investigating a <u>population</u>, it's usually <u>not possible</u> to study <u>every single organism</u> in it.

2) This means that you need to take <u>samples</u> of the population.

3) The samples need to <u>accurately</u> represent the <u>whole population</u>.
   This is so you can use them to <u>draw conclusions</u> about the <u>whole population</u>.

4) To make sure a sample represents the population, it should be <u>random</u>.

Organisms Should Be Sampled At **Random Sites** in an Area

1) <u>Quadrats</u> can be used to take <u>population samples</u> of an organism in an area (see page 147).

2) If you're looking at plant species in a field...

- <u>Divide</u> the field into a <u>grid</u>.
- <u>Label the grid</u> along the bottom and up the side with numbers.
- Use a <u>random number generator</u> (e.g. on a computer or calculator) to select coordinates, e.g. (2,7).
- Place your quadrats at these coordinates to take your <u>samples</u>.

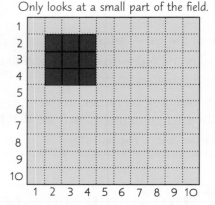

<u>Non-random sampling</u>
Only looks at a small part of the field.

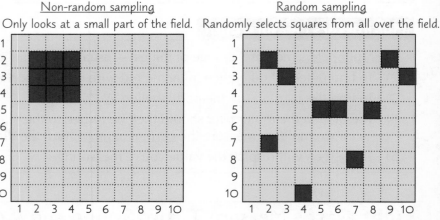

<u>Random sampling</u>
Randomly selects squares from all over the field.

Health Data Should be Taken from **Randomly Selected People**

You need to use <u>random sampling</u> to choose members of the population you're interested in. For example:

A scientist is looking at health data in country X. She wants to know <u>how many</u> people in the country have both <u>Type 2 diabetes</u> and <u>heart disease</u>:

1) <u>Hospital records</u> show that <u>270 196</u> people in the country have Type 2 diabetes.

2) These people are given a <u>number</u> between 1 and 270 196.

3) A <u>random number generator</u> is used to choose the <u>sample group</u>
   — e.g. it selects individuals with the numbers #72 063, #11 822, #193 123, etc.

4) The records of the sample group are used to find the number of people with <u>heart disease</u> in it.

5) The <u>proportion</u> of people in the <u>sample group</u> who have heart disease is worked out.

6) This can be used to <u>estimate</u> the <u>total number</u> of people with Type 2 diabetes who also have heart disease.

Sampling is an important part of an investigation...

Sampling is a really useful way to find out information about the <u>whole population</u> from a <u>smaller group</u>. It's important that the sample is <u>selected randomly</u> though, or the results won't be worth much.

Comparing Results

*Being able to **compare** your results is really important. Here is one way you might do it.*

Percentage Change Allows you to Compare Results

1) When investigating the <u>change</u> in a variable, you may want to <u>compare</u> results that didn't have the <u>same starting value</u>.

- For example, you may want to compare the <u>change in mass</u> of <u>potato cylinders</u> left in different concentrations of <u>sugar solution</u> (see page 32).
- The cylinders probably all had <u>different masses</u> to <u>start with</u>.

2) To do this you can calculate the <u>percentage change</u>. You work it out like this:

$$\text{percentage (\%) change} = \frac{\text{final value} - \text{original value}}{\text{original value}} \times 100$$

3) A <u>positive</u> percentage change means that the value <u>increased</u>.
A <u>negative</u> percentage change means that the value <u>decreased</u>.

EXAMPLE

A student is investigating the effect of the concentration of sugar solution on potato cells. She records the mass of potato cylinders before and after placing them in sugar solutions of different concentrations. The table below shows some of her results.

Potato cylinder	Concentration (mol/dm³)	Mass at start (g)	Mass at end (g)
1	0.0	7.5	8.7
2	1.0	8.0	6.8

Which potato cylinder had the largest percentage change?

Stick each set of results into the <u>equation</u>: $\quad \% \text{ change} = \frac{\text{final value} - \text{original value}}{\text{original value}} \times 100$

The mass at the <u>start</u> is the <u>original value</u>.

potato cylinder 1: $\frac{8.7 - 7.5}{7.5} \times 100 = 16\%$

The mass at the <u>end</u> is the <u>final value</u>.

potato cylinder 2: $\frac{6.8 - 8.0}{8.0} \times 100 = -15\%$ — Here, the mass has <u>decreased</u> so the percentage change is <u>negative</u>.

<u>Compare</u> the results.

16% is greater than 15%. So potato cylinder 1 (in the 0.0 mol/dm³ sugar solution) had the largest percentage change.

Good practical skills are needed when you're doing an investigation...

...but you also need to know about them for your <u>exams</u>. You're guaranteed to be tested on your <u>practical knowledge</u>, so if you've skipped through this section, you'd better <u>go back</u> and <u>read through it again</u>.

Practice Exams

Once you've been through all the questions in this book, you should feel pretty confident about the exams. As final preparation, here is a set of **practice exams** to really get you set for the real thing. The time allowed for each paper is 1 hour 15 minutes. These papers are designed to give you the best possible preparation for your exams.

CGP Practice Exam Paper
GCSE Combined Science

GCSE Combined Science

Biology Paper 1
Foundation Tier

In addition to this paper you should have:
- A ruler.
- A calculator.

Centre name				
Centre number				
Candidate number				

Time allowed:
- 1 hour 15 minutes

Surname	
Other names	
Candidate signature	

Instructions to candidates
- Write your name and other details in the spaces provided above.
- Answer **all** questions in the spaces provided.
- Do all rough work on the paper.
- Cross out any work you do not want to be marked.

Information for candidates
- The marks available are given in brackets at the end of each question.
- There are 70 marks available for this paper.
- You are allowed to use a calculator.
- You should use good English and present your answers in a clear and organised way.
- For Questions 6.5 and 7.2 ensure that your answers have a clear and logical structure, include the right scientific terms, spelt correctly and include detailed, relevant information.

Advice to candidates
- In calculations show clearly how you worked out your answers.

	For examiner's use						
Q	Attempt Nº			Q	Attempt Nº		
	1	2	3		1	2	3
1				5			
2				6			
3				7			
4				8			
			Total				

1 **Figure 1** shows the human respiratory system.

Figure 1

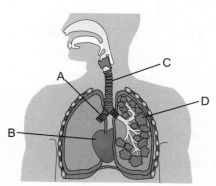

1.1 Which of the labels on **Figure 1** points to the trachea?
Tick **one** box.

☐ A   ☐ B   ☐ C   ☐ D

[1 mark]

1.2 Which of the labels on **Figure 1** shows where gas exchange takes place?
Tick **one** box.

☐ A   ☐ B   ☐ C   ☐ D

[1 mark]

1.3 Cells in the human body are organised into different levels.
Draw **one** line from each description of a level of cell organisation
to the example of that level.

A group of similar cells that work together to carry out a function		Lungs
A group of organs working together to perform a function		Epithelial tissue
A group of different tissues that work together to perform a certain function		Respiratory system

[2 marks]

Question 1 continues on the next page

Turn over ▶

1.4 An athlete ran on a treadmill for 11 minutes. In that time she took 407 breaths.

What was the athlete's average breathing rate in breaths per minute?
Tick **one** box.

☐ 24 ☐ 37 ☐ 48 ☐ 61

[1 mark]

1.5 **Figure 2** shows an alveolus and a blood capillary.

Figure 2

The arrows on the diagram show the net movement of two gases, **A** and **B**.
Name gases **A** and **B**.

Gas **A**: ....

Gas **B**: ....

[2 marks]

2 Plants produce glucose during photosynthesis.

2.1 Complete the word equation for photosynthesis.

carbon dioxide + water ⟶ glucose + ...

[1 mark]

2.2 Name the subcellular structure that absorbs light for photosynthesis.

....

[1 mark]

2.3 The glucose produced in photosynthesis can be used by plants to make cellulose.
What is cellulose used for in plant cells?

....

[1 mark]

2.4 Use a word from the box to complete the sentence below.

damaged	reproduced	respired	differentiated

Plants kept in a greenhouse that has become too hot may stop photosynthesising.

This is because the enzymes needed for photosynthesis are ....

[1 mark]

Question 2 continues on the next page

Turn over ▶

A student is investigating the effect of light intensity on the rate of photosynthesis.
Figure 3 shows the apparatus. **Table 1** shows the student's results.

Figure 3

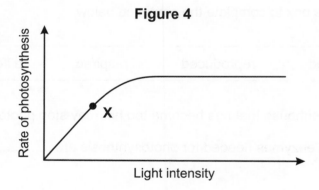

light source

Canadian pondweed

Table 1

Relative light intensity	1	2	3	4	5	6	7	8	9	10
Volume of gas produced in 10 minutes (cm^3)	8	12	18	25	31	13	42	48	56	61

2.5 At which relative light intensity did the student record an anomalous result?

....

[1 mark]

2.6 The student plotted a graph of the rate of photosynthesis against relative light intensity.
Figure 4 shows the student's graph.

Figure 4

Rate of photosynthesis

X

Light intensity

At point **X**, what is the limiting factor of photosynthesis?
Tick **one** box.

☐ oxygen concentration

☐ temperature

☐ light intensity

☐ carbon dioxide concentration

[1 mark]

3 There are a number of digestive enzymes found in the human body.

3.1 Draw **one** line from each digestive enzyme to its function.

Enzyme | Function

Protease

Lipase

Converts lipids into fatty acids and glycerol

Converts starch into sugars

Converts proteins into amino acids

[2 marks]

3.2 Explain why different enzymes catalyse different reactions.

....

....

....

[2 marks]

3.3 Which of the following statements about enzymes is **not** true?
Tick **one** box.

☐ Enzymes are affected by temperature.

☐ Enzymes change the rate of chemical reactions.

☐ Enzymes are changed during reactions.

☐ Enzymes are affected by pH.

[1 mark]

3.4 Explain why reactions catalysed by amylase are important for growth.
Your answer should refer to respiration.

....

....

....

....

[3 marks]

Turn over for the next question

Turn over ▶

4   **Figure 5** shows the rate of transpiration in two plants over 48 hours.

Figure 5

4.1   Define the term transpiration.

....
[1 mark]

4.2   At what time on **day 2** was the rate of transpiration highest for **plant 2**?

....
[1 mark]

4.3   The rate of transpiration for both plants was slower on **day 2** than on **day 1**.
Suggest **one** reason for this.

....
[1 mark]

4.4   Why was the rate of transpiration for both plants very low at night?
Tick **one** box.

☐   Low light intensity at night meant the stomata
opened, allowing less water vapour to escape.

☐   Low light intensity at night meant the stomata
closed, allowing less water vapour to escape.

☐   High temperatures at night meant that less water
evaporated from the surfaces of the plants.

☐   Low temperatures at night meant that water diffused
from the surfaces of the plants at a higher rate.

[1 mark]

Figure 6 shows two stomata on the surface
of a leaf viewed under a microscope.

Figure 6

© MAREK MIS/SCIENCE PHOTO LIBRARY

4.5   Name the cells labelled **X**.

....
[1 mark]

5   A student investigated how well stem cells from a plant grew in four different growth media.

The student placed a block of stem tissue measuring 1 mm × 1 mm × 1 mm onto each growth medium. They were then incubated at 35 °C for two days.

At the end of that time, the blocks were taken out and weighed to see how much they had grown. **Table 2** shows the student's results.

Table 2

Growth medium	% increase in mass
1	120
2	85
3	65
4	90

5.1   Use the results from **Table 2** to complete the bar chart in **Figure 7**.

Figure 7

Growth medium

[3 marks]

5.2   Which growth medium produced the best results?

....

[1 mark]

Question 5 continues on the next page

Turn over ▶

5.3 Give **two** variables that needed to be controlled in this experiment.

1. ....

2. ....

[2 marks]

5.4 Suggest how the student could improve their method to reduce the effect of random errors.

....

....

[2 marks]

5.5 Name the type of reproduction that is taking place when plant tissue is grown from stem cells.

....

[1 mark]

5.6 Suggest **one** benefit of being able to grow stem cells from rare plants.

....

[1 mark]

6   **Figure 8** shows a single-celled organism called *Euglena*, found in pond water.

Figure 8

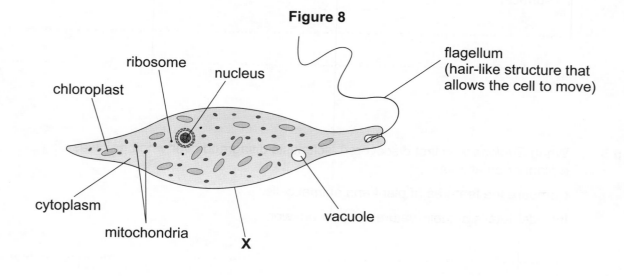

6.1   Name structure **X**.

....

[1 mark]

6.2   *Euglena* is a eukaryote. Which of the following is **not** a eukaryote?
Tick **one** box.

☐ sperm cell   ☐ muscle cell   ☐ fruit fly   ☐ *E. coli* bacteria

[1 mark]

6.3   A scientist viewed an individual *Euglena* under a microscope with × 500 magnification.
He calculated the real length of the *Euglena* to be 0.054 mm.
Calculate the length of the image of the *Euglena*. Give your answer in centimetres.
Use the formula:

image size = real size × magnification

....

....

....

image size = ... cm

[2 marks]

Question 6 continues on the next page

Turn over ▶

6.4 Explain why *Euglena* is able to exchange all of the substances that it needs across its surface.

....

....

[1 mark]

6.5 When *Euglena* was first discovered, scientists disagreed over whether it was a plant or an animal.

Compare the features of plant and animal cells.

Include details of their features in your answer.

....

....

....

....

....

....

....

....

....

....

....

[6 marks]

7   Measles, mumps and rubella are all examples of communicable diseases.

7.1   How is measles spread between people?
Tick **one** box.

☐ By droplets from an infected person's sneeze or cough.

☐ By sexual contact.

☐ By eating contaminated food.

☐ By a vector.

[1 mark]

7.2   The MMR vaccine protects against measles, mumps and rubella.
Explain how vaccination helps to protect the body against a disease.

....

....

....

....

....

....

[4 marks]

7.3   Why might someone **not** want to have the MMR vaccine? Suggest **two** reasons.

1. ....

....

2. ....

....

[2 marks]

Zika virus disease is another example of a communicable disease.
The virus that causes the disease is spread by a mosquito vector.

7.4   Suggest **two** ways that the spread of the Zika virus disease could be reduced.

....

....

....

[2 marks]

7.5   Plants are also affected by diseases.

Plants can be infected by a disease called rose black spot.
When a plant has rose black spot, it is important to strip the leaves off the plant.

Explain why it is important to also destroy the stripped leaves.

....

....

[2 marks]

Turn over for the next question

Turn over ▶

8 Different chemical reagents can be used to test for the presence of certain molecules in samples of food.

8.1 A student prepared a food sample in order to test whether the sample contained protein. What reagent should be used for this test?
Tick **one** box.

☐ Benedict's solution

☐ iodine solution

☐ biuret solution

☐ Sudan III stain solution

[1 mark]

8.2 Suggest **one** measure the student should take to make sure the food test is carried out safely.

....
[1 mark]

The student tested four different food samples for reducing sugars.
She obtained the results shown in **Table 3**.

Table 3

Sample	Colour of sample
A	blue
B	brick-red
C	yellow
D	green

8.3 Name the reagent that the student would have used to test for reducing sugars.

....
[1 mark]

8.4 Which of the samples in **Table 3** did **not** contain reducing sugars?
Tick **one** box.

☐ A   ☐ B   ☐ C   ☐ D

[1 mark]

Lactase is an enzyme involved in digestion. Lactase breaks down a sugar called lactose. The products are the sugars glucose and galactose. These are absorbed into the blood from the small intestine.

8.5 Describe how the small intestine is adapted to absorb molecules such as glucose.

....

....

....

....

[3 marks]

8.6 Lactose intolerance is a digestive problem caused by insufficient production of lactase.

To test a person for lactose intolerance, they are given a drink of lactose solution.
A blood sample is then taken from them every 30 minutes for two hours.
The blood is tested to see how much sugar it contains.

If the person has lactose intolerance, their blood sugar level will **not** rise. Explain why.

....

....

[1 mark]

Digestive problems are also seen in people with blocked bile ducts.

8.7 Bile makes conditions in the small intestine alkaline. Give **one** other function of bile.

....

[1 mark]

8.8 Suggest why people with blocked bile ducts have trouble digesting fats.
Refer to your answer to 8.7.

....

....

....

....

[3 marks]

END OF QUESTIONS

CGP Practice Exam Paper
GCSE Combined Science

GCSE Combined Science

Biology Paper 2
Foundation Tier

In addition to this paper you should have:
- A ruler.
- A calculator.

Centre name				
Centre number				
Candidate number				

Time allowed:
- 1 hour 15 minutes

Surname	
Other names	
Candidate signature	

Instructions to candidates
- Write your name and other details in the spaces provided above.
- Answer **all** questions in the spaces provided.
- Do all rough work on the paper.
- Cross out any work you do not want to be marked.

Information for candidates
- The marks available are given in brackets at the end of each question.
- There are 70 marks available for this paper.
- You are allowed to use a calculator.
- You should use good English and present your answers in a clear and organised way.
- For Questions 7.4 and 9.5 ensure that your answers have a clear and logical structure, include the right scientific terms, spelt correctly and include detailed, relevant information.

Advice to candidates
- In calculations show clearly how you worked out your answers.

For examiner's use

Q	Attempt Nº			Q	Attempt Nº		
	1	2	3		1	2	3
1				5			
2				6			
3				7			
4				8			
				9			
		Total					

1 Hormones control the menstrual cycle.

1.1 How long is a typical menstrual cycle?
Tick **one** box.

☐ 14 days   ☐ 3 months   ☐ 28 days   ☐ 9 months

[1 mark]

1.2 Which hormone causes the release of an egg during the menstrual cycle?
Tick **one** box.

☐ FSH   ☐ LH   ☐ Oestrogen   ☐ Progesterone

[1 mark]

1.3 Some of the hormones involved in the menstrual cycle are released from the pituitary gland.
Describe how these hormones reach their target organs in the reproductive system.

....
[1 mark]

1.4 Give another name for the pituitary gland.

....
[1 mark]

1.5 Give **two** differences between a response controlled by hormones
and a response controlled by nerves.

1. ....

....

2. ....

....
[2 marks]

Turn over for the next question

Turn over ▶

2   **Figure 1** shows a food chain.

Figure 1

algae   limpet   crab   seagull

2.1   Identify the producer in the food chain in **Figure 1**.
Tick **one** box.

☐ algae   ☐ limpet   ☐ crab   ☐ seagull

[1 mark]

2.2   Name **one** organism in the food chain in **Figure 1** that is prey for another organism.

....
[1 mark]

2.3   Limpets are affected by biotic and abiotic factors in their environment.
Which of the following are abiotic factors?
Tick **two** boxes.

☐ temperature

☐ food availability

☐ moisture level

☐ competition

[2 marks]

A student investigated the distribution of limpets on a beach.
The student used a quadrat to take samples at set distances from the tide's lowest point.
Table 1 shows the results.

Table 1

Distance from low-tide point (m)	0	4	8	12	16	20	24	28
Mean number of limpets per quadrat	3	2	14	9	13	24	38	42

2.4 The student plotted a graph of the results.
Complete **Figure 2** by plotting the final **two** results on the graph.

Figure 2

Distance from low-tide point (m)

[2 marks]

2.5 What conclusion can be drawn from the data?
Tick **one** box.

☐ The mean number of limpets is lower at the low-tide point than at 28 m from the low-tide point.

☐ As the distance from the low-tide point increases the number of limpets always increases.

☐ The mean number of limpets increases towards the low-tide point.

☐ The mean number of limpets is constant across the beach.

[1 mark]

2.6 Give **two** possible causes of the variation in limpet distribution.

1. ....

2. ....

[2 marks]

Turn over for the next question

Turn over ▶

3 Fruit flies usually have red eyes.

However, there are a small number of white-eyed fruit flies.

The allele for red eyes (R) is dominant over the allele for white eyes (r).

3.1 What is meant by the term 'allele'?

....

[1 mark]

Figure 3 shows a cross between two heterozygous fruit flies.

Figure 3

	R	r
R		Rr
r		

3.2 Complete **Figure 3**.

[2 marks]

3.3 Give the **two** possible genotypes of fruit flies with red eyes.

....

[1 mark]

3.4 In the genetic cross shown in **Figure 3,** what is the probability of producing offspring with white eyes?
Tick **one** box.

☐ 0.5   ☐ 0.3   ☐ 0.75   ☐ 0.25

[1 mark]

3.5 Fruit flies have the same sex chromosomes as humans.
What combination of sex chromosomes are found in human males?

....

[1 mark]

4 Reproduction can be sexual or asexual.

4.1 Sexual reproduction involves gametes.
Use words from the box to complete the sentences about how gametes form.

different	identical	mitosis	four	meiosis	two

During gamete production the parent cell divides by ....

The number of new cells produced is .... Each new cell only

has a single set of chromosomes and is genetically ....

[3 marks]

4.2 Elephants have 56 chromosomes in their body cells.
How many chromosomes will there be in a single elephant gamete?

....
[1 mark]

A population may become extinct if the environment changes quickly and the population doesn't adapt to the new conditions.

4.3 A population that reproduces asexually might be more likely to become extinct than a population that reproduces sexually. Suggest why.

....

....

....

....
[3 marks]

Turn over for the next question

Turn over ▶

5   **Figure 4** shows the yield of tomatoes grown on a farm over a six year period.

Figure 4

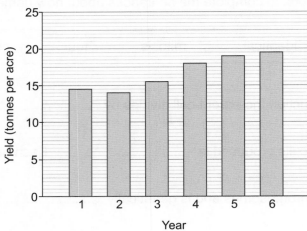

5.1   Explain how selective breeding could have been used to produce the results shown in **Figure 4**.

....

....

[3 marks]

5.2   A new disease has begun to spread in the tomato plants. Explain why the new disease might pose a large threat to the selectively bred tomato plants.

....

....

....

[2 marks]

Some tomato plants have been genetically engineered to be resistant to disease.

5.3   What is genetic engineering?

....

....

[1 mark]

5.4   Give **one** other example of how tomato plants could be genetically engineered.

....

[1 mark]

Some people have concerns about genetically modified crops.

5.5   Genetically modified tomatoes can be grown in enclosed greenhouses, rather than in fields. Suggest how this could reduce concerns about the tomato crop.

....

....

[1 mark]

6   The pancreas plays an important role in controlling the blood glucose level.
Figure 5 shows some of the glands that make up the human endocrine system.

Figure 5

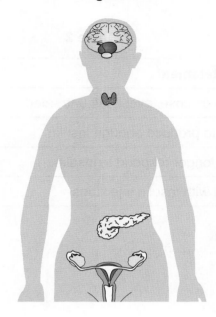

6.1   Label the pancreas on **Figure 5**.

[1 mark]

6.2   When the blood glucose level is too high, the pancreas produces insulin.
Describe how this acts to lower the blood glucose level.

....

....
[1 mark]

Question 6 continues on the next page

Turn over ▶

6.3 People with diabetes have difficulty controlling their blood glucose level.
There are two types of diabetes, type 1 and type 2.

Complete **Table 2** to show whether the statements apply to type 1, type 2 or both.
Put **one** tick in each row.

Table 2

Statement	Type 1	Type 2	Both
Results in a high blood glucose level if left untreated.			
The pancreas fails to produce enough insulin.			
Body cells can no longer respond to insulin.			
Must be treated with insulin injections.			

[4 marks]

Table 3 shows the blood glucose level of a person before and after eating a meal containing carbohydrate.

Table 3

	Before	After
Blood glucose level (mg/dl)	89	146

6.4 Calculate the percentage increase in the person's blood glucose level after the meal.
Give your answer to two significant figures.

....

....

Percentage increase = ... %

[2 marks]

7 A student was investigating the distribution of buttercups in an area around his school.
He counted the number of buttercups in 5 quadrats in five different fields.
His quadrat measured 1 m². His results are shown in **Table 4**.

Table 4

Field	Mean number of buttercups per quadrat
A	10
B	35
C	21
D	37
E	21

7.1 What is the median of the data in **Table 4**?

....

[1 mark]

7.2 A week later, the student repeated his experiment in a sixth field, Field **F**.
His results for each quadrat are shown below:

9   14   19   5   3

Using this data, calculate the mean number of buttercups per m² in Field **F**.

....

....

Mean = ... buttercups per m²

[2 marks]

7.3 Suggest **one** improvement to the student's method.

....

[1 mark]

Question 7 continues on the next page

Turn over ▶

The student observed that the distribution of buttercups changed across Field **A**. Buttercups grow well in damp soil, so the student thinks that the change in the distribution of buttercups is due to variability in the moisture level of the soil across the field. The student wants to investigate this.

7.4 Suggest a hypothesis about the distribution of buttercups in Field **A**, based on the student's observations.

....

....

[1 mark]

7.5 Describe how the student could investigate this hypothesis.

....

....

....

....

....

....

....

....

[4 marks]

8 The peppered moth is an insect that lives on the trunks of trees in Britain.
The moths are prey for birds such as thrushes.

The peppered moth exists in two varieties:

- A light-coloured variety that is better camouflaged on tree trunks in unpolluted areas.
- A dark-coloured variety that is better camouflaged on sooty tree trunks in badly polluted areas.

Figures 6 and **7** show these two varieties of moths on different tree trunks.

Figure 6	**Figure 7**

The dark variety of the moth was first recorded in the North of England in 1848.

It became increasingly common in polluted areas until the 1960s, when the number of soot covered trees declined because of the introduction of new laws.

8.1 The binomial name of the peppered moth is *Biston betularia*.
What is the moth's genus?

....

[1 mark]

8.2 Suggest how the dark variety of moth is likely to have first arisen in the population.

....

[1 mark]

Question 8 continues on the next page

Turn over ▶

8.3 Using the idea of natural selection, explain why the dark variety of moth became more common in soot polluted areas.

....

....

....

....

[3 marks]

The bar charts in **Figure 8** show the percentages of the light and dark varieties of peppered moths in two different towns.

Figure 8

8.4 State which town, **A** or **B**, is the most polluted. Give a reason for your answer.

....

....

[1 mark]

9   A scientist was investigating the reflex actions of males and females.

The scientist made the following hypothesis:

'Males have faster reaction times than females.'

The reaction times of eight participants were tested in the investigation.
Each participant was tapped just below the knee with a small rubber hammer.
When the leg was tapped it automatically kicked outwards at the knee.

The scientist recorded how long it took each participant to respond to
the stimulus of the tap on the leg. Each participant did the test 20 times,
and a mean reaction time was calculated (to 2 decimal places).

The results are shown in **Table 5**.

Table 5

Sex	Participant	Age (years)	Mean reaction time (s)
Female	1	29	0.04
	2	26	0.06
	3	24	0.06
	4	27	0.04
Male	5	19	0.05
	6	22	0.04
	7	25	0.04
	8	20	0.05

9.1   How can you tell that the participants' response was a reflex?
Give **two** reasons.

1. ....

....

2. ....

....

[2 marks]

Question 9 continues on the next page

Turn over ▶

Figure 9 shows the mean reaction times for males and females in the investigation.

Figure 9

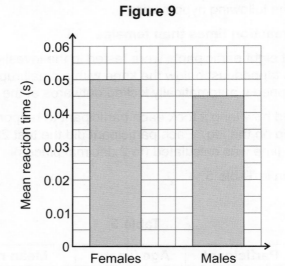

9.2 What can be concluded from the data in **Figure 9**?
Refer back to the scientist's hypothesis in your answer.

....

....
[2 marks]

9.3 Suggest **one** variable that the scientist should have controlled in this experiment.

....
[1 mark]

9.4 Another example of a reflex is the Babinski reflex.
In this reflex, a baby curls its big toe upwards when the sole of its foot is stroked.
The touch stimulus is detected by receptors in the skin and causes a reflex response.

Describe the path taken by a nervous impulse in this reflex, beginning at the receptors.

....

....

....

....

....

....

....

....

....
[6 marks]

END OF QUESTIONS

GCSE Combined Science

Chemistry Paper 1

Foundation Tier

In addition to this paper you should have:
*   A ruler.
*   A calculator.
*   The periodic table (on page 538).

Centre name			
Centre number			
Candidate number			

Time allowed:
*   1 hour 15 minutes

Surname
Other names
Candidate signature

Instructions to candidates
*   Write your name and other details in the spaces provided above.
*   Answer **all** questions in the spaces provided.
*   Do all rough work on the paper.
*   Cross out any work you do not want to be marked.

Information for candidates
*   The marks available are given in brackets at the end of each question.
*   There are 70 marks available for this paper.
*   You are allowed to use a calculator.
*   You should use good English and present your answers in a clear and organised way.
*   For Question 7.5 ensure that your answer has a clear and logical structure, includes the right scientific terms, spelt correctly, and includes detailed, relevant information.

Advice to candidates
*   In calculations show clearly how you worked out your answers.

For examiner's use

Q	Attempt Nº			Q	Attempt Nº		
	1	2	3		1	2	3
1				5			
2				6			
3				7			
4							
			Total				

1 This question is about bonding and elements in the periodic table.

1.1 Which element has 8 electrons in its outer shell?
Tick **one** box.

☐ Oxygen   ☐ Lithium   ☐ Neon   ☐ Nitrogen

[1 mark]

Figure 1 shows a type of bonding.

1.2 What type of bonding is shown in **Figure 1**?
Tick **one** box.

Figure 1

☐ Ionic bonding

☐ Intermolecular bonding

☐ Metallic bonding

☐ Covalent bonding

[1 mark]

1.3 Which element has a structure that is held together by the type of bonding shown in **Figure 1**?
Tick **one** box.

☐ Copper   ☐ Helium   ☐ Chlorine   ☐ Carbon

[1 mark]

The elements in Group 7 of the periodic table are known as the halogens.

1.4 Which of the halogens has the lowest boiling point?
Tick **one** box.

☐ Chlorine   ☐ Fluorine   ☐ Bromine   ☐ Iodine

[1 mark]

1.5 The nuclear symbol for an atom of fluorine is shown below.

$$^{19}_{9}\text{F}$$

How many protons, neutrons and electrons are there in this atom of fluorine?

Protons = ...   Neutrons = ...   Electrons = ...

[3 marks]

The equation for the reaction of chlorine with potassium bromide is:

$$Cl_2 + 2KBr \rightarrow Br_2 + 2KCl$$

1.6 Name the **compound** formed in this reaction.

....

[1 mark]

1.7 Explain why the reactivity of the halogens decreases moving down Group 7.

....

....

[2 marks]

2 Calcium can form the compound calcium carbonate ($CaCO_3$).

The equation for the thermal decomposition of calcium carbonate is:

$$CaCO_3 \rightarrow CaO + CO_2$$

calcium carbonate $\rightarrow$ calcium oxide + carbon dioxide

2.1 When 2560 g of calcium carbonate decomposed, 1130 g of carbon dioxide was formed. Calculate the mass of calcium oxide formed. Give your answer in standard form.

mass of calcium oxide = ... g

[2 marks]

Solid calcium carbonate also reacts with nitric acid:

$$CaCO_{3(s)} + 2HNO_{3(aq)} \rightarrow Ca(NO_3)_{2(aq)} + H_2O_{(l)} + CO_{2(g)}$$

calcium carbonate + nitric acid $\rightarrow$ calcium nitrate + water + carbon dioxide

2.2 What do the symbols (aq) and (s) stand for in the equation above?

(aq): ....

(s): ....

[2 marks]

A scientist carries out the reaction between calcium carbonate and nitric acid in a beaker placed on a mass balance.

2.3 Explain why the reading on the mass balance decreases during the reaction.

....

....

[2 marks]

The reaction produces 3.4 g of calcium nitrate.
The volume of the solution at the end of the reaction is 224 cm³.

2.4 Calculate the concentration of calcium nitrate in g/dm³.
Give your answer to 3 significant figures.

concentration of $Ca(NO_3)_2$ = ... g/dm³

[3 marks]

Turn over for next question

Turn over ▶

3 A student is using fractional distillation to separate a mixture of water, methanol and ethanoic acid.

3.1 What is the meaning of the term 'mixture'?

....

....

[1 mark]

3.2 Why is fractional distillation described as a physical method of separating substances?

☐ No chemical reactions take place during fractional distillation.

☐ The student needs to move the apparatus during the distillation.

☐ Chemical bonds are broken in fractional distillation.

☐ Fractional distillation involves heating.

[1 mark]

The apparatus the student is using is shown in **Figure 2**.

Figure 2

3.3 Name the piece of apparatus labelled **A** in **Figure 2**.

....

[1 mark]

Table 1 shows the boiling points of the compounds in the student's mixture.

Table 1

Compound	Boiling point in °C
Water	100
Methanol	65
Ethanoic acid	118

3.4 The student plans to collect the first two fractions in test tubes.
Which compound will be left in the **flask** at the end of the distillation?
Give a reason for your answer.

Compound: ....

Reason: ....

[2 marks]

3.5 The student wants to collect a pure sample of methanol.
Which temperature should she heat the mixture to?
Tick **one** box.

☐ 30 °C

☐ 43 °C

☐ 58 °C

☐ 78 °C

[1 mark]

3.6 Methanol is toxic.
Suggest **two** safety precautions the student should take
when carrying out the fractional distillation.

1. ....

2. ....

[2 marks]

Another student wants to use simple distillation to separate a mixture of
methanol and isobutanal. The boiling point of isobutanal is 63 °C.

3.7 Why is simple distillation **not** suitable for separating a mixture of methanol and isobutanal?

....

....

[1 mark]

Turn over for next question

Turn over ▶

4   **Table 2** shows the volume of gas produced in 60 seconds
when four different metals reacted with dilute sulfuric acid.
The metal was the only variable that changed.

Table 2

Metal	Volume of gas produced in cm³
Sodium	97
Calcium	81
Magnesium	62
Zinc	28

4.1   Draw a bar chart on the grid in **Figure 3** using all of the data from **Table 2**.

Figure 3

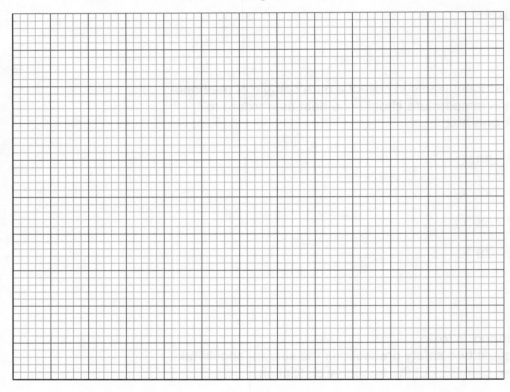

Metal

[2 marks]

4.2   Name the gas produced during the reactions.

....

[1 mark]

4.3   Use **Table 2** to predict the volume of gas that would be produced in the reaction between
sulfuric acid and iron, if all other variables were kept the same.

volume of gas = ... cm³

[1 mark]

One of the products of the reaction of sodium with dilute sulfuric acid is sodium sulfate, Na_2SO_4.

4.4 Calculate the relative formula mass (M_r) of sodium sulfate.
Relative atomic masses (A_r): O = 16, Na = 23, S = 32

M_r of sodium sulfate = ...

[1 mark]

4.5 Use the equation below to calculate the percentage mass of sodium in sodium sulfate.
Give your answer to 3 significant figures.

$$\text{percentage mass of an element in a compound} = \frac{A_r \times \text{number of atoms of that element}}{M_r \text{ of the compound}} \times 100$$

percentage mass of sodium = ... %

[2 marks]

An aqueous solution of sodium sulfate can be electrolysed.

4.6 What is the name given to a solution that can conduct electricity?

....

[1 mark]

4.7 What is formed at the anode when an aqueous solution of sodium sulfate is electrolysed?

....

[1 mark]

4.8 Name the product formed at the cathode when an aqueous solution of sodium sulfate is electrolysed. Give a reason for your answer.

Product at cathode: ....

Reason: ....

....

[2 marks]

Turn over for next question

Turn over ▶

5 The elements in Group 1 of the periodic table are known as the alkali metals.
The first three Group 1 metals are lithium, sodium, and potassium.

5.1 Group 1 metals can react with non-metals to form ionic compounds.
What is the charge on a Group 1 ion in an ionic compound?
Tick **one** box.

☐ +2

☐ +3

☐ −1

☐ +1

[1 mark]

A student watched his teacher carefully place small pieces of lithium, sodium and potassium into cold water. His observations are recorded in **Table 3**.

Table 3

Metal	Observations
lithium	Fizzes, moves across surface.
sodium	Fizzes strongly, moves quickly across surface, appears to melt.
potassium	Fizzes violently, moves very quickly across surface, appears to melt and a flame is seen.

He decides that the order of reactivity of the three metals is:

- potassium (most reactive)

- sodium

- lithium (least reactive)

5.2 Give **two** pieces of evidence from **Table 3** that support the student's conclusion.

1. ....

....

2. ....

....

[2 marks]

5.3   Explain the pattern of reactivity that the student has noticed.
Give your answer in terms of the outer electrons of the atoms.

....

....

....

....

[3 marks]

5.4   Which of the following is correct balanced equation
for the reaction between potassium and water?
Tick **one** box.

☐ $2K + H_2O \rightarrow 2KOH + H_2$

☐ $2K + H_2O \rightarrow K_2O + H_2$

☐ $2K + 2H_2O \rightarrow 2KOH + H_2$

☐ $2K + H_2O \rightarrow 2KOH + O_2$

[1 mark]

5.5   Choose the statement that explains why the solution produced
when potassium reacts with water is alkaline.
Tick **one** box.

☐   It contains potassium ions.

☐   It contains water.

☐   It contains an ionic compound.

☐   It contains hydroxide ions.

[1 mark]

5.6   What is the electronic structure of lithium?

....

[1 mark]

Turn over for next question

Turn over ▶

6   **Figure 4** shows the apparatus used by a student to measure the temperature change of a reaction between a piece of magnesium and dilute hydrochloric acid.

Figure 4

Thermometer

Glass Beaker

Bubbles of gas

Dilute hydrochloric acid

Magnesium

6.1   Suggest **two** changes that the student could make to the apparatus in order to reduce heat loss from her experiment.

1. ....

....

2. ....

....

[2 marks]

6.2   What is the dependent variable in the student's experiment?

....

[1 mark]

6.3   A close up of the thermometer used during the experiment is shown in **Figure 5**.

Figure 5

50 °C

40 °C

What value does each **small division** on the scale of the thermometer represent?
Tick **one** box.

☐ 0.1 °C

☐ 10 °C

☐ 1 °C

☐ 2 °C

[1 mark]

The student recorded the initial temperature of the dilute hydrochloric acid.
She added the magnesium to the acid.
She then measured the temperature of the reaction mixture every 10 seconds.
The student's results are shown on the graph in **Figure 6**.

Figure 6

6.4 Using the graph in **Figure 6**, give the highest temperature
of the mixture that the student recorded.

Highest temperature = ... °C

[1 mark]

6.5 The initial temperature of the acid was 17 °C.
Use this information and your answer from **6.4** to estimate
the total change in temperature of the reaction mixture.

....

Temperature change = ... °C

[2 marks]

6.6 State whether this reaction was exothermic or endothermic. Explain your answer.

....

....

[1 mark]

Turn over for next question

Turn over ▶

442

7 The structure and bonding of elements and compounds affects their properties.

7.1 Sodium and chlorine can react together to form an ionic compound.
Figure 7, below, is a dot and cross diagram showing this reaction.

Complete the right-hand side of **Figure 7** by adding the charges of **both** ions
and adding the electrons to the outer shell of the **chloride** ion.

Figure 7

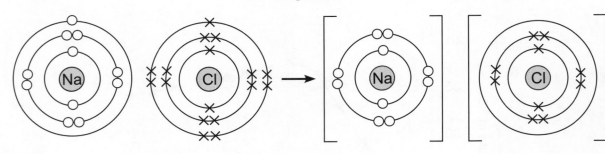

[2 marks]

Table 4 shows some properties of five substances, **A-E**.

Table 4

Substance	Melting point in °C	Boiling point in °C	Does it conduct electricity when solid?	Does it conduct electricity when dissolved or molten?
A	−210	−196	No	No
B	−219	−183	No	No
C	801	1413	No	Yes
D	115	445	No	No
E	1083	2567	Yes	Yes

7.2 At which temperature would substance **B** be a gas?
Tick **one** box.

☐ −207 °C

☐ −184 °C

☐ 63 °C

☐ −220 °C

[1 mark]

7.3 Substance **A** is made up of small, covalently bonded molecules.
Explain why substance **A** has a relatively low melting point.

....

....

[2 marks]

7.4 Look at **Table 4**. One of the substances, **A-E**, is an ionic compound.
Use the information in the table to suggest which of the substances is ionic.
Explain your answer.

....

....

....

[2 marks]

7.5 **Table 5** contains information about some of the properties of diamond and graphite.

Table 5

	Hardness	**Melting point**	**Conducts electricity?**
Diamond	Hard	High	No
Graphite	Soft	High	Yes

Explain these properties of diamond and graphite
in terms of their structure and bonding.

....

....

....

....

....

....

....

....

....

....

[6 marks]

END OF QUESTIONS

GCSE Combined Science

Chemistry Paper 2
Foundation Tier

In addition to this paper you should have:
- A ruler.
- A calculator.
- The periodic table (on page 538).

Centre name				
Centre number				
Candidate number				

Time allowed:
- 1 hour 15 minutes

Surname	
Other names	
Candidate signature	

Instructions to candidates
- Write your name and other details in the spaces provided above.
- Answer **all** questions in the spaces provided.
- Do all rough work on the paper.
- Cross out any work you do not want to be marked.

Information for candidates
- The marks available are given in brackets at the end of each question.
- There are 70 marks available for this paper.
- You are allowed to use a calculator.
- You should use good English and present your answers in a clear and organised way.
- For Questions 3.4 and 7.3 ensure that your answer has a clear and logical structure, includes the right scientific terms, spelt correctly, and includes detailed, relevant information.

Advice to candidates
- In calculations show clearly how you worked out your answers.

	For examiner's use						
Q	Attempt Nº			Q	Attempt Nº		
	1	2	3		1	2	3
1				5			
2				6			
3				7			
4							
			Total				

1   This question is about resources and crude oil.

1.1   What is the meaning of the term 'finite resource'?
Tick **one** box.

☐   A resource that is natural product.

☐   A resource that is used up more quickly than it can be replaced.

☐   A resource that can be replaced fairly quickly.

☐   A resource that can be burned to produce energy.

[1 mark]

Table 1 shows the time it takes for some different resources to form.

Table 1

Resource	Time it takes to form in years
Resource 1	4000
Resource 2	10^7
Resource 3	1
Resource 4	65 000

1.2   Which of the resources is a renewable resource?
Tick **one** box.

☐   Resource 1

☐   Resource 2

☐   Resource 3

☐   Resource 4

[1 mark]

1.3   **Figure 1** shows a technique used to separate crude oil into groups of hydrocarbons.

Figure 1

Name the technique shown in **Figure 1**.

....

[1 mark]

Question 1 continues on the next page

Turn over ▶

1.4 The technique shown in **Figure 1** relies on the properties of the groups of hydrocarbons.
Complete the sentences. Use words from the box.

boiling points	decomposes	evaporates	melting points	melts	reactivities

Before it enters the column, the crude oil is heated until it ....

Different hydrocarbons from the crude oil then leave the column at different points

because they have different ....

[2 marks]

1.5 The products listed in **Table 2** are groups of hydrocarbons
produced using the technique shown in **Figure 1**.

Table 2

Product	Approximate length of carbon chain
Petrol	8
Kerosene	15
Diesel oil	20
Bitumen	>40

Which of these products will be collected closest to the point marked **X** on **Figure 1**?
Tick **one** box.

☐ Petrol

☐ Kerosene

☐ Diesel oil

☐ Bitumen

[1 mark]

1.6 Which of the products in **Table 2** could be cracked to produce diesel oil?
Tick **one** box.

☐ Petrol

☐ Kerosene

☐ Bitumen

☐ None of them

[1 mark]

1.7 Which type of substance is a product of cracking?
Tick **one** box.

☐ Alkene

☐ Salt

☐ Polymer

☐ Catalyst

[1 mark]

2 A student carried out a chromatography experiment to identify an unknown food colouring.

This is the method used:

1. Draw a pencil baseline on a sheet of paper.
   Add a spot of the unknown food colouring to the baseline.

2. Add spots of two reference food colourings, **A** and **B**, to the baseline.

3. Place the sheet of paper in a beaker containing a small amount of solvent.
   Put a lid on the beaker.

4. When the solvent has almost reached the top of the piece of paper,
   remove the paper and leave it to dry.

2.1 What is the purpose of the solvent in this experiment?
Tick **one** box.

☐ It is a reactant

☐ It is the stationary phase

☐ It is a catalyst

☐ It is the mobile phase

[1 mark]

2.2 Only a small amount of solvent is used so that it does not touch the baseline
when the paper is first placed in the beaker.
Why should the solvent not touch the baseline?

....
[1 mark]

2.3 How could the student test the reproducibility of the experiment?

....

....

....
[2 marks]

Figure 2 shows the chromatogram produced during the experiment.

Figure 2

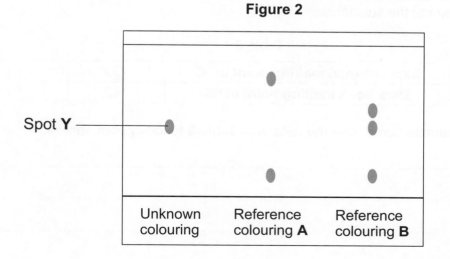

Spot **Y**

| Unknown colouring | Reference colouring **A** | Reference colouring **B** |

Question 2 continues on the next page

Turn over ▶

2.4 Which of the three food colourings is most likely to be a pure substance?
Use **Figure 2** to justify your answer.

....

....

[1 mark]

2.5 What is the minimum number of substances in reference colouring **B**?

....

[1 mark]

2.6 The R_f value for spot **Y** is calculated using the equation:

$$R_f = \frac{\text{distance moved by spot Y from the baseline}}{\text{distance moved by solvent from the baseline}}$$

Calculate the R_f value for spot **Y** on **Figure 2**.
Give your answer to two significant figures.

R_f value = ...

[5 marks]

In another experiment the student measured the melting point
of a sample of a substance found in a different food colouring.
Table 3 shows his result, as well as the data book value
for the melting point of the substance.

Table 3

Experimental melting point in °C	133
Data book melting point in °C	142

2.7 Is the student's sample pure? Use the data from **Table 3** to justify your answer.

....

....

....

[1 mark]

3   **Figure 3** shows how the concentration of carbon dioxide
in the atmosphere has changed since 1700.

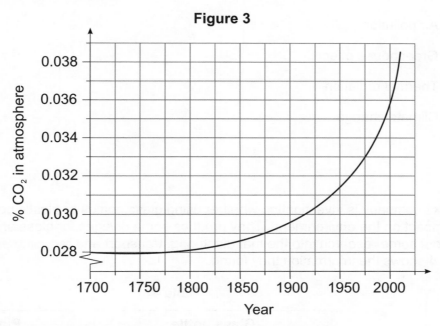

Figure 3

3.1   Use **Figure 3** to describe how the concentration of carbon dioxide
in the atmosphere has changed since 1700.

....

....

....

[2 marks]

3.2   Which piece of information would help convince a scientist that the data in **Figure 3** is valid?
Tick **one** box.

☐   The data covers a long period of time.

☐   The data has been published in a book.

☐   The percentage of CO_2 has been given to three decimal places.

☐   The data has been peer-reviewed.

[1 mark]

Figure 4 shows a process that takes place in Earth's atmosphere.

Figure 4

long wavelength
radiation

short wavelength
radiation

Question 3 continues on the next page

Turn over ▶

3.3 What is the name of the process shown in **Figure 4**?
Tick **one** box.

☐ Air pollution

☐ Greenhouse effect

☐ Thermal radiation

☐ Climate change

[1 mark]

3.4 A drinks company is investigating whether using glass bottles or plastic bottles will have less impact on the environment. They produce some designs for glass and plastic bottles and carry out some research into the manufacturing, transport and recycling processes for each. **Table 4** shows the information they found.

Table 4

	Glass bottle	**Plastic bottle**
CO_2 given out during production	255 g	193 g
Mass of bottle	402 g	44 g
CO_2 given out transporting by road	39 g	12 g
Recycled content	Contains 83% recycled material.	Contains no recycled material.
Recycling	Can be recycled endlessly. The company estimates 65% of these bottles would be recycled after use.	Can be recycled once or twice. The company estimates 55% of these bottles sold would be recycled after use.

Use the information in **Table 4** and your own knowledge to compare the environmental impacts of using glass bottles and using plastic bottles.

....

....

....

....

....

....

....

[4 marks]

4 A student is investigating how the rate of the reaction between calcium carbonate and sulfuric acid is affected by the concentration of the acid.

The student uses the following method:

- Weigh out 0.7 g of calcium carbonate.
- Add the calcium carbonate to an excess of 7.3 g/dm³ sulfuric acid in a conical flask.
- Use a gas syringe to collect the gas given off by the reaction.
- Measure and record the volume of gas produced every 10 s.
- Repeat the experiment using sulfuric acid with a concentration of 14.6 g/dm³.

4.1 To make each run a fair test, the student keeps the mass of calcium carbonate the same. Suggest **two** other variables that the student should keep the same to make each run a fair test.

1. ....

2. ....

[2 marks]

4.2 The gas produced by the reaction is carbon dioxide.
Which test could be used to confirm that the gas is carbon dioxide?
Tick **one** box.

☐ Holding a lit splint at the open end of a test tube containing the gas.

☐ Putting damp litmus paper into a test tube containing the gas.

☐ Putting a glowing splint inside a test tube containing the gas.

☐ Bubbling the gas through a solution of calcium hydroxide.

[1 mark]

The graph in **Figure 5** shows the student's results for the first experiment, using 7.3 g/dm³ sulfuric acid, and the second experiment, using 14.6 g/dm³.

Figure 5

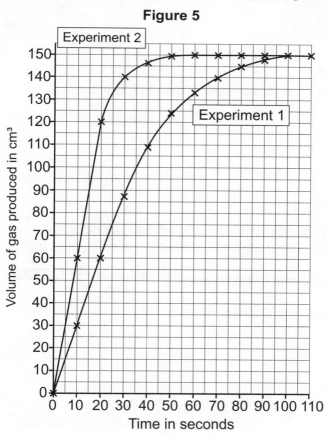

Question 4 continues on the next page

Turn over ▶

4.3 Use **Figure 5** to determine how much gas had been produced in each experiment after 30 seconds.

Volume of gas produced after 30 seconds in Experiment 1 = ... cm³

Volume of gas produced after 30 seconds in Experiment 2 = ... cm³

[2 marks]

4.4 Describe one way in which the shapes of the curves in **Figure 2** show that the rate of reaction was faster in Experiment 2 than in Experiment 1.

....

....

[1 mark]

4.5 In terms of collision theory, explain why concentration affects the rate of a reaction.

....

....

[2 marks]

4.6 The reaction also produces calcium sulfate. **Figure 6** shows how the student used a mass balance and a weighing boat to measure the mass in grams of calcium sulfate produced in Experiment 2.

Figure 6

empty weighing boat   weighing boat with calcium sulfate

```
1.36
```
mass balance
```
2.22
```

Calculate the mass of calcium sulfate formed in Experiment 2.

mass of calcium sulfate formed = ... g

[1 mark]

4.7 Use **Figure 5** and your answer to question **4.6** to calculate the mean rate of reaction during Experiment 2. The mean rate of reaction is calculated using the equation:

$$\text{mean rate of reaction} = \frac{\text{amount of product formed}}{\text{time taken}}$$

Give your answer to 2 significant figures.

mean rate of reaction = ... g/s

[3 marks]

5   Alkanes are hydrocarbon compounds found in crude oil. **Table 5** shows
     how the boiling points of some alkanes change as the molecules get bigger.

Table 5

Alkane	Molecular formula	Boiling point (°C)
Propane	C_3H_8	−42
Butane	C_4H_{10}	−1
Pentane	C_5H_{12}	
Hexane	C_6H_{14}	69
Heptane	C_7H_{16}	98

5.1   On **Figure 7**:

   • plot the boiling points of propane, butane, hexane and heptane against
     number of carbon atoms,
   • draw a smooth curve through the points you have plotted.

Figure 7

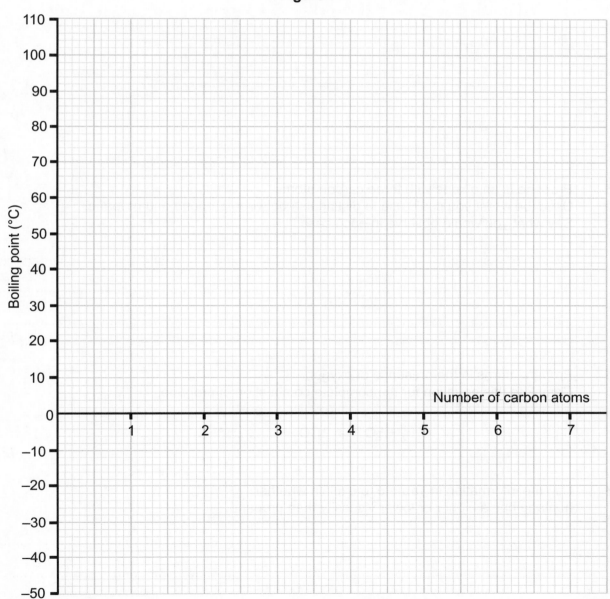

[2 marks]

Question 5 continues on the next page

Turn over ▶

5.2 Use your graph to estimate the boiling point of pentane.

.... °C

[1 mark]

5.3 What is the general formula of the alkanes? Tick **one** box.

☐ C_nH_{2n}

☐ C_nH_{2n+1}

☐ C_nH_{2n+2}

☐ C_nH_{2n-1}

[1 mark]

5.4 Propane is an alkane with three carbon atoms.
Draw the displayed formula of propane.

[1 mark]

5.5 Propene is an alkene with three carbon atoms.
Describe a test you could use to distinguish between propene and propane.
Say what you would observe in each case.

....

....

....

[3 marks]

5.6 Propane burns in the presence of oxygen.
Complete this equation for the complete combustion of propane.

$$C_3H_8 + 5O_2 \rightarrow 3CO_2 + ...$$

[2 marks]

5.7 Use the information in **Table 5** to explain whether
heptane has a higher or lower viscosity than propane.

....

....

....

[2 marks]

6 Nitrogen dioxide is an atmospheric pollutant that irritates the respiratory system. It is thought that there is a link between exposure to nitrogen dioxide and the severity of asthma attacks in people with asthma.

Figure 8 shows the results of a study carried out by a group of scientists. The study compared atmospheric nitrogen dioxide levels with the severity of asthma attacks suffered by men under the age of 40 working in a city centre. The severity of asthma attacks were measured on a scale of 1 to 10, with 10 being the most severe.

Figure 8

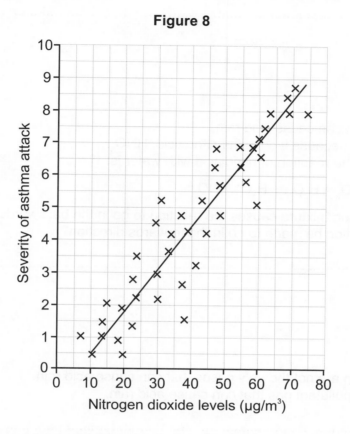

6.1 Describe the relationship between the level of nitrogen dioxide in the air and the severity of asthma attacks shown in **Figure 8**.

....

....

[1 mark]

6.2 The scientists hope to draw a conclusion about the link between the nitrogen dioxide level and the severity of asthma attacks.

Suggest why they cannot use the results shown in **Figure 8** to draw a conclusion that applies to **everyone**.

....

....

[1 mark]

Question 6 continues on the next page

Turn over ▶

6.3 Where do the oxides of nitrogen in the air come from?
Suggest why levels of nitrogen oxides can be particularly high in cities.

....

....

....

....

[3 marks]

6.4 Oxides of nitrogen can cause acid rain.
Acid rain is acidic because it contains nitric acid, HNO_3.
The equation for the reaction of nitric acid with water is:

$$HNO_3 + H_2O \rightleftharpoons H_3O^+ + NO_3^-$$

Heating the reaction mixture causes the reaction to go in the backwards direction.
How can the reaction be made to go in the forwards direction?

....

[1 mark]

6.5 Oxides of nitrogen are not the only gases that can cause acid rain.
Name **one** other pollutant gas that can cause acid rain.

....

[1 mark]

7   In the UK, the majority of our drinking water is produced from treating groundwater or surface water. Drinking water can also be made by treating sea water or waste water.

7.1   Producing water that is safe to drink from sea water is expensive.
Suggest why some countries produce drinking water by this method.

....

[1 mark]

7.2   What is the name of the process used to remove salt from sea water?
Tick **one** box.

☐ Filtration   ☐ Desalination   ☐ Sterilisation   ☐ Cracking

[1 mark]

7.3   A teacher gives a student a sample of sea water, and asks her to produce a sample of pure water from it. Plan a method that the student could use to remove the salt from the sea water.

....

....

....

....

....

....

....

....

[6 marks]

7.4   Sewage treatment plants process sewage and release clean, treated water back into the environment. The first step in the treatment of sewage is screening.
What happens in the screening step?
Tick **one** box.

☐ Chlorine is added to the sewage to kill microorganisms.

☐ The sewage is placed into large storage tanks and allowed to settle.

☐ Anaerobic digestion is used to break down the sewage.

☐ Large bits of material (such as grit) are removed from the sewage.

[1 mark]

7.5   Following screening, sedimentation is used to separate the effluent from the sludge.
Describe what happens to the effluent before it can be returned to the environment.

....

....

....

[2 marks]

END OF QUESTIONS

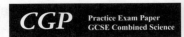

GCSE Combined Science
Physics Paper 1
Foundation Tier

Centre name				
Centre number				
Candidate number				

In addition to this paper you should have:
- A ruler.
- A calculator.
- The Physics Equation sheet (on page 538).

Time allowed:
- 1 hour 15 minutes

Surname
Other names
Candidate signature

Instructions to candidates
- Write your name and other details in the spaces provided above.
- Answer **all** questions in the spaces provided.
- Do all rough work on the paper.
- Cross out any work you do not want to be marked.

Information for candidates
- The marks available are given in brackets at the end of each question.
- There are 70 marks available for this paper.
- You are allowed to use a calculator.
- You should use good English and present your answers in a clear and organised way.
- For Questions 5.1 and 7.7 ensure that your answers have a clear and logical structure, include the right scientific terms, are spelt correctly and include detailed, relevant information.

Advice to candidates
- In calculations, show clearly how you worked out your answers.

For examiner's use

Q	Attempt Nº			Q	Attempt Nº		
	1	2	3		1	2	3
1				5			
2				6			
3				7			
4							
			Total				

1   A representation of the particles of a substance is shown in **Figure 1**.

Figure 1

1.1   Name the state of matter of the substance shown in **Figure 1**.

....

[1 mark]

1.2   The substance in **Figure 1** is heated. This increases the particle's internal energy.
Which of the particle's energy stores is energy transferred to?
Tick **two** boxes.

☐   potential energy

☐   nuclear energy

☐   chemical energy

☐   kinetic energy

☐   magnetic energy

[2 marks]

Figure 2 shows a sketch of the heating curve for a 1.0 kg sample of the substance.

Figure 2

1.3   Identify the state of matter of the substance at point **Z**.

....

[1 mark]

Question 1 continues on the next page

Turn over ▶

1.4 At which point in **Figure 2** has the substance reached its boiling point?
Tick **one** box.

☐ V
☐ W
☐ X
☐ Z

[1 mark]

Between points **V** and **W**, 334 000 J is supplied to the 1.0 kg sample of the substance.

1.5 Which of the following statements is true?
Tick **one** box.

☐ The specific latent heat of fusion of the substance is 334 000 J/kg.

☐ The specific heat capacity of the substance is 334 000 J/kg.

☐ The specific latent heat of vaporisation of the substance is 334 000 J/kg.

[1 mark]

1.6 Calculate the minimum amount of energy that would need to be
transferred from a 5.00 kg sample of the substance to freeze it.
Use the correct equation from the Physics Equation Sheet on page 538.

....

....

Energy = ... J

[2 marks]

2 A student wants to find the density of an ornament.
Figure 3 shows the ornament.

Figure 3

4.0 cm

4.0 cm

4.0 cm

2.1 Estimate the volume of the ornament by calculating the volume of the cube shown in **Figure 3**.
Give your answer in cm³.

....

....

Volume = ... cm³

[2 marks]

The student decides to measure the volume accurately using a eureka can and measuring cylinder.

He fills a eureka can with water so that it is full up to the base of the spout.
When he places the ornament in the eureka can, water will pour into a measuring cylinder.
Figure 4 shows the eureka can before and after the ornament has been added.

Figure 4

eureka can

measuring cylinder

water

ornament

Before   **After**

Question 2 continues on the next page

Turn over ▶

Figure 5 shows two measuring cylinders, **A** and **B**, that the student could use to collect water from the eureka can.

Figure 5

2.2 State and explain which cylinder the student should use for his experiment.

....

....

[1 mark]

2.3 The student finds that the volume of the ornament is 0.000058 m³.
He measures the mass of the ornament to be 0.435 kg.

Use the following equation to calculate the density of the ornament.

$$density = \frac{mass}{volume}$$

....

....

Density = ... kg/m³

[2 marks]

3 A home owner wants to wrap insulation around her hot water tank to reduce unwanted energy transfers. She needs to choose between three different types of insulation.

She does an experiment to test which type of insulation would be the best to use. She fills a beaker with hot water and wraps one type of insulation around it, as shown in **Figure 6**.

Figure 6

She measures the temperature decrease of the water after 5 minutes.
She repeats this experiment with each type of insulation.

3.1 State the independent variable in this investigation.

....

[1 mark]

3.2 State **two** control variables in this investigation.

1. ....

2. ....

[2 marks]

The home owner repeats her experiment three times for each type of insulation.
Her results for one type of insulation are shown in **Table 1**.

Table 1

Temperature decrease (°C)			
1	**2**	**3**	**Mean**
21.9	22.2	20.1	

3.3 Use the data in **Table 1** to calculate the mean temperature decrease for the insulation.

....

....

Mean temperature decrease = ... °C

[2 marks]

Question 3 continues on the next page

Turn over ▶

The home owner finds the temperature decrease for each type of insulation is roughly the same. She realises this is due to the way she set up the apparatus shown in **Figure 6**.

3.4   Using **Figure 6**, identify the mistake the home owner has made.
Explain why this mistake would have caused the temperature decreases
recorded to be roughly the same for each type of insulation.

....

....

....

[3 marks]

3.5   Which of the following best describes how the homeowner should insulate her tank
to minimise unwanted energy transfers to the surroundings?
Tick **one** box.

☐   With a thick layer of material that has a low thermal conductivity.

☐   With a thin layer of material that has a low thermal conductivity.

☐   With a thick layer of material that has a high thermal conductivity.

☐   With a thin layer of material that has a high thermal conductivity.

[1 mark]

The home owner also wishes to use more energy from renewable energy resources
to reduce her energy bills. She wants to generate electricity either using the wind
or directly from the Sun.

3.6   Give **one** other example of a renewable energy resource.

....

[1 mark]

Table 2 gives some data about the costs and savings of generating electricity using
solar panels or a wind turbine.

Table 2

	Installation cost	Average annual energy bill saving
Solar panels	£6000	£375
Wind turbine	£10 000	£500

3.7   The home owner expects to move house in 10 years time.
Evaluate whether she would save money by having solar panels installed.
Use data from **Table 2** in your answer.

....

....

....

[2 marks]

4 A student is investigating the two electrical circuits shown in **Figure 7**.
The resistors and batteries used in each circuit are identical.

Figure 7

Circuit A   Circuit B

4.1 Which statement correctly describes the total resistance of circuit B?
Tick **one** box.

☐ It is half as large as the resistance of circuit A.

☐ It is the same as the resistance of circuit A.

☐ It is twice as large as the resistance of circuit A.

[1 mark]

4.2 Compare the current in circuits A and B. Explain your answer.

....

....
[2 marks]

4.3 The total potential difference across the resistor in circuit A is 12 V.
Which statement about the potential difference across the resistors in circuit B is true?
Tick **one** box.

☐ The potential difference across each resistor is 6 V.

☐ The potential difference across each resistor is 12 V.

☐ The potential difference across each resistor is 24 V.

[1 mark]

4.4 The resistor in circuit A has a resistance of 4.0 Ω. The current through it is 3.0 A.
Use the following equation to calculate the power dissipated by the resistor in circuit A.

power = (current)^2 × resistance

Choose the correct unit from the box.

| **joules** | **watts** | **newtons per metre** |

....

....

Power = ...

Unit = ...
[3 marks]

Question 4 continues on the next page

Turn over ▶

The student considers adding one of the components in **Figure 8** to circuit A.

Figure 8

4.5 What happens to the resistance of component **C** as the intensity of light that falls on it increases?
Tick **one** box.

☐ The resistance increases.

☐ The resistance remains constant.

☐ The resistance decreases.

[1 mark]

4.6 Suggest **one** application for component **D**.

....

....

[1 mark]

4.7 On the axes in **Figure 9**, sketch the *I-V* characteristic of component **E**.

Figure 9

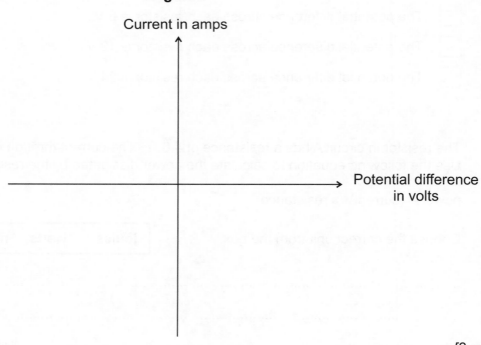

[2 marks]

5 A student uses the circuit shown in **Figure 10** to investigate how the length of the test wire affects its resistance.

Figure 10

5.1 Describe a method the student could use for her investigation.
Include steps to make sure the results are as accurate as possible.

....

....

....

....

....

....

....

....

....

....

....

....

....

[6 marks]

Question 5 continues on the next page

Turn over ▶

468

The student records her results in **Table 3**.

Table 3

Length / cm	Resistance / mΩ
5	6.7
10	13.4
15	20.1
20	26.8
25	33.5

5.2 **Figure 11** shows an incomplete graph of the student's results. Using **Table 3**, complete **Figure 11** by plotting the remaining points. Draw a line of best fit.

Figure 11

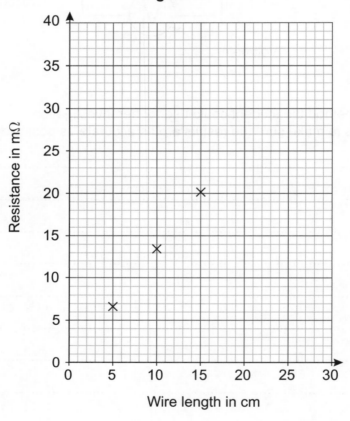

Wire length in cm

[2 marks]

5.3 Predict the resistance of a test wire with a length of 30 cm.

Resistance = ... mΩ

[1 mark]

5.4 Give **one** conclusion that can be made from **Figure 11**.

....

....

[1 mark]

6 At the start of a roller coaster ride a carriage is raised by a chain lift through a vertical height of 40 m to point **W**, as shown in **Figure 12**. It is stopped at point **W** and then released to follow the track through points **X**, **Y** and **Z**.

Figure 12

6.1 At which two points does the carriage have the same amount of energy in its gravitational potential energy store? Tick **one** box.

☐ **X** and **Z**

☐ **W** and **Y**

☐ **Y** and **Z**

☐ **W** and **Z**

[1 mark]

6.2 At which point does the car have the most energy in its kinetic energy store?
Tick **one** box.

☐ **W**

☐ **X**

☐ **Z**

[1 mark]

The mass of a full carriage is 1 500 000 g. Gravitational field strength = 9.8 N/kg.

6.3 Write down the equation that links gravitational potential energy, mass, height and gravitational field strength.

....

[1 mark]

6.4 Calculate the energy transferred to the gravitational potential energy store of a full carriage as it is raised by the chain lift to point **W**.

....

....

Energy transferred = ... J

[2 marks]

Question 6 continues on the next page

Turn over ▶

A different type of roller coaster uses a spring system to launch a carriage forward.
A compressed spring extends, causing an energy transfer that launches the carriage.

6.5 State the energy store that energy is transferred from when the compressed spring extends.

....

[1 mark]

6.6 State the equation linking efficiency, useful energy output and total energy output.

....

[1 mark]

6.7 The spring system stores 59.5 kJ of energy when it is compressed.
When a carriage is launched, 18.0 kJ of this energy is usefully
transferred to the kinetic energy store of the carriage.

Calculate the efficiency of the spring system.
Give your answer to three significant figures.

....

....

Efficiency = ...

[2 marks]

6.8 Explain why lubricating the moving parts of the carriage will increase its speed.
Include the energy store that energy is usefully transferred to in your answer.

....

....

....

....

....

[3 marks]

7   **Table 4** gives details of some isotopes.

Table 4

Isotope	Symbol	Type of decay
Radium-226	$^{226}_{88}\text{Ra}$	alpha
Radon-222	$^{222}_{86}\text{Rn}$	alpha
Radon-224	$^{224}_{86}\text{Rn}$	beta
Bismuth-210	$^{210}_{83}\text{Bi}$	alpha, beta
Bismuth-214	$^{214}_{83}\text{Bi}$	alpha, beta
Lead-210	$^{210}_{82}\text{Pb}$	beta

7.1   Calculate the number of neutrons in a bismuth-214 nucleus.

....
                                                                                              [1 mark]

7.2   Explain why bismuth-210 and bismuth-214 are isotopes of each other.

....

....
                                                                                              [2 marks]

7.3   Using data from **Table 4**, complete the equations in **Figure 13** to show how
      the following isotopes decay.

Figure 13

$$^{226}_{88}\text{Ra} \longrightarrow \boxed{} + \boxed{^{4}_{2}\text{He}}$$

$$^{210}_{82}\text{Pb} \longrightarrow \boxed{} + \boxed{^{0}_{-1}\text{e}}$$

                                                                                              [2 marks]

Question 7 continues on the next page

Turn over ▶

Figure 14 shows the activity-time graph of a sample of polonium-210.

Figure 14

7.4 Using the graph in **Figure 14**, determine the time it takes for the activity of the sample to drop from 80 Bq to 10 Bq.

Time taken = ... days

[1 mark]

7.5 Determine the half-life of polonium-210.

Half-life = ... days

[1 mark]

Polonium-210 emits alpha radiation. Scientists who work with it must be particularly careful to avoid radioactive contamination.

7.6 Define the term radioactive contamination.

....

....

[1 mark]

Another isotope of polonium, polonium-217, emits both alpha and beta particles.

7.7 A human body can be contaminated by radioactive atoms on the inside or on the outside. Explain and compare the dangers from alpha and beta radiation in both of these situations.

....

....

....

....

....

....

....

[4 marks]

END OF QUESTIONS

GCSE Combined Science

Physics Paper 2

Foundation Tier

In addition to this paper you should have:
- A ruler.
- A calculator.
- The Physics Equation sheet (on page 538).

Centre name				
Centre number				
Candidate number				

Time allowed:
- 1 hour 15 minutes

Surname	
Other names	
Candidate signature	

Instructions to candidates
- Write your name and other details in the spaces provided above.
- Answer **all** questions in the spaces provided.
- Do all rough work on the paper.
- Cross out any work you do not want to be marked.

Information for candidates
- The marks available are given in brackets at the end of each question.
- There are 70 marks available for this paper.
- You are allowed to use a calculator.
- You should use good English and present your answers in a clear and organised way.
- For Questions 3.6 and 7.3 ensure that your answers have a clear and logical structure, include the right scientific terms, are spelt correctly and include detailed, relevant information.

Advice to candidates
- In calculations, show clearly how you worked out your answers.

For examiner's use						
Q	Attempt Nº			Q	Attempt Nº	
	1	2	3		1	2	3
1				5			
2				6			
3				7			
4							
			Total				

1   A student is given apparatus to investigate the relationship between the force on a spring and its extension. The apparatus is set up as shown in **Figure 1**. The hook is assumed to have zero mass.

Figure 1

1.1   Placing one of the masses on the hook exerts a force of 1 N on the bottom of the spring.
A force is exerted by the clamp on the other end of the spring.
What is the size of the force exerted on the spring by the clamp?
Tick **one** box.

☐   0.5 N

☐   1 N

☐   1.5 N

☐   2 N

[1 mark]

1.2   Explain why more than one force is needed to deform a spring.

....

....

[1 mark]

1.3   Name the type of error which may be reduced by the use of the tape marker at the end of the spring when taking extension measurements.
Tick **one** box.

☐   zero error

☐   systematic error

☐   random error

[1 mark]

The student used the apparatus in **Figure 1** to collect data and plot the graph shown in **Figure 2**.

Figure 2

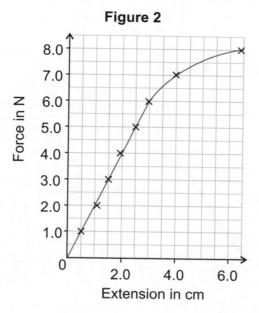

1.4   Estimate the maximum force that can be applied to the spring before the limit of proportionality is reached. Use **Figure 2** to justify your estimate.

....

....

....

[2 marks]

1.5   Use the graph to find the force needed to produce an extension of 0.015 m.

Force = ... N

[2 marks]

1.6   Use the following equation to calculate the spring constant of the spring.

Spring constant = force ÷ extension

....

....

Spring constant = ... N/m

[2 marks]

Turn over for the next question

Turn over ▶

2   A swimmer swims a length of a 20 m swimming pool.
The distance-time graph in **Figure 3** shows the swimmer's motion.

Figure 3

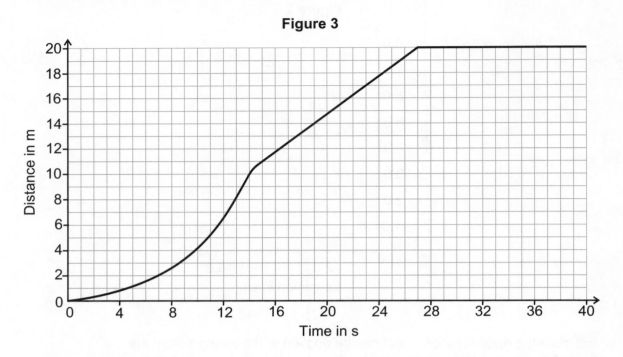

Between 15 and 27 seconds the swimmer is travelling at constant speed.

2.1   State the resultant force on the swimmer between 15 and 27 seconds.

Force = ... N

[1 mark]

2.2   Using **Figure 3**, calculate the speed of the swimmer between 15 and 27 seconds.

....

....

Speed = ... m/s

[2 marks]

2.3   Between which of the following distances was the swimmer travelling fastest?
Tick **one** box.

☐ Between 14 metres and 15 metres.

☐ Between 9 metres and 10 metres.

☐ Between 0 metres and 1 metre.

[1 mark]

A camera travels along the length of the pool to film the swimmer.
It starts from rest at the same time as the swimmer.
It travels at a constant speed and reaches the end of the pool in 23 s.

2.4 Use the following equation to calculate the speed of the camera.

$$\text{speed} = \frac{\text{distance travelled}}{\text{time}}$$

Give your answer to 2 significant figures.

....

....

Speed = ... m/s

[2 marks]

2.5 Draw a distance-time graph on **Figure 3** to show the motion of the camera.

[2 marks]

2.6 The swimmer swims back to their starting position.
Which of the following statements is true when they have returned to their starting position?
Tick **one** box.

☐ The magnitude of the swimmer's displacement is 40 m.

☐ The distance the swimmer has travelled is 20 m.

☐ The magnitude of the swimmer's displacement is 0 m.

☐ The distance the swimmer has travelled is 0 m.

[1 mark]

Turn over for the next question

Turn over ▶

478

3   Electromagnetic waves are a type of transverse wave.
A trace of a transverse wave is displayed in **Figure 4**.

Figure 4

3.1   Calculate the amplitude of the wave in **Figure 4**.

....

Amplitude = ... cm

[1 mark]

3.2   What is the frequency of a wave?
Tick **one** box.

☐   The amount of energy carried by the wave

☐   How long it takes for a complete wave to be produced.

☐   The number of complete waves that pass a point each second.

☐   The average displacement of a point on a wave from the rest position.

[1 mark]

3.3   Infrared radiation is emitted by some TV remote controls. Give **one** other use of infrared.

....

[1 mark]

When infrared radiation reaches a material it can do three things:
(1) be absorbed, (2) bounce back, or (3) pass straight through it.

A student sets up the experiment shown in **Figure 5** to test whether a material absorbs infrared.
The TVs will switch on if infrared radiation from the remote control reached them.
The student believes that if the material absorbs the infrared radiation, the TVs will remain off.

Figure 5

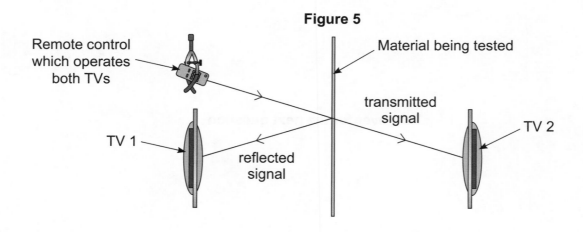

3.4 **Variable 1** and **Variable 2** are listed below. What types of variable are they?
Tick **one** box for **Variable 1** and **one** box for **Variable 2**.

	Independent	Dependent	Control
Variable 1: Distance of remote from material	☐	☐	☐
Variable 2: Type of material being tested	☐	☐	☐

[2 marks]

The student makes the hypothesis:
'Only dark-coloured materials absorb infrared signals.'
The student's results are shown in **Table 1**.

Table 1

Material	Which TVs respond?	Signal absorbed?
white paper	TV 1 and TV 2	no
black paper	neither	yes
white woollen blanket	neither	yes
black woollen blanket	neither	yes

3.5 Explain whether the student's results in **Table 1** support their hypothesis.

....

....

[1 mark]

3.6 Remote controls can use infrared waves or radio waves to send signals to devices.
Describe the similarities and differences between infrared waves and radio waves.

....

....

....

....

....

....

....

[4 marks]

Turn over for the next question

Turn over ▶

4   A student sets up the apparatus shown in **Figure 6** to investigate a wave on a string. The student adjusts the frequency of the signal generator until there is a clear wave on the string.

Figure 6

27.5 cm

4.1   State **one** safety precaution that the student should take when doing this experiment.

....

....

[1 mark]

4.2   What is the wavelength of the wave on the string shown in **Figure 6**?
Tick **one** box.

☐   5.50 cm

☐   11.0 cm

☐   13.75 cm

☐   27.5 cm

[1 mark]

4.3   Write down the equation that links wave speed, frequency and wavelength.

....

[1 mark]

4.4   The signal generator is set to 120 Hz. Calculate the speed of the wave on the string.

....

....

Speed = ... m/s

[2 marks]

4.5 The student sets up a wave on another string and calculates its speed.
She repeats this four times with the same string. Her results are:

  12.8 m/s   13.4 m/s   13.3 m/s   32.9 m/s

Identify any anomalous results in the set.
Describe how such anomalous results should be dealt with.

....

....

....

....

[3 marks]

The student decides to investigate how the diameter of the string is related to wave speed.
She will use four strings made of the same material with different diameters.

4.6 The student plans to measure the diameters of the strings using a 30 cm ruler.
Explain why this equipment is unsuitable.
Suggest a more suitable piece of equipment that could be used.

....

....

....

[2 marks]

The student's results are shown in **Table 2**.

Table 2

String diameter (mm)	0.26	0.68	1.33	2.15
Wave speed (m/s)	25.8	9.86	5.04	3.12

4.7 Give **one** conclusion that can be made from the results in **Table 2**.

....

....

[1 mark]

4.8 The student wants to present her results as a graph.
Suggest a suitable type of graph she could use. Justify your choice.

....

....

....

[2 marks]

Turn over for the next question

Turn over ▶

5 A skydiver jumps from an aeroplane and his motion is recorded.
Figure 7 shows the velocity-time graph of his fall.

Figure 7

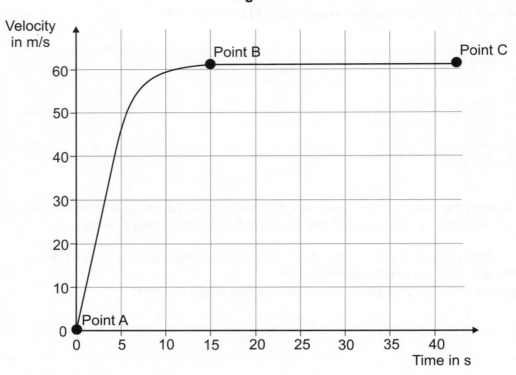

5.1 In the absence of air resistance, all objects accelerate towards the ground at the same rate. State the magnitude of this acceleration.

....

[1 mark]

5.2 Points A, B and C are labelled on **Figure 7**.
Draw **one** line from each part of the skydiver's fall to the correct description of his motion at this time.

| | The skydiver has a positive acceleration |

Between Point A and Point B

| | The skydiver is decelerating |

Between Point B and Point C

| | The skydiver is moving at a constant velocity |

[2 marks]

5.3 After 15 seconds the skydiver reaches his terminal velocity.
Name the contact force acting on the skydiver at this time.

....

[1 mark]

5.4   Write down the equation that links weight, mass and the gravitational field strength.

....

[1 mark]

5.5   The skydiver has a mass of 80.0 kg. Calculate his weight.
Use gravitational field strength = 9.8 N/kg.

....

....

Weight = ... N

[2 marks]

5.6   Once the skydiver has jumped, the plane accelerates away.
Write down the equation which links force, mass and acceleration.

....

[1 mark]

5.7   The plane experiences a resultant driving force of 58 500 N as it accelerates.
The plane has a mass of 4680 kg.
Calculate the acceleration of the plane.

....

....

....

Acceleration = ... m/s²

[3 marks]

Turn over for the next question

Turn over ▶

6 Table 3 shows data from the Highway Code about stopping distances for a well-maintained car travelling on dry roads at various speeds.

Table 3

Speed (km/h)	Thinking distance (m)	Braking distance (m)	Stopping distance (m)
32	6	6	12
64	12		36
96	18	55	73

6.1 Complete **Table 3** by calculating the missing braking distance.

[1 mark]

6.2 The data in **Table 3** was obtained by observing a large number of drivers and calculating average distances. Explain why a large sample of people was used.

....

....

....

[2 marks]

6.3 A car is travelling down a road. A hazard appears ahead.
Which of the following factors will the thinking distance of the car depend on?
Tick **two** boxes.

☐ Whether the driver is tired.

☐ Whether the road is wet.

☐ How worn the tyres are.

☐ The speed the car is travelling at.

☐ The mass of the car.

[2 marks]

75 000 J of work must be done to stop the car. The braking force of the car is 5000 N.

6.4 Write down the equation that links distance, force and work done.

....

[1 mark]

6.5 Calculate the braking distance of the car.

....

....

Distance = ... m

[3 marks]

7 A student passes a current through a straight wire.
The current is flowing into the paper.

7.1 Which of the following shows the magnetic field around the wire?
Tick **one** box.

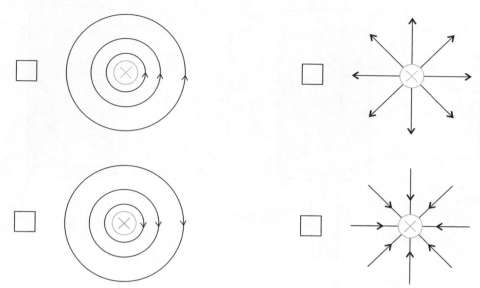

[1 mark]

7.2 A bar magnet is placed near the wire and experiences a force.
State **two** ways that the force on the magnet could be decreased
without removing it from the wire's magnetic field completely.

1. ....

....

2. ....

....

[2 marks]

Question 7 continues on the next page

Turn over ▶

486

7.3 The student coils the wire and inserts an iron core to form an electromagnet.
Figure 8 shows a bar magnet and an iron nail hanging from the electromagnet.

Figure 8

Predict what will happen to the bar magnet and the nail when the electromagnet is disconnected from the battery in each case. Justify your answer.

....

....

....

....

....

....

....

....

....

....

....

....

[6 marks]

END OF QUESTIONS

Topic B1 — Cell Biology

Page 19
Microscopy
Q1   real size = image size ÷ magnification
           = 2.4 mm ÷ 40
           = 0.06 mm *[1 mark]*
       0.06 × 1000 = **60 μm** *[1 mark]*

Page 22
Warm-Up Questions
1)   mitochondria
2)   Any two from: e.g. plant cells have a rigid cell wall and animals do not. / Plant cells have a permanent vacuole and animals do not. / Plant cells contain chloroplasts and animals do not.
3)   False
Bacterial cells have a single loop of DNA instead.
4)   electron microscope
5) 4.5×10^{-4} μm

Exam Questions
1   bacterial cell *[1 mark]*
2.1   C *[1 mark]*
2.2   allows photosynthesis to take place *[1 mark]*
2.3   making proteins *[1 mark]*
3.1   How to grade your answer:
     Level 0:   There is no relevant information. *[No marks]*
     Level 1:   There is a brief explanation of how to prepare a slide. *[1 to 2 marks]*
     Level 2:   There is a detailed explanation of how to prepare a slide. *[3 to 4 marks]*
     Here are some points your answer may include:
     Add a drop of water to the middle of a clean slide.
     Cut up an onion and separate it out into layers.
     Use tweezers to peel off some epidermal tissue from the bottom of one of the layers.
     Use tweezers to place the epidermal tissue into the water on the slide.
     Add a drop of iodine solution/stain.
     Place a cover slip on top without trapping any air bubbles.
3.2   real size = 7.5 mm ÷ 100 = 0.075 mm *[1 mark]*
      0.075 × 1000 = **75 μm** *[1 mark]*

Page 28
Chromosomes and Mitosis
Q1 a) 11 ÷ (62 + 11) = 0.150...
       0.150... × 100 = **15%** *[1 mark]*
    b) E.g. she could see the X-shaped chromosomes in the middle of the cells. / She could see the arms of the chromosomes being pulled apart *[1 mark]*.

Page 29
Warm-Up Questions
1)   differentiation
2)   The cell has a hair-like shape, which gives it a large surface area to absorb water and minerals from the soil.
3)   2
4)   in the nucleus
5)   True

Exam Questions
1

[1 mark for each correct link]

2.1

[1 mark for arrow at shoot tip, 1 mark for arrow at root tip]

2.2   E.g. stem cells can be used to make clones *[1 mark]* of crop plants that have useful features / that aren't killed by a disease *[1 mark]*.
2.3   E.g. paralysis / diabetes *[1 mark]*

Page 30
Diffusion
Q1 a) The ink will diffuse / spread out through the water *[1 mark]*. This is because the ink particles will move from where there is a higher concentration of them (the drop of ink) to where there is a lower concentration of them (the surrounding water) *[1 mark]*.
    b) The ink particles will diffuse / spread out faster *[1 mark]*.
Q2   The larger the surface area of the membrane the faster the diffusion rate *[1 mark]*. This is because more particles can pass through at the same time *[1 mark]*.

Page 32
Osmosis
Q1   Water will move out of the piece of potato by osmosis *[1 mark]*, so its mass will decrease *[1 mark]*.

Page 35
Exchanging Substances
Q1   Surface area:
      (2 × 2) × 2 = 8
      (2 × 1) × 4 = 8
      8 + 8 = 16 μm^2 *[1 mark]*
      Volume:
      2 × 2 × 1 = 4 μm^3 *[1 mark]*
      So the surface area to volume ratio is **16 : 4**, or **4 : 1** *[1 mark]*.

Page 36
More on Exchanging Substances
Q1   E.g. they have a large surface area. / They have a moist lining for dissolving gases. / They have very thin walls. / They have a good blood supply. *[1 mark]*
Q2   The damage to the villi is likely to reduce the surface area for absorption *[1 mark]*. Therefore, less iron can be absorbed from the digested food in the small intestine into the blood *[1 mark]*.

Pages 38-39
Warm-Up Questions
1)   diffusion
2)   True
3)   They increase the surface area.
4)   E.g. alveoli (in the lung)
5)   Stomata

6)   E.g. it is made up of lots of thin plates which give a large surface area. / The plates have lots of blood capillaries. / The plates have a thin layer of surface cells.

Exam Questions

1.1

[1 mark for dye particles spread out evenly]

1.2   A lower temperature would decrease the rate of diffusion *[1 mark]*.

2.1   The movement of substances from an area of lower concentration to an area of higher concentration, requiring energy. *[1 mark]*

2.2   Movement of mineral ions from the soil into root hair cells *[1 mark]*
Movement of nutrients, such as glucose, from the gut into the blood *[1 mark]*

3.1   partially permeable membrane *[1 mark]*

Remember that osmosis always takes place across a partially permeable membrane.

3.2   The liquid level on side B will fall. *[1 mark]*

This is because water will flow from a less concentrated solution to a more concentrated solution.

4.1

Cylinder	1	2	3	4
Length after 24 hours (mm)	40	43	51	55
Change in length (mm)	**−10**	**−7**	**+1**	+5

[1 mark]

4.2   The concentration of the sugar solution that cylinder 4 was placed in must have been lower than the concentration of the solution inside the potato cells *[1 mark]*, so the cylinder increased in length as water entered the cells by osmosis *[1 mark]*.

Topic B2 — Organisation

Page 43
Investigating Enzymatic Reactions

Q1   2.5 min × 60 = 150 seconds *[1 mark]*
1000 ÷ 150 = 6.666... = **6.7 s⁻¹** *[1 mark*

Pages 47-48
Warm-Up Questions

1)   organ
2)   active site
3)   amylase
4)   glycerol and fatty acids
5)   False

Proteases are made in the stomach, pancreas and small intestine.

6)   E.g. break up the food using a pestle and mortar. Then transfer the ground up food to a beaker and add some distilled water. Next, stir the mixture with a glass rod, and finally filter the solution using a funnel lined with filter paper.

Exam Questions

1.1   A *[1 mark]*
1.2   Bile makes conditions in the small intestine **alkaline** *[1 mark]*. Bile also emulsifies **lipids** *[1 mark]*.
2.1   40 °C *[1 mark]*
2.2   optimum temperature *[1 mark]*
3.1   The enzyme has a specific shape which will only fit with one type of substrate *[1 mark]*.

3.2   It would affect the bonds holding the enzyme together and change the shape of the enzyme's active site/ denature the enzyme *[1 mark]*. This would mean the substrate would no longer fit into it so the enzyme wouldn't work anymore *[1 mark]*.

A similar thing happens when the pH or the temperature is too high — the bonds are disrupted and the shape of the active site may change.

4.1   Biuret solution *[1 mark]*
4.2   Yes, because when iodine solution was added, it turned blue-black *[1 mark]*.
4.3   Yes, because when Sudan III stain solution was added, the mixture separated out into two layers with a red top layer *[1 mark]*.
5.1   To prevent the starch coming into contact with amylase in the syringe, which would have started the reaction before he had started the stop clock *[1 mark]*.
5.2   Rate = 1000 ÷ 60 = 16.666... *[1 mark]*
= **17 s⁻¹ (2 s.f.)** *[1 mark]*

Page 49
The Lungs

Q1   304 ÷ 8 = **38 breaths per minute** *[1 mark]*

Page 52
Circulatory System — Blood Vessels

Q1   2.175 1 × 1000 = 2175 ml *[1 mark]*
2175 ÷ 8.7 = **250 ml/min** *[1 mark]*

Q2   They have a big lumen to help the blood flow despite the low pressure *[1 mark]*. They have valves to keep the blood flowing in the right direction *[1 mark]*.

Page 53
Circulatory System — Blood

Q1   They help the blood to clot at a wound *[1 mark]*.
Q2   To carry oxygen from the lungs to all the cells in the body *[1 mark]*.

Pages 54-55
Warm-Up Questions

1)   bronchi
2)   They supply oxygenated blood to the heart itself.
3)   Makes the heart beat regularly.
4)   They carry blood back to the heart.
5)   True

Exam Questions

1.1   aorta *[1 mark]*
1.2   It pumps blood around the body. *[1 mark]*
1.3   vena cava *[1 mark]*

2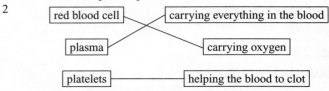

[2 marks for all lines correct, otherwise 1 mark for one line correct.]

3   The shape gives it a large surface area for absorbing oxygen *[1 mark]*.
4.1   492 ÷ 12 = **41 breaths per minute** *[1 mark]*
4.2   Resting heart rate is controlled by a group of cells in the right atrium wall that act as a pacemaker *[1 mark]*.
5.1   How to grade your answer:
Level 0:   There is no relevant information. *[No marks]*
Level 1:   There are some relevant points explaining how the structure of a capillary allows it to carry out its function. *[1 to 2 marks]*

Level 2: There is a clear, detailed explanation of how the structure of a capillary allows it to carry out its function. *[3 to 4 marks]*

Here are some points your answer may include:
Capillaries have gaps in their walls.
This means that substances can diffuse in and out.
Their walls are usually only one cell thick.
This means that diffusion is very fast because there is only a short distance for molecules to travel.

5.2 150 s ÷ 60 = 2.5 min
1155 ÷ 2.5 = **462 ml/min** *[2 marks for correct answer, otherwise 1 mark for correct working.]*

Make sure you read the question carefully — if you gave your answer in ml/second you wouldn't have got all the marks available.

Page 59
Warm-Up Questions
1) the coronary arteries
2) An artificial heart could be fitted.
3) A mechanical device that is put into a person to pump blood if their own heart fails.

Exam Questions
1.1

Description of treatment	Name of treatment
Tubes that are put inside arteries to keep them open	**stents**
Drugs that reduce cholesterol in the blood	**statins**

[1 mark for each correct answer]

1.2 E.g. a person has to remember to take them regularly. / They can cause unwanted side effects. / It takes time for them to work *[1 mark]*.
2.1 biological valves *[1 mark]*, mechanical valves *[1 mark]*
2.2 E.g. it requires surgery, which could lead to bleeding/infection.
/ There could be problems with blood clots *[1 mark]*.
3.1 fatty material/fatty deposit *[1 mark]*
3.2 The fatty material causes the coronary arteries to become narrow, so blood flow to the heart muscle is reduced *[1 mark]*. This reduces (or stops) the delivery of oxygen to the heart muscle *[1 mark]*.

Page 65
Warm-Up Questions
1) False
2) It can be spread from person to person or between animals and people.
3) True
4) cancer

Exam Questions
1 A disease that cannot be spread between people or between animals and people *[1 mark]*.
2

	Benign	Malignant
The tumour is made up of a mass of cells formed by uncontrollable division and growth.	✓	✓
The tumour cells can break off and travel into the bloodstream.		✓
The tumour is cancerous.		✓

[1 mark for each correct row]

3.1 A risk factor is something that is linked to an increased chance of getting a certain disease *[1 mark]*.
3.2 e.g. smoking *[1 mark]*
3.3 e.g. ionising radiation *[1 mark]*

Page 69
The Rate of Transpiration
Q1 Aloe vera, because the transpiration rate will be higher in the hot, dry area *[1 mark]*, so the aloe vera will have fewer stomata to help conserve water *[1 mark]*.
Q2 As it gets darker, the stomata begin to close *[1 mark]*.
This means that very little water can escape *[1 mark]*.
So the rate of transpiration decreases *[1 mark]*.

Pages 70-71
Warm-Up Questions
1) At the growing tips of shoots and roots.
2) palisade layer
3) False
4) light intensity / temperature / air flow / humidity

Exam Questions
1.1 spongy mesophyll tissue *[1 mark]*
1.2 epidermal tissue *[1 mark]*
2.1 phloem *[1 mark]*
2.2 To allow the cell sap to flow through *[1 mark]*.
2.3 translocation *[1 mark]*
3.1 guard cells *[1 mark]*
3.2 Condition B, because the stoma has closed to reduce water loss *[1 mark]*.
4.1 They are made of dead cells joined end to end *[1 mark]* with no end walls between them and therefore a hole down the middle *[1 mark]*. They're strengthened with a material called lignin *[1 mark]*.
4.2 transpiration *[1 mark]*
5.1 A, because transpiration is faster when the temperature is higher / when the humidity is lower *[1 mark]*.
5.2 How to grade your answer:
Level 0: There is no relevant information. *[No marks]*
Level 1: There are some relevant points explaining how the rate of water loss would be affected by windy weather, but some detail is missing. *[1 to 2 marks]*
Level 2: There is a clear, detailed explanation of how the rate of water loss would be affected by windy weather. *[3 to 4 marks]*

Here are some points your answer may include:
Water is lost more quickly on windy days.
This is because fast-moving air sweeps away the water vapour around the leaf.
This causes the concentration of water vapour inside the leaf to always be higher than outside.
This means water vapour diffuses out quickly.

Topic B3 — Infection and Response

Page 77
Warm-Up Questions
1) True
2) By sexual contact.
3) inside cells
4) A red skin rash.
5) tobacco mosaic virus
6) It causes purple or black spots to develop on the leaves, which can then turn yellow and drop off.

Exam Questions
1 Malaria is caused by a virus *[1 mark]*.
Malaria is caused by a protist, not a virus.
2.1 hand-washing *[1 mark]*
Hand-washing before cooking food can reduce the spread of the disease.
Vaccinations given to chickens (not people) can also reduce the spread.
2.2 vaccinating people *[1 mark]*
3.1 The first symptoms are flu-like *[1 mark]*.

3.2   E.g. pain when the infected person urinates. / Thick yellow or green discharge from the vagina or penis *[1 mark]*.

3.3   E.g. fever / stomach cramps / vomiting /diarrhoea *[1 mark]*

Page 80
Fighting Disease — Vaccination
Q1   Basia's white blood cells recognise the antigens on the flu virus and rapidly produce antibodies, which kill the pathogen *[1 mark]*. Cassian's white blood cells don't recognise the antigens, so it takes a while for them to produce antibodies and he becomes ill in the meantime *[1 mark]*.

Pages 83-84
Warm-Up Questions
1) The skin stops pathogens getting inside the body and releases substances that kill them.
2) To destroy pathogens that enter the body.
3) Unique molecules on the surface of a pathogen.
4) Through a mutation.
5) Whether the drug works and has the effect you're looking for.

Exam Questions
1.1   Aspirin — Willow
Digitalis — Foxgloves
Penicillin — Mould
[2 marks for three correct lines, otherwise 1 mark for one correct line.]
1.2   painkiller *[1 mark]*
1.3   antibiotic *[1 mark]*
2.1   phagocytosis *[1 mark]*
2.2   Antibodies are produced by **white blood cells** *[1 mark]*. They attach to specific antigens on the surface of the **pathogen** *[1 mark]*.
3.1   human volunteers *[1 mark]*
3.2   Neither the patient or the doctor know who is receiving the drug and who is receiving the placebo *[1 mark]*.
4.1   They trap particles that could contain pathogens *[1 mark]*.
4.2   They move the mucus up to the back of the throat where it can be swallowed *[1 mark]*.
4.3   (hydrochloric) acid *[1 mark]*
5.1   How to grade your answer:
Level 0:   There is no relevant information. *[No marks]*
Level 1:   There is a brief explanation of how vaccination against rubella can prevent a person catching the disease or how having a large number of vaccinated people in a population reduces the risk of rubella for people who are not vaccinated. *[1 to 2 marks]*
Level 2:   There is some explanation of how vaccination against rubella can prevent a person catching the disease and how having a large number of vaccinated people in a population reduces the risk of rubella for people who are not vaccinated. *[3 to 4 marks]*
Level 3:   There is a clear and detailed explanation of how vaccination against rubella can prevent a person catching the disease and how having a large number of vaccinated people in a population reduces the risk of rubella for people who are not vaccinated. *[5 to 6 marks]*
Here are some points your answer may include:
When a person is vaccinated against rubella, they are injected with dead or inactive rubella viruses.
The dead or inactive viruses carry antigens, which cause the body to produce antibodies to attack them.
If rubella viruses infect the body after this, white blood cells can quickly produce lots of antibodies to defeat the virus.
If a large number of people in a population are vaccinated against rubella, then there are fewer people who are able to pass the disease on.

This means that even someone who hasn't been vaccinated is less likely to catch the disease.
5.2   E.g. they may be worried that they will have a bad reaction to a vaccine. / Vaccines don't always work and so the person might not be given immunity *[1 mark]*.

Topic B4 — Bioenergetics

Page 87
The Rate of Photosynthesis
Q1   a)   C *[1 mark]*
     b)   E.g. CO_2 level / temperature *[1 mark]*.

Pages 89-90
Warm-Up Questions
1) chlorophyll
2) light
Energy is transferred to chloroplasts from the environment by light.
3) False
Photosynthesis is endothermic.
4) True

Exam Questions
1.1   glucose — $C_6H_{12}O_6$
oxygen — O_2
water — H_2O *[2 marks for 2 correct lines, 1 mark for one correct line.]*
1.2 CO_2 *[1 mark]*
2.1   carbon dioxide + **water** → glucose + **oxygen** *[2 marks — 1 mark for each correct answer.]*
2.2   cellulose *[1 mark]*
2.3   storage as oils *[1 mark]*
3.1   it is insoluble *[1 mark]*
3.2   When photosynthesis is not happening, the plant can't produce glucose, so uses stored starch instead *[1 mark]*.
4.1   The rate of photosynthesis is increasing as the concentration of carbon dioxide is increased *[1 mark]*.
4.2   The concentration of carbon dioxide *[1 mark]*.
4.3   The rate of photosynthesis is no longer increasing as the concentration of carbon dioxide is increased *[1 mark]*. The concentration of carbon dioxide is no longer the limiting factor / light intensity or temperature is now the limiting factor *[1 mark]*.
At this point, photosynthesis won't go any faster because another factor is limiting the rate.
4.4   Enzymes needed for photosynthesis will work more slowly at low temperatures *[1 mark]*.
5.1   By counting the number of bubbles produced / by measuring the volume of gas produced in a given time/at regular intervals *[1 mark]*.
5.2   Rate of photosynthesis/number of bubbles in a given time/volume of gas in a given time *[1 mark]*.
5.3   light intensity *[1 mark]*
5.4   E.g. carbon dioxide concentration in the water / temperature / the plant being used *[1 mark]*.

Page 93
Exercise
Q1   Running is a more intense type of exercise than walking *[1 mark]*, so more anaerobic respiration will be taking place in the muscles *[1 mark]*. Anaerobic respiration produces lactic acid, so running will lead to more lactic acid being in the blood *[1 mark]*.

Page 95
Warm-Up Questions
1) True
2) fermentation

3)   e.g. increases breathing rate / increases breath volume / increases heart rate
4)   urea

Exam Questions

1.1   glucose $\rightarrow$ lactic acid *[1 mark]*

1.2   Muscles start using anaerobic respiration when they don't get enough **oxygen** *[1 mark]*. This causes a build up of **lactic acid** *[1 mark]*. After anaerobic respiration stops, the body is left with an oxygen **debt** *[1 mark]*.

2   protein *[1 mark]*

3.1   Any two from: e.g. aerobic respiration uses oxygen, anaerobic respiration does not. / Glucose is broken down fully during aerobic respiration but is only partially broken down during anaerobic respiration. / Aerobic respiration doesn't produce lactic acid, anaerobic respiration does. / Aerobic respiration releases more energy than anaerobic respiration. *[2 marks]*

3.2   glucose + **oxygen** $\rightarrow$ carbon dioxide + **water** *[2 marks — 1 mark for each correct answer.]*

Topic B5 — Homeostasis and Response

Page 100

The Nervous System

Q1   A fast, automatic response to a stimulus *[1 mark]*.

Q2   a)   muscle *[1 mark]*

     b)   The heat stimulus is detected by receptors in the hand *[1 mark]*, which send impulses along a sensory neurone to the CNS *[1 mark]*. The impulses are transferred to a relay neurone *[1 mark]*. They are then transferred to a motor neurone and travel along it to the effector/muscle *[1 mark]*.

Page 101

Investigating Reaction Time

Q1   a)   242 + 256 + 253 + 249 + 235 = 1235 *[1 mark]*
         1235 ÷ 5 = **247 ms** *[1 mark]*

     b)   Any two from: e.g. the hand each person used to click the mouse / the computer equipment/programme used / the amount of energy drink they consumed / the type of energy drink used / the time between consuming the energy drink and taking the test *[2 marks]*.

Page 102

Warm-Up Questions

1)   E.g. body temperature / blood glucose level / water content.
2)   synapse
3)   True
4)   E.g. use the same person to catch the ruler each time. / The person should always use the same hand to catch the ruler. / The ruler should always be dropped from the same height.

Exam Questions

1   sensory neurone *[1 mark]*

2.1   appearance of red triangle *[1 mark]*

2.2   cells in the eye / light receptor cells *[1 mark]*

2.3   muscles (in hand controlling mouse) *[1 mark]*

2.4   343 × 3 = 1029
         1029 – 328 – 346 = **355 ms** *[2 marks for the correct answer, otherwise 1 mark for the correct working]*

Page 105

Controlling Blood Glucose

Q1   Curve 2, because it starts rising after curve 1 starts to rise *[1 mark]*. Insulin is released when the blood glucose concentration gets too high, so insulin must be the second curve *[1 mark]*.

Page 107

Warm-Up Questions

1)   In the blood.
2)   thyroid
3)   False
Type 2 diabetes is where a person becomes resistant to their own insulin.
4)   eating a carbohydrate-controlled diet / taking regular exercise

Exam Questions

1

Hormone	Gland the hormone is released from
Testosterone	Testes
Adrenaline	Adrenal gland
Oestrogen	Ovaries

[1 mark for each correct row]

2   Insulin is released by the **pancreas** *[1 mark]*. Liver and muscle cells convert glucose into **glycogen** *[1 mark]*.

Page 112

Warm-Up Questions

1)   testosterone
2)   FSH/follicle-stimulating hormone
3)   oestrogen and progesterone
4)   A chemical that disables or kills sperm.
5)   False

Exam Questions

1.1   E.g. facial hair in males / breasts in females *[1 mark]*

1.2   Every 28 days *[1 mark]*

2   diaphragm *[1 mark]*

3.1   It is involved in the growth and maintenance of the uterus lining *[1 mark]*.

3.2   LH / luteinising hormone *[1 mark]*

3.3   They stop the hormone FSH from being released *[1 mark]*, which stops eggs maturing *[1 mark]*.

Topic B6 — Inheritance, Variation and Evolution

Page 116

Meiosis

Q1   23 *[1 mark]*

Page 119

Warm-Up Questions

1)   True
2)   two
3)   XX

Exam Questions

1   egg — 23 *[1 mark]*
         fertilised egg — 46 *[1 mark]*

2.1   A polymer made up of two strands *[1 mark]*.

2.2   Its genome *[1 mark]*.
Remember, an organism's genome is its entire set of genetic material. A gene is a short section of DNA and a chromosome is a really long structure, which contains genes.

2.3   DNA contains genes *[1 mark]*. Each gene codes for a certain sequence of amino acids *[1 mark]*. The sequence of amino acids are put together to make a specific protein *[1 mark]*.

3.1   asexual *[1 mark]*

3.2   They will be genetically identical *[1 mark]*.
Remember, asexual reproduction produces clones — offspring are exactly the same as the parent.

Page 122
Inherited Disorders
Q1   75% / 3 in 4 chance *[1 mark]*

Page 123
Family Trees
Q1   Ff *[1 mark]*

Page 125
Warm-Up Questions
1)   An allele.
2)   The characteristics an organism has.
3)   It's a genetic disorder where a baby is born with extra fingers or toes.
4)   E.g. it will help to stop people suffering. / Treating disorders costs a lot of money.

Exam Questions
1   heterozygous — having two different alleles
homozygous — having two of the same allele
genotype — the mix of alleles in an organism
[2 marks for all lines correct, 1 mark for one correct line.]

2.1

[1 mark for correct genotype of offspring, 1 mark for correct genotypes of gametes]

2.2   1 in 2 / 50% *[1 mark]*
2.3   One does not have cystic fibrosis and is not a carrier *[1 mark]*. The other does not have cystic fibrosis but is carrier of the condition *[1 mark]*.

Page 128
Evolution
Q1   There was a variety of tongue lengths in the moth population *[1 mark]*. Moths with longer tongues got more food/nectar and were more likely to survive *[1 mark]*. These moths were more likely to reproduce and pass on the genes responsible for their long tongues *[1 mark]*. So, over time, longer tongues became more common in the moth population *[1 mark]*.

Page 132
Warm-Up Questions
1)   False
2)   False
3)   When no individuals of a species are left.
4)   A drug that kills bacteria.

Exam Questions
1.1   The appearance of this stingray's ancestors showed **variation** *[1 mark]*. The ancestors that looked like flat rocks were hidden, so were more likely to **survive** *[1 mark]*. They were more likely to reproduce and pass their genes on to the next **generation** *[1 mark]*.
1.2   a mutation *[1 mark]*
2.1   The difference in weight must be caused by the environment *[1 mark]*, because the twins have exactly the same genes *[1 mark]*.
In this case, the environment can mean the amount of food each twin eats or the amount of exercise they each do.
2.2   If they were caused by genes both twins should have the birthmark *[1 mark]*.

Page 133
Selective Breeding
Q1   Select rabbits with floppy ears *[1 mark]* and breed them together to produce offspring *[1 mark]*. Select offspring with floppy ears and breed them together *[1 mark]*. Repeat this over many generations until all of the offspring have floppy ears *[1 mark]*.

Page 136
Warm-Up Questions
1)   True
2)   GM/genetically modified crops
3)   E.g. human insulin

Exam Questions
1   In a population of selectively bred plants, there will be fewer different **alleles** *[1 mark]*. This means if a new disease appears, the plants may be **less resistant** *[1 mark]*. Due to inbreeding, there's also more chance of selectively bred plants having **health problems** *[1 mark]*.
2.1   E.g. to improve the size/quality of their fruit. / To make them resistant to insects/herbicides *[1 mark]*.
2.2   E.g. some people are worried that we might not fully understand the effects of GM crops on human health. / Some people say that growing GM crops will negatively affect the number of wild flowers and insects that live in and around the crops. *[1 mark]*
3.1   Difference between generations 2 and 3 = 5750 − 5375 = 375
Percentage change = (375 ÷ 5375) × 100
= 6.976
= **7%** *[2 marks for the correct answer, otherwise 1 mark for correct working.]*
To work out the percentage change, you first need to work out the difference between generations 2 and 3. You then divide the difference by the original average milk yield (generation 2), and multiply by 100 to convert it into a percentage.
3.2   How to grade your answer:

Level 0:   There is no relevant information. *[No marks]*
Level 1:   There are some relevant points describing how a higher milk yield was produced by selective breeding, but the answer is missing some detail. *[1 to 2 marks]*
Level 2:   There is a clear, detailed explanation of how a higher milk yield was produced by selective breeding. *[3 to 4 marks]*

Here are some points your answer may include:
From the existing cows, the farmer selected the cows that produced the highest average milk yield for breeding.
The farmer then selected the offspring that produced the highest average milk yield for breeding.
The farmer would have continued this process over several generations of cows.
After several generations, the farmer would get cows that are able to produce a very high milk yield.

Page 139
Classification
Q1   B and C *[1 mark]*
Q2   *Castor* *[1 mark]*

Page 140
Warm-Up Questions
1)   True
2)   True
3)   genus
4)   species

Exam Questions
1.1   Prokaryotes *[1 mark]*
1.2   Carl Woese *[1 mark]*

2.1 E.g. from gradual replacement by minerals. / From casts and impressions. / From preservation in places where no decay happens *[1 mark]*.

2.2 Many early organisms were soft-bodied, so their tissue decayed away completely *[1 mark]*. Geological activity may have destroyed some of the fossils that were already formed in rock *[1 mark]*.

2.3 They show how much or how little different organisms have changed over time *[1 mark]*.

3.1 Species C *[1 mark]*

3.2 Yes, you would expect Species D to look similar to Species E because they share a recent common ancestor, so they are closely related/have similar genes *[1 mark]*.

Topic B7 — Ecology

Page 141

Competition

Q1 Any three from: e.g. light / water / space / mineral ions *[3 marks]*.

Q2 The water boatmen would not have to compete with the diving beetles for food *[1 mark]* so there would be more food for the water boatmen *[1 mark]*.

Page 144

Adaptations

Q1 a) A behavioural adaptation *[1 mark]*.

b) E.g. it has webbed feet/flippers to help it swim for food *[1 mark]*. / It has a thick layer of fat to help it keep in heat *[1 mark]*.

Page 145

Food Chains

Q1 a) grass *[1 mark]*

b) three *[1 mark]*

c) grasshopper *[1 mark]*

d) The population of grasshoppers could increase *[1 mark]* as there's nothing to eat them *[1 mark]*. The population of snakes could decrease *[1 mark]* as there's nothing for them to eat *[1 mark]*.

Page 146

Warm-Up Questions

) e.g. territory/space / mates

) e.g. moisture level / light intensity / temperature / carbon dioxide level / wind intensity/direction / oxygen level / soil pH/mineral content

) False

Food chains always start with a producer.

) it would decrease

Exam Questions

.1 A habitat is the place where an organism lives *[1 mark]*.

.2 community *[1 mark]*

.1 tertiary consumer *[1 mark]*

.2 The algae are producers *[1 mark]*. They are the source of biomass/energy for the food chain *[1 mark]*.

.1 It doesn't sweat *[1 mark]*.

.2 Any two from: e.g. it lives in burrows. / It holds its tail over its head. / It lies in the shade. / It lies with its limbs spread out wide. *[2 marks]*

Page 147

Using Quadrats

Q1 1200 ÷ 0.25 = 4800
4800 × 0.75 = **3600 tulips in total**
[2 marks for correct answer, otherwise 1 mark for correct working]

Pages 151-152

Warm-Up Questions

1) E.g. a quadrat.

2) e.g. rain / snow / hail

3) To break down/decay dead matter and animal waste.

4) Through burning.

Exam Questions

1 Energy from the sun makes water **evaporate** *[1 mark]*. When warm water vapour gets higher up, the water vapour cools and **condenses** *[1 mark]*. Water falls from the clouds as **precipitation** *[1 mark]*.

2.1 E.g. the number of poppies increases with increasing distance from the wood *[1 mark]*.

2.2 E.g. moisture level / soil pH / soil mineral content / wind intensity / wind direction *[1 mark]*.

3.1 eating *[1 mark]*

3.2 respiration *[1 mark]*

3.3 Microorganisms break down/decay the dead matter *[1 mark]* and return carbon to the air as carbon dioxide through respiration *[1 mark]*.

3.4 photosynthesis *[1 mark]*

4.1 Grass species = 47 squares out of 100
= (47 ÷ 100) × 100 = **47%** *[1 mark]*

Remember, to calculate percentage cover of an organism in a quadrat you count the number of squares which are more than half covered by the organism.

4.2 E.g. because there may have been too many blades of grass to count each one individually / it's hard to count individual blades of grass *[1 mark]*.

Page 159

Warm-Up Questions

1) Biodiversity is the variety of different species of organisms on Earth, or within an ecosystem.

2) e.g. toxic chemicals for farming / household waste in landfill

3) methane and carbon dioxide

4) True

5) The cutting down of forests.

Exam Questions

1.1 Hedgerows provide a habitat for lots of types of organisms *[1 mark]*.

1.2 The animal species can be bred in captivity *[1 mark]*. This makes sure that some individuals will survive if the species dies out in the wild *[1 mark]*. These individuals can then be released into the wild to replace a population that has been wiped out *[1 mark]*.

2.1 E.g. smoke *[1 mark]*, acidic gases *[1 mark]*.

2.2 E.g. sewage/toxic chemicals from industry can pollute lakes/rivers/oceans. / Fertilisers/other chemicals used on land can be washed into water *[1 mark]*.

2.3 E.g. the human population size is increasing *[1 mark]*, people around the world are demanding a higher standard of living *[1 mark]*.

2.4 This reduces the amount of land taken over for landfill, so ecosystems can be left alone *[1 mark]*.

3 How to grade your answer:

Level 0: There is no relevant information. *[No marks]*

Level 1: There is a brief explanation of how deforestation contributes to global warming. The answer lacks coherency. *[1 to 2 marks]*

Level 2: There is some explanation of how deforestation contributes to global warming, and the answer has some structure. *[3 to 4 marks]*

Level 3: There is a clear and detailed explanation of how deforestation contributes to global warming. *[5 to 6 marks]*

Here are some points your answer may include:
Trees take in carbon dioxide/CO_2 from the atmosphere during photosynthesis.

So cutting down trees means that less carbon dioxide/CO_2 is removed from the atmosphere.

Trees 'lock up' some of the carbon in their wood.

So removing trees means that less is locked up.

Carbon dioxide/CO_2 is released when trees are burnt to clear land.

Microorganisms feeding on dead wood release carbon dioxide/CO_2 through respiration.

Carbon dioxide is a greenhouse gas.

An increase in greenhouse gas levels causes global warming.

Topic C1 — Atomic Structure and the Periodic Table

Page 161

Atoms

Q1   protons = atomic number = 31 *[1 mark]*

electrons = protons = 31 *[1 mark]*

neutrons = mass number – atomic number
    = 70 – 31 = **39** *[1 mark]*

Page 163

Isotopes

Q1   E.g. isotopes are atoms with the same number of protons but a different number of neutrons / isotopes have the same atomic number but different mass numbers *[1 mark]*.

Q2   Relative atomic mass =

$$\frac{(92.2 \times 28) + (4.7 \times 29) + (3.1 \times 30)}{92.2 + 4.7 + 3.1} \text{ [1 mark]}$$

$$= \frac{2581.6 + 136.3 + 93}{100} = \frac{2810.9}{100}$$

$$= 28.109 = \textbf{28.1 } \textit{[1 mark]}$$

Page 164

Compounds

Q1 $(2 \times Na) + (1 \times C) + (3 \times O) = \textbf{6 } \textit{[1 mark]}$

Q2   Aluminium — **2 atoms**, sulfur — **3 atoms** and oxygen — **12 atoms** *[1 mark]*.

Page 166

Chemical Equations

Q1 $2Fe + 3Cl_2 \rightarrow 2FeCl_3$ *[1 mark]*

Q2   a) water $\rightarrow$ hydrogen + oxygen *[1 mark]*

b) $2H_2O \rightarrow 2H_2 + O_2$
    [1 mark for correct reactants and products, 1 mark for correctly balancing]

Pages 167-168

Warm-Up Questions

1)   The total number of protons and neutrons.

2)   An element is a substance made up of atoms that all have the same number of protons in their nucleus.

3)   False

4)   calcium chloride

5) $2K + 2H_2O \rightarrow 2KOH + H_2$

Exam Questions

1.1

Relative charge of a proton	Relative charge of a neutron
+1	0

[1 mark]

1.2   in the nucleus *[1 mark]*

1.3   8 *[1 mark]*

Atoms have the same number of protons as electrons. This is what makes them neutral.

1.4   1 *[1 mark]*

2.1   12 *[1 mark]*

2.2   11 *[1 mark]*

2.3   Na *[1 mark]*

3.1   methane and oxygen *[1 mark]*

3.2   carbon dioxide and water *[1 mark]*

3.3   oxygen/O_2 *[1 mark]*

3.4 $CH_4 + \textbf{2O}_2 \rightarrow CO_2 + \textbf{2}H_2O$ *[1 mark]*

4.1 $\textbf{H}_2\textbf{SO}_4 + \textbf{2NH}_3 \rightarrow (NH_4)_2SO_4$ *[1 mark for correct reactants, 1 mark for correctly balancing the equation]*

4.2   4 *[1 mark]*

These elements are hydrogen, sulfur, oxygen and nitrogen.

4.3   8 *[1 mark]*

There are 4 hydrogen atoms in NH_4 and there are two lots of NH_4 present in the formula of ammonium sulfate.

5.1   Isotopes are different forms of the same element, which have the same number of **protons** *[1 mark]* but different numbers of **neutrons** *[1 mark]*.

5.2   5 *[1 mark]*

The number of protons in an atom is equal to its atomic number.

5.3 $(20 \times 10) + (80 \times 11) = 1080$

Relative atomic mass $= 1080 \div 100 = \textbf{10.8}$

[3 marks for correct answer, otherwise 1 mark for calculating sum of (isotope abundance × isotope mass number), 1 mark for dividing by 100.]

Page 174

Fractional Distillation

Q1   Ethanol *[1 mark]*. Ethanol has the second lowest boiling point and will be collected once all the methanol has been distilled off and the temperature increased *[1 mark]*.

Page 175

Warm-Up Questions

1)   False

2)   evaporation / crystallisation

3)   the top

Exam Questions

1.1   Put the paper in a beaker of solvent *[1 mark]*.

1.2   Pencil marks are insoluble/won't dissolve in the solvent / pen would dissolve in the solvent *[1 mark]*.

2   Step 1 is to dissolve the ammonium sulfate *[1 mark]*.

Step 2 is to remove the sharp sand *[1 mark]*.

Step 3 is to evaporate the water and produce dry crystals of ammonium sulfate *[1 mark]*.

3.1   How to grade your answer:

Level 0:   There is no relevant information. *[No marks]*

Level 1:   Some steps of the method and some relevant safety precautions are included, but the answer is not in a logical order. Following the method given would not produce the results desired. *[1 to 2 marks]*

Level 2:   Most of the method and safety precautions are described, but the steps may not be in a completely logical order and some detail may be missing. *[3 to 4 marks]*

Level 3:   The method and safety precautions are described in full, with the steps given in a logical order. Following the method would produce the results desired. *[5 to 6 marks]*

Here are some points your answer may include:

Method

Put the solution of propanone and water in the flask and heat it.

Monitor the temperature using the thermometer.

Heat the mixture until the temperature reaches around 56 °C. 56 °C is the boiling point of propanone, so at this temperature the propanone in the solution will start to evaporate and turn into a gas.

The boiling point of water is higher (100 °C), so at 56 °C the water will remain as a liquid.

The propanone gas travels from the flask into the condenser. In the condenser, the gas is cooled and condenses/turns back into a liquid.

The liquid propanone runs out of the condenser and is collected in the beaker.

The water is left behind in the flask.

Safety precautions

Take care with Bunsen burner/heat source.

Alternatively, use a heat source that doesn't involve a flame, such as a water bath or electric heater.

Avoid touching hot glassware.

Make sure no solution gets on the outside of the flask where it could catch fire.

Make sure the flask is tightly sealed so no propanone gas escapes.

Work in a fume cupboard.

Wear a lab coat, gloves and goggles.

3.2   fractional distillation *[1 mark]*

The boiling points of water and methanoic acid are too close together to allow them to be separated by simple distillation, so fractional distillation must be used.

Page 178
Electronic Structure
Q1   The inner shells are always filled first *[1 mark]*.

Q2   2,8,8 or

[1 mark]

Page 181
Warm-Up Questions
1)   In the 'plum pudding' model, the atom is a ball of positive charge, with negatively charged electrons scattered in this ball.

2)   a)   2

     b)   8

3)   Mendeleev left gaps in his table so that elements with similar properties stayed in the same groups.

Exam Questions
1.1   by atomic weight *[1 mark]*

1.2   by atomic number *[1 mark]*

1.3   They have the same number of electrons in their outer shell *[1 mark]*.

2.1

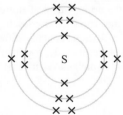

[1 mark]

It's fine if you used dots instead of crosses to show the electrons in your diagram.

2.2   Group 6 *[1 mark]*

2.3   Any one from: oxygen / selenium / tellurium / polonium / livermorium *[1 mark]*

2.4   2 *[1 mark]*

Page 184
Group 1 Elements
Q1   lithium + water → lithium hydroxide + hydrogen *[1 mark]*

Page 186
Group 7 Elements
Q1 $Br_2 + 2NaI \rightarrow 2NaBr + I_2$ *[1 mark]*

Pages 188-189
Warm-Up Questions
1)   positive ions

2)   Any two from: e.g. strong / can be bent or hammered into different shapes (malleable) / conduct heat / conduct electricity / high melting point / high boiling point.

3)   lithium chloride / LiCl

4)   negative

5)   Group 0

Exam Questions
1.1   fluorine *[1 mark]*.

1.2   iodine *[1 mark]*

2.1   alkali metals *[1 mark]*

2.2   To the right of the line *[1 mark]*. Since it does not conduct electricity, it must be a non-metal *[1 mark]*.

3.1   They have a single outer electron which is easily lost so they are very reactive *[1 mark]*.

3.2   potassium hydroxide *[1 mark]* and hydrogen *[1 mark]*

3.3   The outer electron is further from the nucleus and so less attracted to the nucleus *[1 mark]*.

4.1   ionic bonds *[1 mark]*

4.2   displacement reaction *[1 mark]*

4.3   Chlorine is more reactive than iodine *[1 mark]*, because more reactive elements displace less reactive elements in displacement reactions / chlorine displaces iodine from the potassium iodide *[1 mark]*.

4.4   Group 0 elements don't need to lose or gain electrons to have a full outer shell. / Group 0 elements already have a full outer shell *[1 mark]*.

Topic C2 — Bonding, Structure and Properties of Matter

Page 190
Ions
Q1   Noble gas electronic structures have a full shell of outer electrons *[1 mark]*, which is a very stable structure *[1 mark]*.

Page 192
Ionic Bonding
Q1   The transfer of one electron from one atom to another *[1 mark]*.

Q2

[1 mark for arrow showing electron transferred from potassium to bromine, 1 mark for correct outer shell electron configurations (with or without inner shells), 1 mark for correct charges]

Page 194
Ionic Compounds
Q1   a)   It will have a high melting point *[1 mark]* because a lot of energy is needed to break the strong attraction between the ions/the strong ionic bonds *[1 mark]*.

     b)   When melted, the ions are free to move, so they can carry electric charge *[1 mark]*.

     c)   The compound contains magnesium and sulfide ions. Magnesium is in Group 2 so forms 2+ ions *[1 mark]*, and sulfur is in Group 6 so forms 2– ions *[1 mark]*. The charges balance with one of each ion, so the empirical formula is MgS *[1 mark]*.

Warm-Up Questions
1)   A charged particle
2)   1–
3)   high
4)   True
5) $Al(OH)_3$

Exam Questions
1.1

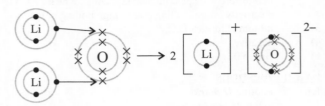

[1 mark for correct electron arrangement and charge on lithium ion, 1 mark for correct electron arrangement and charge on oxygen ion]

1.2   LiCl *[1 mark]*
2.1   Sodium ions have a 1+ charge and chloride ions have a 1– charge *[1 mark]* so one sodium ion is needed to balance the charge on one chloride ion *[1 mark]* (so the empirical formula is NaCl).
2.2   Sodium chloride contains many strong ionic bonds *[1 mark]* which require a lot of energy to break *[1 mark]*.
2.3   In solid sodium chloride, the ions are held in place, so cannot conduct electricity *[1 mark]*. In molten sodium chloride, the ions are free to move, so can conduct electricity *[1 mark]*.
2.4   Dissolve it in water/solution *[1 mark]*.

Page 198
Covalent Bonding
Q1

[1 mark for 3 shared pairs of electrons, 1 mark for correct number of electrons in outer shell of each atom (with or without inner shells on nitrogen)]

Page 199
Warm-Up Questions
1)   A chemical bond made by the sharing of a pair of electrons between two atoms.
2)   1
3)   False
Most simple molecular substances are gases or liquids at room temperature.
4)   covalent bonds

Exam Questions
1.1   8 *[1 mark]*
1.2   3 *[1 mark]*
1.3   0 *[1 mark]*
All the bonds in the molecule are single covalent bonds — you get double bonds in molecules like oxygen.
2

[1 mark for showing 1 pair of shared electrons between H atoms]

3.1   1 *[1 mark]*
3.2   The forces of attraction between molecules/intermolecular forces are very weak, so are easily overcome *[1 mark]*.
3.3   Hydrogen chloride isn't charged / doesn't contain any ions or delocalised electrons to carry a charge *[1 mark]*.

Page 200
Polymers
Q1 $(C_2H_3Cl)_n$ *[1 mark]*

Page 201
Giant Covalent Structures
Q1   E.g. graphite contains layers of carbon atoms *[1 mark]* arranged in hexagons *[1 mark]*. Each carbon atom forms three covalent bonds *[1 mark]*. There are no covalent bonds between the sheets *[1 mark]*.

Page 204
Warm-Up Questions
1)   True
2)   solid
3)   E.g. diamond is much harder than graphite. Diamond doesn't conduct electricity whereas graphite does.
4)   The layers of atoms/ions in metals are able to slide over each other.

Exam Questions
1

Diamond	A structure of carbon in which each carbon atom forms four covalent bonds.
	A carbon structure shaped like a closed tube or hollow ball.
Graphite	A layered structure in which each carbon atom forms three covalent bonds.

[1 mark for each correctly drawn line]

2.1   In a giant covalent structure, all of the atoms are bonded to each other with strong covalent bonds *[1 mark]*. It takes lots of energy to break these bonds and melt the solid *[1 mark]*.
2.2   E.g. diamond / graphite / silicon dioxide *[1 mark]*
3.1   A metal mixed with another metal (or element) *[1 mark]*.
3.2   The delocalised electrons are free to move *[1 mark]*, so can carry thermal/heat energy *[1 mark]*.
3.3   Iron is a metal, so has a regular arrangement of atoms *[1 mark]*, which means that they can slide over each other *[1 mark]*, making iron soft. Steel contains different sized atoms *[1 mark]* which makes it harder for them to slide over each other *[1 mark]* (which makes it hard).

Page 207
States of Matter
Q1 a) solid *[1 mark]*
    b) liquid *[1 mark]*
    c) liquid *[1 mark]*
    d) gas *[1 mark]*

Page 208
Warm-Up Questions
1)   Solid
2)   True
3)   The forces of attraction increase and lots of bonds form between the gas particles, so the gas becomes a liquid.
4) $Na^+_{(aq)}$

Exam Questions

1 In solids, there are **strong** *[1 mark]* forces of attraction between particles, which hold them in fixed positions in a **regular** *[1 mark]* arrangement. The particles don't **move** *[1 mark]* from their positions, so solids keep their shape. The **hotter** *[1 mark]* the solid becomes, the more the particles in the solid vibrate.

2.1 C *[1 mark]*

2.2 Boiling/evaporation *[1 mark]*

2.3 The particles are free to move about / only have weak forces of attraction between them *[1 mark]*, so they spread out to fill the container *[1 mark]*.

Topic C3 — Quantitative Chemistry

Page 209
Relative Formula Mass

Q1 a) A_r of C = 12 and A_r of O = 16
M_r of CO_2 = 12 + (2 × 16) = **44** *[1 mark]*

b) A_r of Li = 7, A_r of O = 16 and A_r of H = 1
So M_r of LiOH = 7 + 16 + 1 = **24** *[1 mark]*

c) A_r of H = 1, A_r of S = 32
and A_r of O = 16
M_r of H_2SO_4 = (2 × 1) + 32 + (4 × 16)
= **98** *[1 mark]*

Q2 A_r of K = 39, A_r of O = 16
and A_r of H = 1
M_r of KOH = 39 + 16 + 1 = 56 *[1 mark]*
$\frac{39}{56}$ × 100 = **70%** *[1 mark]*

Page 210
Conservation of Mass

Q1 Total mass on the left hand side
= $M_r(H_2SO_4)$ + 2 × $M_r(NaOH)$
M_r of H_2SO_4 = (2 × 1) + 32 + (4 × 16) = 98
2 × M_r of NaOH = 2 × (23 + 16 + 1) = 80
So total mass on the left hand side
= 98 + 80 = **178** *[2 marks for 178, 1 mark for either 98 or 80]*
Total mass on right hand side
= $M_r(Na_2SO_4)$ + 2 × $M_r(H_2O)$
M_r of Na_2SO_4 = (2 × 23) + 32 + (4 × 16) = 142
2 × M_r of H_2O = 2 × [(2 × 1) + 16] = 36
142 + 36 = **178** *[2 marks for 178, 1 mark for either 142 or 36]*
The total M_r on the left-hand side is equal to the total M_r on the right-hand side, so mass is conserved *[1 mark]*.

Page 211
Conservation of Mass

Q1 One of the reactants is a gas *[1 mark]* and the products are solid, liquid or aqueous *[1 mark]*.

Q2 The mass will decrease *[1 mark]*.

Page 212
Concentrations of Solutions

Q1 Volume = 15 ÷ 1000
= 0.015 dm^3 *[1 mark]*
Concentration = mass ÷ volume
= 0.6 ÷ 0.015
= **40 g/dm^3** *[1 mark]*

Pages 213-214
Warm-Up Questions

1) The sum of the relative atomic masses of all the atoms in a compound.

2) (2 × 1) + 16 = 18

3) True

4) One of the reactants is a gas that is found in air, and all the products are solids, liquids or in solution.

5) g/dm^3

Exam Questions

1 111 *[1 mark]*
M_r of $CaCl_2$ = 40 + (35.5 × 2) = 111

2 magnesium fluoride, MgF_2 *[1 mark]*

3 48.6 + 26.4 = **75.0 kg** *[1 mark]*

4 M_r of $Zn(CN)_2$ = 65 + ((12 + 14) × 2) = **117** *[1 mark]*

5.1 M_r of $Ca(OH)_2$ = 40 + ((16 + 1) × 2) = **74** *[1 mark]*

5.2 Total mass of reactants = 18.5 g + 31.5 g = 50 g
So mass of calcium nitrate = 50 g – 9 g = **41 g** *[1 mark]*

6.1 M_r of $MgCO_3$ = 24 + 12 + (16 × 3) = **84** *[1 mark]*

6.2 The mass will decrease *[1 mark]*

7.1 1500 ÷ 1000 = **1.5 dm^3** *[1 mark]*
1000 cm^3 = 1 dm^3

7.2 mass = concentration × volume = 12 × 1.5 = **18 g**
[2 marks for correct answer, otherwise 1 mark for correct working.]

8.1 concentration = mass ÷ volume = 40 ÷ 0.25 = **160 g/dm^3**
[2 marks for correct answer, otherwise 1 mark for correct working.]

8.2 M_r of KOH = 39 + 16 + 1 = 56
Percentage mass of potassium in KOH
= $\frac{A_r \text{ of potassium} \times \text{number of atoms of potassium}}{M_r \text{ of potassium hydroxide}}$ × 100
= $\frac{39 \times 1}{56}$ × 100 = 69.642...% = **69.6%**
[3 marks for correct answer rounded to 3 s.f., otherwise 2 marks for correct answer not rounded to 3 s.f., or 1 mark for correct M_r of KOH.]

Topic C4 — Chemical Changes

Page 216
Acids, Bases and Their Reactions

Q1 calcium carbonate + hydrochloric acid
→ calcium chloride + carbon dioxide + water *[1 mark for calcium chloride, 1 mark for carbon dioxide and water]*
$CaCO_3$ + 2HCl → $CaCl_2$ + CO_2 + H_2O
[1 mark for the correctly balanced equation]

Page 218
Warm-Up Questions

1) 0-14

2) Neutral

3) False
Universal indicator turns green if it is added to a substance with a pH of 7.

4) $CaCO_3$

5) Copper sulfate and water

Exam Questions

1.1 OH^- *[1 mark]*

1.2 neutralisation *[1 mark]*

2.1 Alkalis *[1 mark]*

2.2 2HNO₃ + Mg(OH)₂ → **Mg(NO₃)₂ + 2H₂O**
[1 mark for formulas of both products correct, 1 mark for putting a 2 in front of H_2O to balance the equation]

3.1 Calcium chloride *[1 mark]*

3.2 The salt will be contaminated by the indicator *[1 mark]*.

3.3 How to grade your answer:
Level 0: There is no relevant information. *[No marks]*
Level 1: Simple statements are made relating to relevant scientific techniques, however points are not linked, and the answer lacks detail.
[1 to 2 marks]

Level 2: A coherent answer is given that follows a logical order and shows a good understanding of the relevant scientific techniques, including filtration and crystallisation. However, some detail may be missing. *[3 to 4 marks]*

Level 3: A detailed and coherent description of a relevant scientific technique is given. The answer shows a clear understanding of the techniques of filtration and crystallisation. *[5 to 6 marks]*

Here are some points your answer may include:
Gently warm the hydrochloric acid using a Bunsen burner/ water bath, then turn off the Bunsen burner/remove the acid from the water bath.
Add the calcium carbonate to the warmed hydrochloric acid until no more reacts / there is calcium carbonate at the bottom of the flask.
Use filter paper and a funnel to filter the solution, in order to remove any unreacted calcium carbonate.
Crystallise the solution by gently heating it using a water bath/electric heater to evaporate off some of the water.
Then leave the solution to cool.
Crystals of calcium chloride/the soluble salt should form.
The crystals can be filtered out of the solution and then dried.

Page 220
Metals and Their Reactivity
Q1 $2Na_{(s)} + 2H_2O_{(l)} \rightarrow 2NaOH_{(aq)} + H_{2(g)}$
[1 mark for correct reactants and products, 1 mark for correctly balancing, 1 mark for state symbols]

Page 221
Extracting Metals
Q1 $2PbO + C \rightarrow 2Pb + CO_2$
[1 mark for the correct products, 1 mark for the correctly balanced equation]
Q2   Carbon is less reactive than calcium and therefore will not reduce calcium oxide / Calcium is more reactive than carbon, so calcium oxide won't be reduced by carbon *[1 mark]*.

Page 222
Warm-Up Questions
1)   True
2)   magnesium chloride
3)   A metal hydroxide and hydrogen

Exam Questions
1   Magnesium *[1 mark]*
2.1   potassium/sodium/calcium *[1 mark]*
2.2   copper *[1 mark]*
Metals below hydrogen in the reactivity series don't react with acids.
2.3   The reaction with iron would be less violent than with zinc *[1 mark]* because iron is less reactive/ lower in the reactivity series than zinc *[1 mark]*.
2.4   potassium/sodium/calcium/magnesium *[1 mark]*
Carbon can only be used to extract metals that are below it in the reactivity series. Metals above carbon must be extracted using electrolysis.
3.1   The copper was displaced from its salt *[1 mark]*.
3.2   Zinc is more reactive/higher in the reactivity series than copper *[1 mark]*.
3.3   e.g. iron *[1 mark]*
Metal X must be more reactive than copper (as it displaces copper from copper sulfate), but less reactive than zinc (which it doesn't displace from zinc sulfate).

Page 224
Electrolysis
Q1   a)   chlorine gas/Cl_2 *[1 mark]*
       b)   calcium atoms/Ca *[1 mark]*

Page 226
Electrolysis of Aqueous Solutions
Q1   a)   bromine gas/Br_2 *[1 mark]*
       b)   copper atoms/Cu *[1 mark]*

Page 227
Warm-Up Questions
1)   The cathode
2)   True
3)   Hydrogen gas

Exam Questions
1   When molten sodium chloride is electrolysed, the **negative** *[1 mark]* chloride ions move towards the anode and form chlorine gas. At the cathode, the **sodium** *[1 mark]* ions gain electrons.
The sodium chloride is molten, so there are no hydrogen ions present to compete with the sodium ions at the cathode.
2.1 Pb^{2+} *[1 mark]*
2.2 Br^- *[1 mark]*
2.3   Molten lead *[1 mark]*
2.4 Br_2 *[1 mark]*

Topic C5 — Energy Changes

Page 230
Reaction Profiles
Q1

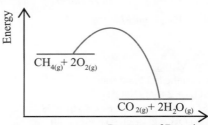

[1 mark for correct axes, 1 mark for correct energy levels of reactants and products, 1 mark for correct shape of curve linking the reactants to the products]

Page 231
Warm-Up Questions
1)   True
2)   E.g. in hand warmers/self-heating cans/burning fuels.
3)   It will decrease.
4)   endothermic
5)   The overall energy change/the energy given out in the reaction.

Exam Questions
1   thermal decomposition *[1 mark]*
2.1   E.g. to ensure that they are the same temperature before beginning the reaction/ to know their initial temperature *[1 mark]*.
2.2   E.g. to insulate the cup/reduce the amount of heat lost to the surroundings *[1 mark]*.
2.3   The student should repeat the experiment under the same conditions *[1 mark]*. The measurement is repeatable if the student obtains similar results in both repeats *[1 mark]*.
3   C *[1 mark]*

Topic C6 — The Rate and Extent of Chemical Change

Page 236

Warm-Up Questions

1) E.g. the rusting of iron is a reaction that happens very slowly. Burning/combustion is a very fast reaction.
2) They must collide with enough energy / the activation energy.
3) Breaking a reactant into smaller pieces increases its surface area to volume ratio. This means there is a greater surface area available for collisions to occur on, so the rate of reaction is increased.
4) True

Exam Questions

1.1 The rate would increase *[1 mark]*.
1.2 The rate would increase *[1 mark]*.
2.1 A *[1 mark]*
2.2 C *[1 mark]*
2.3 Increasing the temperature means that the reactant particles move faster *[1 mark]*, so collisions between reactant particles are more frequent *[1 mark]*. The particles also have more energy *[1 mark]*, so more collisions have enough energy to make the reaction happen *[1 mark]*.

3.1

[1 mark]

3.2

[1 mark for curve drawn with a lower maximum]

Page 240

Graphs of Reaction Rate Experiments

Q1 E.g.

[1 mark for correctly marking on all 6 points, 1 mark for choosing a sensible scale for the axes, 1 mark for drawing a line of best fit]

Page 241

Working Out Reaction Rates

Q1 Mean rate = amount of reactant used ÷ time
    = 6.0 g ÷ 200 s *[1 mark]*
    = 0.03 g/s *[1 mark]*

Pages 244-245

Warm-Up Questions

1) e.g. a mass balance / gas syringe / stopwatch / timer
2) Reaction A
3) False
A steep tangent on a rate graph means that the rate of reaction is fast at that point in time.
4) The backwards reaction

Exam Questions

1.1 The reaction is reversible *[1 mark]*.
1.2 As A and B react, their concentrations will **fall** *[1 mark]* and the rate of the forwards reaction will decrease. As C and D are made, the **backwards** *[1 mark]* reaction speeds up. After a while, the amounts of products and reactants will remain **constant** *[1 mark]*. The system is at equilibrium.
2.1 stopwatch/stopclock/timer *[1 mark]*
2.2 gas syringe *[1 mark]*
2.3 E.g. mass balances are very accurate / give very accurate results *[1 mark]*.
2.4 E.g. potentially harmful gases are released into the room *[1 mark]*.
3.1 17 cm³ *[1 mark]*
3.2 Manganese(IV) oxide was the most effective catalyst *[1 mark]* because it led to the greatest volume of oxygen being produced over the time period measured/increased the rate of reaction by the greatest amount *[1 mark]*.
3.3 Draw tangents to each of the curves at 2 minutes *[1 mark]*, and compare how steep they are *[1 mark]*. A steeper tangent means a faster rate (and vice versa) *[1 mark]*.
4 How to grade your answer:
   Level 0: There is no relevant information. *[No marks]*
   Level 1: Simple statements are made which demonstrate some understanding of how colour change or the formation of a precipitate can be used to investigate the rate of reaction. The response lacks detail or logical structure. *[1 to 2 marks]*
   Level 2: The method is described in relevant detail and demonstrates a broad understanding of how colour change or the formation of a precipitate can be used to investigate the rate of reaction. The answer follows a logical structure. *[3 to 4 marks]*

   Here are some points your answer may include:
   Add one of the reactants to a conical flask.
   Place the conical flask over a black mark or cross that can be seen through the solution.
   Add the second reactant to the conical flask.
   The solution will turn cloudy.
   Use a stopwatch to measure the time taken for the mark to disappear.
   The faster the mark disappears, the faster the rate of reaction.
   Repeat the experiment using different concentrations of reactant Y.
   All other variables must be kept constant.

5.1 mean rate of reaction = amount of product formed ÷ time
    mean rate of reaction = 46 ÷ 250 = **0.18 cm³/s**
    [3 marks for a rate between 0.17 cm³/s and 0.19 cm³/s, otherwise 1 mark for correct working and 1 mark for correct units]
   Remember that the reaction is complete at the point where the line goes flat, so the total reaction time is 250 seconds.
5.2 mean rate of reaction = amount of product formed ÷ time
    mean rate of reaction = (44 − 29) ÷ (150 − 40) = 15 ÷ 110
    mean rate of reaction = 0.1363... = **0.14** cm³/s
    [3 marks for correct answer, otherwise 1 mark for calculating change in x (110) and 1 mark for calculating change in y (15)]

Topic C7 — Organic Chemistry

Page 247
Hydrocarbons
Q1 $C_2H_6 + 3\frac{1}{2}O_2 \rightarrow 2CO_2 + 3H_2O$ or
$2C_2H_6 + 7O_2 \rightarrow 4CO_2 + 6H_2O$
***[1 mark for correct reactants and products,
1 mark for correctly balancing]***

Page 249
Fractional Distillation
Q1   The diagram shows that hydrocarbons with shorter chains drain out further up the column *[1 mark]*, so petrol has a shorter chain than diesel *[1 mark]*.

Page 251
Cracking
Q1 $C_5H_{12} \rightarrow C_2H_4 + C_3H_8$ *[1 mark]*

Pages 252-253
Warm-Up Questions
1)   methane, ethane, propane, butane
2)   (single) covalent bonds
3)   They release lots of energy when burnt.
4)   long-chain/large hydrocarbons

Exam Questions
1   ethane *[1 mark]*
2   Flammability decreases and viscosity increases. *[1 mark]*
3.1   butane *[1 mark]*
3.2 C_4H_{10} *[1 mark]*
3.3   Any two from: e.g. polymers / solvents / lubricants / detergents *[2 marks — 1 mark for each correct answer]*
4   Oxygen reacts with a fuel and energy is released. *[1 mark]*
5.1 $C_9H_{20} \rightarrow \mathbf{C_7H_{16}} + \mathbf{C_2H_4}$ *[1 mark]*
5.2   When bromine water is shaken with heptane, it remains orange in colour *[1 mark]*. When bromine water is shaken with ethene, it turns from orange to colourless *[1 mark]*.
Ethene is an alkene, so it turns bromine water colourless. Heptane is an alkane, so it doesn't react with bromine water.
6.1   A *[1 mark]*
6.2   Hydrocarbons with longer chains have higher boiling points *[1 mark]*. The column is hot at the bottom and gets cooler as you go up *[1 mark]*. The longer hydrocarbons condense back to liquids and drain out of the column at the higher temperatures lower down *[1 mark]*.

Topic C8 — Chemical Analysis

Page 257
Interpreting Chromatograms
Q1 $R_f = \frac{6.3}{8.4} = \mathbf{0.75}$ *[1 mark]*

Pages 260-261
Warm-Up Questions
1)   Impurities in a substance will increase the boiling point of the substance and may also cause the substance to boil across a range of temperatures.
2)   e.g. paint/cleaning products/fuels/medicines/ cosmetics/fertilisers/metal alloys/food/drink
3)   Chromatography separates out the substances present in a mixture.
4)   False
An R_f value represents the ratio between the distance travelled by a dissolved substance and the distance travelled by the solvent.

Exam Questions
1

[3 marks — 1 mark for each correctly drawn line.]
2   Substance B only *[1 mark]*
Impurities lower the melting point of a substance, and may cause the sample to melt across a range of temperatures. Substance B is the only substance in the table that has an experimental melting point that is exactly the same as the data book value, so it is the only pure substance.
3   The brown group *[1 mark]*
4.1   B *[1 mark]*
4.2   C *[1 mark]*
4.3 R_f = distance moved by substance ÷ distance moved by solvent
$R_f = 9.0 ÷ 12.0 = \mathbf{0.75}$
[2 marks for correct answer, otherwise 1 mark for correctly substituting the values into the formula for R_f.]

Topic C9 — Chemistry of the Atmosphere

Page 264
Climate Change and Greenhouse Gases
Q1   The sun gives out short wavelength radiation *[1 mark]* which is reflected back by the Earth as long wavelength/ thermal radiation *[1 mark]*. The thermal radiation is absorbed by greenhouse gases in the atmosphere *[1 mark]*. Greenhouse gases give out the thermal radiation in all directions including back towards the Earth, causing the temperature to rise *[1 mark]*.

Pages 268-269
Warm-Up Questions
1)   Volcanoes
2)   e.g. limestone / coal
3)   e.g. coal / crude oil / natural gas
4)   True
5)   e.g. acid rain / respiratory problems

Exam Questions
1.1   When green plants first evolved, the Earth's early atmosphere was mostly **carbon dioxide** *[1 mark]* gas. These plants produced **oxygen** *[1 mark]* by the process of photosynthesis. Some of the **carbon** *[1 mark]* from dead plants eventually became 'locked up' in fossil fuels.
1.2 $6\mathbf{CO_2} + 6\mathbf{H_2O} \rightarrow C_6H_{12}O_6 + 6\mathbf{O_2}$
[1 mark for both CO_2 and O_2 formulas correct, 1 mark for correct balancing of H_2O]
1.3   C *[1 mark]*
2.1   Natural gas *[1 mark]*
Natural gas, crude oil and coal are the three fossil fuels you need to know about.
2.2   combustion / oxidation *[1 mark]*
2.3   e.g. particulates / soot *[1 mark]*
2.4   E.g. if breathed in, they can cause respiratory problems. / They reflect sunlight back into space, causing global dimming *[2 marks — 1 mark for each correct description]*.
2.5   It doesn't have any colour or smell *[1 mark]*.
3.1   Methane *[1 mark]*

3.2 Greenhouse gases give out the thermal radiation in all directions *[1 mark]*, so some of the radiation is returned to earth *[1 mark]* where it warms the surface of the planet *[1 mark]*.

3.3 Any two from: e.g. deforestation / burning fossil fuels / agriculture / using landfill sites *[2 marks — 1 mark for each correct answer]*

3.4 E.g. rising sea levels / increased flooding / changes in rainfall / more frequent/severe storms / changes in temperature *[1 mark]*.

3.5 E.g. tax companies and individuals based on the amount of greenhouse gases they emit. / Put a limit on the emissions of all greenhouse gases a company can make. / Invest in research and technology to reduce emissions or capture greenhouse gases before they are released *[1 mark]*.

4 How to grade your answer:
Level 0: There is no relevant information. *[No marks]*
Level 1: There is a brief description of how carbon dioxide was removed from the atmosphere by the oceans, plants and algae, and/or how this led to the formation of coal. However some details are missing or incorrect and the answer lacks structure. *[1 to 2 marks]*
Level 2: There is a detailed description of how the oceans and plants and algae removed carbon dioxide from the atmosphere, and how this led to the formation of coal. The answer is clearly written and logically structured. *[3 to 4 marks]*
Here are some points your answer may include:
Carbon dioxide was removed from the atmosphere by dissolving in the oceans.
The dissolved carbon dioxide formed carbonates/sediments/carbon-containing compounds in the ocean.
Green plants and algae took in carbon dioxide during photosynthesis.
When marine plants and algae died, they were buried on the seabed.
Over a long time, the dead plants were squashed down, forming coal.

Topic C10 — Using Resources

Page 275

Warm-Up Questions
1) e.g. wool / rubber
2) True
3) Any two from: e.g. saves energy needed to make new metals / saves limited supplies of metals from the earth / cuts down on the amount of waste going to landfill.
4) To assess the effect a product would have on the environment over the course of its life.

Exam Questions
1.1 A natural resource that can be remade at least as fast as we use it *[1 mark]*.
1.2 E.g. reuse the cans / recycle the aluminium / use fewer cans *[1 mark]*.
2.1 How to grade your answer:
Level 0: There is no relevant information. *[No marks]*
Level 1: There is a brief discussion of some environmental impacts of each type of bag. The points made are basic, don't link together and don't cover all of the information given in Table 1. If a conclusion is present it may not link to the points made. *[1 to 2 marks]*

Level 2: There is a logical discussion of possible environmental impacts of each type of bag, but there is limited detail. There is a good coverage of the information given in Table 1 and the answer has some structure. A clear conclusion is given. *[3 to 4 marks]*
Level 3: There is a clear and detailed discussion of the possible environmental impacts of each type of bag. The answer has a logical structure and makes good use of the information given in Table 1. A conclusion is present that fits with the points given in the answer. *[5 to 6 marks]*
Here are some points your answer may include:
The raw materials used to make plastic bags come from crude oil, which is a non-renewable resource.
Obtaining crude oil from the ground and processing it uses a lot of energy and results in air pollution due to the release of greenhouse gases.
The raw materials used to make paper bags come from trees. Trees are a renewable resource, although they take up land that could be used for other uses e.g. growing crops.
Cutting down trees and processing the raw timber requires energy.
This energy is often generated by burning fossil fuels, which releases harmful greenhouse gases into the atmosphere.
The manufacture of plastic bags involves many industrial processes (e.g. fractional distillation, cracking, polymerisation), which all require large amounts of energy.
As this energy often comes from burning fossil fuels, the manufacture causes the release of pollution (e.g. greenhouse gases) into the atmosphere.
The waste from the manufacturing of plastic bags can be used to make other products, which reduces the amount of waste being sent to landfill.
Manufacturing paper bags also requires lots of energy. This could come from burning fossil fuels and so would generate pollution, such as greenhouses gases, which have a negative impact on the environment.
The manufacture of paper bags also creates lots of waste, which has to be disposed of and may cause pollution (e.g. if sent to landfill).
Plastic bags are reusable, which could reduce the amount of waste sent to landfill.
Paper bags are usually not reusable, which could increase the amount of waste sent to landfill.
Plastic bags are not biodegradable so will stay in the environment for a long time if disposed of in landfill sites.
Plastic bags can release toxic substances into the ground and pollute the land.
Plastic bags that end up in the oceans can harm marine life and pollute the water.
Plastic bags can be recycled, which would reduce the need to extract raw materials to make new bags.
Paper bags are biodegradable so will break down more easily than plastic bags if sent to landfill sites, reducing the impact on the environment.
Paper bags are also non-toxic, so won't releases poisonous/toxic substances into the environment after being disposed of.
Paper bags can be recycled, which would reduce the need to gather raw materials to make new bags.
2.2 E.g. some things can't be measured, so depend upon a person's own judgement *[1 mark]*. Companies might use selective LCAs to make their product look more environmentally-friendly for advertising purposes *[1 mark]*.

Page 276
Potable Water and Water Treatment
Q1 E.g. the water is filtered using a wire mesh, and then using filter beds *[1 mark]*. The filtered water is then sterilised using chlorine / ozone / ultraviolet light *[1 mark]*.

Page 279
Potable Water and Water Treatment
Q1 Screening — sewage is screened to remove any large bits of material and grit *[1 mark]*.
Sedimentation — heavier solids sink to the bottom to form sludge, while the lighter effluent floats on the top *[1 mark]*.

Pages 280-281
Warm-Up Questions
1) E.g. the levels of dissolved salts in the water aren't too high. / The water has a pH of between 6.5 and 8.5. / There aren't any bacteria or other microbes in the water.
2) True
3) effluent and sludge
4) True

Exam Questions
1.1 Screening *[1 mark]*
1.2 Bacteria *[1 mark]*
2.1 Water that is safe to drink *[1 mark]*.
2.2 To remove any solids from the water *[1 mark]*.
2.3 e.g. chlorine / ozone / ultraviolet light *[1 mark]*
3.1

X

[1 mark]

3.2 When the water evaporates, it is separated from any soluble impurities, which are left in the flask *[1 mark]*. Condensation turns the steam back into liquid water, so it can be collected easily *[1 mark]*.
3.3 E.g. neutralise it / add acid until the pH is 7 *[1 mark]*.
3.4 All the seawater will have evaporated from the round bottomed flask *[1 mark]*.
3.5 The crystals are salts that were in the seawater before it was distilled *[1 mark]*.
The salts won't evaporate with the water, so they get left in the flask.
4.1 E.g. to remove any pollutants *[1 mark]* so that the water doesn't cause health problems / damage the environment *[1 mark]*.
Pollutants could be organic matter, bacteria and viruses etc.
4.2 Effluent is treated by aerobic digestion *[1 mark]* and sludge is treated by anaerobic digestion *[1 mark]*. In both processes, bacteria is used to break down the effluent/sludge *[1 mark]*.
4.3 E.g. it might contain harmful chemicals *[1 mark]*.
Industrial waste always needs further treatment before it is safe to return to the environment.
5.1 Seawater is passed through a membrane, which lets water molecules pass through *[1 mark]*, but traps the salts *[1 mark]*.
5.2 It requires a lot of energy *[1 mark]*.

Topic P1 – Energy

Page 285
Mechanical Energy Transfer
Q1 Energy is transferred mechanically *[1 mark]* from the kinetic energy store of the wind *[1 mark]* to the kinetic energy store of the windmill *[1 mark]*.

Page 286
Kinetic and Potential Energy Stores
Q1 The change in height is 5.0 m. So the energy transferred from the gravitational potential energy store is:
$E_p = mgh = 2.0 \times 9.8 \times 5.0 = 98$ J *[1 mark]*
This is transferred to the kinetic energy store of the object, so $E_k = 98$ J *[1 mark]*
$E_k = \frac{1}{2}mv^2$
so $v^2 = 2E_k \div m$ *[1 mark]*
$= (2 \times 98) \div 2.0$ *[1 mark]*
$= 98$ m²/s²
$v = \sqrt{98} = 9.899...$
$= \textbf{9.9 m/s (to 2 s.f.)}$ *[1 mark]*

Page 288
Specific Heat Capacity
Q1 $\Delta E = mc\Delta\theta$
so $\Delta\theta = \Delta E \div (m \times c)$ *[1 mark]*
$= 50\,000 \div (5 \times 4200)$
$= 2.380...$ °C *[1 mark]*
So the new temperature
$= 5 + 2.380... = 7.380...$
$= \textbf{7 °C (to 1 s.f.)}$ *[1 mark]*

Page 290
Investigating Specific Heat Capacity
Q1 $E = P \times t = 80 \times 200$ *[1 mark]*
$= 16\,000$ J *[1 mark]*
$\Delta E = mc\Delta\theta$, so
$c = \Delta E \div (m \times \Delta\theta)$ *[1 mark]*
$= 16\,000 \div (2 \times 20)$ *[1 mark]*
$= \textbf{400 J/kg°C}$ *[1 mark]*

Pages 291-292
Warm-Up Questions
1) Any two from: mechanically (by a force doing work) / electrically (work done by when a current flows) / by heating / by radiation.
2) Energy is transferred (mechanically) from the chemical energy store of the person's arm to the kinetic energy stores of the arm and the ball.
3) True
4) A lorry travelling at 60 miles per hour.
5) Energy can be transferred usefully, stored or dissipated, but can never be created or destroyed.

Exam Questions
1 The thermal energy store of the metal block *[1 mark]*
2

A skydiver falling from an aeroplane.	elastic potential
A substance undergoing a nuclear reaction.	gravitational potential
A piece of burning coal.	chemical
	nuclear

[3 marks for all correct, otherwise 2 marks for 2 correct or 1 mark for 1 correct]
3.1 The elastic potential energy store of the spring *[1 mark]*
3.2 kinetic energy = ½ × mass × speed² / $E_k = \frac{1}{2}mv^2$ *[1 mark]*
Allow velocity instead of speed in the relationship.

3.3 $E_k = \frac{1}{2} \times 0.20 \times 0.9^2$ *[1 mark]*
   $= \textbf{0.081 J}$ *[1 mark]*

4.1 gravitational potential energy = mass × gravitational field strength × height / $E_p = mgh$ *[1 mark]*

4.2 Rearrange $E_p = mgh$ for h:
   $h = E_p \div (m \times g)$ *[1 mark]*
   $= 137.2 \div (20 \times 9.8)$ *[1 mark]*
   $= \textbf{0.7 m}$ *[1 mark]*

4.3 Energy is transferred from the gravitational potential energy store *[1 mark]* to the kinetic energy store of the load *[1 mark]*.

4.4 Some of the energy would also be transferred to thermal energy store of the air (and the thermal energy store of the load) *[1 mark]*.

5 change in thermal energy = mass × specific heat capacity × temperature change / $\Delta E = mc\Delta\theta$
   So, $c = \Delta E \div (m \times \Delta\theta)$ *[1 mark]*
   $c = 36\,000 \div (0.5 \times 80)$ *[1 mark]*
   $= \textbf{900 J/kg °C}$ *[1 mark]*

Page 293
Power

Q1 $P = E \div t$
   $t = 2 \times 60 = 120$ s *[1 mark]*
   $P = 4800 \div 120$ *[1 mark]*
   $= \textbf{40 W}$ *[1 mark]*

Page 295
Efficiency

Q1 efficiency = useful output energy transfer
   $\div$ total input energy transfer
   $= 225 \div 300$ *[1 mark]*
   $= \textbf{0.75}$ *[1 mark]*

Q2 efficiency = useful power output ÷ total power input
   $= 900 \div 1200 = 0.75$ *[1 mark]*
   useful output energy transfer
   = efficiency × total input energy transfer *[1 mark]*
   $= 0.75 \times 72\,000$ *[1 mark]*
   $= \textbf{54\,000 J}$ *[1 mark]*

Page 296
Warm-Up Questions

1) Power is the rate of energy transfer/doing work.
2) 1 J/s
3) E.g. its thickness/thermal conductivity
4) A material with a high thermal conductivity.
5) Some energy is always dissipated, so less than 100% of the input energy transfer is transferred usefully.

Exam Questions

1.1 power = work done ÷ time / $P = W \div t$ *[1 mark]*
1.2 1 kJ = 1000 J
   $P = 1000 \div 20$ *[1 mark]*
   $= \textbf{50 W}$ *[1 mark]*
1.3 E.g. by lubricating any moving parts *[1 mark]*
1.4 It will be faster. *[1 mark]*
The motor transfers the same amount of energy, but over a shorter time.
2.1 Any one from: e.g. by heating the fan / by heating the surroundings / transferred away by sound waves *[1 mark]*.
2.2 2 kJ = 2 × 1000 = 2000 J *[1 mark]*
   useful output energy transfer
   = total input energy transfer – wasted output energy transfer
   = 7250 – 2000
   $= \textbf{5250 J}$ *[1 mark]*
2.3 efficiency = $\dfrac{\text{useful output energy transfer}}{\text{total input energy transfer}}$
   $= \dfrac{5250}{7250}$ *[1 mark]*
   $= 0.72413... = \textbf{0.72 (to 2 s.f.)}$ *[1 mark]*

Page 304
Warm-Up Questions

1) Any two from: coal / oil / natural gas.
2) Fossil fuels can be used to generate electricity at any time, but solar power cannot be used at night and is not reliable in cloudy weather.
3) Any one from: e.g. bio-fuels can be used to run vehicles / electricity generated using renewable resources can be used to power vehicles.
4) Any two from: e.g. it releases greenhouse gases and contributes to global warming / it causes acid rain / coal mining damages the landscape.
5) True

Exam Questions

1 wind *[1 mark]*
2 They can produce sulfur dioxide and cause acid rain. *[1 mark]*
3.1 E.g. Heating *[1 mark]*.
3.2 Any two from: e.g. it's expensive to build new renewable power plants / people don't want to live near new power stations / some renewable energy resources aren't very reliable, so they could not be used on their own / it's expensive to switch to cars running on renewable energy *[1 mark for each correct answer]*
4.1 How to grade your answer:
   Level 0: There is no relevant information. *[No marks]*
   Level 1: Some points are made about the environmental impact and reliability of wind power and hydro-electric power, but the energy resources are not directly compared. Answer lacks detail and structure. *[1 to 2 marks]*
   Level 2: At least three valid comparisons are made about the environmental impact and the reliability of wind power and hydro-electric power. Answer has some detail and structure. *[3 to 4 marks]*
   Level 3: At least four valid comparisons are made about the environmental impact and the reliability of wind power and hydro-electric power. Answer is detailed and well-structured. *[5 to 6 marks]*
   Here are some points your answer may include:
   Wind turbines do not do any permanent damage to the landscape.
   Building a hydro-electric power plant does damage the landscape, as it involves flooding a valley.
   Hydro-electric power stations have a larger impact on the local environment than wind turbines since animals and plants in the flooded valley lose their habitats.
   Wind turbines and hydro-electric power stations produce no pollution once they are built.
   However, plants in valleys flooded for hydro-electric power stations can rot, producing greenhouse gases which lead to global warming.
   Hydro-electric power is reliable in countries that have regular rainfall, but wind turbines are unable to produce electricity when wind stops or when the wind is too strong.
   Hydro-electric power stations can respond straight away when there is additional demand, but the power supplied by wind turbines cannot be increased.
4.2 E.g. they cause no pollution *[1 mark]*

Topic P2 — Electricity

Page 306
Charge and Resistance Calculations

Q1 $V = IR$ so $R = V \div I$ *[1 mark]*
   $= 230 \div 5.0$ *[1 mark]*
   $= \textbf{46 }\Omega$ *[1 mark]*

Page 309
I-V Characteristics
Q1 As the current through the lamp increases, the temperature of its filament increases *[1 mark]* causing its resistance to increase *[1 mark]*. A larger resistance means less current can flow per unit potential difference, and so the graph gets shallower *[1 mark]*.

Page 311
Warm-Up Questions
1)

2) Electric current is a flow of electric charge.
3) Ohms / Ω
4) Any one from: e.g. a wire / a fixed resistor
5) In parallel.
6) A graph that shows how the current flowing through a component changes as the potential difference across it varies.

Exam Questions
1.1 $Q = It$ / charge flow = current × time *[1 mark]*.
1.2 Convert from minutes into seconds:
2 minutes = 120 seconds
$Q = It$
$= 0.30 \times 120$
$= \mathbf{36\ C}$
[2 marks for correct answer, otherwise 1 mark for correctly converting from minutes to seconds]
1.3 A filament lamp is a **non-linear** *[1 mark]* component. As the temperature of the filament increases, the **resistance** *[1 mark]* of the lamp increases.
2.1

component X

[1 mark for adding the ammeter in line with component X, 1 mark for adding the voltmeter across component X]
2.2 A straight line *[1 mark]*. Component X is a resistor, which is an ohmic/linear component *[1 mark]*.

Page 313
Sensing Circuits
Q1 E.g.

[1 mark for all symbols correct, 1 mark for the LDR connected in series with a resistor and a source of potential difference, 1 mark for the bulb connected in parallel with the LDR]

Page 315
Series Circuits
Q1 $R_{total} = 4 + 5 + 6 = 15\ \Omega$ *[1 mark]*
$V = I \times R = 0.6 \times 15$ *[1 mark]*
$= \mathbf{9\ V}$ *[1 mark]*

Page 317
Parallel Circuits
Q1 The total current through the circuit decreases *[1 mark]* as there are fewer paths for the current to take *[1 mark]*. The total resistance of the circuit increases *[1 mark]* as, using $V = IR$, a decrease in the total current means an increase in the total resistance *[1 mark]*.

Page 319
Warm-Up Questions
1) Any one from: e.g. in automatic night lights / outdoor lighting / burglar detectors.
2) The resistance decreases.
3) The components are all connected in a line between the ends of the power supply.
4) True
5) The total resistance is the sum of all the resistances.
6) Two resistors connected in series.

Exam Questions
1 Total resistance is equal to the sum of the individual resistances. *[1 mark]*
2.1 $R_{total} = R_1 + R_2$
$= 3 + 2$ *[1 mark]* $= \mathbf{5\ \Omega}$ *[1 mark]*
2.2 0.4 A *[1 mark]*. Current is the same throughout a series circuit *[1 mark]*.
2.3 $V_{total} = V_1 + V_2$
$V_2 = V_{total} - V_1$
$= 4.0 - 1.6$ *[1 mark]*
$= \mathbf{2.4\ V}$ *[1 mark]*
3.1 When current flows, the LED will be lit. *[1 mark]*
3.2 When the lights are switched off, the resistance of the LDR increases *[1 mark]*. As a result the total resistance of the circuit also increases, since it is equal to the sum of the individual resistances *[1 mark]*.

Page 321
Power of Electrical Appliances
Q1 $E = P \times t$ so $P = E \div t$ *[1 mark]*
$= 6000 \div 30$ *[1 mark]*
$= \mathbf{200\ W}$ *[1 mark]*
Q2 $E = P \times t$ *[1 mark]*
$= 250 \times (2 \times 60 \times 60)$
$= 1\ 800\ 000\ J$ *[1 mark]*
$E = 375 \times (2 \times 60 \times 60)$
$= 2\ 700\ 000\ J$ *[1 mark]*
So change in energy is
$2\ 700\ 000 - 1\ 800\ 000$
$= \mathbf{900\ 000\ J}$ *[1 mark]*

Page 322
More on Power
Q1 $E = Q \times V$
$= 10\ 000 \times 200$ *[1 mark]*
$= \mathbf{2\ 000\ 000\ J}$ *[1 mark]*
Q2 $P = V \times I$
$= 12 \times 4.0$ *[1 mark]*
$= \mathbf{48\ W}$ *[1 mark]*
Q3 $R = P \div I^2$ *[1 mark]* $= 2300 \div 10.0^2$ *[1 mark]*
$= \mathbf{23\ \Omega}$ *[1 mark]*

Page 325
Warm-Up Questions
1) The live wire, neutral wire, and earth wire.
2) Energy is transferred electrically to the thermal energy store of the heating element.
3) power = (current)^2 × resistance / $P = I^2R$
4) The network of cables and transformers that distributes electricity across the country.

Exam Questions
1.1 **Step-up** *[1 mark]* transformers are used between the power station and the transmission cables. This increases the **potential difference** *[1 mark]*, so that power may be transferred more efficiently.
1.2 230 V ac *[1 mark]*
2.1 $P = VI$ / power = potential difference × current *[1 mark]*
2.2 $P = VI$
$I = \dfrac{P}{V}$
$= \dfrac{2760}{230}$ *[1 mark]*
$= \mathbf{12\ A}$ *[1 mark]*
2.3 E.g. volume of water / starting temperature *[1 mark]*
2.4 Energy transferred = power × time / Power is the rate of energy transfer *[1 mark]*. So kettle B will transfer more energy in the same time *[1 mark]*.

Topic P3 — Particle Model of Matter

Page 329
Measuring Density
Q1 Gemstone's mass = 0.019 kg
$= 0.019 × 1000$
$= 19$ g *[1 mark]*
Gemstone's volume = volume of water pushed out of eureka can = 7.0 cm^3
$\rho = m ÷ V$
$= 19 ÷ 7.0$ *[1 mark]*
$= 2.714...$
$= \mathbf{2.7\ g/cm^3}$ **(to 2 s.f.)** *[1 mark]*

Page 331
Specific Latent Heat
Q1 $E = m × L = 0.25 × 120\,000$ *[1 mark]*
$= \mathbf{30\,000\ J}$ *[1 mark]*

Pages 332-333
Warm-Up Questions
1) In a solid, the particles are close together and are held in a regular, fixed pattern.
2) A measure of how much mass there is in a certain space.
3) It increases.
4) The specific latent heat of vaporisation of a substance is the amount of energy needed to change 1 kg of that substance from a liquid to a gas.
5) J/kg

Exam Questions
1 If a liquid is heated to a certain temperature it starts to boil and turns into a **gas** *[1 mark]*. Another process that causes this change of state is **evaporation** *[1 mark]*.
2.1 The densities of each of the toy soldiers are the same, but their masses may vary. *[1 mark]*
2.2 200 g = 0.2 kg
density = mass ÷ volume = 0.2 ÷ (2.5 ×10^{-5}) *[1 mark]*
$= \mathbf{8000\ kg/m^3}$ *[1 mark]*
3 $E = mL = 0.40 × 1200$ *[1 mark]*
$= \mathbf{480\ J}$ *[1 mark]*
4.1 The volume of the pendant *[1 mark]*.
The mass of the pendant *[1 mark]*.

4.2 E.g. measure the mass of the pendant using the mass balance *[1 mark]*. Fill the eureka can with water to just below the spout, then place the measuring cylinder beneath the spout *[1 mark]*. To measure the volume of the pendant, submerge the pendant in the water, catching the displaced water in the measuring cylinder *[1 mark]*. Measure the volume of the displaced water, which is equal to the volume of the pendant *[1 mark]*. Divide the mass of the pendant by the volume of the pendant to find the density *[1 mark]*.

With questions where you have to describe a method, make sure your description is clear and detailed. You could also pick up some of the marks by describing how you'd do repeats, take averages and other ways in which you'd make it a fair test.

5.1 The substance is melting *[1 mark]*.
5.2 Melting point = −7 °C *[1 mark]*
Boiling point = 58 °C *[1 mark]*
6 How to grade your answer:
Level 0: There is no relevant information. *[No marks]*
Level 1: There is a brief explanation of what happens to the particles in the gas as the container is heated. *[1 to 2 marks]*
Level 2: An attempt is made to use the particle model to explain how gas particles create pressure in a sealed container. This is linked to a brief explanation of why the pressure of the gas increases as the container is heated. *[3 to 4 marks]*
Level 3: The particle model is used to provide a clear explanation of how gas particles create pressure in a sealed container. This is used to give a detailed explanation of why the pressure of the gas increases. *[5 to 6 marks]*
Here are some points your answer may include:
In a sealed container, the gas particles are free to move around.
The particles collide with the walls of the container.
Each collision exerts a force on the walls.
The overall force creates an outward pressure.
When the container is heated, energy is transferred to the particles' kinetic energy stores.
This means that the particles move faster.
Since the particles are moving faster, they collide with the container walls more often.
So the force exerted on the container walls, and therefore the pressure, increases as the container is heated.

Topic P4 — Atomic Structure

Page 337
Types of Nuclear Radiation
Q1 E.g. Alpha would not be suitable because it is stopped by a few cm of air or a sheet of paper *[1 mark]*. It would not be able to pass through the packaging to sterilise the equipment *[1 mark]*.

Page 338
Nuclear Equations
Q1 $14 + 4 = \mathbf{18}$ *[1 mark]*
The mass number of a nucleus reduces by 4 during alpha decay, so to find what the mass number would have been before the decay, you need to add 4 on.
Q2 $^{219}_{86}Rn \rightarrow ^{215}_{84}Po + ^{4}_{2}He$
[1 mark for correct layout, 1 mark for correct symbol for an alpha particle, 1 mark for total atomic and mass numbers being equal on both sides]

Page 341
Half-Life
Q1   16 seconds *[1 mark]*
41 is half of 82, meaning the activity of the sample halved in 16 seconds. Remember, half-life is the time taken for the activity of a sample to fall to half of its starting value.
Q2   Initial count-rate = 168 cps
     After 1 half-life, count-rate = $168 \div 2 = 84$ cps
     After 2 half-lives, count-rate = $84 \div 2 = 42$ cps
     After 3 half-lives, count-rate = $42 \div 2 = 21$ cps *[1 mark]*
     So, it took 3 half-lives for the count-rate to drop to 21 cps.
     This means that 60 minutes is equal to 3 half-lives *[1 mark]*.
     So, the half-life of the sample = $60 \div 3$
                   = **20 minutes** *[1 mark]*

Pages 344-345
Warm-Up Questions
1)   Evidence from alpha particle scattering experiments showed that the plum pudding model could not be correct. The evidence suggested that atoms were mostly empty space, and that most of the mass was in the centre of the atom as a small, positive nucleus.
2)   An atom contains a tiny, positively charged, nucleus made up of protons and neutrons. The nucleus is surrounded by electrons, which orbit the nucleus in energy levels.
3)   Electromagnetic radiation.
4)   A positive ion.
Atoms are neutral overall. If an atom loses an electron, it has more positive protons than negative electrons. So it now has a positive charge.
5)   The mass number tells you the total number of protons and neutrons.
6)   Alpha decay: mass number decreases by 4 and the atomic number decreases by 2.
     Gamma decay: the mass and atomic numbers don't change.
7)   Contamination occurs when radioactive atoms get onto or inside an object. Irradiation occurs is when radiation from a radioactive sources reaches an object.
8)   Gamma radiation is less ionising than alpha or beta radiation, so it does the least harm as it passes through the body.

Exam Questions
1.1   Protons *[1 mark]*, neutrons *[1 mark]*
1.2   Atoms with the same atomic number but a different mass number *[1 mark]*.
2

Particle	Charge	Number present in an atom of iodine-131
Proton	positive	53
Neutron	zero	78
Electron	negative	53

[1 mark for each correct answer]

The bottom number in $^{131}_{53}I$ is the atomic number, which is the number of protons. The top number is the total number of protons and neutrons. So there are $131 - 53 = 78$ neutrons.
3

[1 mark for each correct line]
4.1   Beta (particles) *[1 mark]*, because the radiation passes through the paper, but not the aluminium *[1 mark]*.
4.2   E.g. a Geiger-Muller tube (and counter) *[1 mark]*
5.1   28 minutes *[1 mark]*
The initial activity is 740 Bq. Half of this is $740 \div 2 = 370$ Bq. The activity falls to this level between 20 and 30 minutes, so from the options, 28 minutes must be the half-life.

5.2   Irradiation from the source isn't much of a concern because alpha radiation only travels a few centimetres in air and cannot get through the skin to damage organs *[1 mark]*. However, if the student's hands are contaminated by atoms of the radioactive source, they could end up inside her body, where the alpha radiation would do a lot of damage as it is highly ionising *[1 mark]*.

Topic P5 — Forces

Page 348
Weight, Mass and Gravity
Q1   a) $W = mg = 5 \times 9.8$ *[1 mark]*
            = **49 N** *[1 mark]*
    b) $W = 5 \times 1.6$ *[1 mark]* = **8 N** *[1 mark]*

Page 349
Resultant Forces and Work Done
Q1   20 cm = 0.2 m *[1 mark]*
     $W = Fs = 20 \times 0.2$ *[1 mark]*
           = **4 J** *[1 mark]*

Page 350
Warm-Up Questions
1)   friction
2)   the magnitude of the vector
3) a) kg
    b) N
4)   Add the forces together.

Exam Questions
1.1   force *[1 mark]*
1.2   14 kg *[1 mark]*
2.1 $800 - (300 + 200) =$ **300 N** *[1 mark]* **down** *[1 mark]*
2.2 $x - 400 = 0 \Rightarrow x =$ **400 N** *[1 mark]*
3.1   Work done = force × distance / $W = Fs$ *[1 mark]*
3.2 $W = 44\,000 \times 750$ *[1 mark]*
         = **33 000 000 J** *[1 mark]*
         = **33 000 kJ** *[1 mark]*
Remember, to convert from J to kJ, divide by 1000.

Page 352
Forces and Elasticity
Q1   2 cm = 0.02 m *[1 mark]*
     $F = ke$ so $k = F \div e$ *[1 mark]*
             = $1 \div 0.02$ *[1 mark]*
             = **50 N/m** *[1 mark]*

Page 354
Investigating Springs
Q1   2.5 cm = 0.025 m *[1 mark]*
     $E_e = \frac{1}{2}ke^2 = \frac{1}{2} \times 40 \times (0.025)^2$ *[1 mark]*
        = **0.0125 J** *[1 mark]*

Page 355
Warm-Up Questions
1)   true
2)   false
3)   metres

Exam Questions
1.1 $F = ke$ / Force = spring constant × extension *[1 mark]*
1.2 $k = F \div e$ *[1 mark]*
        = $4 \div 0.05$ *[1 mark]*
        = **80 N/m** *[1 mark]*
2.1   E.g. the spring used (so the spring constant remains the same) *[1 mark]*

2.2   E.g. the mass attached to the spring / the force applied to the spring *[1 mark]*

2.3   Extension = 4.0 cm = 0.040 m
Work done = $\frac{1}{2} \times 175 \times 0.040^2$ *[1 mark]*
= **0.14** *[1 mark]* **J** *[1 mark]*
You can read the extension from the graph. Don't forget to convert it to m.

Page 356
Distance, Displacement, Speed, Velocity
Q1 $s = vt$ so $v = s \div t$ *[1 mark]*
= 200 ÷ 25 *[1 mark]*
= **8 m/s** *[1 mark]*

Page 357
Acceleration
Q1 $u = 0$ m/s, $v = 7$ m/s, $a = g = 9.8$ m/s^2,
$s = (v^2 - u^2) \div 2a$ *[1 mark]*
= (49 – 0) ÷ (2 × 9.8) *[1 mark]*
= **2.5 m** *[1 mark]*

Page 358
Distance-Time Graphs
Q1   E.g.

[1 mark for a curved line with an increasing positive gradient, 1 mark for the line becoming a straight line with a positive gradient, 1 mark for the line then becoming horizontal]

Page 359
Velocity-Time Graphs
Q1   E.g.

[1 mark for a straight, horizontal line representing constant speed, 1 mark for a straight line with a positive gradient representing constant acceleration, 1 mark for a straight, horizontal line at a different velocity to the initial velocity to represent a different constant speed]

Q2

[1 mark for an upwards curved acceleration line to 20 m/s, 1 mark for a straight line representing steady speed, 1 mark for a straight line representing deceleration]

Page 361
Warm-Up Questions
1)   Speed is a scalar, velocity is a vector / velocity has a direction, speed does not.
2)   a)   E.g. 3 m/s
      b)   E.g. 30 m/s
      c)   E.g. 250 m/s
Your answers may be slightly different to these, but as long as they're about the same size, you should be fine to use them in the exam.

3)   true
4)   a flat section.
5)   0 N.

Exam Questions
1   acceleration = (10 – 2.0) ÷ 20 *[1 mark]*
= **0.4 m/s^2** *[1 mark]*

2.1   The cyclist travels at a constant speed (of 3 m/s) between 5 s and 8 s *[1 mark]*, then decelerates (with decreasing deceleration) between 8 s and 10 s *[1 mark]*.

2.2   Acceleration is given by the gradient of a velocity-time graph.
change in y = 3 – 0 = 3 m/s
change in x = 5 – 2 = 3 s
acceleration = 3 ÷ 3 *[1 mark]* = **1 m/s^2** *[1 mark]*

3.1   Distance = speed × time / $s = vt$ *[1 mark]*

3.2   Distance rolled = 0.46 × 2.4 *[1 mark]*
= 1.104 *[1 mark]*
= **1.1 m (to 2 s.f.)** *[1 mark]*

3.3 $v^2 - u^2 = 2as$
$a = \dfrac{v^2 - u^2}{2s}$ *[1 mark]*
$= \dfrac{12^2 - 0^2}{2 \times 8}$ *[1 mark]*
= **9 m/s^2** *[1 mark]*

Page 362
Newton's First and Second Law
Q1 $F = ma = (80 + 10) \times 0.25$ *[1 mark]*
= **22.5 N** *[1 mark]*

Page 363
Newton's Third Law
Q1   Any one from: e.g the gravitational force of the Earth attracts the car and the gravitational force of the car attracts the Earth *[1 mark]* / the car exerts a normal contact force down against the ground and the normal contact force from the ground pushes up against the car *[1 mark]* / the car (tyres) pushes the road backwards and the road pushes the car (tyres) forwards *[1 mark]*.

Page 366
Warm-Up Questions
1)   true
2)   Boulder B
Boulder B needs a greater force to accelerate it by the same amount as boulder A.
3)   true
This is Newton's Third Law.

Exam Questions
1.1   The ball exerts a force of –520 N on the bat *[1 mark]*.
1.2   The acceleration of the ball will be **greater than** that of the bat because it has a smaller mass. *[1 mark]*
1.3   Force = mass × acceleration
acceleration = force ÷ mass *[1 mark]*
= 520 ÷ 1.6 *[1 mark]*
= **325 m/s^2** *[1 mark]*

2.1   0 N *[1 mark]*
The van is travelling at a constant speed in one direction so the resultant force must be zero.

2.2   The driving force decreases *[1 mark]*
The wind blowing in the opposite direction to the van's movement increases *[1 mark]*

2.3 $F = ma$
= 2500 × 1.4 *[1 mark]*
= **3500 N** *[1 mark]*
opposite to the direction of motion *[1 mark]*

Page 368
Braking Distance

Q1   Energy in car's kinetic energy store
$= \frac{1}{2} \times m \times v^2$
$= \frac{1}{2} \times 1000 \times 10^2$ *[1 mark]*
$= 50\ 000$ J *[1 mark]*
To stop the car, the brakes must do work to transfer all the energy away from the car's kinetic energy store:
$\frac{1}{2} \times m \times v^2 = F \times d$ *[1 mark]*
So $F \times d = 50\ 000$
Rearrange for F:
$F = 50\ 000 \div d$
$= 50\ 000 \div 50$ *[1 mark]*
$= \textbf{1000 N}$ *[1 mark]*

Page 369
Reaction Times

Q1   a) $v^2 - u^2 = 2as$
$v^2 = 2 \times 9.8 \times 0.162 + 0$ *[1 mark]* $= 3.1752$ m²/s²
$v = \sqrt{3.1752} = 1.781...$ m/s *[1 mark]*
$a = \Delta v \div t$ so
$t = \Delta v \div a$ *[1 mark]*
$= 1.781... \div 9.8$ *[1 mark]* $= 0.181...$ s
$= \textbf{0.18 s (to 2 s.f.)}$ *[1 mark]*

    b)   His reaction time is longer in the evening *[1 mark]* so whilst driving, he may take longer to react to a hazard, meaning his thinking distance would be longer *[1 mark]*.

Page 370
Warm-Up Questions

1)   reaction time / speed / tiredness / drugs / alcohol.
2)   The braking distance.
3)   Large decelerations may lead to brakes overheating/ the car skidding.
4)   true

Exam Questions

1.1   Thinking distance *[1 mark]*.
1.2   The distance the car travels during its deceleration whilst the brakes are being applied *[1 mark]*.
2.1   It reduces the frictional force of the tyres on the road, which increases the braking distance *[1 mark]*.
2.2   E.g. decrease their speed *[1 mark]*.
2.3   Energy transferred from:
The car's kinetic energy stores *[1 mark]*
Energy transferred to:
The brakes' thermal energy stores *[1 mark]*
3.1   Average reaction time $= (0.24 + 0.19 + 0.23) \div 3$ *[1 mark]*
$= 0.22$ s *[1 mark]*
3.2   E.g. use the same ruler in each test / add a ball of modelling clay to the bottom of the ruler to help it fall straight down each time / repeat the test more times and take an average *[1 mark]*.

Topic P6 – Waves

Page 373
Wave Speed

Q1 $7.5 \div 100 = 0.075$ m *[1 mark]*
wave speed = frequency × wavelength,
so frequency = wave speed ÷ wavelength *[1 mark]*
$= 0.15 \div 0.075$ *[1 mark]*
$= \textbf{2 Hz}$ *[1 mark]*

Page 376
Refraction

Q1   E.g.

[1 mark for correctly drawing the boundary and the normal
1 mark for drawing an incident ray at the correct angle,
1 mark for drawing the refracted ray at the correct angle]

Page 377
Warm-Up Questions

1)   E.g. If an object is dropped into calm water, ripples spread out. The ripples don't carry the water or the object away with them though. / If a guitar string is strummed, the sound waves don't carry the air away from the guitar. If they did, a wind would be created.
2)   In a longitudinal wave, the vibrations are parallel to the direction of travel/energy transfer.
3)   rarefactions
4)   true

Exam Questions

1.1   E.g. The particles vibrate at right angles to the direction of energy transfer *[1 mark]*
1.2   5 cm *[1 mark]*
1.3   2 m *[1 mark]*
2.1   The wavelength of the sound waves *[1 mark]*.
2.2   wave speed = frequency × wavelength / $v = f\lambda$ *[1 mark]*
2.3 $v = f\lambda$
$= 50.0 \times 6.8$ *[1 mark]*
$= \textbf{340}$ *[1 mark]* m/s *[1 mark]*

Pages 384-385
Warm-Up Questions

1)   gamma rays
2)   7
3)   Gamma rays are created by changes in the nucleus of an atom.
4)   E.g. Infrared cameras / heating / cooking
5)   Any two from: e.g. sunburn / the skin can age prematurely / the risk of skin cancer is increased.

Exam Questions

1   visible light *[1 mark]*
2.1   X-rays *[1 mark]*
2.2   E.g. Exposure could cause cancer / cell mutations / damage cells *[1 mark]*.
3.1   low-frequency infrared *[1 mark]*
3.2   They don't travel faster than radio signals because all electromagnetic waves travel at the same speed in a vacuum *[1 mark]*.
4.1   Any one from: e.g. time temperature increase is measured over / type/size of beaker / the amount of water in each beaker / the size/thickness of each piece of card / the distance of each thermometer from the beaker / the height of each thermometer *[1 mark]*.
4.2   Any one from: e.g. be careful when pouring/ carrying hot water / don't touch the beakers until they have cooled down *[1 mark]*.
4.3   29 °C *[1 mark]*
4.4   More infrared radiation is emitted from matt surfaces than from shiny surfaces *[1 mark]*.
4.5   Any one from: e.g. repeat the experiment and calculate averages / use infrared detectors instead of thermometers *[1 mark]*

Topic P7 — Magnetism and Electromagnetism

Page 388
Electromagnetism
Q1   E.g. for current out of the page:

*[1 mark for concentric circles getting further apart,
1 mark for arrows on field lines with correct direction]*

Page 390
Warm-Up Questions
1)

2)   The direction of the magnetic field.
3)   By wrapping it into a spring-shaped coil.

Exam Questions
1.1

[1 mark for arrows on all lines pointing north to south].

1.2   Attraction *[1 mark]* — opposite poles attract *[1 mark]*.
2   Cobalt is an example of a **magnetic material** *[1 mark]*.
       The force between a piece of cobalt and a bar
       magnet is always **attractive** *[1 mark]*.
3.1   Concentric circles around the wire / circles centred
       on the wire *[1 mark]*. The field will be in a
       clockwise direction around the wire *[1 mark]*.

*If you need to state the direction of a circular field, it's usually easiest to
describe the field as either going clockwise or anticlockwise.*

3.2   The field lines of the loops line up *[1 mark]*.
       The field lines are now closer, meaning the
       magnetic field is stronger *[1 mark]*.

Biology Practice Paper 1

Pages 402-415
1.1   C *[1 mark]*
A is a bronchus, B is the heart and D is an alveolus.
1.2   D *[1 mark]*
1.3   Epithelial tissue — A group of similar cells that work
       together to carry out a function.
       Respiratory system — A group of organs working together to
       perform a function.
       Lungs — A group of different tissues that work together to
       perform a certain function.
       *[2 marks for all lines correct, otherwise 1 mark for
       one line correct]*
1.4   37 *[1 mark]*
*When you're calculating a rate, you always divide by time. So here, you
need to divide the number of breaths by the number of minutes.*
1.5   Gas A — oxygen *[1 mark]*
       Gas B — carbon dioxide *[1 mark]*
2.1   oxygen *[1 mark]*
2.2   chloroplast *[1 mark]*
2.3   making cell walls *[1 mark]*
2.4   damaged *[1 mark]*
2.5   6 *[1 mark]*

2.6   light intensity *[1 mark]*
3.1   Protease — Converts proteins into amino acids.
       Lipase — Converts lipids into fatty acids and glycerol.
       *[2 marks for two lines correct, otherwise 1 mark for
       one line correct]*
3.2   The active sites of different enzymes have different
       shapes *[1 mark]*. The substance involved in a reaction has
       to fit into the active site for the enzyme to work *[1 mark]*.
3.3   Enzymes are changed during reactions *[1 mark]*.
3.4   In order to grow, organisms need to transfer energy using
       respiration *[1 mark]*. Cells need glucose for respiration
       [1 mark]. Amylase provides this glucose by breaking
       down starch *[1 mark]*.
4.1   The loss of water from a plant *[1 mark]*.
4.2   9 a.m. *[1 mark]*
Each division on the x-axis is one hour.
4.3   E.g. day 2 was colder. / Day 2 was less windy. / Day 2 was
       wetter/more humid. / The light intensity was lower on day 2
       [1 mark].
4.4   Low light intensity at night meant the stomata closed,
       allowing less water vapour to escape. *[1 mark]*.
4.5   guard cells *[1 mark]*
5.1

*[3 marks — 1 mark for a suitable y-axis scale, 2 marks for
all bars correct (or 1 mark if two or more bars correct)]*

5.2   Growth medium number 1 *[1 mark]*
5.3   Any two from: e.g. the temperature in the incubator / the
       size of the tissue samples/blocks / the volume of growth
       medium used *[2 marks — 1 mark for each correct answer]*.
5.4   E.g. grow multiple blocks of stem tissue on
       each growth medium *[1 mark]* and find the
       mean for each growth medium *[1 mark]*.
5.5   asexual reproduction *[1 mark]*
5.6   E.g. to prevent the species from going extinct *[1 mark]*.
6.1   cell membrane *[1 mark]*
6.2   *E.coli* bacteria *[1 mark]*
E. coli bacteria are prokaryotes.
6.3   image size = 0.054 × 500 *[1 mark]*
               = 27 mm
               = **2.7 cm** *[1 mark]*
6.4   *Euglena* is a single-celled organism so has a large
       surface area compared to its volume *[1 mark]*.
6.5   How to grade your answer:
       Level 0: No relevant information is given. *[No marks]*
       Level 1: There is a brief comparison of plant and
                 animal cells, including at least one similarity
                 and one difference. *[1 to 2 marks]*
       Level 2: There is a comparison of plant and animal
                 cells, including at least two similarities and two
                 differences. Some descriptions of subcellular
                 structures are included. *[3 to 4 marks]*
       Level 3: There is a detailed comparison of plant and
                 animal cells, including at least three similarities
                 and three differences. Detailed descriptions of
                 subcellular structures are included. *[5 to 6 marks]*

Here are some points your answer may include:

Similarities:

Both plant and animal cells have a nucleus, which controls the cell's activities.

Both plant and animal cells contain cytoplasm, which is where most of the cell's chemical reactions take place.

Plant cells and animal cells both have a cell membrane, which controls what goes in and out of the cell.

Mitochondria are found in both plant cells and animal cells — these are where most of the reactions for aerobic respiration take place.

Both plant cells and animal cells have ribosomes, which are where proteins are made.

Differences:

Chloroplasts, the site of photosynthesis, are present in plant cells, but not in animal cells.

Plant cells have a cell wall, which supports and strengthens the cell, but animal cells do not.

Plant cells contain a permanent vacuole, containing cell sap, but animal cells do not.

7.1   By droplets from an infected person's sneeze or cough *[1 mark]*.

7.2   How to grade your answer:

Level 0:   There is no relevant information. *[No marks]*

Level 1:   There are some relevant points explaining how vaccination helps to protect the body against disease but the answer is missing some detail. *[1 to 2 marks]*

Level 2:   There is a clear, detailed explanation of how vaccination helps to protect the body against disease. *[3 to 4 marks]*

Here are some points your answer may include:

The body is injected with small amounts of dead or inactive pathogens.

These pathogens have antigens on their surface, which cause the white blood cells in the body to produce antibodies.

Antibodies attack/kill the pathogens.

If live pathogens of the same type appear again, the white blood cells can quickly produce lots of antibodies to kill the pathogens so the person doesn't get ill.

7.3   E.g. vaccines don't always give you immunity. Some people have a bad reaction to a vaccine *[2 marks — 1 mark for each correct answer]*.

7.4   E.g. stop the mosquitoes from breeding. Protect people from mosquito bites using mosquito nets *[2 marks — 1 mark for each correct answer]*.

7.5   To prevent the fungus spreading to other plants *[1 mark]* by being carried by wind or water *[1 mark]*.

8.1   biuret solution *[1 mark]*

8.2   E.g. make sure the area is well ventilated / wear safety goggles / wear gloves / use a funnel when pouring liquids *[1 mark]*.

8.3   Benedict's solution *[1 mark]*

8.4   A *[1 mark]*

Benedict's solution is blue, and so the sample where it stays blue has no reducing sugars.

8.5   It is covered in many villi that provide a large surface area for diffusion (and active transport) to occur across *[1 mark]*. The villi have a thin wall/single layer of surface cells, which decreases the distance for diffusion to occur across *[1 mark]*. They also have a good blood supply to assist quick absorption *[1 mark]*

8.6   A person with lactose intolerance has little or no lactase to break down the lactose in the drink, so there will be little or no sugar to be absorbed from the small intestine *[1 mark]*.

8.7   Bile emulsifies/breaks down fats *[1 mark]*.

8.8   Fat in the small intestine would not be emulsified/broken down into small droplets *[1 mark]*. This would mean that there is a low surface area for lipase to work on *[1 mark]*, meaning a slow rate of fat digestion *[1 mark]*.

Biology Practice Paper 2

Pages 416-430

1.1   28 days *[1 mark]*

1.2   LH *[1 mark]*

1.3   The hormones are carried in the blood to their target organs *[1 mark]*.

1.4   master gland *[1 mark]*

1.5   Any two from: nerve-controlled responses are fast-acting while hormone-controlled responses have a slower action. / Nerve-controlled responses act for a short time while hormone-controlled responses act for long time. / Nerve-controlled responses act on a precise area while hormone-controlled responses act more generally. *[2 marks — 1 mark for each correct answer]*

2.1   algae *[1 mark]*

2.2   limpet / crab *[1 mark]*

2.3   temperature *[1 mark]*, moisture level *[1 mark]*

2.4

[1 mark for each point plotted correctly]

2.5   The mean number of limpets is lower at the low-tide point than at 28 m from the low-tide point *[1 mark]*.

2.6   Any two from: e.g. variation in competition/predation/ food availability/moisture level/temperature/oxygen level *[2 marks — 1 mark for each correct answer]*

3.1   A form/version of a gene *[1 mark]*.

3.2

	R	r
R	RR	Rr
r	Rr	rr

[2 marks for all genotypes correct, otherwise 1 mark for one or two correct.]

3.3   RR and Rr *[1 mark]*

3.4   0.25 *[1 mark]*

3.5   XY *[1 mark]*

4.1   meiosis *[1 mark]*, four *[1 mark]*, different *[1 mark]*

4.2   28 *[1 mark]*

4.3   Asexual reproduction happens by mitosis *[1 mark]*. This means there's no genetic variation in the offspring *[1 mark]*. The offspring may not have characteristics that are suited to the new conditions and so the population can't adapt to the new conditions *[1 mark]*.

5.1   The highest yielding tomato plants from the first year could have been selected *[1 mark]* and been bred together *[1 mark]*. This could have been repeated every year *[1 mark]*.

5.2   The number of different alleles/genetic variation in the selectively bred tomato population might be low *[1 mark]*. This would mean it's less likely that the tomato plants will have (alleles for) disease resistance *[1 mark]*.

5.3   A process in which genes from one organism are introduced into the genome of another organism *[1 mark]*.

5.4   E.g. to be resistant to herbicides / to be resistant to insects / to produce bigger fruit / to produce more fruit *[1 mark]*.

5 The genetically engineered tomatoes are less likely to affect wild plant populations *[1 mark]*.

1

Pancreas

[1 mark]

2 Insulin causes glucose to move out of the blood and into cells *[1 mark]*.

3

Statement	Type 1	Type 2	Both
Results in a high blood glucose level if left untreated.			✓
The pancreas fails to produce enough insulin.	✓		
Body cells can no longer respond to insulin.		✓	
Must be treated with insulin injections.	✓		

[4 marks — 1 mark for each tick]

.4 percentage increase = $((146 − 89) ÷ 89) × 100$
$= 64\%$ **(2s.f.)**
[2 marks for correct answer, otherwise 1 mark for correct working.]

.1 **21** *[1 mark]*
To find the median, you write out all the results from lowest to highest, e. 10, 21, 21, 35, 37. 21 is in the middle of the list, so it is the median.

.2 $(9 + 14 + 19 + 5 + 3) ÷ 5$
$= 50 ÷ 5$
$= \textbf{10 buttercups per m}^2$ *[2 marks for correct answer, otherwise 1 mark for correct working.]*

.3 E.g. use more quadrats in each field *[1 mark]*.

.4 E.g. more buttercups grow where there is a higher moisture level in the soil *[1 mark]*.

.5 How to grade your answer:
Level 0: There is no relevant information. *[No marks]*
Level 1: There is a brief description of how the student could investigate whether the change in distribution of buttercups is due to variability in the moisture level of the soil. *[1 to 2 marks]*
Level 2: There is a detailed description of how the student could investigate whether the change in distribution of buttercups is due to variability in the moisture level of the soil. *[3 to 4 marks]*
Here are some points your answer may include:
He could use a transect across Field A.
To do this he should mark out a line across the field.
Then he should record the number of buttercups in quadrats placed next to each other/at intervals along the line.
He should also measure the moisture level of the soil at each sampling point (e.g. with a probe).

.1 *Biston [1 mark]*

.2 As a result of mutation(s) *[1 mark]*.

.3 The dark variety is less likely to be eaten by predators in soot polluted areas (because they are better camouflaged) *[1 mark]* so they are more likely to survive to reproduce *[1 mark]*, meaning that the genes for dark colouring are more likely to be passed on to the next generation and become more common in the population *[1 mark]*.

.4 Town B is the most polluted because it contains a higher percentage of dark moths *[1 mark]*.

9.1 Their reaction time was very fast *[1 mark]*.
Their response was involuntary/automatic *[1 mark]*.
If you have to think about what response to give then it's not a reflex action.

9.2 The males in this experiment had a faster mean reaction time than the females *[1 mark]*, so the data supports the scientist's hypothesis *[1 mark]*.

9.3 E.g. the age of the participants. / The strength of the tap on the knee. / Caffeine consumption of the participants prior to the investigation. *[1 mark]*

9.4 How to grade your answer:
Level 0: There is no relevant information. *[No marks]*
Level 1: There is a brief description of some parts of the path taken by a nervous impulse in the reflex. *[1 to 2 marks]*
Level 2: There is some description of the path taken by a nervous impulse in the reflex, but some detail is missing. *[3 to 4 marks]*
Level 3: There is a clear and detailed description of the path taken by a nervous impulse in the reflex. *[5 to 6 marks]*
Here are some points your answer may include:
The impulse travels along a sensory neurone to the central nervous system/spinal cord.
When the impulse reaches a synapse between the sensory neurone and a relay neurone, it triggers chemicals to be released.
These chemicals cause impulses to be sent along the relay neurone.
When the impulse reaches a synapse between the relay neurone and a motor neurone, chemicals are released again which cause impulses to be sent along the motor neurone.
The impulse then reaches the muscle, which contracts to curl the big toe upwards.

Chemistry Practice Paper 1

Pages 431-443

1.1 Neon *[1 mark]*
1.2 Metallic bonding *[1 mark]*
1.3 Copper *[1 mark]*
1.4 Fluorine *[1 mark]*
1.5 Protons = **9** *[1 mark]*
Neutrons = $19 − 9 = \textbf{10}$ *[1 mark]*
Electrons = **9** *[1 mark]*
Remember: number of protons = atomic number, number of neutrons = mass number − atomic number, number of electrons (in a neutral atom) = number of protons.
1.6 potassium chloride *[1 mark]*
1.7 Moving down Group 7, the outer electron shell gets further from the nucleus *[1 mark]*, and so it becomes harder for the halogens to gain an extra electron *[1 mark]*.
2.1 $2560 − 1130 = 1430$ g
$= \textbf{1.43} × \textbf{10}^3$ **g**
[2 marks for correct answer given in standard form, otherwise 1 mark for correct answer not given in standard form.]
Remember, the total mass of the products must always be the same as the total mass of the reactants.
2.2 (aq): aqueous/dissolved in water *[1 mark]*
(s): solid *[1 mark]*
2.3 The reaction produces carbon dioxide gas *[1 mark]*.
This escapes from the beaker, reducing the mass of the reaction mixture *[1 mark]*.

2.4 E.g. 224 cm³ ÷ 1000 = 0.224 dm³
3.4 g ÷ 0.224 dm³ = 15.17... g/dm³
= **15.2 g/dm³ (3 s.f.)**
[3 marks for correct answer given to 3 s.f. or 2 marks for correct answer not given to 3 s.f., otherwise 1 mark for converting from cm³ to dm³.]
Remember, to get from cm³ to dm³ you have to divide by 1000.

3.1 Two or more elements or compounds that are not chemically combined together / don't have any chemical bonds between them *[1 mark]*.

3.2 No chemical reactions take place during fractional distillation *[1 mark]*.

3.3 fractionating column *[1 mark]*

3.4 Compound: ethanoic acid *[1 mark]*
Reason: it has the highest boiling point *[1 mark]*.

3.5 78 °C *[1 mark]*

3.6 Any two from: e.g. wear gloves / wear a lab coat / wear goggles / work in a fume cupboard.
[2 marks — 1 mark for each sensible precaution.]

3.7 The boiling points of methanol and isobutanal are very similar *[1 mark]*.

4.1 E.g.

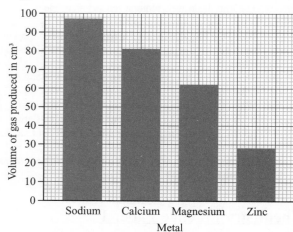

[1 mark for sensible scale on the vertical axis, 1 mark for all 4 bars plotted correctly]
Make sure any graphs you draw fill at least two-thirds of the space given.

4.2 hydrogen *[1 mark]*

4.3 e.g. 17 cm³ *[1 mark for answer in range 1-27 cm³.]*
To answer this question you need to remember than iron is below zinc in the reactivity series. This means it reacts more slowly with the acid, and so not as much gas is produced in 60 seconds.

4.4 $M_r = (2 \times 23) + 32 + (4 \times 16)$
$= 46 + 32 + 64$
$= \textbf{142}$ *[1 mark]*

4.5 percentage mass of an element in a compound
$$= \frac{A_r \times \text{number of atoms of that element}}{M_r \text{ of the compound}} \times 100$$
percentage mass of sodium $= \frac{23 \times 2}{142} \times 100$
$= 32.394...$
$= \textbf{32.4 (3 s.f.)}$
[2 marks for correct answer given to 3 s.f., otherwise 1 mark for correct answer not given to 3 s.f.]
You can still get the marks here if you got the wrong value for the M_r in 4.4 and used that in your calculation. Just make sure you did the right calculation and that your answer is correct for the value of M_r you used.

4.6 electrolyte *[1 mark]*

4.7 oxygen *[1 mark]*
There are no halide ions present in the solution, so it is OH⁻ ions from the water that lose electrons at the anode, forming O_2 (and H_2O).

4.8 Product at cathode: hydrogen *[1 mark]*
Reason: sodium is more reactive than hydrogen *[1 mark]*.

5.1 +1 *[1 mark]*

5.2 Any two from: e.g. potassium fizzes more than sodium, which fizzes more than lithium. / Potassium moves more quickly than sodium, which moves more quickly than lithium. / Potassium appears to melt and a flame is seen, sodium appears to melt but no flame is seen and lithium do not appear to melt.
[2 marks — 1 mark for each correct observation]

5.3 As you go down Group 1 the outer electron gets further from the nucleus *[1 mark]*. This means that the outer electron is more easily lost because it is less attracted to the nucleus *[1 mark]*. So reactivity increases as you go down Group 1/from lithium to sodium to potassium *[1 mark]*.

5.4 $2K + 2H_2O \rightarrow 2KOH + H_2$ *[1 mark]*

5.5 It contains hydroxide ions *[1 mark]*.

5.6 2, 1 *[1 mark]*

6.1 Any two from: e.g. have a lid on the beaker. / Use insulation (e.g. cotton wool) around the beaker. / Use a polystyrene beaker. *[2 marks — 1 mark for each correct answer]*

6.2 temperature change *[1 mark]*
The dependent variable is the variable you measure.

6.3 1 °C *[1 mark]*

6.4 37.5 °C *[1 mark]*

6.5 Temperature change = final temperature − initial temperature
$= 37.5 - 17 = \textbf{20.5 °C}$
[2 marks for correct answer, otherwise 1 mark for writing correct expression for calculating the temperature change]
If your answer to 6.4 was wrong, you can still have both marks for correctly subtracting 17 from it to find the temperature change.

6.6 The reaction was exothermic as the temperature of the surroundings increased during the reaction *[1 mark]*.

7.1

[1 mark for adding seven crosses and one dot to outer shell of Cl⁻ ion, 1 mark for correct charge on both ions.]

7.2 63 °C *[1 mark]*
Substance B is a gas at temperatures above its boiling point of −183 °C. 63 °C is the only temperature given which is higher than −183 °C, so substance B must be a gas at this temperature.

7.3 The molecules in substance A are only attracted to each other by weak intermolecular forces *[1 mark]* which don't need much energy to break/overcome *[1 mark]*.

7.4 Substance C *[1 mark]*. It can conduct electricity when molten or dissolved but not when solid *[1 mark]*.

7.5 How to grade your answer:
Level 0: There is no relevant information. *[No marks]*
Level 1: A brief attempt is made to explain one or two of these properties in terms of structure and bonding. *[1 to 2 marks]*
Level 2: Some explanation of two or three of the properties, in terms of their structure and bonding, is given. *[3 to 4 marks]*
Level 3: Clear and detailed explanation of all three of the properties, in terms of their structure and bonding, is given. *[5 to 6 marks]*
Here are some points your answer may include:
Diamond
Each carbon atom in diamond forms four covalent bonds, making it very hard.
Because it is made up of lots of covalent bonds, which take a lot of energy to break, diamond has a very high melting point.
There are no free/delocalised electrons or ions in the structure of diamond, so it can't conduct electricity.

Graphite
Each carbon atom in graphite forms three covalent bonds, creating sheets of carbon atoms that can slide over each other. The carbon layers are only held together weakly, which is what makes graphite soft.
The covalent bonds between the carbon atoms take a lot of energy to break, giving graphite a very high melting point. Only three out of each carbon's four outer electrons are used in bonds, so graphite has lots of free/delocalised electrons which can conduct electricity.

Chemistry Practice Paper 2

Pages 444-457

1.1 A resource that is used up more quickly than it can be replaced *[1 mark]*.
1.2 Resource 3 *[1 mark]*
1.3 fractional distillation *[1 mark]*
1.4 Before it enters the column, the crude oil is heated until it **evaporates** *[1 mark]*. Different hydrocarbons from the crude oil then leave the column at different points because they have different **boiling points** *[1 mark]*.
1.5 Petrol *[1 mark]*
1.6 Bitumen *[1 mark]*
1.7 Alkene *[1 mark]*
2.1 It is the mobile phase *[1 mark]*
2.2 So the spots of food colouring do not dissolve into the solvent in the beaker *[1 mark]*.
2.3 The student could get another person to do the chromatography experiment too, using the same method and conditions *[1 mark]*, and check that the results from both experiments are similar *[1 mark]*.
2.4 The unknown food colouring is most likely to be pure, as it has only formed one spot on the chromatogram *[1 mark]*.
2.5 three *[1 mark]*
2.6 E.g.
distance moved by spot **Y** from the baseline = 1.9 cm
distance moved by solvent from the baseline = 4.1 cm
R_f = 1.9 ÷ 4.1
= 0.4634...
= 0.46 (2 s.f.)
[5 marks for correct answer in range 0.43-0.50 given to 2 s.f. or 4 marks for correct answer in range 0.43-0.50 not given to 2 s.f., otherwise 1 mark for distance moved by spot Y in range 1.8-2.0 cm, 1 mark for distance moved by solvent in range 4.0-4.2 cm, 1 mark for correctly substituting values into equation.]
2.7 The student's sample is not pure, as its melting point is lower than the data book value for the melting point of the substance *[1 mark]*.
3.1 The concentration of carbon dioxide in the atmosphere has increased over time *[1 mark]*. It stayed roughly the same for the first 75 years before increasing slowly from 1775, then increasingly more rapidly after 1900 *[1 mark]*.
3.2 It has been peer-reviewed *[1 mark]*.
3.3 Greenhouse effect *[1 mark]*
3.4 How to grade your answer:
Level 0: There is no relevant information. *[No marks]*
Level 1: There are some correct and relevant points, but no overall comparison of the environmental impacts. *[1 to 2 marks]*
Level 2: A range of correct and relevant points are made, leading to an overall comparison of the environmental impacts. *[3 to 4 marks]*
Here are some points your answer may include:
Less carbon dioxide is given out manufacturing a plastic bottle than manufacturing a glass bottle.

Transporting plastic bottles produces less carbon dioxide than transporting glass bottles (as they are lighter).
Glass bottles are made mostly from recycled glass.
Plastic bottles are usually produced from new raw materials, using up more crude oil.
More glass bottles than plastic bottles get recycled.
More carbon dioxide is given out manufacturing and transporting glass bottles than plastic bottles, but less waste is produced/less new raw materials are needed as glass bottles are easier to recycle.
Less carbon dioxide is given out manufacturing and transporting plastic bottles than glass bottles, but more waste is produced/more raw materials are needed as plastic bottles are harder to recycle.

4.1 surface area of the calcium carbonate *[1 mark]*
temperature *[1 mark]*
4.2 Bubbling the gas through a solution of calcium hydroxide *[1 mark]*.
4.3 Volume of gas produced after 30 seconds in Experiment 1
= 86-88 cm³ *[1 mark]*
Volume of gas produced after 30 seconds in Experiment 2
= 139-141 cm³ *[1 mark]*
You get the marks for any answer within each range.
4.4 E.g. the curve for Experiment 2 starts off steeper than the curve for Experiment 1. / The curve for Experiment 2 flattens out more quickly than the curve for Experiment 1, with the same total amount of gas produced *[1 mark]*.
4.5 Increasing the concentration increases the number of particles in the reaction mixture *[1 mark]*. This increases the frequency of collisions *[1 mark]*.
4.6 mass of calcium sulfate formed = mass of weighing boat with calcium sulfate – mass of weighing boat
mass of calcium sulfate formed = 2.22 – 1.36
= 0.86 g *[1 mark]*
4.7 From the graph, the reaction finished after 55 seconds.
So time taken = 55 seconds
mean rate of reaction = 0.86 ÷ 55
= 0.01563...
= 0.016 g/s (2 s.f.)
[3 marks for correct answer in range of 0.014-0.016, given to 2 s.f. or 2 marks for correct answer in range of 0.014-0.016 not given to 2 s.f., otherwise 1 mark for time of 55-60 seconds taken from graph]

5.1

[1 mark for all four points correctly plotted, 1 mark for a smooth curve that passes through all the points]

5.2 E.g. 36 °C
[1 mark for correct reading of the graph drawn in 5.1]
Even if the graph you drew in question 5.1. was wrong, if you've used it correctly to find a value for the boiling point of a molecule with 5 carbon atoms, you get the mark here.

5.3 C_nH_{2n+2} **[1 mark]**

5.4

[1 mark]

5.5 Add a few drops of bromine water to both compounds and shake **[1 mark]**. With propane, nothing will happen **[1 mark]**. Propene will decolourise the bromine water / turn the solution from orange to colourless **[1 mark]**.

5.6 $C_3H_8 + 5O_2 \rightarrow 3CO_2 + $**$4H_2O$**
[1 mark for correctly giving H_2O as the missing product, 1 mark for correct number in front of H_2O.]

5.7 Heptane has a higher viscosity than propane **[1 mark]**, as its molecular formula shows that it has more atoms in its carbon chain/has a longer carbon chain/is a bigger molecule **[1 mark]**.

6.1 As the level of nitrogen dioxide increases, the severity of asthma attacks increases / there is a positive correlation between the nitrogen dioxide level and severity of asthma attacks **[1 mark]**

6.2 E.g. the scientists only collected data from men. / The scientists only collected data from people under 40. / The severity of asthma attacks might be affected by another pollutant which happens to be abundant in the same areas as nitrogen dioxide. **[1 mark]**

6.3 Oxides of nitrogen are formed when nitrogen and oxygen from the air react at high temperatures **[1 mark]**. This happens when fuel is burned in car engines **[1 mark]**. In cities, there are lots of cars, so the levels of nitrogen oxides tend to be higher **[1 mark]**.

6.4 Cool the reaction mixture. / Reduce the temperature the reaction is carried out at **[1 mark]**.

6.5 E.g. sulfur dioxide **[1 mark]**

7.1 E.g. they don't have enough fresh water / groundwater / surface water to treat and use as drinking water **[1 mark]**.

7.2 Desalination **[1 mark]**

7.3 How to grade your answer:
Level 0: There is no relevant information. **[No marks]**
Level 1: There is a brief description of the method to distil seawater, but many details are missing or incorrect. **[1 to 2 marks]**
Level 2: There is some explanation of the method used to distil sea water. Most of the information is correct, but a few small details may be incorrect or missing. **[3 to 4 marks]**
Level 3: There is a clear, detailed and fully correct explanation of the method used to distil sea water in the lab. **[5 to 6 marks]**
Here are some points your answer may include:
Pour the sea water into a (round bottom) flask.
Attach the flask to a condenser and secure both with clamps.
Connect a supply of cold water to the condenser.
Place a beaker under the condenser to collect the fresh water.
Place a Bunsen burner under the round bottom flask and heat the sea water slowly.
The water will boil and form steam.
The steam will condense back to pure liquid water in the condenser and be collected in the beaker as it runs out.
Continue to heat the (round bottom) flask until all the water has evaporated.

7.4 Large bits of material (such as grit) are removed from the sewage **[1 mark]**.

7.5 The effluent undergoes aerobic biological treatment **[1 mark]**. Aerobic bacteria break down any organic matter that is present **[1 mark]**.

Physics Practice Paper 1

Pages 458-472

1.1 liquid **[1 mark]**
1.2 potential energy **[1 mark]**, kinetic energy **[1 mark]**
1.3 gas **[1 mark]**
There are two flat bits on the graph that show changes of state. The first must show the substance melting and the second must show it boiling. So at Z it must be a gas.
1.4 X **[1 mark]**
1.5 The specific latent heat of fusion of the substance is 334 000 J/kg. **[1 mark]**
1.6 $E = mL = 5.00 \times 334\,000$ **[1 mark]**
= **1 670 000 J** **[1 mark]**
2.1 Volume = length × width × height
= $4.0 \times 4.0 \times 4.0$ **[1 mark]**
= **64 cm³** **[1 mark]**
2.2 He should use cylinder A. The graduations are smaller on cylinder A, so the student will be able to make more accurate measurements **[1 mark]**.
2.3 density = $0.435 \div 0.000058$ **[1 mark]**
= **7500 kg/m³** **[1 mark]**
3.1 The type of insulation **[1 mark]**.
3.2 Any two from, e.g. thickness of insulation / starting temperature of the water / length of time water is left to cool / volume of water used / the beaker used / temperature of the room **[1 mark for each]**
3.3 Mean temperature = $(21.9 + 22.2 + 20.1) \div 3$ **[1 mark]**
= **21.4 °C** **[1 mark]**
3.4 E.g. the insulation does not cover the top of the beaker **[1 mark]**. This means a lot of energy is being lost from the top of the beaker **[1 mark]**. The amount of energy lost through the insulation is small in comparison, meaning that the decrease in energy is roughly the same each time **[1 mark]**.
3.5 With a thick layer of material that has a low thermal conductivity. **[1 mark]**
3.6 E.g. biofuel / waves / hydroelectricity / the tides **[1 mark]**
3.7 In 10 years she would save £375 × 10 = £3750 on her energy bill **[1 mark]**. This would not cover the £6000 cost of installing the solar panels, so the home owner would not save money **[1 mark]**.
4.1 It is twice as large as the resistance of circuit A. **[1 mark]**
4.2 E.g. The current is higher in circuit A **[1 mark]**. When potential difference is the same, the greater the resistance in the circuit, the smaller the current. Potential difference is the same in both circuits so the current in circuit A is higher because its resistance is lower **[1 mark]**.
4.3 The potential difference across each resistor is 6 V. **[1 mark]**
4.4 power = $3.0^2 \times 4.0$ **[1 mark]** = **36** **[1 mark]** watts **[1 mark]**
4.5 The resistance decreases **[1 mark]**.
4.6 E.g. a car engine temperature sensor / an electronic thermostat **[1 mark]**.

4.7

[1 mark for zero current at negative potential differences, 1 mark for curve into positive-gradient at a non-zero positive potential difference]

5.1   How to grade your answer:

Level 0:   There is no relevant information. *[No marks]*

Level 1:   There is a brief description of how to calculate the resistance of different lengths of wire. The answer is missing key details. *[1 to 2 marks]*

Level 2:   There is a brief summary of the experimental procedure, including one way to ensure accurate results. The answer states which quantities need to be measured and explains how they can be used to calculate the resistance of the wire. *[3 to 4 marks]*

Level 3:   There is full, clear and logical description of the experimental procedure. The answer states which quantities need to be measured and how they can be used to calculate the resistance of the wire. At least two ways to ensure the results of the experiment will be accurate are given. *[5 to 6 marks]*

Here are some points your answer may include:

Procedure

Attach a crocodile clip to the wire level with 0 cm on the ruler.
Attach the second crocodile clip to the wire, e.g. 5 cm from the first clip.
Write down the length of the wire between the clips.
Close the switch, then record the current through the wire and the potential across it.
Rearrange $V = IR$ to $R = V \div I$ and use this equation to calculate the resistance of the wire.
Repeat the procedure several times, moving the second crocodile clip further along each time to create a longer wire, e.g. move it 5 cm along each time to create wires of lengths 10 cm, 15 cm, 20 cm and 25 cm.
Plot a graph of resistance against wire length to see the relationship between the two.

Improving accuracy

If the wires heat up their resistance will increase, making the results less accurate.
To reduce the heating effect:
1. Switch off the circuit between measurements to allow the circuit to cool down / stop the circuit heating up.
2. Use a battery with a low potential difference / only use low currents (as the larger the current, the more the circuit will heat up).
Repeat all wire length measurements to ensure the correct length is measured. Draw lines on the crocodile clips as distance markers, to ensure the distance is being measured between the same points each time.
Tape the wire down onto the ruler to ensure the wire is straight and there are no kinks.
Ensure that the length measurements are taken at eye level to avoid errors due to parallax.

Make sure the same part of the crocodile clip is in contact with the wire each time it is moved or the resistance of the crocodile clip may affect the results.
Repeat the measurements of potential difference and current several times for each length of wire and use them to calculate a mean resistance for each length of wire.
This will minimise the amount of random error in the results and allow anomalous results to be easily identified.

5.2

[1 mark for points correctly plotted, 1 mark for sensible line of best fit]

5.3   40 mΩ *[1 mark for value between 39 and 41 mΩ]*

5.4   As the length of the wire increases, its resistance increases *[1 mark]*.

6.1   **W** and **Y** *[1 mark]*

6.2   **X** *[1 mark]*

6.3   Gravitational potential energy = mass × gravitational field strength × height / GPE = $m \times g \times h$ *[1 mark]*

6.4   mass = 1 500 000 g = 1500 kg
Gravitational P.E. = 1500 × 9.8 × 40.0 *[1 mark]*
                       = **588 000 J** *[1 mark]*

6.5   elastic potential energy store (of the spring) *[1 mark]*

6.6   efficiency = $\dfrac{\text{useful energy output}}{\text{total energy output}}$ *[1 mark]*

6.7   efficiency = $\dfrac{18.0}{59.5}$ *[1 mark]*
                = 0.3025... = **0.303 (to 3 s.f.)** *[1 mark]*

You could also have given the efficiency as a percentage.
To get a percentage, multiply by 100: 0.303 × 100 = 30.3%

6.8   Lubricating the moving parts of the carriage will decrease the energy lost due to frictional forces *[1 mark]*. This means more energy will be transferred to the kinetic energy store of the carriage *[1 mark]*. Kinetic energy = $\frac{1}{2}mv^2$, so the velocity/speed will increase *[1 mark]*.

7.1   214 − 83 = **131 neutrons** *[1 mark]*

7.2   Because they have the same number of protons/are the same element *[1 mark]* and have a different number of neutrons/have a different mass number *[1 mark]*.

7.3

$^{222}_{86}\text{Rn}$ *[1 mark]*

$^{210}_{83}\text{Bi}$ *[1 mark]*

7.4   420 days *[1 mark]*

7.5   Half-life when activity drops to half original total.
Activity after 1 half-life = 80 ÷ 2 = 40 Bq
Using **Figure 14**, when activity = 40 Bq, time = 140 days.
Therefore, half-life = **140 days** *[1 mark]*

7.6 Contamination is when unwanted radioactive atoms are on or inside an object *[1 mark]*.

7.7 How to grade your answer:
Level 0: There is no relevant information. *[No marks]*
Level 1: There is a brief explanation on the dangers of alpha and beta contamination, but little to no comparison between them. The answer has little or no clear structure. *[1 to 2 marks]*
Level 2: There is a clear explanation and comparison of the dangers of alpha and beta contamination both inside and outside the body. The answer is well structured. *[3 to 4 marks]*
Here are some points your answer may include:
Inside the body, the release of alpha particles is more dangerous than the release of beta particles.
This is because alpha particles are more ionising than beta particles, so they can cause more damage to cells.
Outside the body, the release of beta particles is more dangerous than the release of alpha particles.
This is because alpha particles are easily absorbed by thin barriers, so it is unlikely to pass through the skin if the contaminating atoms are outside the body.
But beta particles from contaminating atoms outside the body can pass through skin and damage internal organs.

Physics Practice Paper 2

Pages 473-486

1.1 1 N *[1 mark]*
The spring is still, so the forces acting on it must be balanced.

1.2 If only one force was applied this would simply cause the spring to move in the direction of the force. *[1 mark]*

1.3 random error *[1 mark]*
Using a marker ensures that you're always measuring the length of the spring from the same point.

1.4 E.g. 6.0 N (allow estimate from 5.5 N up to 6.5 N) *[1 mark]*. The graph is a straight line up to that point which shows extension and force are proportional *[1 mark]*.

1.5 0.015 m = 1.5 cm
From the graph a force of 3.0 N causes this extension.
[1 mark for evidence of conversion to 1.5 cm. 1 mark for correct force.]

1.6 spring constant = 3.0 ÷ 0.015 *[1 mark]* = **200 N/m** *[1 mark]*

2.1 0 N *[1 mark]*
When an object is travelling at a constant speed in a fixed direction it is not accelerating and so the resultant force will be zero.

2.2 Speed is the gradient of a distance-time graph.
change in vertical axis = 20 − 11 = 9 m
change in horizontal axis = 27 − 15 = 12 s
speed = 9 ÷ 12 *[1 mark]* = **0.75 m/s** *[1 mark]*

2.3 Between 9 metres and 10 metres *[1 mark]*.
The swimmer is travelling fastest when the gradient of the graph is steepest.

2.4 speed = 20 ÷ 23 = 0.8695... m/s *[1 mark]*
= **0.87 m/s (to 2 s.f.)** *[1 mark]*

2.5

[1 mark for straight line, 1 mark for correct start and end points]

2.6 The magnitude of the swimmer's displacement is 0 m. *[1 mark]*

3.1 amplitude = 5 squares tall, one square = 1 cm tall
amplitude = 5 × 1 = **5 cm** *[1 mark]*

3.2 The number of complete waves that pass a point each second. *[1 mark]*

3.3 E.g. heating/cooking/infrared cameras *[1 mark]*

3.4 Variable 1 — Control *[1 mark]*
Variable 2 — Independent *[1 mark]*

3.5 The hypothesis is not supported as the white woollen blanket is not dark-coloured but has absorbed the signal *[1 mark]*.

3.6 How to grade your answer:
Level 0: There is no relevant information. *[No marks]*
Level 1: There is a clear description of at least one similarity and one difference between the features and properties of infrared waves and radio waves. *[1 to 2 marks]*
Level 2: There is a clear description of multiple similarities and differences between the features and properties of infrared waves and radio waves. *[3 to 4 marks]*
Here are some points your answer may include:
Both infrared and radio waves are electromagnetic waves.
They are both transverse waves.
The vibrations in both types of wave are perpendicular to the direction of energy transfer.
Both types of wave travel at the same speed through air or a vacuum.
Radio waves have a longer wavelength than infrared waves.
Radio waves have a lower frequency than infrared waves.

4.1 E.g. wear goggles in case string snaps / remain standing so that they can get out of the way of any falling masses. *[1 mark]*

4.2 11.0 cm *[1 mark]*
Each half-wave is 27.5 ÷ 5 = 5.5 cm.
So one full wave is 5.5 × 2 = 11.0 cm.

4.3 wave speed = frequency × wavelength / $v = f \times \lambda$ *[1 mark]*

4.4 wavelength = 11.0 cm = 0.110 m
wave speed = 120 × 0.110 *[1 mark]*
= **13.2 m/s or 13 m/s (to 2 s.f.)** *[1 mark]*

4.5 32.9 m/s is anomalous *[1 mark]*. The student should try to identify a reason for the anomalous result *[1 mark]*. If it is found to be due to an error, it should be ignored and not included when calculating the mean *[1 mark]*.

4.6 It is not suitable as the resolution of a ruler is too low *[1 mark]*. A micrometer/Vernier callipers would be more suitable *[1 mark]*.
Micrometers and vernier callipers have a much higher resolution than rulers.

4.7 As diameter decreases, wave speed increases / As diameter increases, wave speed decreases *[1 mark]*.

4.8 A scatter/line graph *[1 mark]*. Diameter and speed are both continuous variables *[1 mark]*.

5.1   9.8 m/s² *[1 mark]*

5.2   Between Point A and Point B —
The skydiver has a positive acceleration *[1 mark]*
Between Point B and Point C —
The skydiver is moving at a constant velocity *[1 mark]*

5.3   Air resistance / friction / drag *[1 mark]*

5.4   weight = mass × gravitational field
strength / $W = mg$ *[1 mark]*

5.5 $W = 80.0 \times 9.8$ *[1 mark]* = **784 N** *[1 mark]*

5.6   force = mass × acceleration / $F = ma$ *[1 mark]*

5.7 $a = F \div m$ *[1 mark]*
     $= 58\,500 \div 4680$ *[1 mark]* = **12.5 m/s²** *[1 mark]*

6.1 $36 - 12 = $ **24 m** *[1 mark]*

6.2   Reaction times vary from person to person *[1 mark]*.
A large sample will give a more accurate average *[1 mark]*.

6.3   Whether the driver is tired. *[1 mark]*
The speed the car is travelling at. *[1 mark]*

6.4   Work done = force × distance *[1 mark]*

6.5   Rearranging work done = force × distance for distance:
distance = work done ÷ force *[1 mark]*
     $= 75\,000 \div 5000$ *[1 mark]* = **15 m** *[1 mark]*

7.1

           [1 mark]
You need to use the right-hand thumb rule for this.

7.2   Decrease the current *[1 mark]*.
Move the magnet further from the wire *[1 mark]*.

7.3   How to grade your answer:

Level 0:   There is no relevant information. *[No marks]*

Level 1:   Predictions of what will happen to the bar
magnet and nail are given and a brief reason is
given for at least one of the predictions.
[1 to 2 marks]

Level 2:   Predictions of what will happen to the bar
magnet and nail are given. There is some
explanation for each prediction, or a detailed
account of one of them. *[3 to 4 marks]*

Level 3:   Predictions of what will happen to the bar
magnet and nail are given. There is a clear
and detailed explanation for each prediction.
[5 to 6 marks]

Here are some points your answer may include:
The bar magnet will remain attached to the electromagnet.
The bar magnet is a permanent magnet.
When the current stops flowing in the wire, the wire has no
magnetic field around it.
With the bar magnet attached, the iron core remains an
induced magnet, as it's in the bar magnet's magnetic field.
Permanent magnets and induced magnets always attract
each other.
So the bar magnet will remain stuck to the iron core
(assuming the magnetic force is greater than the weight of
the magnet).
The nail will fall off.
The nail was an induced magnet as it was in the magnetic
field of the electromagnet.
When the current stops flowing, the electromagnet and the
nail both lose their magnetism.
This means there is no attractive force keeping them together,
so the nail will fall off.

Glossary

Glossary

Abiotic factor	A non-living factor in an environment.
Acceleration	A change in velocity in a certain amount of time.
Accurate result	A result that is really close to the true answer.
Acid	A substance with a pH of less than 7 that forms H^+ ions in water.
Activation energy	The minimum amount of energy that reactant particles must have when they collide in order to react.
Active transport	The movement of particles against a concentration gradient (from an area of lower concentration to an area of higher concentration) using energy from respiration.
Activity (radioactive)	The number of nuclei of a sample that decay per second.
Adaptation	A feature that helps an organism to survive in the conditions of its natural environment.
Aerobic respiration	Respiration that uses oxygen. It produces carbon dioxide and water.
Air resistance	The frictional force caused by air on a moving object.
Alkali	A substance with a pH of more than 7 that forms OH^- ions in solution.
Alkali metal	An element in Group 1 of the periodic table. E.g. sodium, potassium etc.
Alkane	A saturated hydrocarbon with the general formula C_nH_{2n+2}. E.g. methane, ethane etc.
Alkene	An unsaturated hydrocarbon that contains a carbon-carbon double bond and has the general formula C_nH_{2n}. E.g. ethene, propene etc.
Allele	An alternative version of a gene.
Alloy	A metal that is a mixture of two or more metals, or a mixture involving metals and non-metals.
Alpha decay	A type of radioactive decay in which an alpha particle is given out from a decaying nucleus.
Alpha particle	A positively-charged particle made up of two protons and two neutrons (a helium nucleus).
Alpha particle scattering experiment	An experiment in which alpha particles were fired at gold foil to see if they were deflected. It led to the plum pudding model being abandoned in favour of the nuclear model of the atom.
Alternating current (ac)	Current that is constantly changing direction.
Alveolus	A tiny air sac in the lungs, where gas exchange occurs.
Amino acid	A small molecule that is a building block of proteins.
Ammeter	A component used to measure the current through a component. It is always connected in series with the component.
Amplitude	The maximum displacement of a point on a wave from its undisturbed position.
Anaerobic respiration	Respiration without oxygen. It produces lactic acid in humans, and carbon dioxide and ethanol in plants and yeast.
Angle of incidence	The angle the incident ray of a wave makes with the normal at a boundary.
Angle of refraction	The angle a refracted ray makes with the normal when a wave refracts at a boundary.
Anion	A particle with a negative charge, formed when one or more electrons are gained.

Glossary

Anomalous result	A result that doesn't fit in with the rest of the data.
Antibiotic	A drug used to kill or prevent the growth of bacteria.
Antibiotic resistance	When bacteria aren't killed by an antibiotic.
Antibody	A protein produced by white blood cells in response to the presence of an antigen (e.g. on the surface of a pathogen).
Antigen	A molecule on the surface of a cell. Foreign antigens trigger white blood cells to make antibodies.
Antitoxin	A protein produced by white blood cells that stops toxins from working.
Artery	A blood vessel that carries blood away from the heart.
Asexual reproduction	When organisms reproduce by mitosis to produce genetically identical offspring.
Atmosphere	The layer of air that surrounds a planet.
Atom	A neutral particle made up of protons and neutrons in the nucleus, with electrons surrounding the nucleus.
Atomic number	The number of protons in the nucleus of an atom. It's also known as proton number.
Base	A substance that reacts with acids in neutralisation reactions.
Behavioural adaptation	A way in which an organism behaves that helps it to survive in its environment.
Beta decay	A type of radioactive decay in which a beta particle is given out from a decaying nucleus.
Beta particle	A high-speed electron emitted in beta decay.
Bias	Unfairness in the way data is presented, possibly because the presenter is trying to make a particular point (sometimes without knowing they're doing it).
Binomial system	The system used in classification for naming organisms using a two-part Latin name.
Bio-fuel	A renewable energy resource made from plant products or animal dung.
Biodiversity	The variety of different species of organisms on Earth, or within an ecosystem.
Biotic factor	A living factor in an environment.
Braking distance	The braking distance is the distance a vehicle travels after the brakes are applied until it comes to a complete stop, as a result of the braking force.
Capillary	A type of blood vessel involved in the exchange of materials at tissues.
Carbohydrase	A type of digestive enzyme that catalyses the breakdown of a carbohydrate (like starch) into simple sugars. Amylase is a carbohydrase.
Carbon footprint	A measure of the amounts of greenhouse gases released by a product, a service or an event.
Cardiovascular disease	Disease of the heart or blood vessels.
Catalyst	A substance that increases the speed of a reaction, without being changed or used up.
Categoric data	Data that comes in clear categories, e.g. blood type (A+, B−, etc.), metals (copper, zinc, etc.).
Cation	A particle with a positive charge, formed when one or more electrons are lost.

Glossary

Cell membrane	A membrane surrounding a cell, which holds it together and controls what goes in and out.
Cell wall	A structure surrounding some cell types, which gives strength and support.
Cellulose	A molecule which strengthens cell walls in plants and algae.
Central nervous system (CNS)	The brain and spinal cord. It's where reflexes and actions are coordinated.
Chemical bond	The attraction of two atoms for each other, caused by the sharing or transfer of electrons.
Chlorophyll	A green substance found in chloroplasts which absorbs light for photosynthesis.
Chloroplast	A structure found in plant cells and algae. It is the site of photosynthesis.
Chromatogram	The pattern of spots formed as a result of separating a mixture using chromatography.
Chromatography	An analytical method used to separate the substances in a mixture based on how the components interact with a mobile phase and a stationary phase.
Chromosome	A long molecule of DNA found in the nucleus. Each chromosome carries many genes.
Climate change	A change in the Earth's climate. E.g. global warming, changing rainfall patterns etc.
Clinical trial	A set of drug tests on human volunteers.
Clone	An organism that is genetically identical to another organism.
Closed system	A system where neither matter nor energy can enter or leave. The net change in total energy in a closed system is always zero.
Collision theory	The theory that in order for a reaction to occur, particles must collide with sufficient energy.
Combustion	An exothermic reaction between a fuel and oxygen.
Communicable disease	A disease that can spread between individuals.
Community	The populations of different species living in a habitat.
Compound	A substance made up of atoms of at least two different elements, chemically joined together.
Concentration	The amount of a substance in a certain volume of solution, given in units of 'units of amount of substance'/'units of volume'.
Conservation of energy principle	Energy can be transferred usefully from one energy store to another, stored or dissipated — but it can never be created or destroyed.
Contamination (radioactive)	The presence of unwanted radioactive atoms on or inside an object.
Continuous data	Numerical data that can have any value within a range (e.g. length, volume or temperature).
Contraceptive	A method of preventing pregnancy. Some methods use hormones and some do not.
Control experiment	An experiment that's kept under the same conditions as the rest of an investigation, but doesn't have anything done to it.
Control variable	A variable in an experiment that is kept the same.
Coordination centre	An organ (e.g. the brain, spinal cord or pancreas) that processes information from receptors and organises a response from the effectors.

Glossary

Coronary artery	A blood vessel which supplies blood to the heart muscle.
Coronary heart disease	A disease in which fatty deposits build up in the coronary arteries, causing them to become narrow.
Correlation	A relationship between two variables.
Covalent bond	A chemical bond formed when atoms share a pair of electrons.
Covalent substance	A substance where the atoms are held together by covalent bonds.
Cracking	The process that is used to break long-chain hydrocarbons down into shorter, more useful hydrocarbons. Two types of cracking are catalytic cracking and steam cracking.
Crystallisation	The formation of solid crystals as water evaporates from a solution. For example, salt solutions undergo crystallisation to form solid salt crystals.
Current	The flow of electric charge. The size of the current is the rate of flow of charge. Measured in amperes (A).
Cystic fibrosis	An inherited disorder of the cell membranes caused by a recessive allele.
Cytoplasm	A gel-like substance in a cell where most of the chemical reactions take place.
Deforestation	The cutting down of forests (large areas of trees).
Delocalised electron	An electron that isn't associated with a particular atom or bond and is free to move within a structure.
Density	A substance's mass per unit volume.
Dependent variable	The variable in an experiment that is measured.
Diabetes	A condition that affects the body's ability to control its blood glucose level.
Differentiation	The process by which a cell becomes specialised for its job.
Diffusion	The spreading out of particles from an area of higher concentration to an area of lower concentration.
Diode	A circuit component that only allows current to flow through it in one direction. It has a very high resistance in the other direction.
Direct current (dc)	Current that always flows in the same direction.
Displacement	The straight-line distance and direction from an object's starting position to its finishing position.
Displacement reaction	A reaction where a more reactive element replaces a less reactive element in a compound.
Displayed formula	A chemical formula that shows the atoms in a covalent compound and all the bonds between them.
Distance-time graph	A graph showing how the distance travelled by an object changes over a period of time.
Distillation	A way of separating out a liquid from a mixture. You heat the mixture until the bit you want evaporates, then cool the vapour to turn it back into a liquid.
Distribution	Where organisms are found within an area.
DNA	Deoxyribonucleic acid. The molecule in cells that stores genetic information.
Dominant allele	An allele whose characteristic always appears in an organism, whether it has two copies of the allele or only one.

Glossary

Double-blind trial	A clinical trial where neither the doctors nor the patients know who has received the drug and who has received the placebo until all the results have been gathered.
Drag	The frictional force caused by any fluid (a liquid or gas) on a moving object.
Earth wire	The green and yellow wire in an electrical cable that only carries current when there's a fault. It stops exposed metal parts of an appliance from becoming live.
Ecosystem	The interaction of a community of organisms with the non-living parts of their environment.
Effector	Either a muscle or gland which responds to nervous impulses.
Efficacy	Whether something, e.g. a drug, works or not.
Efficiency	The proportion of input energy transfer which is usefully transferred. Also the proportion of input power which is usefully output.
Elastic deformation	An object undergoing elastic deformation will return to its original shape and length once any forces being applied to it are removed.
Elastic object	An object which can be elastically deformed.
Elastic potential energy store	Anything that has been stretched or compressed, e.g. a spring, has energy in its elastic potential energy store.
Electrode	An electrical conductor which is submerged in the electrolyte during electrolysis.
Electrolysis	The process of breaking down a substance using electricity.
Electrolyte	A liquid or solution used in electrolysis to conduct electricity between the two electrodes.
Electromagnet	A solenoid with an iron core.
Electromagnetic (EM) spectrum	A continuous spectrum of all the possible wavelengths of electromagnetic waves.
Electron	A negatively charged particle that orbits the nucleus of an atom.
Electron shell	A region of an atom that contains electrons. It's also known as an energy level.
Electronic structure	The number of electrons in an atom (or ion) of an element and how they are arranged.
Electrostatic force	A force of attraction between opposite charges.
Element	A substance that is made up only of atoms with the same number of protons.
Empirical formula	A chemical formula showing the simplest possible whole number ratio of atoms in a compound.
Endothermic reaction	A reaction which takes in energy from the surroundings.
Energy level	A region of an atom that contains electrons. It's also known as an electron shell.
Energy store	A means by which an object stores energy. There are different types of energy store: thermal (or internal), kinetic, gravitational potential, elastic potential, chemical, magnetic, electrostatic and nuclear.
Enzyme	A protein that acts as a biological catalyst.
Equilibrium (physics)	A state in which all the forces acting on an object are balanced, so the resultant force is zero.

Glossary

Equilibrium (reactions)	The point at which the rates of the forward and backward reactions in a reversible reaction are the same, and so the amounts of reactants and products in the reaction container don't change.
Eukaryotic cell	A complex cell, such as a plant or animal cell.
Evolution	The changing of the inherited characteristics of a population over time.
Excretion	The removal of waste products from the body.
Exothermic reaction	A reaction which transfers energy to the surroundings.
Extinction	When no living individuals of a species remain.
Extremophile	An organism that's adapted to live in seriously extreme conditions.
Fair test	A controlled experiment where the only thing being changed is the independent variable.
Family tree	A diagram that shows how a characteristic is inherited in a group of related people.
Feedstock	A raw material used to produce other substances through industrial processes.
Fermentation	The process of anaerobic respiration in yeast cells.
Fertilisation	The fusion of a male and a female gamete during sexual reproduction.
Fertility	The ability to conceive a child.
Filtration	A physical method used to separate an insoluble solid from a liquid.
Finite resource	A resource that isn't replaced at a quick enough rate to be considered replaceable.
Flammability	How easy it is to ignite a substance.
Fluid	A substance that can flow — either a liquid or a gas.
Force	A push or a pull on an object caused by it interacting with something.
Formulation	A useful mixture with a precise purpose made by following a formula.
Fossil	The remains of an organism from many years ago, which is found in rock.
Fossil fuel	The fossil fuels are coal, oil and natural gas. They're non-renewable energy resources that we burn to generate electricity.
Fossil record	The history of life on Earth preserved as fossils.
Fraction	A group of hydrocarbons that condense together when crude oil is separated using fractional distillation. E.g. petrol, naphtha, kerosene etc.
Fractional distillation	A process that can be used to separate substances in a mixture according to their boiling points.
Frequency	The number of complete waves passing a certain point per second. Measured in hertz, Hz.
Friction	A force that opposes an object's motion. It acts in the opposite direction to motion.
Functional adaptation	Something that goes on inside an organism's body which helps it to survive in its environment.
Gamete	A sex cell, e.g. an egg cell or a sperm cell in animals.
Gamma decay	A type of radioactive decay in which a gamma ray is given out from a decaying nucleus.
Gamma ray	A high-frequency, short-wavelength electromagnetic wave.
Geiger-Müller tube	A particle detector that is used with a counter to measure count rate.

Glossary

Gene	A short section of DNA, found on a chromosome. A gene contains the instructions needed to make a protein, so it controls the development of a characteristic.
General formula	A formula that can be used to find the molecular formula of any member of a homologous series.
Genetic engineering	The process of cutting out a useful gene from one organism's genome and putting it into another organism's cells.
Genetically modified (GM) crop	A crop which has had its genes modified using genetic engineering.
Genome	All of the genetic material in an organism.
Genotype	What alleles you have, e.g. Tt.
Geothermal power	A renewable energy resource where energy is transferred from the thermal energy stores of hot rocks underground and is used to generate electricity or to heat buildings.
Giant covalent structure	A large molecule made up of a very large number of atoms held together by covalent bonds (also known as a macromolecule).
Gland	An organ that produces and secretes hormones.
Global dimming	The decrease in the amount of sunlight reaching the Earth's surface due to an increase in the amount of particulates in the atmosphere.
Global warming	The increase in the average temperature of the Earth.
Glycogen	A molecule that acts as a store of glucose in liver and muscle cells.
Gradient	The slope of a line graph. It shows how quickly the variable on the y-axis changes with the variable on the x-axis.
Gravitational potential energy (g.p.e) store	Anything that has mass and is in a gravitational field has energy in its gravitational potential energy store.
Greenhouse effect	When greenhouse gases in the atmosphere absorb long wavelength radiation and re-radiate it in all directions, including back towards Earth, helping to keep the Earth warm.
Greenhouse gas	A gas that can absorb long wavelength radiation.
Group	A column in the periodic table.
Guard cell	A type of cell found on either side of a stoma. A pair of these cells controls the stoma's size.
Habitat	The place where an organism lives.
Haemoglobin	A red pigment found in red blood cells which carries oxygen.
Half-life	The time it takes for the number of nuclei of a radioactive isotope in a sample to halve. OR The time it takes for the count rate (or activity) of a radioactive sample to fall to half its initial level.
Hazard	Something that could cause harm (e.g. fire, electricity, etc.).
Heterozygous	When an organism has two alleles for a particular gene that are different.
Homeostasis	The regulation of conditions inside your body and cells in order to maintain a stable internal environment.

Glossary

Homologous series	A group of chemicals that react in a similar way because they have the same functional group. E.g. the alcohols or the carboxylic acids.
Homozygous	When an organism has two alleles for a particular gene that are the same.
Hormone	A chemical messenger which travels in the blood to act on a target cell.
Hydrocarbon	A compound that is made from only hydrogen and carbon.
Hypothesis	A possible explanation for a scientific observation.
I-V characteristic	A graph of current against potential difference for a component.
Inbreeding	When closely related animals or plants are bred together.
Incomplete combustion	When a fuel burns but there isn't enough oxygen for it to burn completely. Products can include carbon monoxide and carbon particulates. Also known as partial combustion.
Independent variable	The variable in an experiment that is changed.
Indicator	A substance that changes colour above or below a certain pH.
Induced magnet	An object that turns into a magnet when it is placed inside another magnetic field.
Inelastic deformation	An object undergoing inelastic deformation will not return to its original shape and length once the forces being applied to it are removed.
Infrared (IR) radiation	A type of electromagnetic wave that is given out by all objects. It can also be absorbed by objects which makes the object hotter.
Inherited disorder	A disorder caused by a faulty allele, which can be passed on to an individual's offspring.
Insoluble	A substance is insoluble if it does not dissolve in a particular solvent.
Insulin	A hormone produced and secreted by the pancreas when the blood glucose level is too high. It causes cells to take up more glucose from the blood, reducing the blood glucose level.
Interdependence	Where, in a community, different species depend on each other for things such as food, shelter, pollination and seed dispersal.
Intermolecular force	A force of attraction that exists between molecules.
Internal energy	The total energy that a system's particles have in their kinetic and potential energy stores.
Ion	A charged particle formed when one or more electrons are lost or gained from an atom or molecule.
Ionic bond	A strong attraction between oppositely charged ions.
Ionic compound	A compound that contains positive and negative ions held together in a regular arrangement (a lattice) by electrostatic forces of attraction.
Ionic lattice	A closely-packed regular arrangement of particles held together by electrostatic forces of attraction.
Ionising radiation	Radiation that has enough energy to knock electrons off atoms.
Irradiation	Exposure to radiation.
Isotope	A different form of the same element, which has atoms with the same number of protons (atomic number), but a different number of neutrons (and so different mass number).
Joules	The standard unit of energy.

Glossary

Kinetic energy store	Anything that's moving has energy in its kinetic energy store.
Latent heat	The energy required to change the state of a substance without changing its temperature.
Lattice	A closely-packed regular arrangement of particles.
Life cycle assessment	An assessment of the environmental impact of a product over the course of its life.
Light-dependent resistor (LDR)	A resistor whose resistance is dependent on light intensity. The resistance decreases as light intensity increases.
Limit of proportionality	The point beyond which the force applied to an elastic object is no longer directly proportional to the extension of the object.
Limiting factor	A factor which prevents a reaction from going any faster.
Line of action (of a force)	A straight line passing through the point at which the force is acting in the same direction as the force.
Linear graph	A straight line graph.
Lipase	A type of digestive enzyme that catalyses the breakdown of lipids into fatty acids and glycerol, in the small intestine.
Litmus	A single indicator that's blue in alkalis and red in acids.
Live wire	The brown wire in an electrical cable that carries an alternating potential difference from the mains.
Longitudinal wave	A wave in which the vibrations are along the same line as the direction of energy transfer.
Lubricant	A substance used between two objects to reduce friction between surfaces.
Magnetic field	A region where magnetic materials (like iron and steel) experience a force.
Magnetic material	A material (such as iron, steel, cobalt or nickel) which is attracted to magnets.
Mass number	The total number of protons and neutrons in an atom.
Mean (average)	A measure of average found by adding up all the data and dividing by the number of values there are.
Median (average)	A measure of average found by selecting the middle value from a data set arranged in order from smallest to largest.
Meiosis	A type of cell division where a cell divides twice to produce four genetically different gametes. It occurs in the reproductive organs.
Menstrual cycle	A monthly sequence of events during which the body prepares the lining of the uterus (womb) in case it receives a fertilised egg, and releases an egg from an ovary. The uterus lining then breaks down if the egg has not been fertilised.
Meristem tissue	Tissue found at the growing tips of plant shoots and roots that is able to differentiate into any type of plant cell.
Metabolism	All the chemical reactions that happen in a cell (or in the body).
Metal	An element that can form positive ions when it reacts.
Metal ore	Rocks that are found naturally in the Earth's crust containing enough metal to make the metal profitable to extract.
Metallic bond	The attraction between metal ions and delocalised electrons in a metal.
Microwave	A type of electromagnetic wave that can be used for cooking and satellite communications.

Glossary

Mitochondria	Structures in a cell where most of the reactions for aerobic respiration take place.
Mitosis	A type of cell division where a cell divides once, to form two new identical cells.
Mixture	A substance made from two or more elements or compounds that aren't chemically bonded to each other.
Mobile phase	In chromatography, the mobile phase is a gas or liquid where the molecules are able to move.
Mode (average)	A measure of average found by selecting the most frequent value from a data set.
Model	A simple way of describing or showing what's going on in real life.
Molecule	A particle made up of at least two atoms held together by covalent bonds.
Molecular formula	A chemical formula showing the actual number of atoms of each element in a compound.
Motor neurone	A nerve cell that carries electrical impulses from the CNS to effectors.
MRSA	A strain of bacteria that is resistant to most known antibiotics.
Mutation	A random change in an organism's DNA.
National grid	The network of transformers and cables that distributes electrical power from power stations to consumers.
Natural resource	A resource formed without human input.
Natural selection	The process by which species evolve.
Nervous system	The organ system in animals that allows them to respond to changes in their environment.
Neurone	A nerve cell. Neurones transmit information around the body, including to and from the CNS.
Neutral substance	A substance with a pH of 7.
Neutral wire	The blue wire in an electrical cable that current in an appliance normally flows through. It is around 0 V.
Neutralisation reaction	The reaction between acids and bases that leads to the formation of neutral products — usually a salt and water.
Neutron	A particle found in the nucleus of an atom. It has no charge.
Newton's First Law	An object will remain at rest or travelling at a constant velocity unless it is acted on by a resultant force.
Newton's Second Law	The acceleration of an object is directly proportional to the resultant force acting on it, and inversely proportional to its mass.
Newton's Third Law	When two objects interact, they exert equal and opposite forces on each other.
Non-communicable disease	A disease that cannot spread between individuals.
Non-contact force	A force that can act between objects that are not touching.
Non-metal	An element that doesn't form positive ions when it reacts, with the exception of hydrogen.
Non-renewable energy resource	An energy resource that is non-renewable cannot be made at the same rate as it's being used.
Normal (at a boundary)	A line that's perpendicular (at 90°) to a surface at the point of incidence (where a wave hits the surface).

Glossary

Nuclear model	An accepted theory which describes the atom as having a tiny, positively charged nucleus surrounded by shells which are occupied by negative electrons.
Nucleus (atom)	The centre of an atom, containing protons and neutrons.
Nucleus (of a cell)	A structure found in animal and plant cells which contains the genetic material that controls the activities of the cell.
Obesity	A condition where a person has an excessive amount of body fat, to the point where it poses a risk to their health.
Ohmic conductor	A conductor with resistance that is constant at a constant temperature. It has a linear *I-V* characteristic.
Optimum dose	The dose of a drug that is most effective and has few side effects.
Optimum level (in the body)	A level of something (e.g. water, ions or glucose) that enables the body to work at its best.
Organ	A group of different tissues that work together to perform a function.
Organ system	A group of organs working together to perform a function.
Organic compound	A chemical compound that contains carbon atoms.
Osmosis	The movement of water molecules across a partially permeable membrane from a region of higher water concentration to a region of lower water concentration.
Oxidation	A reaction where electrons are lost or oxygen is gained by a species.
Oxygen debt	The amount of extra oxygen that your body needs after exercise.
Paper chromatography	An analytical technique that can be used to separate and analyse coloured substances.
Parallel circuit	A circuit in which every component is connected separately to the positive and negative ends of the battery.
Partially permeable membrane	A membrane with tiny holes in it, which lets some molecules through but not others.
Pathogen	A microorganism that causes disease, e.g. a bacterium, virus, protist or fungus.
Peer-review	The process in which other scientists check the results and explanations of an investigation before they are published.
Period	A row in the periodic table.
Period (of a wave)	The time taken for one complete wave to pass a certain point.
Periodic table	A table of all the known elements, arranged in order of atomic number so that elements with similar chemical properties are in groups.
Permanent magnet	An object that always has its own magnetic field around it.
Permanent vacuole	A structure in plant cells that contains cell sap.
pH scale	A scale from 0 to 14 that is used to measure how acidic or alkaline a solution is.
Phagocytosis	The process by which white blood cells engulf (surround) pathogens and digest them.
Phenotype	The characteristics you have, e.g. brown eyes.
Phloem	A type of plant tissue which transports food substances (dissolved sugars) around a plant.
Photosynthesis	The process by which plants use energy to convert carbon dioxide and water into glucose and oxygen.

Glossary

Physical change	A change where you don't end up with a new substance — it's the same substance as before, just in a different form. (A change of state is a physical change.)
Placebo	A substance that is like a drug being tested, but which doesn't do anything.
Plasma	The liquid part of blood, which carries blood cells and other substances around the body.
Platelet	A small fragment of a cell found in the blood, which helps blood to clot at a wound.
Plum pudding model	A disproved theory of the atom as a ball of positive charge with electrons inside it.
Polydactyly	An inherited disorder caused by a dominant allele, where a person has extra fingers or toes.
Polymer	A long chain molecule that is formed by joining lots of smaller molecules (monomers) together.
Potable water	Water that is safe for drinking.
Potential difference	The driving force that pushes electric charge around a circuit, measured in volts (V). Also known as pd or voltage.
Power	The rate of transferring energy (or doing work). Normally measured in watts (W).
Precipitate	A solid that is formed in a solution during a chemical reaction.
Precise result	When all the data is close to the mean.
Predator	An animal that hunts and kills other animals for food.
Prediction	A statement based on a hypothesis that can be tested.
Pressure	The force per unit area exerted on a surface.
Prey	An animal that is hunted and killed by another animal for food.
Primary consumer	An organism in a food chain that feeds on a producer.
Producer	An organism at the start of a food chain that makes its own food using energy from the Sun.
Product	A substance that is formed in a chemical reaction.
Prokaryotic cell	A small, simple cell, e.g. a bacterium.
Protease	A type of digestive enzyme that catalyses the breakdown of proteins into amino acids, in the stomach and small intestine.
Protein	A large biological molecule made up of long chains of amino acids.
Protist	A type of pathogen. Protists are often transferred to other organisms by a vector.
Proton	A positively charged particle found in the nucleus of an atom.
Punnett square	A type of genetic diagram.
Pure substance	A substance that only contains one compound or element throughout.
Quadrat	A square frame enclosing a known area. It is used to study the distribution of organisms.
Radiation dose	A measure of the risk of harm to your body due to exposure to radiation.
Radio wave	A type of electromagnetic wave mainly used for radio and TV signals.
Radioactive decay	The random process of a radioactive substance giving out radiation from the nuclei of its atoms.

Glossary

Radioactive substance	A substance that spontaneously gives out radiation from the nuclei of its atoms.
Random error	A difference in the results of an experiment caused by unpredictable events, e.g. human error in measuring.
Range	The difference between the smallest and largest values in a set of data.
Rate of reaction	How fast the reactants in a reaction are changed into products.
Ray	A straight line showing the path along which the wave moves.
Ray diagram	A diagram that shows the path of light waves.
Reactant	A substance that reacts in a chemical reaction.
Reaction profile	A graph that shows how the energy in a reaction changes as the reaction progresses (also known as an energy level diagram).
Reaction time	The time taken for a person to react after an event (e.g. seeing a hazard).
Reactivity series	A list of elements arranged in order of their reactivity. The most reactive elements are at the top and the least reactive at the bottom.
Receptor	A group of cells that are sensitive to a stimulus (e.g. receptor cells in the eye detect light).
Recessive allele	An allele whose characteristic only appears in an organism if it has two copies of the allele.
Reduction	A reaction where electrons are gained or oxygen is lost.
Reflex	A fast, automatic response to a stimulus.
Refraction	When a wave changes direction as it passes across the boundary between two materials at an angle to the normal.
Relative atomic mass (A_r)	The average mass of the atoms of an element measured relative to the mass of one atom of carbon-12. The relative atomic mass of an element is the same as its mass number in the periodic table.
Relative formula mass (M_r)	All the relative atomic masses (A_r) of the atoms in a compound added together.
Relay neurone	A nerve cell that carries electrical impulses from sensory neurones to motor neurones.
Renewable energy resource	An energy resource that is renewable is one that is being, or can be, made at the same rate (or faster) than it's being used.
Repeatable result	A result that will come out the same if the experiment is repeated by the same person using the same method and equipment.
Repeating unit	The shortest repeating section of a polymer.
Reproducible result	A result that will come out the same if someone different does the experiment.
Resistance	Anything in a circuit that reduces the flow of charge. Measured in ohms, Ω.
Respiration	The process of breaking down glucose to transfer energy, which goes on in every cell.
Resultant force	A single force that can replace all the forces acting on an object to give the same effect as the original forces acting altogether.
Reversible reaction	A reaction where the products of the reaction can themselves react to produce the original reactants.

Glossary

R_f **value**	In chromatography, the ratio between the distance travelled by a dissolved substance and the distance travelled by a solvent.
Ribosome	A structure in a cell, where proteins are made.
Right-hand thumb rule	The rule to work out the direction of the magnetic field around a current-carrying wire. Your thumb points in the direction of the current, and your fingers curl in the direction of the magnetic field.
Risk	The chance that a hazard will cause harm.
Risk factor	Something that is linked to an increased chance that a person will develop a disease.
S.I. unit	A standard unit of measurement, recognised by scientists all over the world.
Scalar	A quantity that has magnitude but no direction.
Secondary consumer	An organism in a food chain that eats a primary consumer.
Selective breeding (artificial selection)	When humans select the plants or animals that are going to breed together, so that the genes for useful characteristics become more common in the population.
Sensory neurone	A nerve cell that carries electrical impulses from a receptor in a sense organ to the CNS.
Series circuit	A circuit in which every component is connected in a line, end to end.
Sex chromosome (humans)	One of the 23rd pair of chromosomes, X or Y. Together they determine whether an individual is male or female.
Sexual reproduction	When two gametes combine to produce a new individual that is genetically different.
Significant figure	The first significant figure of a number is the first non-zero digit. The second, third and fourth significant figures follow on immediately after it.
Simple distillation	A way of separating a liquid out from a mixture if there are large differences in the boiling points of the substances.
Simple molecule	A molecule made up of only a few atoms held together by covalent bonds.
Solar cell	A device that generates electricity directly from the Sun's radiation.
Solenoid	A coil of wire.
Solute	A substance dissolved in a solvent to make a solution.
Solution	A mixture made up of one substance (the solute) dissolved in another (the solvent).
Solvent	A liquid in which another substance (a solute) can be dissolved.
Solvent front	The point the solvent has reached up the filter paper during paper chromatography.
Species	A group of similar organisms that can reproduce to give fertile offspring.
Specific heat capacity	The amount of energy (in joules) needed to raise the temperature of 1 kg of a material by 1°C.
Specific latent heat (SLH)	The amount of energy needed to change 1 kg of a substance from one state to another without changing its temperature. (For cooling, it is the energy released by a change in state.)
Specific latent heat of fusion	The specific latent heat for changing between a solid and a liquid (melting or freezing).
Specific latent heat of vaporisation	The specific latent heat for changing between a liquid and a gas (evaporating, boiling or condensing).
Stable community	A community where all the species and environmental factors are in balance. This means that the population sizes stay about the same.

Glossary

Standard form	A number written in the form $A \times 10^n$, where A is a number between 1 and 10.
State of matter	The form which a substance can take — e.g. solid, liquid or gas.
State symbol	The letter, or letters, in brackets that are placed after a substance in an equation to show what physical state it's in. E.g. gaseous carbon dioxide is shown as $CO_{2(g)}$.
Statins	A group of drugs that are used to decrease the risk of heart and circulatory disease.
Stationary phase	In chromatography, the stationary phase is a solid or really thick liquid where molecules are unable to move.
Stem cell	An undifferentiated cell that can become one of many different types of cell, or produce more stem cells.
Stent	A wire mesh tube that's put inside an artery to help keep it open.
Stimulus	A change in the environment.
Stoma	A tiny hole in the surface of a leaf.
Stopping distance	The distance covered by a vehicle in the time between the driver spotting a hazard and the vehicle coming to a complete stop. It's the sum of the thinking distance and the braking distance.
Structural adaptation	A feature of an organism's body structure that helps it to survive in its environment.
Sustainable development	An approach to development that takes into the account the needs of present society while not damaging the lives of those in the future.
Synapse	A connection between two neurones.
System	The object, or group of objects, that you're considering.
Systematic error	An error that is consistently made throughout an experiment.
Tangent	A straight line that touches a curve at a particular point without crossing it.
Terminal velocity	The maximum velocity a falling object can reach without any added driving forces. It's the velocity at which the resistive forces (drag) acting on the object match the force due to gravity (weight).
Tertiary consumer	An organism in a food chain that eats a secondary consumer.
Theory	A hypothesis which has been accepted by the scientific community because there is good evidence to back it up.
Thermal conductivity	A measure of how quickly an object transfers energy by heating through conduction.
Thermal decomposition	A reaction where one substance chemically changes into at least two new substances when it's heated.
Thermal insulator	A material with a low thermal conductivity.
Thermistor	A resistor whose resistance is dependent on the temperature. The resistance decreases as temperature increases.
Thinking distance	The distance a vehicle travels during the driver's reaction time (before the brakes have been applied).
Three-core cable	An electrical cable containing a live wire, a neutral wire and an earth wire.
Tissue	A group of similar cells that work together to carry out a function.
Toxicity	How harmful something is, e.g. a drug.
Toxin	A poison. Toxins are often produced by bacteria.
Transect	A line which can be used to study the distribution of organisms across an area.

Glossary

Transformer	A device which can change the potential difference of an ac supply.
Translocation	The movement of food substances (e.g. dissolved sugars) around a plant.
Transpiration stream	The movement of water from a plant's roots, through the xylem and out of the leaves.
Transverse wave	A wave in which the vibrations are perpendicular (at 90°) to the direction of energy transfer.
Tumour	A growth of abnormal cells.
Ultraviolet (UV) radiation	A type of electromagnetic wave, the main source of which is sunlight.
Uncertainty	The amount of error measurements might have.
Universal indicator	A wide range indicator that changes colour depending on the pH of the solution that it's in.
Urea	A waste product (produced from the breakdown of proteins in the liver).
Vaccination	Injecting dead or inactive pathogens to produce an immune response that will help to protect you against the same pathogen in the future.
Valid result	A repeatable and reproducible result from an experiment designed to be a fair test.
Valve	A structure in the heart or in a vein that prevents blood from flowing in the wrong direction.
Variation	The differences that exist between individuals.
Vector (in disease)	An organism that transfers a disease from one animal or plant to another, which doesn't get the disease itself.
Vector (physics)	A quantity which has both magnitude (size) and a direction.
Vein	A blood vessel that carries blood to the heart.
Velocity	The speed and direction of an object.
Velocity-time graph	A graph showing how the velocity of an object changes over a period of time.
Virus	A tiny disease-causing agent that can only replicate within body cells.
Viscosity	How runny or gloopy a substance is.
Visible light	The part of the electromagnetic spectrum that we can see with our eyes.
Voltmeter	A component used to measure the potential difference across a component. Always connected in parallel with the component.
Wave	A vibration that transfers energy without transferring any matter.
Wavelength	The length of a full cycle of a wave, e.g. from a crest to the next crest.
Weight	The force acting on an object due to gravity.
White blood cell	A blood cell that is also part of the immune system, defending the body against disease.
Work done	The energy transferred when a force moves an object through a distance, or by a moving charge.
X-ray	A high-frequency, short-wavelength electromagnetic wave. It is mainly used in medical imaging and treatment.
Xylem	A type of plant tissue which transports water and mineral ions around a plant.

Index

Index

The Periodic Table

							Group 0

Periods

1

Group 1   Group 2

Relative atomic mass

Atomic (proton) number

The periodic table showing:

Period	Group 1	Group 2										Group 3	Group 4	Group 5	Group 6	Group 7	Group 0

1: H (Hydrogen, relative atomic mass 1, atomic number 1); He (Helium, 4, 2)

2: Li (Lithium, 7, 3), Be (Beryllium, 9, 4); B (Boron, 11, 5), C (Carbon, 12, 6), N (Nitrogen, 14, 7), O (Oxygen, 16, 8), F (Fluorine, 19, 9), Ne (Neon, 20, 10)

3: Na (Sodium, 23, 11), Mg (Magnesium, 24, 12); Al (Aluminium, 27, 13), Si (Silicon, 28, 14), P (Phosphorus, 31, 15), S (Sulfur, 32, 16), Cl (Chlorine, 35.5, 17), Ar (Argon, 40, 18)

4: K (Potassium, 39, 19), Ca (Calcium, 40, 20), Sc (Scandium, 45, 21), Ti (Titanium, 48, 22), V (Vanadium, 51, 23), Cr (Chromium, 52, 24), Mn (Manganese, 55, 25), Fe (Iron, 56, 26), Co (Cobalt, 59, 27), Ni (Nickel, 59, 28), Cu (Copper, 63.5, 29), Zn (Zinc, 65, 30), Ga (Gallium, 70, 31), Ge (Germanium, 73, 32), As (Arsenic, 75, 33), Se (Selenium, 79, 34), Br (Bromine, 80, 35), Kr (Krypton, 84, 36)

5: Rb (Rubidium, 85, 37), Sr (Strontium, 88, 38), Y (Yttrium, 89, 39), Zr (Zirconium, 91, 40), Nb (Niobium, 93, 41), Mo (Molybdenum, 96, 42), Tc (Technetium, [98], 43), Ru (Ruthenium, 101, 44), Rh (Rhodium, 103, 45), Pd (Palladium, 106, 46), Ag (Silver, 108, 47), Cd (Cadmium, 112, 48), In (Indium, 115, 49), Sn (Tin, 119, 50), Sb (Antimony, 122, 51), Te (Tellurium, 128, 52), I (Iodine, 127, 53), Xe (Xenon, 131, 54)

6: Cs (Caesium, 133, 55), Ba (Barium, 137, 56), La (Lanthanum, 139, 57), Hf (Hafnium, 178, 72), Ta (Tantalum, 181, 73), W (Tungsten, 184, 74), Re (Rhenium, 186, 75), Os (Osmium, 190, 76), Ir (Iridium, 192, 77), Pt (Platinum, 195, 78), Au (Gold, 197, 79), Hg (Mercury, 201, 80), Tl (Thallium, 204, 81), Pb (Lead, 207, 82), Bi (Bismuth, 209, 83), Po (Polonium, [209], 84), At (Astatine, [210], 85), Rn (Radon, [222], 86)

7: Fr (Francium, [223], 87), Ra (Radium, [226], 88), Ac (Actinium, [227], 89), Rf (Rutherfordium, [261], 104), Db (Dubnium, [262], 105), Sg (Seaborgium, [266], 106), Bh (Bohrium, [264], 107), Hs (Hassium, [277], 108), Mt (Meitnerium, [268], 109), Ds (Darmstadtium, [271], 110), Rg (Roentgenium, [272], 111), Cn (Copernicium, [285], 112), Nh (Nihonium, [286], 113), Fl (Flerovium, [289], 114), Mc (Moscovium, [289], 115), Lv (Livermorium, [293], 116), Ts (Tennessine, [294], 117), Og (Oganesson, [294], 118)

The Lanthanides (atomic numbers 58-71) and the Actinides (atomic numbers 90-103) are not shown in this table.

Physics Equations Sheet

In each physics paper you have to sit for GCSE Combined Science, you'll be given an equations sheet listing some of the equations you might need to use. That means you don't have to learn them, but you still need to be able to pick out the correct equations to use and be really confident using them. The equations sheet won't give you any units for the equation quantities — so make sure you know them inside out.

The equations you'll be given in the exam are all on this page. You can use this page as a reference when you're doing the exam questions in each topic, and the Practice Papers at the end of the book.

elastic potential energy = ½ × spring constant × (extension)²	$E_e = \frac{1}{2}ke^2$
change in thermal energy = mass × specific heat capacity × temperature change	$\Delta E = mc\Delta\theta$
thermal energy for change of state = mass × specific latent heat	$E = mL$
(final velocity)² − (initial velocity)² = 2 × acceleration × distance	$v^2 - u^2 = 2as$
period = $\dfrac{1}{\text{frequency}}$	